19th International Conference on Textures of Materials (ICOTOM19 2021)

IOP Conference Series: Materials Science and Engineering
Volume 1121

Online
1-4 March 2021

Editors:

Hirofumi Inoue
Yoshimasa Takayama
Naoki Yoshinaga

ISBN: 978-1-7138-4606-2
ISSN: 1757-8981

Printed from e-media with permission by:

Curran Associates, Inc.
57 Morehouse Lane
Red Hook, NY 12571

Some format issues inherent in the e-media version may also appear in this print version.

Institute of Physics
Dirac House, Temple Back
Bristol BS1 6BE UK

Phone: 44 1 17 929 7481
Fax: 44 1 17 920 0979

techtracking@iop.org

Additional copies of this publication are available from:

Curran Associates, Inc.
57 Morehouse Lane
Red Hook, NY 12571 USA
Phone: 845-758-0400
Fax: 845-758-2633
Email: curran@proceedings.com
Web: www.proceedings.com

TABLE OF CONTENTS

Preface

Peer review declaration on ICOTOM19

A Brief Overview of Texture and Anisotropy 1
Anthony D. Rollett, Günter Gottstein

Texture Observation and Control in Metal Manufacturing: Theory and Practice 11
Leo A.I. Kestens, Jesus Galan Lopez, Hadi Pirgazi, Tuan Nguyen-Minh, Roumen H. Petrov

Understanding cross boundary twin behaviours in AZ31 alloy by a composite Schmid factor 21
Q L Huang, C F Guo, R L Xin

Evolutions of Mechanical Properties and Macro Textures of AZ91D sheets by Hot Rolling and Subsequent Annealing 28
S Kaneko, S Takenouchi, S M Lee, H Utsunomiya

Texture Evolution During Cold Forming of Rectangular Hollow Section 34
A Kaijalainen, V Javaheri, O Nousiainen, J Tulonen, P Steen, J Kömi

Crystallographic orientation on raft-like structure developed by tensile deformation in Cu-Fe dual phase alloy sheet 40
N. Koga, S. Tomono, O. Umezawa

Adiabatic shear bands formation in polycrystalline aluminium 46
I Mania, H Paul, R Chulist, P Petrzak

Observation of Inhomogeneous Deformation in a Cold-Rolled Ti-added Ultra-Low Carbon Steel using High-Precision Markers Drawn by Focused Ion Beam 52
T Morikawa, R Kurosaka, M Tanaka, T Ichie, K Murakami

Texture and mechanical properties of Cu alloy by cryogenic high-speed rolling 57
S Lee, R Muchime, R Matsumoto, H Utsunomiya

Suppression of serration of Al-Mg sheet by periodic indentation 63
H Utsunomiya, N Ochi, S Koshi, K Natori, R Matsumoto

New Insight into the development of deformation texture in face-centered cubic material 69
Gyan Shankar, Deepak Kumar, Satyam Suwas

Recrystallization behaviour of IF steel at the interface of Al junction 76
K Okuda, K Han, R Kainuma

A phase-field investigation of recrystallization boundary migration into heterogeneous deformation energy fields: Effects of dislocation boundary sharpness 81
R Li, V Yadav, N Moelans, Y Zhang, D Juul Jensen

Growth of Grains in the Third Orientation in an Inhomogeneous Matrix Consisting of Two Orientation Groups - A Modified Potts–Monte Carlo Simulation 87
Kunio Ito

The Origin of the Cube ({001}<100>) Texture in Non-oriented Electrical Steel Sheets 93
Youliang He, M Mehdi, E J Hilinski, L A I Kestens, A Edrisy

Effects of Fe, Si, and Cu on Recrystallization Behavior in High Purity Aluminum Foil 99
T Yamanoi

Texture evolutions in aluminum and Al-3%Mg alloy subjected to shear deformation and subsequent annealing 105
Yoshimasa Takayama, Yihe Xu, Tsuyoshi Yoshida, Hiroki Tanaka, Yusuke Onuki, Shigeo Sato

Strong rotated cube textures in thin cold-rolled potassium-doped tungsten sheets during annealing up to 1300 °C 111
D Tarras Madsen, U M Ciucani, A Hoffmann, W Pantleon

Secondary recrystallization in grain-oriented silicon steel 117
Y Ushigami

Grain growth in soft magnetic ferritic stainless steels under compressive stresses at high temperatures 125
S. Suzuki, Y. Onuki, M. Uchida, S. Sato, T. Naruse, M. Watanabe, T. Sato, T. Ebata

Variant Selection in Phase Transformation and its Influence on Texture and Martensite Starting Temperature in Steel 131
T Tomida, S Sato

Orientation dependence of transformation induced plasticity in high carbon bainitic steel 137
R Ueji, Y Kimura, K Ushioda, T Ohmura, T Inoue, A Shibata

Variant selection during β to α transformation for Ti-6Al-4V alloy produced by Selective Laser Melting printing 143
H. Xiang, L. A. I. Kestens, W. Van Paepegem

Cyclic ring fiber textures in single tungsten fiber-reinforced tungsten composites 149
U M Ciucani, L Haus, H Gietl, J Riesch, W Pantleon

Improving Ductility in Dual-Phase Steel by Cold Rolling and Intercritical Annealing 155
Alok Kumar Singh, Basudev Bhattacharya, Somjeet Biswas

Twin induced Strain Hardening, Grain Fragmentation, and Texture Evolution during Cold Compression of CP-Ti 161
Devesh Kumar Chouhan, Somjeet Biswas

The role of deformation twins in recrystallization texture formation of the FeGa alloy 167
V A Milyutin, I V Gervasyeva

Fracture toughness of hot rolled pure magnesium: Correlation with microstructure and texture 173
Gautam C.Prakash, H. N. Bar, S. Sivaprasad, S. Tarafder, Somjeet Biswas

Change in intragranular misorientation during stress relaxation in Al-Cu-Mg-Mn alloy subjected to continuous cyclic bending 179
Takumi Hoshino, Kouki Miura, Yoshimasa Takayama, Hideo Watanabe

Change in intragranular misorientation during stress relaxation behavior in Cu-Ni-Si alloy subjected to continuous cyclic bending 185
Tatsuya Fukutomi, Narumi Komei, Yoshimasa Takayama, Hideo Watanabe

Heterogeneity of microstructure, texture and mechanical properties along the building direction of Ti-6Al-4V alloy developed by SLM 191
C Widomski, D Solas, T Baudin, F Brisset, S Lebel, A-L Helbert

The influence of the crystallographic texture and phase composition of Ti-Nb-Zr alloys with shape memory and superelasticity on their functional properties 197
M M Zaripova, M G Isaenkova, V A Fesenko, A V Osintsev

Microstructural study of duplex stainless steel after turning using EBSD and X-ray diffraction analysis 203
J Capek, P Minarik, M Neslusan, K Trojan, N Ganev

η-fiber microstructure and texture evolutions in ultra-thin silicon steel 209
N Zhang, L Meng, B Zhang, C X He, G Ma, Y Han, X Chen

Influence of substructure inhomogeneity on the anisotropy of physical properties of textured materials 215
O A Krymskaya, M G Isaenkova, Y A Perlovich, V A Fesenko

Dependence of Thermal Expansion of Zr-Based Products on their Crystallographic Texture 221
Sergey Stolbov, Margarita Isaenkova, Yuriy Perlovich, Andrey Tenishev, Olga Krymskaya, Vladimir Mikhalchik, Kristina Klyukova

Effect of post-rolling cooling on the hot-rolled microstructure and texture of a new medium-carbon steel 227
V Javaheri, S Sadeghpour, A Kaijalainen, M R Kamali, J Kömi

Texture-related biological properties of severely deformed titanium 233
D Wojtas, A Mzyk, J Kawalko, K Trembecka-Wójciga, K Wierzbanowski, G Imbir, M Marzec, L Maj, A Jarzębska, M Bieda-Niemiec, R Chulist, K Sztwiertnia, W Pachla

Secondary Recrystallization of Grains with Cube Orientation for Pure Iron Tape 239
D Okai, A Yamamoto, T Doi, H Adachi

Evolution of recrystallization texture for Cu-30% Zn alloy sheets with high Young's modulus in the transverse direction 244
Hirofumi Inoue, Fumito Ituchi, Tetsuo Cho

Stereological analysis of triple line orientations 250
B J Schuessler, D P Field

Depth Profile of Residual Stresses to Analyze Textures in Extruded A6XXX 256
Shogo Oda, Shun-Ichiro Tanaka

Using synchrotron radiation XRD technique to investigate active slip systems during tensile deformation in pure magnesium 262
Masahiro Hirata, Daisuke Okai, Hiroki Adachi

Evaluation of active slip systems during deformation by In-situ XRD in precipitation hardening Mg Alloys 268
Tomoki Yoshikawa, Masahiro Hirata, Daisuke Okai, Hiroki Adachi

3D simulation of texture evolution induced grain coarsening in FCC polycrystals during severe plastic deformation 274
Chi Zhang, Laszlo S Toth

Process parameter influence on deformation and recrystallization textures in Al alloys 280
Jurij J Sidor, Qingge Xie, Purnima Chakravarty, Gyula Pal

Influence of laser beam scanning strategy in the selective laser melting of 316L steel powder on macrostress 286
M G Isaenkova, A V Yudin, A E Rubanov, A V Osintsev, L A Degadnikova

Regularities of Crystallographic Texture Formation in Products Obtained by Selective Laser Powder Melting 292
Margarita Isaenkova, Yuriy Perlovich, Anatoliy Rubanov, Vladimir Fesenko, Artyom Yudin

Microstructural anisotropy in Electron Beam Melted 316L stainless steels 298
Deepak Kumar, Gyan Shankar, Satyam Suwas

Author Index

ICOTOM 19 (2021)

Preface

It is our great pleasure to welcome all of you to the 19th International Conference on Textures of Materials (ICOTOM-19), which is held in Japan from March 1 to 4, 2021. First and foremost, we would like to thank all of participants for understanding that the conference was postponed by six months and held virtually, in consideration of COVID-19 pandemic.

ICOTOM19 should have been held at Osaka Prefecture University (OPU), Sakai, Japan from September 6 – 11, 2020. The organizing committee decided in April, 2020 to postpone holding the conference by six months, as better situation would be expected. Further, the committee selected a virtual format as the most appropriate plan when holding actual conference at OPU became unrealistic in consideration of the current situation regarding the COVID-19 pandemic.

The first Virtual conference belongs to the series of ICOTOM meetings with a history of 52 years. The conference started in Clausthal in 1969 and it has been held about every 3 years as follows: Cracow-1971, Pont-à-Mousson-1973, Cambridge-1975, Aachen-1978, Tokyo-1981, Noordwijkerhout-1984, Santa Fe-1987, Avignon-1990, Clausthal-1993, Xian-1996, Montreal-1999, Seoul-2002, Leuven-2005, Pittsburgh-2008, Mumbai-2011, Dresden-2014 and St. George-2017. It is indeed our great honor to hold an ICOTOM conference in Japan or organized by Japanese colleagues again after 40 years.

Following the tradition of ICOTOM conferences, ICOTOM-19 focuses on the fundamental understanding of the basic processes underlying the formation of texture and its relation to the properties. ICOTOM-19 thus provides a forum for the presentation and discussion on recent progress in crystallographic texture and related mechanical and functional properties of all kinds of polycrystalline materials. We invite all the scientists and engineers from many different areas working under the common theme of crystallographic orientation and texture to exchange ideas with the aim of linking basic research with an application.

The proceedings contain 49 papers, including the precious Plenary Lectures by Prof. Rollett and Prof. Kestens, with a significant knowledge in the research field on the crystallographic orientation, texture and related properties. We hope that these papers will be attractive and useful for all researchers in this field.

We would like to thank the many colleagues who helped in organizing the conference and especially Virtual Conference Team members, Prof. Makoto Hasegawa, Dr. Yusuke Onuki, Dr. Natsuko Sugiura, Dr. Shigehiro Takajo, Dr. Yasuaki Tanaka and Prof. Hiroshi Utsunomiya. Prof. Masakazu Kobayashi, Mr. Toshiaki Takasaki, G.T. Center and reviewers also made substantial contributions to the editing of the proceedings.

We should also thank Prof. Yasuyuki Kaneno, Prof. Shigeo Sato and Mr. Seiichi Suzuki for their devoted contributions to the realistic conference preparation.

Finally, we would like to express our thanks to The Light Metal Educational Foundation, Inc., The Amada Foundation, The Iron and Steel Institute of Japan, The Japan Institute of Metals and Materials for their financial supports and many companies and organizations for their encouragements.

February 9, 2021

Editors
Hirofumi Inoue[1]
Yoshimasa Takayama[2]
Naoki Yoshinaga[3]

1 Osaka Prefecture University, Japan
2 Utsunomiya University, Japan
3 Nippon Steel Corporation, Japan

ICOTOM19 committees

International committee

- Anthony Rollett (USA) – Chairman
- Matthew Barnett (Australia)
- Raúl Bolmaro (Argentina)
- Shihoon Choi (South Korea)
- Olaf Engler (Germany)
- Hirofumi Inoue (Japan)
- Dorte Juul Jensen (Denmark)
- Leo Kestens (Belgium)
- Adam Morawiec (Poland)
- João Quinta da Fonseca (UK)
- Indradev Samajdar (India)
- Werner Skrotzki (Germany)
- Satyam Suwas (India)
- Laszlo Toth (France)
- Stuart Wright (USA)
- Liang Zuo (China)

Local organizing committee

- Hirofumi Inoue, Osaka Prefecture University (co-chair)
- Yoshimasa Takayama, Utsunomiya University (co-chair)
- Naoki Yoshinaga, Nippon Steel (co-chair)
- Masahiko Demura, National Institute for Materials Science
- Makoto Hasegawa, Yokohama National University
- Takehiko Hiraga, The University of Tokyo
- Yasuyuki Kaneno, Osaka Prefecture University
- Masakazu Kobayashi, Toyohashi University of Technology
- Katsushi Matsumoto, Kobe Steel
- Katsuyoshi Michibayashi, Nagoya University
- Tatsuya Morikawa, Kyushu University
- Hirobumi Morita, Oxford Instruments
- Kaneharu Okuda, JFE Steel
- Yusuke Onuki, Ibaraki University
- Shigeo Sato, Ibaraki University
- Toshiya Shibayanagi, University of Toyama
- Natsuko Sugiura, Nippon Steel
- Shigeru Suzuki, Tohoku University

- Seiichi Suzuki, TSL Solutions
- Shigehiro Takajo, JFE Steel
- Yorinobu Takigawa, Osaka Prefecture University
- Hiroki Tanaka, UACJ
- Yasuaki Tanaka, Nippon Steel
- Hiroshi Utsunomiya, Osaka University
- Tomoaki Yamanoi, Showa Denko

Local advisory committee

- Kunio Ito, The University of Tokyo, Professor Emeritus
- Hiroshi Fukutomi, Yokohama National University, Professor Emeritus
- Kazuyoshi Sekine, Yokohama National University, Former Professor, Present: High Pressure Instutute of Japan, Adviser
- Kohsaku Ushioda, Osaka University, Kanazawa University, National Institute for Materials Science

IOP Conf. Series: Materials Science and Engineering 1121 (2021) 011002 doi:10.1088/1757-899X/1121/1/011002

Peer review declaration on ICOTOM19

All papers published in this volume of *IOP Conference Series: Materials Science and Engineering* have been peer reviewed through processes administered by the Editors. Reviews were conducted by expert referees to the professional and scientific standards expected of a proceedings journal published by IOP Publishing.

- **Type of peer review: Single-blind**

Single-anonymous: authors' identities are known to the reviewers, reviewers' identities are hidden from authors

Double-anonymous: author and reviewer identities are hidden to each other

Triple-blind: author and reviewer identities are hidden to each other, and from the Editor(s)

Open: author and reviewer identities are known to each other

- **Describe criteria used by Reviewers when accepting/declining papers. Was there the opportunity to resubmit articles after revisions?**

The criteria for accepting papers are if they have (i) novelty, (ii) giving a solution for pending issue or (iii) possibility of progress in the fields related to the conference. In addition, an appropriate format and English are confirmed.

- **Conference submission management system:**

The conference is generally managed by a conference management system, Confit, which is supplied by Atlas Co., Ltd, Japan.

- **Number of submissions received:**

55

- **Number of submissions sent for review:**

55

- **Number of submissions accepted:**

53

- **Acceptance Rate (Number of Submissions Accepted / Number of Submissions Received X 100):**

96%

- **Average number of reviews per paper:**

1.0

- **Total number of reviewers involved:**

57 (32 persons who acted as reviewer)

IOP Conf. Series: Materials Science and Engineering 1121 (2021) 011002 doi:10.1088/1757-899X/1121/1/011002

- **Any additional info on review process (ie plagiarism check system):**

Chief and vice-chief reviewers confirmed all of reviewer's reports and revised papers.

- **Contact person for queries:**

Mr. Takasaki, GT Center, Kyoto, Japan t.takasaki@gtcenter.co.jp

IOP Conf. Series: Materials Science and Engineering 1121 (2021) 012001 doi:10.1088/1757-899X/1121/1/012001

A Brief Overview of Texture and Anisotropy

Anthony D. Rollett[1], **Günter Gottstein**[2]
[1]5000 Forbes Ave., Pittsburgh, PA 15213 USA
[2]Institute of Physical Metallurgy and Materials Physics, RWTH Aachen University, Germany
E-mail: [1]rollett@andrew.cmu.edu
E-mail: [2]Gottstein@imm.rwth-aachen.de

Abstract. A brief overview of the state of texture and anisotropy is provided with the motive of inspiring younger readers to engage in this topic. The International Conference on Texture of Materials *ICOTOM* has been active since 1969 up through the recent 19th meeting in Japan in 2021. The series initially focused on the problem of reconstructing three-dimensional orientation distributions from diffraction data which typically provided two-dimensional projections in the form of pole figures following the pioneering work of Bunge [1] and Roe [2]. In recent years, the advent of automated orientation mapping in the scanning electron microscope [3] and 3D mapping via synchrotron x-rays [4][5] has provided vastly more detailed data on texture and, crucially, has connected texture more closely with microstructure. Alongside this has been the development of simulation tools to predict texture formation and the anisotropic properties of polycrystalline materials. This has mostly been a accomplished via a mix of mesoscale models, e.g. [6], and more detailed methods that include microstructure. The latter are predominantly based on the finite element method complemented by the spectral method [7].

1. Introduction

From the earliest days of x-ray diffraction, researchers realized that the patterns from polycrystalline samples being captured on film were sometimes anisotropic in an obvious fashion, e.g., the work of Wever on changes in preferred orientation from rolling aluminum sheet [8]. Eventually interference counters replaced film [9], no doubt helped by the strong interest in radioactivity at the time. Within a few years, Geiger counters were in regular use for transmission measurements of pole figures, e.g., Decker *et al.* [10]. Although the variation in absorbance as a function of transmission through a sample can be estimated, Schulz's invention of the back reflection method diminished the challenges of quantitative analysis of pole figure data [11]. Shortly thereafter, Hu *et al.* showed how to combine transmission and reflection data to obtain complete pole figures [12]. Bunk *et al.* worked out an apparatus for translating large samples under the x-ray beam for coarse-grained samples [13]. For what became the standard approach of pole figures measured in reflection, the problem of defocussing and the almost inevitable roll-off in intensity towards the edge required careful calibration of each instrument, which is documented in standard texts [14]. Interpretation of pole figure data, however, was contentious because, except for a few instances where a very few orientations were identifiable, most textures were too complex for quantitative analysis. The key development in texture analysis came in the 1960s with the convergent development of mathematical and numerical analysis of orientation distributions by Bunge [1] and Roe [2]. The latter, however, developed his analysis for polymers at a time when the research community associated that class of materials had less interest than in metals, e.g., [15]. Roe moved onto other problems whereas Bunge devoted his whole career to the subject and is commemorated with an award in his name issued at each meeting of the International Conference on Textures of Materials (ICOTOM). Both Bunge and Roe realized that the spherical harmonic functions used in physics could be adapted for use in analyzing pole figure data. More specifically, it is possible to write down linear equations between the coefficients derived from fitting the (spherical) pole figure data and those for the underlying three-dimensional orientation distribution. This approach is often referred to as the "series expansion method" because of the mathematics used. The relationship between pole figure data and texture is also often referred to as the *fundamental equation of texture* because inverting it to compute the orientation distribution function or ODF enabled fully quantitative description of texture.

2. Ghost Problem

With the theoretical foundation developed by Bunge and the availability of sufficient computer power it became possible to compute the orientation distribution function from several pole figures, the number depending on crystal symmetry. Since a pole figure is the projection of the ODF along a crystallographic direction, a series expansion of both in terms of spherical harmonics leads to a relation between the coefficients in both series expansions, so that the ODF coefficients can be calculated from several incomplete pole figures. As remarked above, this was a real quantum leap in texture research since now a new level of texture analysis and interpretation was reached, and in the 1970s texture research was dominated by the measurement of important texture types and a computation of their respective ODF. Soon it was realized, however, that in the computed ODF orientation appeared which obviously did not exist in the pole figure, particularly for very pronounced textures. The reason was soon discovered. The so called 'ghost orientations' owed to the symmetry of X-ray reflection, which did not discriminate between a direction (hkl) and $(\bar{h}\bar{k}\bar{l})$. Therefore, only the even coefficient of the ODF series expansion could be determined, whereas the odd coefficients remained undetermined and therefore caused artificial values in the ODF. Texture research in the 1980s was essentially dedicated to this problem. Lücke and coworkers computed a 'ghost map' for the prominent texture types in fcc metals or decomposed the ODF in a set of ideal orientations with respective scatter to compute the volume fraction of the main components. Bunge tried to break the symmetry by forcing the ODF intensity positive in the entire orientation space (typically the Euler space) or by setting the ODF value to zero where virtually no intensity was expected. Also, other approaches were proposed for instance by Williams, Imhof, Matthies Vinel (WIMV) [16] or by the application of specific criteria like maximum entropy algorithms (Schaeben) [17]. In the end it turned out that the so-called "true ODF" remained undetermined within a certain albeit small range. Any ODF from that range would render the same pole figures. This problem was essentially solved by the development of fast, large scale single grain orientation measurements by orientation imaging microscopy with EBSD, see Section 5.

3. Simulation of Texture Development and Anisotropy

Within a few years of the solution of the problem of generating orientation distributions from pole figure data so that texture could be understood in 3D, efforts began to predict texture development under plastic deformation according the physics of dislocation motion, i.e., computing the contribution of each slip system as $d\tau \cdot \mathbf{b} \otimes \mathbf{n}$. Taylor had already made such a prediction for tensile deformation of fcc metals [18] but the advent of computers made this routine. Bishop & Hill provided theory that reduced the problem to a search through 28 discrete stress states activating multiple slip (in each grain) [19] although further work was needed to arrive at a compatible set of slip rates. Through the efforts of Kallend & Davies [20] as well as (less well known) Leffers [21], it became apparent that the Taylor model, i.e., boundary condition of uniform strain in each grain produced better agreement with experiment than assuming uniform stress (and, by implication, using Schmid factors to predict slip activity). The imperfect agreement obtained prompted much discussion about the boundary conditions and the "relaxed constraints" approach of Honneff & Mecking [22] provided one of the earliest indications of the influence of grain shape on plastic deformation. Eshelby theory [23] came to be applied to the interaction between a given grain and its surroundings which culminated in the widely used viscoplastic self-consistent algorithm of Lebensohn and Tomé [6]. Many workers have incorporated so-called "crystal plasticity" into finite element codes, e.g., Dawson and co-workers [24] which has enabled the effects of the inevitable gradients in strain and stress to be taken into account in simulations. Spectral methods have also been developed for modeling elasto-viscoplastic polycrystals and have certain advantages [7]. Nevertheless, our ability to predict texture development with continuum models remains imperfect which suggests that simulating the behavior of large populations of dislocations may ultimately be required; this approach has already had some success at simulating strain hardening [25].

Understanding the anisotropic properties of materials is closely related to quantitative descriptions of texture and calculation of texture development. Nye's classic text on the properties of crystals [26], followed by Newnham's expansion [27] to a wider range of properties provide a theoretical basis and many properties of polycrystals can be estimated as a volume average of the single crystal behavior. Even for elastic response, however, one must choose between different boundary conditions. Just as mentioned above for texture modeling, the simplest lower (Reuss) and upper (Voigt) bounds on the elastic stiffness assume either iso-stress or iso-strain; many use the Hill average of these two [28]. Depending on the choice, the fitted coefficients for the ODF of a material lead to a very efficient calculation of any type of elastic modulus in any direction [29]. Plastic anisotropy is more complex than for elasticity but uses the same approach as described above: instead of repeating increments of strain in the same direction to accumulate total (plastic) strain, the directionality of, e.g., strength is calculated by imposing different strain increments on the same texture. Early work was reported by Kallend & Davies, for example [30] and many details are available in textbooks such as Kocks, Tomé and Wenk [14]. The most common way to visualize the results is to plot yield surfaces, i.e., the variation in yield stress as a function of direction in relation to a reference frame embedded in the material. Although the volume invariance in plastic deformation effectively eliminates the hydrostatic component of stress (and strain), one still has five components from which to draw pairs for plots. The reader should beware of relying on only plotting pairs of, say, principal components or the pi-plane. The practical consequences of plastic anisotropy appear in metal working processes such as sheet forming where embedding plastic anisotropy in a finite element code enables quantitative evaluation of the influence of texture [31]. It is also important to remember that strain anisotropy may be larger in magnitude than stress anisotropy, which is apparent in the variation in the "r-value" or Lankford coefficient that is closely related to the capability of sheet metals to undergo deep drawing [32].

4. Texture in Geological Materials

In contrast to texture research in metallurgy, where the measurement and prediction of anisotropy of processed material was of primary concern, texture research in geology served mainly to reveal and understand the geological history of minerals. When reading geological literature, it is important to note that the term texture typically relates to the morphology of a sample rather than to its crystallographic texture, which is referred to in geology as preferred orientation. Research on geological materials is substantially more complicated than in metals due to the fact that most minerals have a lower crystal symmetry than metallic materials, which dominantly have a cubic or in fewer cases a hexagonal crystal structure, whereas minerals often show only triclinic symmetry. This required the measurement of many more pole figures and computation of high order series expansion in order to obtain full information on the orientation distribution. On the other hand, geological materials have typically a much larger grain size, which makes the measurement with conventional X-ray texture goniometers virtually impossible. Therefore, crystallographic textures in geological materials are typically measured by neutron diffraction in transmission mode where a larger number of grains is encountered by a neutron beam on its way through the volume. Such measurements cannot be performed in a private laboratory but requires access to large research facilities, and owing to the low interaction of neutrons with crystalline materials the acquisition of pole figures usually takes a long time. Nevertheless, in the course of time texture research in geology has advanced to a most valuable tool for earth sciences, q.v. Wenk's chapter on geological textures in [14].

5. Electron Back Scatter Diffraction (EBSD)

Most researchers in materials science accept Electron Back Scatter Diffraction (EBSD) as an everyday characterization tool albeit one requiring additional care in sample preparation to remove surface damage. Although advances continue to be made in terms of both hardware and the software to analyze the results, most of the technique is described in the book by Schwartz *et al.* [3] and an encyclopedia article by Rollett & Barmak [33]. Once it became clear that individual Kikuchi maps could be indexed automatically [34][35], for which we note that the application of the Hough transform proved to be a crucial image processing step [36], then interfacing to the SEM to control the beam implemented automated mapping. Given that commercial EBSD systems are highly reliable when damage-free samples are scanned, it is useful in the limited space to offer some pros and cons from a texture perspective. For typical grain sizes in the range $10 - 100\ \mu m$, choosing a scan size and step size to obtain good resolution of each grain often means that the field of view only includes a few dozen grains. This is *not* enough to describe the texture of most materials unless the texture is very strong. A rule of thumb is that one needs ~ 500 grains to represent most textures and more quantitative guidance was given by Matthies & Wagner [37]. Another caution has to do with the "inverse pole figure color" that is so often used, mostly, one suspects, because the resulting figures are pleasingly colorful: by assigning color to each pixel based on which crystal direction is closest to a chosen sample direction (generally, the surface normal), the 3-parameter nature of orientation is reduced to a 2-parameter description. Accordingly, the reader is encouraged to experiment with other color schemes. EBSD surpasses traditional texture measurement, of course, by revealing local variations in orientation which have revealed important details about orientation gradients, for example [38][39][40]. As discussed in section 7, EBSD opened up the study of grain boundaries and interfaces in general.

6. Controversies in Texture

Despite the use of the Schultz method and the application of point counters the measurement of pole figures in the 1950s remained a tedious and time-consuming procedure, since the counter intensity was usually recorded on a time-linear recorder which required the manual transcription of a linear time-intensity profiles on meter long recorder paper into an intensity distribution in the stereographic projection. This difficulty was essentially removed by the pole figure plotter, where the intensity was associated with a specific color and plotted in a stereographic projection. While the recording of pole figures was substantially simplified by these developments, the analysis and interpretation of the pole figures remained difficult since the pole figures usually consisted of continuous intensity distributions. Despite differences in detail four types of pole figures of rolled sheet were identified in fcc metals, namely the low alloy, high temperature type, the so called 'copper-type' texture (Fig. 1) and its associated annealing texture (Fig. 2). The "cube texture" and the high alloy low temperature type, the so called "brass-texture" with the respective "brass recrystallization texture" after annealing of the rolled sheet. Two kinds of analytical descriptions

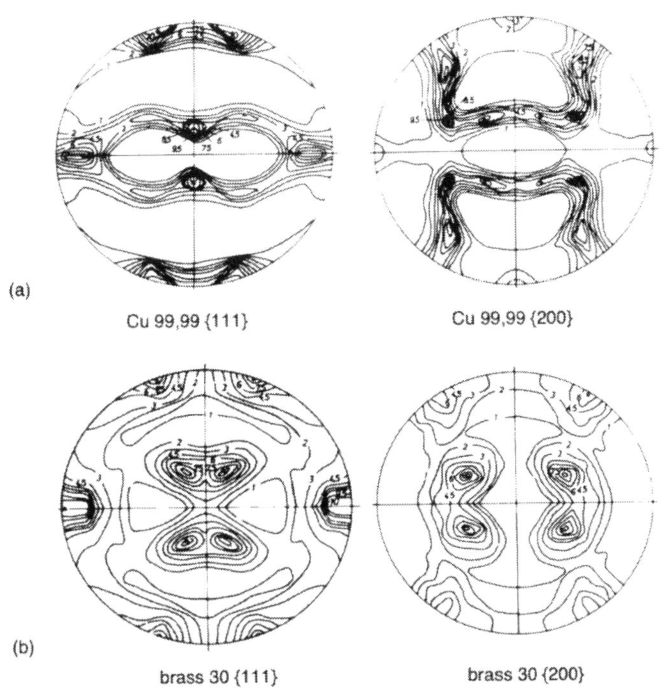

Figure 1. Rolling texture of Cu and Cu30Zn (brass30) in terms of their 111 and 200 pole figures.

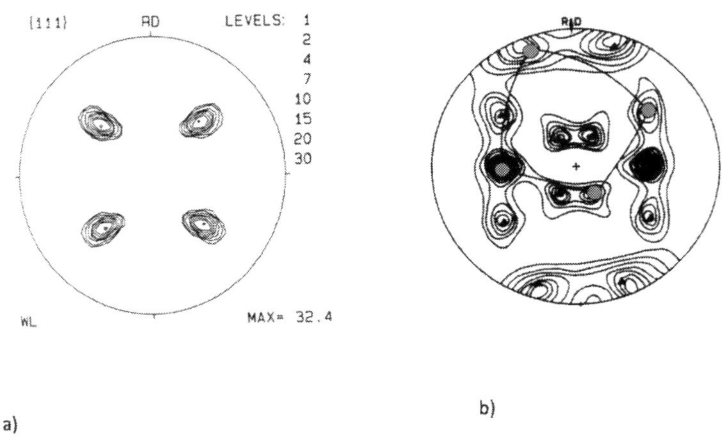

Figure 2. 111 pole figures of the annealing textures of pure Al (a) and Cu30Zn (b).

of the continuous intensity distributions were proposed, namely the partial fiber (i.e., a rotation about a specific crystallographic axis) approach and the scattered ideal orientation approach. Eventually the latter description became widely accepted but it required extensive TEM work to identify the major ideal orientations, notably the S-orientation (i.e., $(123)[63\bar{4}]$) besides copper and brass orientation. It is interesting to mention in this context that the ODF representation of rolling textures is nowadays typically described by respective fibers in orientation (Euler) space for both fcc (Fig. 3) and bcc metals (Fig. 4). A major scientific dispute arose about the reason for the two different types of rolling textures, i.e. between brass and copper type texture. The brass texture was attributed to cross slip by one school and deformation twinning by another, until it finally could became evident from TEM work that the low temperature texture was substantially influenced by deformation twinning. The fiercest classical controversy, however, was fought over the development of the recrystallization texture, occasionally touching even the personal level. Dillamore and coworkers associated the recrystallization texture on the basis of transmission electron microscopy and deformation texture simulations according to the Taylor theory (Sect. 3) with a dominant nucleation process during recrystallization (oriented nucleation, ON) [41] whereas Lücke and coworkers promoted the theory of dominant growth of recrystallized grains with a specific orientation relation to the deformed microstructure, specifically in fcc metals and alloys the famous 40°⟨111⟩ rotation (oriented growth, OG) which they derived from growth selection experiments [42]. Only after extensive TEM and EBSD work, refined texture analysis and advanced recrystallization simulation results [43] is it nowadays obvious that both processes, nucleation and growth, and maybe even elastic anisotropy [44] play a role.

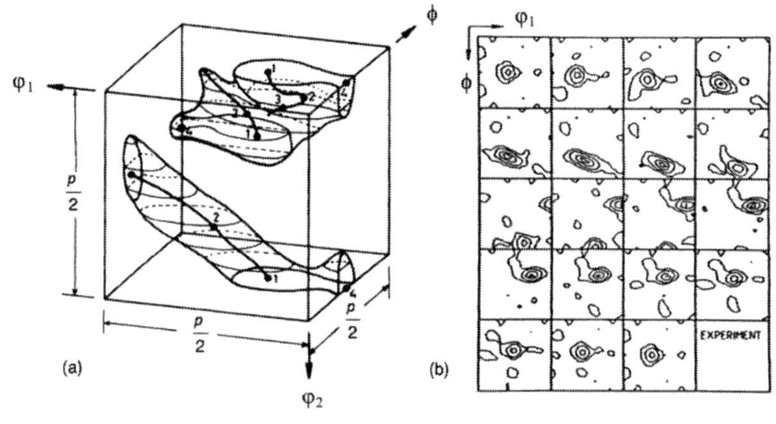

Figure 3. ODF of rolled CU in 3D view (a) and 5° sections parallel to ϕ_2 (b).

7. Interfacial Texture and Properties

A major advance, and extension from classical topics, was to consider the crystallographic character of grain boundaries as *interface texture* and to evaluate it in an analogously statistical fashion to bulk or volumetric texture. This development depended almost entirely on the availability of EBSD, section 5, that could provide large area orientation maps with large numbers of grains, each pair of which has a distinct boundary. The obvious limitation of not knowing the inclination of each individual boundary on a planar cross-section was overcome via a stereological and statistical approach in which sufficient examples of (the zones of traces of) boundaries of each misorientation class were accumulated in a stereogram [45][46]. By normalizing the accumulated intensities and using the local crystal frame as a reference, the distribution of grain boundary normals for each misorientation class is revealed. It quickly became apparent, e.g., that symmetric tilt boundaries did not exhibit any unusually high frequency whereas low energy surfaces predict low energy grain boundaries. Moreover, a strong (anti-)correlation emerged between grain boundary frequency versus energy [47] and the

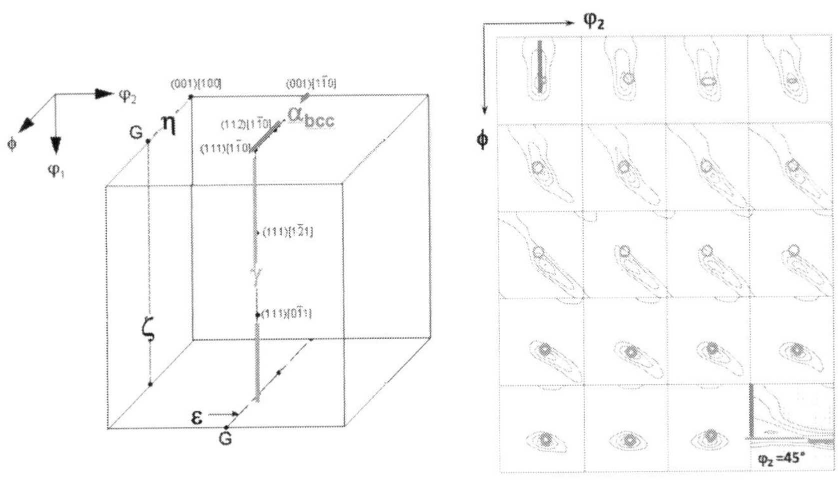

Figure 4. Fibers in the ODFs of rolled and annealed bcc materials.

simulated grain boundary energies of grain boundaries were well correlated with experimentally derived values [48]. Measurement of interfacial energies has long been (mostly) performed by measuring dihedral angles at triple junctions on the assumption that local equilibrium holds. Being able to perform automated serial sectioning with EBSD [49] opened up a wide range of investigation into 3D microstructure [50], including properties of grain boundaries such as energy. The key step in extracting energies from measurements of dihedral angles was to recognize that all the data had to be considered together [51] and that the capillarity vector [52] was the best basis for obtaining reliable results [53]. Although most attention has been given to grain boundaries, surfaces can be characterized in a similar fashion [54], as well as heterophase interfaces [55], and that surface energies can be linked to grain boundary energies.

8. Synchrotron x-rays for Grain Mapping, Diffraction Microscopy

Although the application of synchrotron radiation (x-rays) to materials science in general and texture in particular has a long history, e.g., [56], it is in the past decade that this activity has flowered. A recent book by Poulsen [57] provides a great deal of detail about the various techniques that are now available. Apart from substantial improvements in the resolution of detectors as well as the speed at which data can be read out, the key development was to devise ways in which to identify sets of diffraction spots that originate from the same grain (orientation). This was the major algorithmic and computational challenge because, unlike EBSD, illuminating a polycrystalline sample with x-rays inevitably results in diffraction from multiple grains at any given rotational position of the sample. Nevertheless in its various forms, diffraction microscopy [4] can be used to map 3D polycrystals in a completely non-destructive manner. In one setting with the detector placed far enough away from the sample to identify Bragg rings, known as far-field, each grain is indexed for orientation ($\sim 0.01°$), center of mass ($\sim 20\mu m$) and elastic strain ($\sim 10^{-4}$), where the resolution is noted with each quantity. In another setting with the detector very close to the sample, known as near field, Bragg rings cannot be distinguished but the resulting orientation map has a resolution slightly coarser than a micron, albeit without the elastic strain information. Thanks to the non-destructive quality of the technique, it is easy to understand that many different types of microstructural evolution can be performed from mechanical deformation to grain growth. Many examples of the application of diffraction microscopy can be found in the recent review by Bernier et al. [4] and further development continues, e.g. [58][59].

9. Conclusion and Prognosis

This article provides a brief summary of the development of the subject of texture (*fabric* in geology) and a selection of its achievements, which have been transformed into practical tools for analysis in many cases. For example, including elastic anisotropy in finite element or spectral calculations is considered routine and adding plastic anisotropy to that is straightforward, albeit with a non-trivial computational cost. Measuring millions of orientations in EBSD in a few hours is considered routine, which while not guaranteeing statistically valid texture measurement, certainly provides large volumes of unambiguously single orientation data. Looking forward, however, one should ask what challenges are apparent at this point. One example is that of the evolution of texture on a local basis within grains. Throughout the literature there are examples of comparisons between both 2D and 3D orientation mapping of successive stages of (plastic) deformation versus simulations which show good statistical agreement but much variation at the local scale across individual grains [60]. One can speculate that the constitutive relations commonly employed that capture the physics-based laws for slip systems do not represent dislocation motion well enough. There are, however, a number of other ideas that have been put forward and all of these deserve to be tested as hypotheses. Another example is that of grain growth which has long been considered to be a straightforward example of curvature-driven coarsening, see, e.g., [61]. Despite the empirical result that polycrystal coarsening obeys (in some limiting sense) a parabolic law, $R^2 \propto time$, the growth rate of individual grains is clearly more complicated in reality [62] and does not follow the expectations of the theory for growth or shrinkage of 3D grains in a polycrystalline network [63]. Even these brief examples serve to illustrate that texture is a rich field full of puzzles for the young researcher to tackle and solve.

10. References

[1] Bunge H J 1965 *Zeitschrift Fur Metallkunde* **56** 872
[2] Roe R J 1965 *Journal of Applied Physics* **36** 2024
[3] Schwartz A J, Kumar M, Adams B L and Field D P 2009 *Electron Backscatter Diffraction in Materials Science* 2nd ed (New York: Springer)
[4] Bernier J V, Suter R M, Rollett A D and Almer J 2020 *Annual Reviews in Materials Research* **50** 395–436
[5] Poulsen H 2020 *Current Opinion in Solid State and Materials Science* **24** 100820 ISSN 1359-0286 URL `http://www.sciencedirect.com/science/article/pii/S1359028620300188`
[6] Lebensohn R A and Tomé C N 1993 *Acta metallurgica et materialia* **41** 2611–2624
[7] Lebensohn R A and Rollett A D 2020 *Computational Materials Science* **173** 109336 ISSN 0927-0256 URL `http://www.sciencedirect.com/science/article/pii/S0927025619306354`
[8] Wever F 1924 *Zeitschrift für physik* **28** 69–90
[9] Lindemann R and Trost A 1940 *Zeitschrift für Physik* **115** 456–468
[10] Decker B, Asp E and Harker D 1948 *Journal of Applied Physics* **19** 388–392
[11] Schulz L 1949 *Journal of Applied Physics* **20** 1030
[12] Hu H, Sperry P and Beck P 1952 *J. of Metals* 76–81
[13] Bunk W, Lucke K and Masing G 1954 *Zeitschrift für Metallkunde* **45** 584–593
[14] Kocks U F, Tomé C and Wenk H R 1998 *Texture and Anisotropy* (Cambridge University Press, Cambridge, UK)
[15] Wassermann G and Grewen J 2013 *Texturen metallischer Werkstoffe* (Springer-Verlag)
[16] Matthies S, Wenk H R and Vinel G W 1988 *Journal of Applied Crystallography* **21** 285–304
[17] Schaeben H and Fundenberger J J 1994 *Journal of Applied Crystallography* **27** 177–189 part 2
[18] Taylor G 1938 *J. Inst. Metals (U.K.)* **62** 307
[19] Bishop J and Hill R 1951 *Philosophical Magazine* **42** 1298–1307
[20] Kallend J and Davies G 1972 *Philosophical Magazine* **25** 471–490
[21] Leffers T 1968 *physica status solidi (b)* **25** 337–344
[22] Honneff H and Mecking H 1978 *ICOTOM-5, Aachen, W. Germany* **1** 265
[23] Eshelby J D 1957 *Proceedings of the Royal Society of London Series A - Mathematical Physical and Engineering Sciences* **A241** 376–396

[24] Mathur K and Dawson P 1988 *International Journal of Plasticity* **5** 67–94
[25] Berbenni S, Taupin V and Lebensohn R A 2020 *Journal of the Mechanics and Physics of Solids* **135** 103808 ISSN 0022-5096
[26] Nye J F 1957 *Physical Properties of Crystals* (Oxford: Clarendon Press)
[27] Newnham R E 2005 *Properties of Materials* (Oxford: Oxford University Press)
[28] Hill R 1998 *The mathematical theory of plasticity* (Oxford University Press)
[29] Bunge H 1982 *Texture Analysis in Materials Science* (London, UK: Butterworths)
[30] Kallend J and Davies G 1971 *Journal of the Institute of Metals* **5** 257–260
[31] Raabe D, Zhao Z S and Roters F 2001 *Steel Research* **72** 421–426
[32] Rollett A D, Canova G R and Kocks U F 1986 The effect of the cube texture component on the earing behavior of rolled f.c.c. metals *Formability and Metallurgical Structure* vol 1 ed Sachdev A K and Embury J D (TMS, Warrendale, PA) pp 147–157
[33] Rollett A D and Barmak K 2015 Orientation mapping *Physical Metallurgy (Fifth Edition)* vol 1 ed Laughlin D E and Hono K (Elsevier) chap 11, pp 1113–1142 5th ed
[34] Wright S I, Zhao J W and Adams B L 1991 *Textures and Microstructures* **13** 123–131
[35] Jensen D J and Schmidt N H 1991 *Textures and Microstructures* **14** 97–102 part 1-2
[36] Duda R O and Hart P E 1972 *Communications Of The Acm* **15** 11–
[37] Matthies S and Wagner F 1999 Using sets of individual orientations for odf determination *ICOTOM-12* vol 1 ed Szpunar J A (NRC Research Press) pp 40–45
[38] El-Dasher B, Adams B and Rollett A 2003 *Scripta materialia* **48** 141–145
[39] Mishra S K, Pant P, Narasimhan K, Rollett A D and Samajdar I 2009 *Scripta materialia* **61** 273–276
[40] Subedi S, Pokharel R and Rollett A D 2015 *Materials Science and Eng. A* **638** 348–356 ISSN 0921-5093
[41] Dillamore I and Katoh H 1974 *Metal Sci.* **8** 73
[42] Liebmann B, Lucke K, Graham C D, Cahn R W and Dunn C G 1956 *Transactions of the American Institute of Mining and Metallurgical Engineers* **206** 1413–1416
[43] Doherty R D, Hughes D A, Humphreys F J, Jonas J J, Jensen D J, Kassner M E, King W E, McNelley T R, McQueen H J and Rollett A D 1997 *Materials Science And Engineering A-Structural Materials Properties Microstructure And Processing* **238** 219–274
[44] Lee D N and Han H N 2013 *Recent developments in the Study of Recrystallization* 3–59
[45] Saylor D M, Morawiec A and Rohrer G S 2003 *Acta materialia* **51** 3663–3674
[46] Saylor D, El-Dasher B, Adams B and Rohrer G 2004 *Metallurgical and Materials Transactions* **35A** 1981–1989
[47] Rohrer G S, Holm E A, Rollett A D, Foiles S M, Li J and Olmsted D L 2010 *Acta materialia* **58** 5063–5069
[48] Holm E A, Rohrer G S, Foiles S M, Rollett A D, Miller H M and Olmsted D L 2011 *Acta materialia* **59** 5250–5256
[49] Uchic M D, Groeber M A, Dimiduk D M and Simmons J P 2006 *Scripta materialia* **55** 23–28
[50] Rollett A D, Lee S B, Campman R and Rohrer G S 2007 *Annual Review of Materials Research* **37** 627–658
[51] Adams B L, Ta'asan S, Kinderlehrer D, Livshits I, Mason D E, Wu C T, Mullins W W, Rohrer G S, Rollett A D and Saylor D M 1999 *Interface Science* **7** 321–338
[52] Saylor D M and Rohrer G S 2001 *Interface Science* **9** 35–42
[53] Saylor D M, Morawiec A and Rohrer G S 2002 *Journal of The American Ceramic Society* **85** 3081–3083
[54] Saylor D M, Mason D E and Rohrer G S 1998 The influence of surface and grain boundary tangent plane anisotropy on thermal groove geometry in magnesia *Grain Growth in Polycrystalline Materials III (ICGG-3)* ed Weiland H, Adams B L and Rollett A D (TMS) pp 359–364
[55] Lee S B, LeDonne J E, Lim S C V, Beyerlein I J and Rollett A D 2012 *Acta materialia* **60** 1747–1761
[56] Gottstein G 1986 *Scripta metallurgica* **20** 1791–1794
[57] Poulsen H 2004 *Three-dimensional X-ray diffraction microscopy - Mapping polycrystals and their dynamics* (*Springer Tracts In Modern Physics* vol 205) (Springer)
[58] Shade P A, Musinski W D, Obstalecki M, Pagan D C, Beaudoin A J, Bernier J V and Turner T J 2019 *Current Opinion in Solid State and Materials Science* **23** 100763
[59] Shen Y F, Liu H and Suter R M 2020 *Current Opinion in Solid State and Materials Science* **24** 100852
[60] Pokharel R, Lind J, Kanjarla A, Lebensohn R, Li S, Kenesei P, Suter R and Rollett A 2014 *Annual Reviews of Condensed Matter Physics* **5** 317–346
[61] Humphreys J, Rohrer G S and Rollett A 2017 Chapter 11 - grain growth following recrystallization *Recrystallization and Related Annealing Phenomena (Third Edition)* ed Humphreys J, Rohrer G S and Rollett A (Oxford: Elsevier) pp 375 – 429 third edition ed ISBN 978-0-08-098235-9 URL `https://www.sciencedirect.com/science/article/pii/B9780080982359000112`
[62] Bhattacharya A, Shen Y F, Hefferan C M, Li S F, Lind J, Suter R M and Rohrer G S 2019 *Acta Materialia* **167** 40 – 50 URL `http://www.sciencedirect.com/science/article/pii/S1359645419300369`

[63] MacPherson R D and Srolovitz D J 2007 *Nature* **446** 1053–1055

IOP Conf. Series: Materials Science and Engineering 1121 (2021) 012002 doi:10.1088/1757-899X/1121/1/012002

Texture Observation and Control in Metal Manufacturing : Theory and Practice

Leo A.I. Kestens[1,2], Jesus Galan Lopez[(2)], Hadi Pirgazi[1,2], Tuan Nguyen-Minh[1,3] and Roumen H. Petrov[1,2]

[1]Ghent University, Technologiepark 46, 9052 Gent, Belgium
[2]Delft University of Technology, Mekelweg 2, 2628 CD Delft, Netherlands
[3]CRM Group, Technologiepark 48 zone A1b, 9052 Gent, Belgium

Leo.Kestens@ugent.be

Abstract. It is generally known that the crystallographic texture of metal alloys is formed during subsequent solid-state transformations, occurring during manufacturing of the product. Applied to the specific case of metal sheet manufacturing, it implies that the texture of the finished product is the result of the crystallographic phenomena involved in hot rolling, cold rolling and annealing. Austenite-to-ferrite phase transformation, plastic deformation, recrystallization and grain growth are the dominant solid-state transformations occurring during thermo-mechanical processing of steel sheet. Moreover, the crystallographic texture ensuing of a solid-state transformation is a characteristic feature of the physical mechanics underlying this transformation and therefore, a precise understanding of the texture formation mechanisms is an important tool in gaining a better understanding of metal physics phenomena. The present paper will give a brief overview of the current state-of-the-art in these issues.

1. Introduction

The crystallographic texture is the microstructural state variable pertaining to the statistical distribution of crystallographic orientations in a polycrystalline material. Though an early monograph on crystallographic textures of metal alloys was published already in 1939 by Wassermann (2nd edition by Wassermann and Grewen [1]), a real boost to the field was given with the publication of the seminal work by Bunge in 1969 (Mathematische Methoden der Texturanalyse [2]). For a more detailed description of the early development of texture research the reader is referred to Bunge [3].

The research carried out within the texture community can be broadly divided in three different categories: (i) research on texture dependent process-structure-property relations for structural and functional materials, (ii) crystallographic aspects of material science phenomena and (iii) crystallographic phase and orientation contrast for microstructural characterization. The present paper will present a brief and kaleidoscopic overview of recent development of the versatile aspects of texture research.

2. Textures in relation to process, microstructure and properties

2.1. Thermomechanical processing of metal sheet through rolling and annealing

It is well understood that texture plays a dominant role for a number of metal sheet properties. Well-known examples are the Lankford R-value (i.e. the so called normal and planar anisotropy) [4], the magnetic properties of electrical steels [5], the earing behavior of can stock aluminum, the roping/ridging behavior of aluminum [6]. This has motivated the detailed study of texture formation during metal sheet manufacturing for a wide variety of alloys. During slab casting, hot/cold rolling and annealing the texture of the finished product is formed and in each processing step the texture inherited from the previous step may be modified. E.g. during cold rolling a texture is developed that is determined by the plastic velocity field that is induced by a specific rolling configuration. When the sheet is recrystallization annealed afterwards, the cold rolling textures will be transferred to a recrystallization texture.

In general, textures induced by plastic deformation depend on the crystallographic structure of the material (which in turn determines the potential slip or twinning systems), on the specific velocity field of the applied plastic deformation and on the initial texture prior to plastic deformation, but to a lesser extent on the precise chemical composition of the alloy. It is quite remarkable that with the rather coarse and approximate assumptions of the Full Constraint Taylor (FCT) model, ignoring phenomena such as strain hardening or strain localization, the cold deformation texture of single phase alloys can be predicted with reasonable accuracy for low and medium strains if the displacement field and the potentially active slip and twinning systems are known.

The reason for the success of the FCT model, and its more advanced successors, is because of the fact that one single texture component (i.e. a crystal orientation) is distributed over many physical grains of the polycrystalline aggregate. Although the local behavior of each individual grain can be very deviatoric with respect to the theoretical prediction, it is apparently true that these local deviations cancel out in the mean field description of the average crystal rotations. The validity of a homogenized mean-field description during cold rolling of a 6xxx aluminum alloy was recently confirmed in a near-insitu experiment reported by Pirgazi and Kestens [7].

Unfortunately the same level of accuracy cannot be obtained for the prediction of recrystallization textures. Despite decades of intense metallurgical research there are as yet no models available that are able to simulate the texture after recrystallization annealing with sufficient precision so as to reliably predict the texture dependent properties mentioned above (assuming there is an accurate property state model available that allows to express the property under consideration as a function of the texture). One of the reasons is that specifically the nucleation stage during recrystallization (i.e. the initial stage of subgrain growth, coalescence or bulging [8] critically depends on the detailed local features of the deformation structure for which the statistical methods of crystal plasticity models do not have sufficient resolution to provide an accurate description. Hence, advanced recrystallization models need to be supplied with detailed experimental data of the deformation structure (e.g. by EBSD or TKD measurements), which are far from trivial to obtain and which represent an approach that does not allow for a through-process simulation. Perhaps a viable alternative is provided by the full-field crystal plasticity finite element models (CPFEM) [9], which, in principle, are capable of reproducing the detailed features of the deformation microstructure. It remains to be verified, though, whether the microstructural resolution and accuracy of such models are enough to allow for an accurate simulation of thermally activated recovery and recrystallization models.

2.2. Texture formation in non-conventional processes: Additive Manufacturing

Additive manufacturing (AM) based techniques for production of near-net-shape metallic materials have been recently in the centre of attention of many researchers in the fields of materials science and mechanical engineering. AM processes uses computer controlled high energy sources, which layer by layer melts or deposits the metallic powder/feeding wire and produces fully dense components. Texture evolution in the AM processes is based on the directional solidification of metal in the melt-pools with very high cooling rates. Despite the texture study of the rolled sheets in which the crystallographic orientations are considered based on the sample reference frame composed of three reference directions (i.e. RD, TD and ND), crystallographic orientations in the AM products are studied with respect to only one sample reference direction, i.e. the building direction (BD).

Texture of the as-built AM products is a result of (i) the directional solidification in which the preferred solidification direction (i.e. <001> in BCC and FCC crystals [10]) is parallel to the direction of heat flow (i.e. perpendicular to the melt-pool boundaries), and (ii) of the processing parameters and the occurrence of solid state phase transformation during cooling cycles. For example, for the alloys fabricated by selective laser melting (SLM) process, it has been reported that variation of the laser scanning parameters (e.g. laser power, scanning speed) and/or the hatching strategy can change the melt-pool geometry and the resulting crystallographic texture [11-14]. Consequently, different fibre textures such as <001>||BD [15;16], <011>||BD [12] and <111>||BD [17;18] have been observed in BCC and FCC alloys processed by the SLM process.

The occurrence of solid state phase transformation (e.g. FCC to BCC in steels) in alloys with allotropic crystal structures will change the solidification texture in the AM products. Dominant texture components after phase transformation is expected to follow the governing orientation relationship between the two phases. Furthermore, the fast cooling rate of the AM processes results in the formation of variants with equal statistical probability which eventually reduces the overall texture intensity in alloys featuring phase transformation [19;20].

3. Microstructural characterization and data processing based on electron diffraction contrast

In the last decades of the 20th century Electron Back Scatter Diffraction (EBSD) has developed into a powerful and versatile microstructural characterization technique with an optimum combination of reasonable resolution (~30-50 nm in a SEM with Field Emission Gun), large field width (~mm^2) and angular resolution of ~1°. The texture community has largely contributed to the development of this technique. Perhaps the most interesting quality of orientation contrast imaging based on EBSD is the fact that each image represents a huge set of crystallographic data that is ideally suitable for post-processing. Given the fact that artificial intelligence and machine learning algorithms will play an increasing role in the future, it appears that EBSD images are particularly suited for this type of quantitative analysis.

EBSD is currently a mature and routine tool employed for microstructural characterization both in industrial and academic research. The present section highlights 2 recent developments in the field of orientation contrast microscopy: 3D-EBSD and Transmission Kikuchi Diffraction. As EBSD allows for concurrently gathering orientation and microstructural information, it renders EBSD maps suitable to provide information on the multi-variate Grain Size Orientation Distribution Functions, which will be introduced below.

3.1. 3D-EBSD by slice and viewing

For decades, conventional microstructural characterization techniques such as electron backscattering diffraction (EBSD), scanning electron microscopy (SEM) and optical microscopy have been extensively used to uncover microstructural details in different length scales. Among these, EBSD has proven its

IOP Conf. Series: Materials Science and Engineering 1121 (2021) 012002 doi:10.1088/1757-899X/1121/1/012002

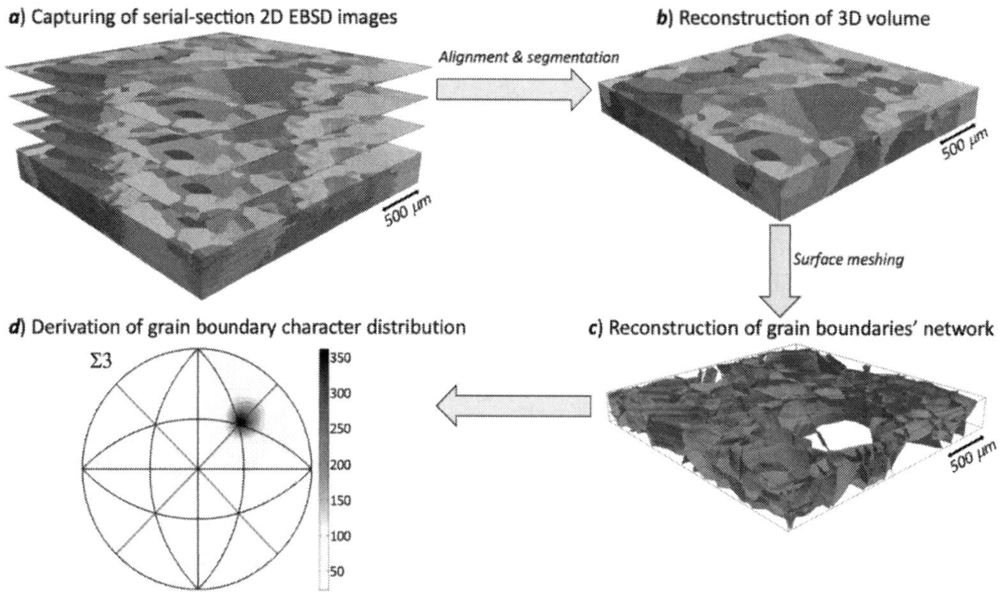

Figure 1. Procedure for 3D reconstruction of microstructure and grain boundaries' network in a large-grained nickel sample based on the serial sectioning technique combined with EBSD.

potential in providing high-resolution digital images in which each pixel contains microstructural and crystallographic information. With the post-processing of these digital images, one can extract tremendous amount of information, regarding for example grain size and distribution, local crystallographic orientation and texture, crystallographic and morphological phases, grain boundary type, etc. The capability of the above-mentioned techniques is limited to the observation from planar surfaces (i.e. two dimensional (2D)). The microstructures, however, are of three-dimensional (3D) nature and a full characterization of many features such as e.g. grain boundary planes and true shape of microstructural constituents demands the utilization of a 3D based characterization technique [21;22]. With the latest progress in equipment design and computational speed, various techniques for 3D characterization of microstructures have been developed. Atom probe tomography [23;24], X-ray tomography[25;26], High-energy X-ray diffraction microscopy (HEDM) [27;28] and 3D-EBSD are the commonly used techniques to uncover the 3D nature of microstructural features at different length scales.

Among these techniques, 3D-EBSD has gotten special attention because on one hand it is an adaptation of the conventional 2D EBSD, and on the other hand it features a balance between high-resolution and large field of observation which is of great interest for characterization of metallic microstructures. 3D-EBSD is the combination of conventional EBSD and tomography based on serial sectioning. The usual method for serial sectioning involves cyclic removal of parallel layers of the sample and then imaging of the planar sections by e.g. the EBSD technique (cf. Fig. 1a) [29;30]. The removal of the material for serial sectioning can be performed with different methods: e.g., mechanical polishing, chemical polishing, Focused Ion Beam (FIB) tomography, Broad Ion Beam tomography (BIB) and laser or electrical discharge ablation [31]. Among these method, FIB tomography and manual serial sectioning are the most frequently used techniques, which have been extensively used to generate 3D micrographs of different metals.

When the serial sectioning experiment is completed and the stack of 2D data are created the data need to be processed. The main step of serial sectioning data processing is data alignment. Data

IOP Conf. Series: Materials Science and Engineering 1121 (2021) 012002 doi:10.1088/1757-899X/1121/1/012002

alignment means to ensure that the spatial registry of each 2D data file is accurate. This step is common for most tomographic methods; however, manually performed experiments usually need more alignment, which must be done before further data processing [32;33]. In the alignment step, the internal features of the microstructure are used for the precise alignment of the collected 3D stack. One generally accepted approach proposed by Lee et al. [34] and further developed by Pirgazi et al. [21;32] consists of a cross correlation procedure based on the minimization of the average misorientation between two adjacent sections. It has been shown that the full alignment procedure produces a more reliable grain boundary plane morphology and continuous orientation gradients inside the grains of a single phase nickel sample with large grains (cf. Figure 1b and c).

The reconstructed grain boundary network extracted from the 3D microstructural volumes have been frequently used to study the five parameter grain boundary character distribution (e.g. [35;36]). Figure 1d represents the distribution of grain boundary plane normal for grain boundaries carrying a S3 crystal misorientation in a polycrystalline nickel specimen. The strong peak at the (111) pole, is an indication of the presence of coherent twin boundaries. This dataset was reconstructed based on 50 EBSD sections spaced by a 7 mm distance to obtain a total volume of 3000x3000x350 mm3 comprising 470 grains.

3.2. *Transmission Kikuchi Diffraction*

3.2.1 Architecture of the TKD systems and working principle. The principle setup of the TKD system developed at Ghent University is shown in Figure 2a, whereas Figure 2b shows a picture taken inside the Quanta 450 SEM chamber with the sample in TKD condition. The sample holder (5) is pre-tilted in the negative direction up to 45°, allowing some degree of freedom for the researcher to search for the optimum tilt angle for each individual measurement. The stage in the case shown in Figure 2b is tilted 15° in positive direction. These settings define the acquisition angle of -30°which is found to be optimum with respect to position of the diffraction pattern on the phosphorous screen and the indexation reliability. In most of the cases we acquired the diffraction patterns at working distances between 4 to 6mm, but the best results are usually obtained at a working distance of ~5mm. Usually we used the incident electron beam (2) with an energy corresponding to 30 or 20 keV accelerating voltage and a and a beam current in the range between 300 pA and 2.3 nA, focused on the transparent part of the different TEM samples(3)-foils or FIB processed samples beam current in the range between 300 pA and 2.3 nA,

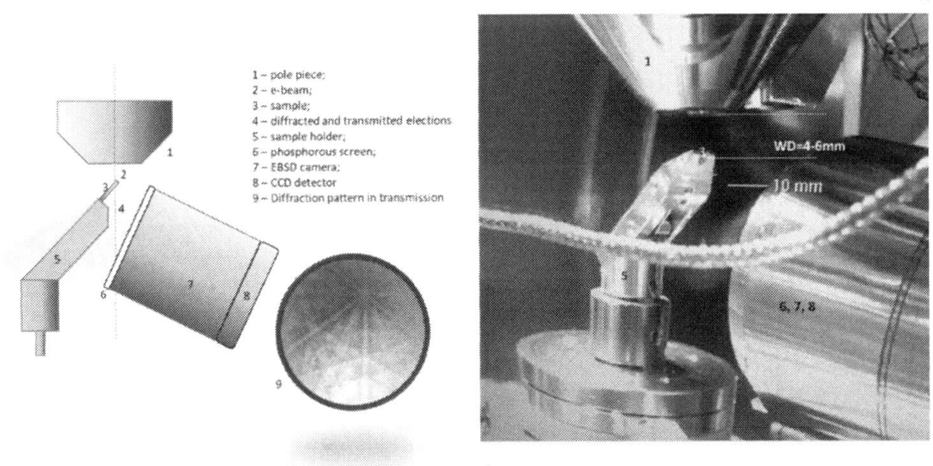

a b

Figure 2. (a) Schematic representation of the architecture and the main elements of TKD system with off axis position of the EBSD detector; (b) Infrared camera image from the microscope chamber with fully inserted EBSD camera for the same configuration.

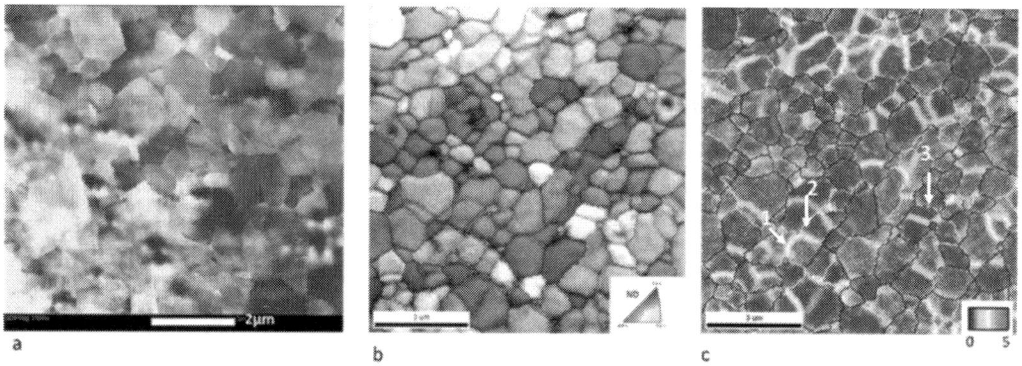

Figure 3. (a) Forward scattered electrons image; (b) Normal direction inverse pole figure map and (c) a kernel average orientation map with superimposed high angle grain boundaries (>15°) in black, low angle grain boundaries (5-15°) of deformed to ε_{vM}=5.4 by high pressure torsion technically pure Al.

focused on the transparent part of the different samples (3) — foils or FIB processed samples. By these setting we were able to obtain a spatial resolution of in the range of 5 to 10nm in case we use the configuration on Figure 2, known as the off-axis setup, and ~4nm in case when we use the on-axis detector configuration. The angular accuracy was better than 1° in all cases.

3.2.2 Results. The example shown in Figure 3 is from pure aluminum, deformed to a von Misses (vM) true strain of 5.4 by high pressure torsion [37]. The observation is made in a plane perpendicular to the torsion axis.

The acquisition parameters are 30kV accelerating voltage, 2.3 nA probe current, working distance 5 mm and tilt angle -30°. The EBSD scan was performed on a hexagonal scan grid with a step size of

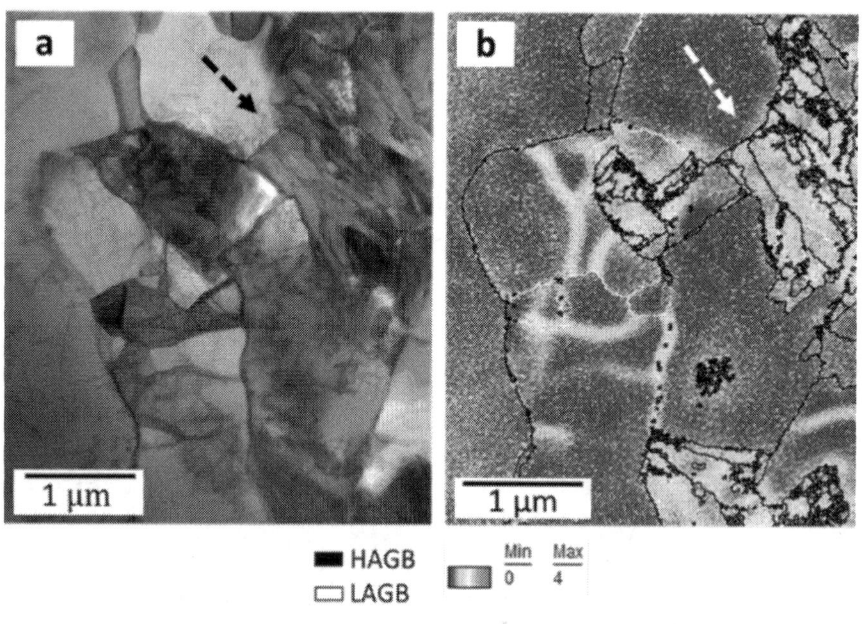

Figure 4. a) TEM image after ultrafast heating an subsequent quenching b) KAM map of the same area obtained from the TKD analysis. Step size 10nm, 30kV, square grid.

IOP Conf. Series: Materials Science and Engineering 1121 (2021) 012002 doi:10.1088/1757-899X/1121/1/012002

10 nm. The original data were post-processed by applying only a confidence index standardization procedure. The Kernel average misorientation map (Figure 3c) is calculated for the 3rd neighbor with upper cut off criterion 5°. The KAM map shows clearly the fragmentation of the Al grains in three stages: (i) strain localization inside the existing grains (green and yellow colored regions)(arrow #1); (ii) formation of the low angle grain boundaries in the heavily distorted regions (arrow#2) and (iii) transition from LAGBs to HAGBs in some regions (arrow #3).

Figure 4a shows a TEM bright field image of a steel with 0.2%C, 1.6 %Mn, 1%Al and 0.5%Si (in mass%). The steel was heated with a heating rate of 800°C/s to 860°C, soaked for 0.2 s and subsequently quenched. The microstructure after this treatment consists of ferrite, martensite, bainite and retained austenite with a grains size of ~1.5μm. The KAM map that was gathered on the same sample, covering the same site as the TEM bright field image of Figure 4a, gives an idea of the sensitivity of the TKD to determination of the dislocation density, cf. Figure 4b. It is clearly shown that the zones with KAM values of the order ~1-2° formed a cellular sub-grain structure. The arrow points to a zone with increased dislocation density in a ferrite grain adjacent to a martensite grain. A nearly excellent correspondence can be observed between the dislocation network observed on the TEM image and the TKD-KAM map.

In summary TKD is a very promising characterization technique, which allows effectively and in a relatively simple way to bridge the resolution gap between TEM and classical EBSD. A minimum effort is required to adjust a standard EBSD system to an off axis TKD system. However, the on line TKD system exhibits a number of advantages – faster acquisition and ability to work at better spatial resolution, but they require dedicated hardware.

3.3. The Grain Size Orientation Distribution Function

The grain size and orientation distribution function, or GSODF, combines, in a single continuous function, the probability distributions of crystallographic orientations and grain sizes [38]. The following method has been proposed to find the GSODF of a microstructure: (i) Calculate the grain size distribution of the material; (ii) divide the total number of grains in bins depending on grain size; (iii) Calculate an ODF for each of these bins (using the exponential method of Bunge [39]) and (iv) find a mathematical correlation between the coefficients of the ODFs calculated in the previous step and grain size. Once the C-coefficients of the ODF are expressed as functions of grain size, d, an ODF dependent on grain size is obtained: $f_d(g)$ (where g represents a triplet of Euler angles $g \equiv \varphi_1, \Phi, \varphi_2$). Then, the

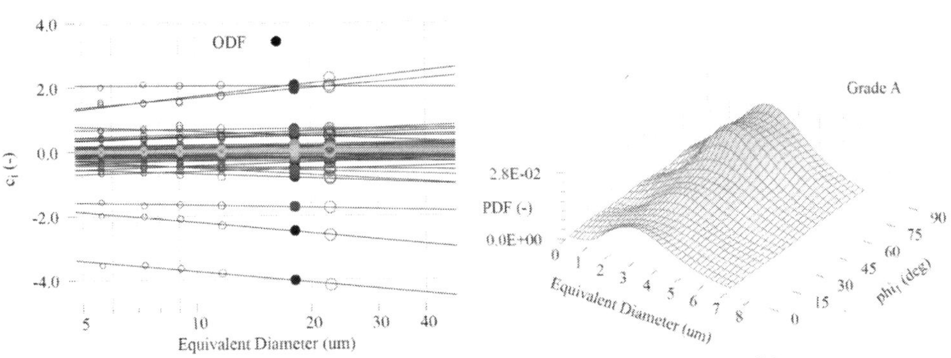

(a) (b)

Figure 5. (a) Linear dependence of C-coefficients with respect to grain size (the coefficients corresponding are represented in blue, turning into red and finally yellow as the harmonic level increases). The coefficients of the global ODF are represented with black dots; (b) Probability distribution function that show the probability of finding a grain with a certain grain size and orientation in the γ-fibre.

GSODF is given by the product of the grain size distribution, $p(d)$, and the size dependent ODF, $f_d(g)$:
$F(d,g) = p(d)f_d(g)$

Although, a priori, it is not obvious how to find the size dependent ODF, the investigation of several low carbon steels has shown that, for these microstructures, a very clear linear relationship is found between the C-coefficients obtained for different grain size ranges and the logarithm of the grain size (see Figure 5a). When the C-coefficients present this simple relationship with respect to grain size, the GSODF can be succinctly displayed using the grain size distribution function and two ODF plots: the first one, or *global ODF*, which corresponds to the conventional ODF, calculated for all the grains of the sample, and the second one, or *slope ODF*, which shows the dependence of intensity on the logarithm of the grain size. In order to obtain the probability density of a material volume element that is part of a grain with a certain size and crystallographic orientation, first the total fraction for that size is found from the size probability function, then it is multiplied by the sum of the intensity for the chosen crystallographic orientation in the global ODF and the correction calculated from the slope ODF for the given size.

The GSODF offers a large number of possibilities for the analysis of microstructures. To begin with, it includes the grain size and orientation distribution functions, which can be calculated as marginal distributions of the GSODF. Moreover, it can be used to study the correlation between both properties. As an example, Figure 5b shows how the GSODF can be used to compare two dual-phase steels. Each of the graphs show the grain size distributions of the grains with orientations along the γ-fibre (<111>//ND). The concept of grain size dependent ODFs can also be applied in modelling. Several examples of how the GSODF is applied to the generation of RVEs for full-field models and in mean-field simulations can be found in [38] and [40].

4. Texture control in non-oriented electrical steels

For decades already texture control in Non-Oriented (NO) electrical steel is the subject of intense study [41]. Unlike for Grain-Oriented (GO) electrical steel there is not a generally accepted manufacturing procedure that guarantees the optimum <001>//ND. Various procedures have been developed on a laboratory scale [42;43], but proofed to be difficult to upscale for industrial processing. Unlike for FCC alloys the {001}<100> cube component is not a common recrystallization component in low-carbon steel after cold rolling and annealing. Nguyen-Minh et al have discovered, however, that the cube component appears in localized micro shear-bands in rotated Goss grains {110}<110> [44].

Strain localization in the form of micro shear bands can be accounted for by geometric softening of heavily deformed polycrystals. The change of the deformation geometry is to soften the high hardening stage of crystals. The condition for this change of deformation configurations is proposed by Dillamore et al [45;46], based on crystal plasticity theory. The transition from homogeneous to local plastic flow of materials is usually marked by a plastic instability point ($d\sigma/d\varepsilon = 0$) on the stress-strain (σ-ε) curve. Beyond this point, geometric softening ($d\sigma/d\varepsilon < 0$) due to local strain accommodation is dominant, and thus grains in shear bands are deformed.

Besides the well-documented case of SBs appearing in the hard {111}<112> grains [47], also the rotated Goss ({110}<110>) oriented crystals, in fact, exhibit the highest Taylor factor value and thus can be considered as the *hardest* orientations of BCC structured materials under the plane strain

IOP Conf. Series: Materials Science and Engineering 1121 (2021) 012002 doi:10.1088/1757-899X/1121/1/012002

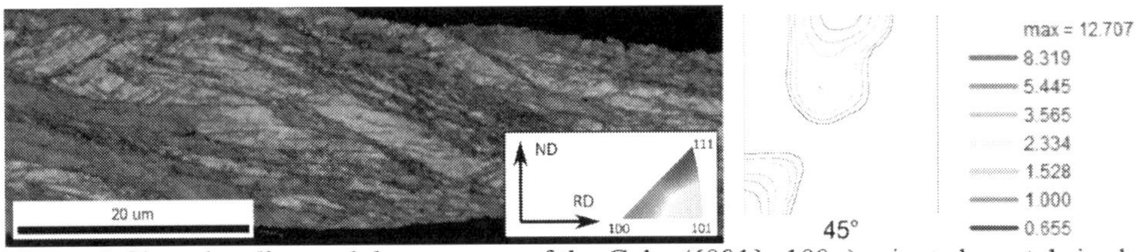

Figure 6. Shear banding and the presence of the Cube ({001}<100>) oriented crystals in shear bands of the rotated Goss ({110}<110>) grain.

compression of the conventional rolling. Geometric softening by micro shear banding, therefore, should be the most prevalent in rotated Goss oriented grains [48]. An investigation by electron backscatter diffraction (EBSD) technique, therefore, has been carried on samples of an Fe-1.2 wt.% Si alloy after the cold rolling of 75% thickness reduction. The rotated Goss oriented grains in cold rolled steel sheet, in general, are not very frequently observed because the {110}<110> orientation is just a minor component of the rolling texture. The resistance of these grains to plane strain compression is very high, but the grains are merely present as a minor transformation product of recrystallization Cube ({001}<100>) austenite grains. Nevertheless, by EBSD measurements on large samples areas (~1 mm^2) with small scanning step sizes (~0.1-0.5 μm), it is possible to find some rotated Goss grains having micro shear bands. Figure 6 shows the presence of Cube oriented crystals in these micro shear bands, which has been predicted by crystal plasticity calculation [44]. Recently, cross rolling and annealing experiments have been implemented on strongly Goss oriented samples [49]. Results of these experiments clearly show the presence of the Cube ({001}<100>) oriented bands in the rotated Goss samples. Moreover, retention and development of the Cube texture are observed in annealed samples [49].

5. Conclusions

In the present paper a very broad overview was given of current state-of-the-art and recent developments in a number of aspects of applied metallurgical research pertaining to texture control in metal manufacturing. It was shown that both in conventional metal sheet manufacturing and in innovative processing technologies such as *Additive Manufacturing*, a detailed analysis of the texture formation can lead to a better understanding of these processes in terms of their physical mechanisms, which in turn may lead to a better texture control and ultimately to improved material properties.

In another register the crystallographic nature of most metal alloys and the preference of texture allows for advanced microstructural characterization by EBSD. It was shown how the added value of orientation contrast microscopy can be further augmented by gathering 3D-EBSD images through a slice-and-view approach and how the resolution of conventional EBSD can be increased down to less than 10 nm by Transmission Kikuchi Diffraction (TKD)

References

[1] Wassermann G, Grewen J. Texturen metallischer Werkstoffe: Springer Berlin Heidelberg; 1939.
[2] Bunge HJ. Mathematische Methoden Der Texturanalyse: Akademie-Verlag; 1969.
[3] Bunge HJ 1988 *Textures and Microstructures* **8** *p*.751210.
[4] Lankford WT 1950 *Trans. ASM* **42** *p*.1197.
[5] Cullity BD, Graham CD. Introduction to Magnetic Materials: Wiley; 2009.
[6] Bennett TA, Petrov RH, Kestens LAI 2009 *Scripta Materialia* **61** *p*.733.
[7] Pirgazi H, Kestens LAI 2021 *Materials Characterization* **(in press)**
[8] Samet-Meziou A, Etter AL, Baudin T, Penelle R 2005 *Scripta Materialia* **53** *p*.1001.
[9] Roters F, Diehl M, Shanthraj P, Eisenlohr P, Reuber C, Wong SL, Maiti T, Ebrahimi A, Hochrainer T, Fabritius HO, Nikolov S, Friák M, Fujita N, Grilli N, Janssens KGF, Jia N, Kok PJJ, Ma D, Meier F, Werner E, Stricker M, Weygand D, Raabe D 2019 *Computational Materials Science* **158** *p*.420.
[10] Kou S. Welding Metallurgy: Wiley; 2003.

[11] Andreau O, Koutiri I, Peyre P, Penot JD, Saintier N, Pessard E, De Terris T, Dupuy C, Baudin T 2019 *Journal of Materials Processing Technology* **264** p.21.
[12] Jadhav SD, Dadbakhsh S, Goossens L, Kruth JP, Van Humbeeck J, Vanmeensel K 2019 *Journal of Materials Processing Technology* **270** p.47.
[13] Sun SH, Hagihara K, Nakano T 2018 *Materials and Design* **140** p.307.
[14] Sun Z, Tan X, Tor SB, Chua CK 2018 *NPG Asia Materials* **10** p.127.
[15] Ghoncheh MH, Sanjari M, Cyr E, Kelly J, Pirgazi H, Shakerin S, Hadadzadeh A, Amirkhiz BS, Kestens LAI, Mohammadi M 2020 *International Journal of Plasticity* **133**
[16] Hadadzadeh A, Amirkhiz BS, Li J, Mohammadi M 2018 *Additive Manufacturing* **23** p.121.
[17] Jones DR, Fensin SJ, Ndefru BG, Martinez DT, Trujillo CP, Gray GT, III 2018 *Journal of Applied Physics* **124**
[18] Oh J, Ishimoto T, Sun S-h, Nakano T 2019 *Journal of Smart Processing* **8** p.151.
[19] Beladi H, Chao Q, Rohrer GS 2014 *Acta Materialia* **80** p.478.
[20] Pirgazi H, Sanjari M, Tamimi S, Shalchi Amirkhiz B, Kestens LAI, Mohammadi M 2021 *Journal of Materials Science* **56** p.844.
[21] Pirgazi H, Glowinski K, Morawiec A, Kestens LAI 2015 *Journal of Applied Crystallography* **48** p.1672.
[22] Pirgazi H, Petrov R, Kestens L. Modeling the magnetic properties of non-oriented electrical steels based on microstructural parameters. Materials Science Forum, vol. 702-703, 2012. p.734.
[23] Gault B, Moody MP, Cairney JM, Ringer SP. Atom Probe Microscopy: Springer New York; 2012.
[24] Miller MK, Kelly TF, Rajan K, Ringer SP 2012 *Materials Today* **15** p.158.
[25] Maire E, Buffière JY, Salvo L, Blandin JJ, Ludwig W, Létang JM 2001 *Advanced Engineering Materials* **3** p.539.
[26] Salvo L, Suéry M, Marmottant A, Limodin N, Bernard D 2010 *Comptes Rendus Physique* **11** p.641.
[27] Jensen DJ, Poulsen HF 2012 *Materials Characterization* **72** p.1.
[28] Rollett AD, Barmak K. 11 - Orientation Mapping, Laughlin DE, Hono K, (eds.) in. Physical Metallurgy (Fifth Edition). Oxford: Elsevier; 2014. p.1113.
[29] Alkemper J, Voorhees PW 2001 *Journal of Microscopy* **201** p.388.
[30] Pirgazi H. Wide field 3D orientation contrast microscopy. Faculty of Engineering and Architecture, vol. PhD: Ghent University, 2015.
[31] Zaefferer S, Wright SI. Three-dimensional orientation microscopy by serial sectioning and EBSD-based orientation mapping in a FIB-SEM, in. Electron Backscatter Diffraction in Materials Science. 2009. p.109.
[32] Pirgazi H 2019 *Materials Characterization* **152** p.223.
[33] Uchic MD. Serial sectioning methods for generating 3D characterization data of grain-and precipitate-scale microstructures, in. Computational Methods for Microstructure-Property Relationships. 2011. p.31.
[34] Lee SB, Rollett AD, Rohrer GS. Three-dimensional microstructure reconstruction using FIB-OIM. Materials Science Forum, vol. 558-559, 2007. p.915.
[35] Pirgazi H, Akbarzadeh A, Petrov R, Sidor J, Kestens L 2008 *Materials Science and Engineering: A* **492** p.110.
[36] Saylor DM, Morawiec A, Rohrer GS 2003 *Acta Materialia* **51** p.3663.
[37] Naghdy S, Percq LL, Serret R, Petrov R, Hertelé S, Kestens L, Verleysen P 2017 *Materials Science and Technology* **33** p.678.
[38] Galan Lopez J, Kestens LAI 2021 *Journal of Applied Crystallography* **54**
[39] Bunge HJ. Texture Analysis in Materials Science: Mathematical Methods: Elsevier Science; 2013.
[40] Galán-López J, Hidalgo J 2020 *Crystals* **10** p.819.
[41] Moses AJ 1990 *IEE Proceedings A - Physical Science, Measurement and Instrumentation, Management and Education* **137** p.233.
[42] Park JY, Oh KH, Ra HY 2000 *ISIJ International* **40** p.1210.
[43] Wang S, Jiang YM, Liang YF, Ye F, Lin JP 2015 *Advances in Materials Science and Engineering* **2015**
[44] Nguyen-Minh T, Sidor JJ, Petrov RH, Kestens LAI 2012 *Scripta Materialia* **67** p.935.
[45] Dillamore IL, Roberts JG, Bush AC 1979 *Metal Science* **13** p.73.
[46] Haratani T, Hutchinson WB, Dillamore IL, Bate P 1984 *Metal Science* **18** p.57.
[47] Ushioda K, Hutchinson WB 1989 *ISIJ International* **29** p.862.
[48] Nguyen-Minh T, Sidor JJ, Petrov RH, Kestens LAI 2015 *IOP Conference Series: Materials Science and Engineering* **82** p.012023.
[49] Mehdi M, He Y, Hilinski EJ, Kestens LAI, Edrisy A 2020 *Acta Materialia* **185** p.540.

Understanding cross boundary twin behaviours in AZ31 alloy by a composite Schmid factor

Q L Huang[1], **C F Guo**[2] **and R L Xin**[3,4]

[1] College of Artificial Intelligence, Southwest University, Chongqing, 400715, China
[2] Department of Chemistry, Zhejiang Normal University, Jinhua, Zhejiang Province, 321004, China
[3] Joint International Laboratory for Light Alloys (MOE), College of Materials Science and Engineering, Chongqing University, Chongqing, 400044, China
[4] Corresponding author.

Email: rlxin@cqu.edu.cn (R. Xin)

Abstract. It is well known that twinning likely nucleates and forms pairs at grain boundaries (GBs) during the formation of hexagonal close-packed alloys. Therefore, the crystallography of GBs should be taken into account to assess the activation preference of twins (and pairs) at GBs. As Schmid factor (SF) is a grain-based parameter, it cannot predict from which GB segment, twinning prefers to nucleate. To solve this problem, recently we proposed a composite Schmid factor (CSF) that incorporates both the SF and a geometric compatibility factor (m') between twin/slip systems in neighbouring grains. In this presentation, we first summarize the definition and calculation method of this parameter. Then, simultaneous twin nucleation and twin (or slip) stimulated twin behaviour in a twin chain were assessed by this parameter. For comparison, SF and m' analyses were also performed. The advantages and limitations of this CSF in assessing twin behaviours were discussed.

1. Introduction

Compared to cubic structured metals, the strain accommodation at grain boundaries (GBs) are more difficult in hexagonal close packed (HCP) metals because of its lower symmetry of crystal structure. Generally, there is one deformation mode dominant, and the others play a minor role due to the large difference in critical resolved shear stress (CRSS) and Schmid factors (SFs). The compatibility between the dominant deformation modes in neighbouring grains could therefore, determine the ability of plasticity at GBs. Consequently, the selection of slip and twin variants in neighbouring grains should be significantly affected by each other [1]. An in-depth understanding of the slip-twin interaction mechanism is of great importance for the development of physics - based crystal plasticity models and the design of new alloys with superior strength and ductility.

Previous studies have indicated that variant selection during twinning in Mg, Ti, and Zr is not only determined by the Schmid rule, but is also related to strain accommodation at neighbouring grain boundaries [2]. This occurs by the activation of slip and twin. Many non-high Schmid twins were observed in deformed HCP metals. This phenomenon can be explained in terms of local strain accommodation by calculating the displacement gradient tensors associated with both twinning and slip [3]. It is also possible to employ the geometric compatibility factor m' [4,5], as initially used to assess the slip transfer in Ni-Al alloys by Luster and Morris [6]. Nevertheless, the relative importance of these two parameters, have not been investigated to date. The purpose of our recent paper was therefore to consider the use of a single parameter that incorporates both SF and m' [7]. Here, simultaneous twin nucleation and twin transfer behaviour at GBs of AZ31 Mg alloy were investigated. The selection of twin variants is analysed below according to this approach.

2. Material and Method

The material studied here is a commercial AZ31 rolled sheet with 30 mm in thickness. The material has typical basal texture and average grain size of 30 μm. A rectangular prism sample of dimensions 5 mm (RD) × 10mm (TD) × 5 mm (ND) was cut from the as-received sheet. Here, RD, TD and ND refer to the rolling direction, transverse direction and normal direction, respectively. The sample was compressed along TD to an engineering strain of 3% at room temperature. The microstructure of the deformed sample was examined on the TD-RD plane by electron backscatter diffraction (EBSD) analysis. It was accomplished using an HKL Channel5 System equipped in a scanning electron microscope (FEI Nova 400 FEG-SEM). More detailed descriptions on experimental data can be found from ref. [4].

As illustrated in figures 1a and 1b, stress concentration can be caused at the common GB when either twinning or dislocation is active in G1. As a consequence, twin may be "transferred" or nucleated in(to) G2. Crystal plasticity finite element simulation indicated that the local stress imposed on T2 (in G2) can be estimated as the form of a simple shear associated with T1 [7]. The resolved value of this local stress on T2 is: $\eta\sigma_0 m_1 m'$, where η, σ_0, m_1 and m' are the local shear stress factor (taken as 1 here), macroscopic stress, Schmid factor for T1 and the geometric compatibility factor between T1 and T2, respectively. In addition, the resolved shear stress due to the homogeneous macroscopic stress is: $\sigma_0 m_2$, where m_2 is the Schmid factor for T2. Therefore, a composite orientation factor, i.e., composite Schmid factor (CSF), which indicates the orientation preference on the activation of different twin variant, was proposed recently as: $CSF = m_2 + \eta m_1 m'$. In principle, the local shear stress factor can be affected by the GB characteristics and the CRSS ratio of different deformation systems.

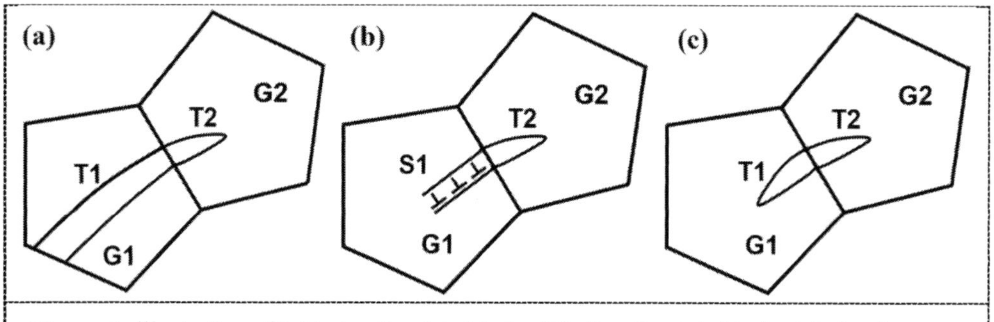

Figure 1. illustration of (a) twin stimulated twin, (b) slip stimulated twin, (c) simultaneous twin nucleation at a GB.

As illustrated in figure 1c, at some GBs, two twins can form simultaneously and grow in opposite directions. For this case, the value of $CSF = (m_1 + m_2)(1 + m')/2$ can be used to assess the activation preference of twin pairs, as will be demonstrated in the following. figure 2a shows an example of simultaneous twin nucleation at the common GB of grains a and b. Based on the Euler angles, twin a and b are determined as variant 5 and 6, respectively. A program was developed to identify twin variant and the detailed algorithm for twin identification can be found in ref. [8]. The pole figures shown in figures 2b and 2c are the outputs of the program. The program also has the function to calculate SF, m' and CSF, and draw the corresponding maps. The methods to calculate these values are briefly described in the following. As shown in figure 3, let b_i, q_i and n_i (i=1 or 2) represents the base vector for twin shear, shear plane normal and twin plane normal of T_i, respectively. s is the loading direction in sample coordinate system. g_1 and g_2 are the orientation matrix for G1 and G2, respectively. The SF for T_i (i=1 or 2) can be calculated as follows:

$$m_i = [s \cdot (g_i^{-1} b_i)][s \cdot (g_i^{-1} n_i)] \quad (1)$$

The geometric compatibility factor between T1 and T2 is calculated as:

$$m' = [(g_1^{-1}b_1)(g_2^{-1}b_2)][(g_1^{-1}n_1)(g_2^{-1}n_2)] \quad (2)$$

Then,

$$CSF = (m_1 + m_2)(1 + m')/2 \quad (3)$$

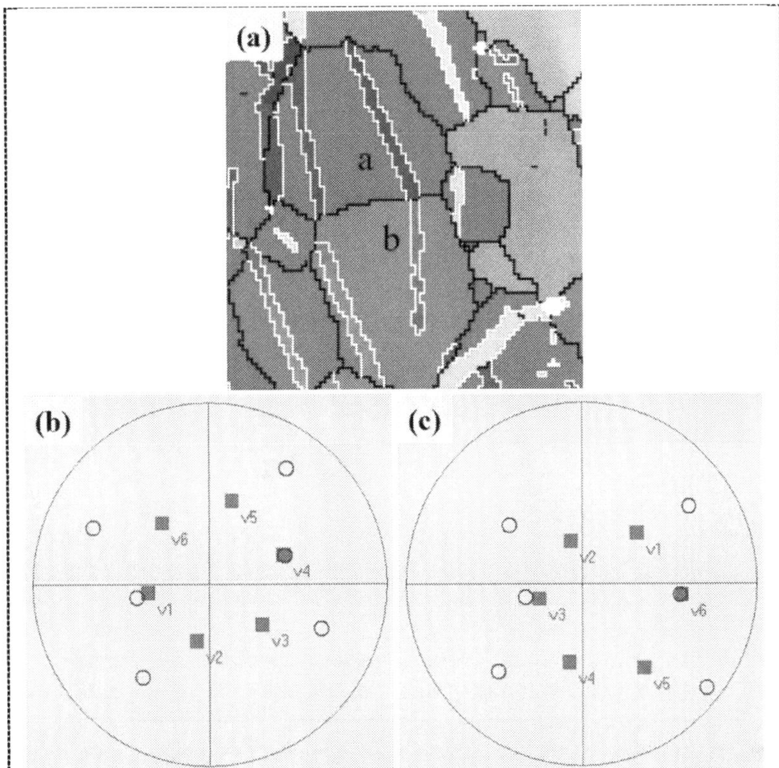

Figure 2. (a) IPF map showing a twin pair formed at the common GB, (b) and (c) the {10-12} pole figures showing the twin variants in grains a and b, respectively. The square and circle symbols indicate the {10-12} poles in matrix and twin, respectively.

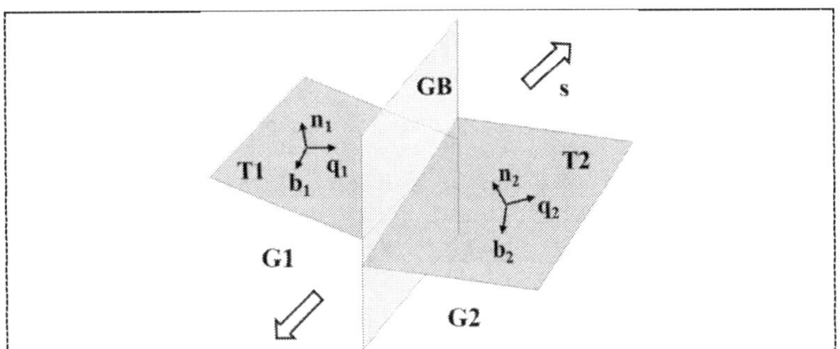

Figure 3. illustration of the basis vectors of T1 and T2.

Based on EBSD scanning data (X, Y, Euler1, Euler2 and Euler3), a SF map can be easily generated since X and Y define the position of grain pixels, and the corresponding SF value can be obtained from Euler1-Euler3. An example of SF map is shown in figure 4a. For the generation of a CSF map, GBs should be first determined, which is judged based on the misorientation angle of two neighbouring pixels in our program. Then CSF values of the GB between two potential twin systems can be obtained by equations 1-3. An example of CSF map is shown in figure 4b. Here, we want to emphasize that SF is grain-based, while CSF is GB-based. That is to say, the different GB segment usually have different CSF values, i.e., different activation preference of twin pairs. As twin likely nucleates from GBs, in theory CSF has superiority over SF in assessing twin activity.

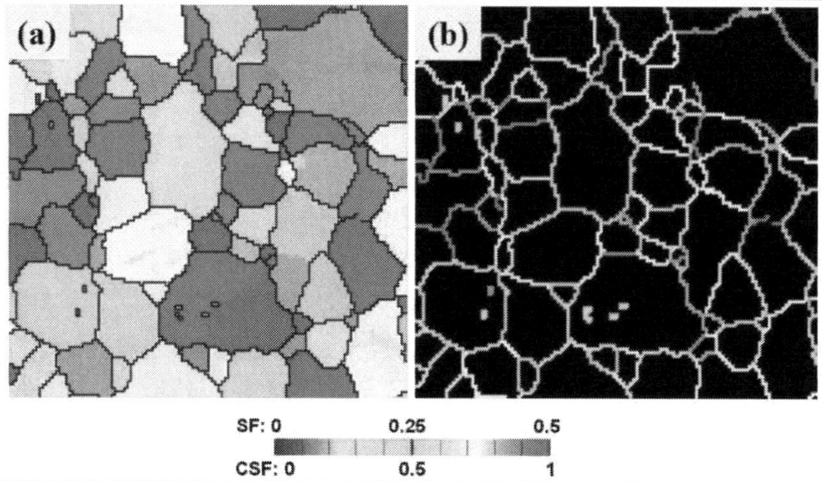

Figure 4. (a) a calculated SF map for twinning, (b) a calculated CSF map for twin pair. Uniaxial compression is loaded along the x direction.

3. Analysis and discussion

Now let's take the activation of twin pair in figure 2a for example. Table 1 shows the calculated SFs (and CSFs) for the potential twins (and pairs) in grains a and b. The values in the second column (or row) shows the SFs for potential twin variants in grain a (or b). The other 36 values are the calculated CSFs for potential twin variant pairs. As judged from SF values, variant v1 and v4 likely nucleate in grain a while v3 and v6 likely nucleate in grain b. Thus, four twin pairs (v1-v3, v1-v6, v4-v3 and v4-v6) prefer to form in terms of SF values. This makes it difficult to predict which twin pair most likely forms. Table 1 shows that 2 out of 36 twin variant combinations lead to relatively large CSF values, 0.816 for v1-v3 and 0.854 for v4-v6.

Table 1. Calculated SF and CSF values for all the potential twins or twin pairs at the a-b GB.

	twin b	v1	v2	v3	v4	v5	v6
twin a	SF	0.086	0.068	0.405	0.069	0.085	0.440
v1	0.457	0.275	0.352	0.816	0.431	0.288	0.442
v2	0.028	0.054	0.043	0.290	0.092	0.091	0.255
v3	0.255	0.175	0.133	0.300	0.218	0.313	0.559
v4	0.463	0.449	0.272	0.410	0.270	0.371	0.854
v5	0.030	0.110	0.079	0.238	0.049	0.055	0.318
v6	0.250	0.227	0.293	0.528	0.170	0.152	0.333

The other potential twin pairs correspond to obviously smaller CSF values. The observed twin pair in figure 2a is v4-v6 with the largest CSF. At least the number of the likely formed twin pairs is reduced to 2 using the single parameter CSF. In previous studies, twin transfer at GBs and twin variant selection have been studied by m'. For comparison, the calculated m' for the potential twin pairs is shown in Table 2. It is clear that there are six variant combinations, giving rise to relatively higher m' values (>0.89). Therefore, it is difficult to predict the most likely formed twin pair using the single parameter of m'. Combining the m' with SF analysis, it is also possible to shortlist the number of twin pairs to 2, v1-v3 and v4-v6. Both have a high m' value of 0.893. Actually, m' is purely geometric and shouldn't have any dependence on the externally applied stress. Therefore, the use of m' should be combined with SF analysis for predicting simultaneous twin nucleation events.

Table 2. Calculated SF and m' values for all the potential twins or twin pairs at the a-b GB.

	twin b	v1	v2	v3	v4	v5	v6
twin a	SF	0.086	0.068	0.405	0.069	0.085	0.440
v1	0.457	0.011	0.343	0.893	0.638	0.064	-0.013
v2	0.028	-0.060	-0.095	0.336	0.891	0.612	0.091
v3	0.255	0.024	-0.177	-0.092	0.343	0.845	0.610
v4	0.463	0.634	0.025	-0.056	0.012	0.352	0.893
v5	0.030	0.891	0.609	0.092	-0.015	-0.036	0.353
v6	0.250	0.352	0.845	0.613	0.063	-0.091	-0.034

figure 5a shows that a twin chain is formed in three grains: d, e and f. Again, the variant of each twin is determined by an in-house program and the results are shown in the form of {10-12} pole figures in figures 5b-5d. Twins d, e and f are identified as v6, v6 and v5, respectively. The SFs (and CSFs) for potential twin (pairs) in grains e and f are listed in Table 3. It is clear that two twin pairs v3-v2 and v6-v5 have relatively large CSF, similar to that shown in Table 1. However, the observed twin pair corresponds to a smaller CSF (0.388 vs. 0.497). The SF for the activated twin is also smaller than a potential variant, 0.199 vs. 0.257 for twin e and 0.197 vs. 0.251 for twin f. As judged from the morphology, twin f was likely stimulated by twin e. If the variant for twin e is fixed as v6, the selected variant v5 for twin f has obvious advantage in term of CSF (compare the values in the bottom row of Table 3).

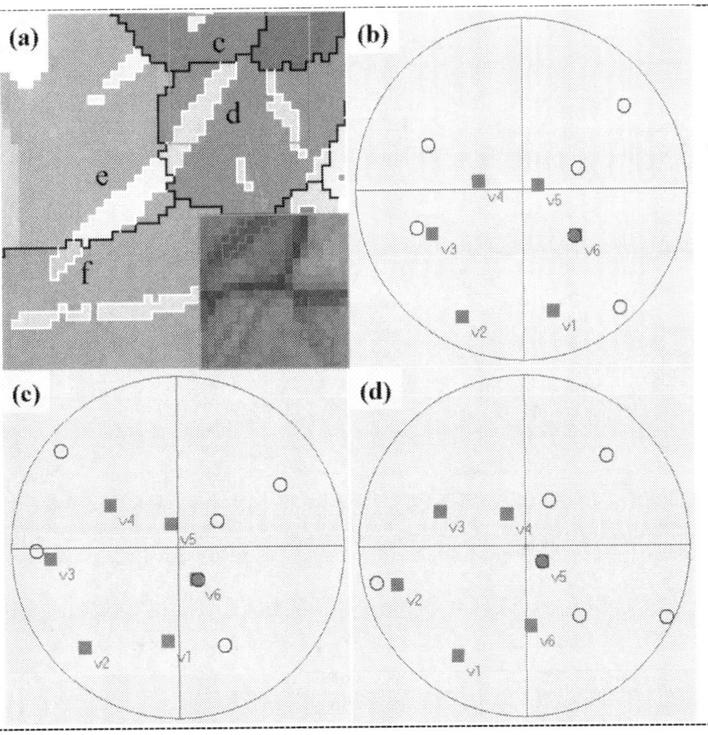

Figure 5. (a) IPF map showing a twin chain formed in grains d-f, (b), (c) and (d) the {10-12} pole figures showing the twin variants in grains d, e and f, respectively. The square and circle symbols indicate the {10-12} poles in matrix and twin, respectively.

Table 3. Calculated SF and CSF values for all the potential twins or twin pairs at the e-f GB.

	twin f	v1	v2	v3	v4	v5	v6
twin e	SF	-0.093	0.251	0.080	-0.107	0.197	0.041
v1	-0.065	-0.137	0.105	0.007	-0.088	0.091	-0.024
v2	-0.023	-0.113	0.198	0.033	-0.065	0.089	0.013
v3	0.257	0.114	0.497	0.292	0.085	0.226	0.151
v4	-0.038	-0.066	0.148	0.041	-0.126	0.091	0.001
v5	-0.052	-0.072	0.101	0.019	-0.156	0.125	-0.007
v6	0.199	0.061	0.223	0.142	0.064	0.388	0.208

The SF and CSF for the potential twin (pairs) in grains d and e are listed in Table 4. The observed twin pairs are v6-v6, having a situation similar to that found in grains e and f. Again, if twin d is fixed as v6, the selected twin pair v6-v6 has obvious activation advantage in term of CSF. The above analysis implies that twin d might nucleate from the c-d common GB. The band contrast image shown as the inset in figure 5a indicates that the dislocations are high near the tip of twin d. SF analysis shows that the three variants of basal slip in grain c have SF values of 0.313, 0.254 and 0.060, respectively. Assume the variant with the largest SF was activated in grain c, the m' between the basal slip and the six twin variants in grain d can be calculated and the CSF for the six twin variants can be obtained as well. Table 5 shows the calculation results. It indicates that the activated twin v6 has a slightly smaller SF value, compared to the potential variant v3 (0.458 vs. 0.479). But the m' for v6 is much larger than that for v3 (0.705 vs. -0.007). Since twinning has polar characteristic, i.e., it likely shears in one direction, but difficult in the opposite direction, there are negative values for m'. Interestingly, the second largest m' values is close to that for v6 (0.627 vs. 0.705). This is not always the case, depending on the relative OR of the different deformation systems. Nevertheless, the variant of twin d can be predicted by combined analysis on SF and m' analysis. The CSF values in Table 5 indicate that the observed twin variant v6 has obvious activation advantage (0.679 vs. the second largest 0.477). As a summary, the CSF analyses in Tables 3-5 indicate that twin d was nucleated at the c-d GB due to the local stress caused by basal slip in grain c. Twin d propagated to the d-e GB and stimulated twin e. Lastly, twin f was stimulated by the stress concentration caused by twin e at the e-f GB.

Table 4. Calculated SF and CSF values for all the potential twins or twin pairs at the d-e GB.

	twin e	v1	v2	v3	v4	v5	v6
twin d	SF	-0.065	-0.023	0.257	-0.038	-0.052	0.199
v1	0.121	0.051	0.073	0.180	0.037	0.035	0.229
v2	0.092	0.019	0.066	0.257	0.027	0.020	0.144
v3	0.479	0.181	0.328	0.677	0.321	0.214	0.281
v4	0.133	0.027	0.054	0.278	0.087	0.059	0.148
v5	0.082	0.008	0.030	0.173	0.032	0.028	0.206
v6	0.458	0.285	0.224	0.325	0.198	0.293	0.605

Table 5. Calculated SF, m' and CSF values for the potential twins or twin pairs at the c-d GB.

twin d	v1	v2	v3	v4	v5	v6
SF	0.121	0.092	0.479	0.133	0.082	0.458
m'	0.097	-0.039	-0.007	0.051	0.627	0.705
CSF	0.152	0.079	0.477	0.149	0.278	0.679

4. Summary

The CSF takes into account the macroscopic stress and the local shear stress from one dominant twin/slip mode in a neighbouring grain. Therefore, it is a GB-based parameter, having the ability to assess the preference of twin nucleation at GBs. Knowing the loading direction of the macroscopic stress, the CSF value (map) can be obtained based on EBSD data. For simultaneous twin nucleation at GBs, there are 36 twin variant combinations and two twin pairs are most likely activated in term of CSF values. CSF analysis well explain the selection of slip-stimulated and twin-stimulated twin variants in AZ31 Mg alloys after uniaxial compression.

Acknowledgements
This project was supported financially by the National Natural Science Foundations of China (Project No. 52071040).

References
[1] Bieler T R, Eisenlohr P, Zhang C, Phukan H J and Crimp M A 2014 *Curr. Opin. Solid State Mater. Sci.* **18** 212
[2] Beyerlein I J, Capolungo L, Marshall P E, McCabe R J and Tome C N 2010 *Philos. Mag.* **90** 2161
[3] Jonas J J, Mu S, Al-Samman T, Gottstein G, Jiang L and Martin E 2011 *Acta Mater.* **59** 2046
[4] Luster J and Morris M A 1995 *Metall. Mater. Trans. A.* **26** 1745
[5] Xin R, Guo C, Xu Z, Liu G, Huang X and Liu Q 2014 *Scripta Mater.* **74** 96
[6] Guo C, Xin R, Ding C, Song B and Liu Q 2014 *Mater. Sci. Eng.* A **609** 92
[7] Xin R, Liu Z, Sun Y, Wang H, Guo C, Ren W and Liu Q 2019 *Int. J. Plasticity* **123** 208
[8] Huang Q and Xin R 2018 *Mater. Charact.* **141** 370

IOP Conf. Series: Materials Science and Engineering 1121 (2021) 012004 doi:10.1088/1757-899X/1121/1/012004

Evolutions of Mechanical Properties and Macro Textures of AZ91D sheets by Hot Rolling and Subsequent Annealing

S Kaneko[1], S Takenouchi[2], S M Lee[3] and H Utsunomiya[3]
[1] Division of Maritime Safety Technology, Japan Coast Guard Academy, 5-1 Wakaba-cho, Kure, Hiroshima 737-8512, Japan

[2] Undergraduate student, Japan Coast Guard Academy, 5-1 Wakaba-cho, Kure, Hiroshima 737-8512, Japan

[3] Division of Materials and Manufacturing Science, Graduate School of Engineering, Osaka University, 2-1 Yamada-oka, Suita, Osaka 565-0871, Japan

kaneko@jcga.ac.jp

Abstract. The mechanical properties and textures of 75% hot unidirectionally rolled and cross rolled commercial magnesium die-casting alloy AZ91D sheets were investigated for the different rolling temperatures 623K and 673K, respectively. As for mechanical properties, tensile testing results show total elongations of both as-unidirectional and as-cross-rolled sheets are enhanced by the repetition of rolling passes and inter-pass heating. The planar anisotropy of tensile strengths and elongations of cross-rolled at 673K are the smallest among the rolling conditions employed in the present study. Annealed sheets demonstrate the significant elongation to failure due to the static recrystallisation at 623K. Macro textures of the as-unidirectional-rolled sheets show typical double-peak (0001) basal textures with inclined peaks towards ±15° in RD. Contrastingly, macro textures of the as-cross-rolled sheets show the significant (0001) basal textures having double peaks at ±10° in TD and concentrically broader orientation distribution in RD and TD.

1. Introduction

Magnesium alloys have very attractive features such as a promising potential of light-weight structural metallic material and high-specific strength to be employed for bodies of motor vehicles, high speed rail rolling stocks and aeroplanes in order to reduce emission gas and improve fuel efficiency [1,2]. Magnesium alloys are mostly used as die-cast products in general and the prevalence of wrought magnesium alloy products, especially rolled sheets, are still limited. This is mainly because crystal structure of magnesium is hexagonal close-packed structure which hinders plastic deformation at room temperature in which the basal slip systems only activate. For improvement of cold workability such as sheet metal forming, texture control to weaken (0001) basal texture of magnesium alloys is highly focused for many years [3-5]. Rare earth element added magnesium alloys tend to avoidably have lower tensile strength in exchange for splendid formability at room temperature [5]. High aluminium content (~9%) magnesium alloy AZ91 has higher tensile strength and good corrosion resistance. However, commercial wrought AZ91 materials are seldom manufactured until rapid solidification continuous roll caster designed for thin slab and forging materials is introduced [6]. Only a few attentions on texture changes of rolled AZ91 sheet have been paid even though the other magnesium alloys are evaluated

[7,8]. It would be preferable that the thin wide AZ91 rolled sheet with weak or double-peak type (0001) basal textures are fabricated using texture control via strain path change in thermo-mechanical process. In this study, the authors investigated the effectiveness and feasibility of strain path change on evolutions of macro textures and anisotropy of mechanical properties of rolled AZ91D sheets.

2. Experimental procedures

A commercial magnesium alloy AZ91D ingot was used in this study. Its chemical composition was listed in the Table 1. The 4mm thick sheets were sliced from an ingot, subsequently being machined into 30mm wide and 60mm long sheets. The sliced sheets were subject to heat treatment in the electric furnace at 703K for 1 hour, followed by water quenching. The quenched AZ91D sheets were rolled at the two different elevated temperatures, 623K and 673K including 30-minutes pre-heating and inter-pass heat treatment for 5 minutes. The total pass numbers of hot rolling were 9 passes and total reduction in thickness was set to 75%. A ϕ 50 mm 2-high laboratory rolling mill was used without lubrication. Two different rolling patterns explained hereinafter were employed as seen in Figure 1. Unidirectional rolling pattern (A in the figure) was defined as a conventional flat rolling in which a sheet was rolled along the longitudinal direction. Cross rolling pattern (B in the figure) was defined as a combination of unidirectional rolling and transverse rolling. In cross rolling pattern, unidirectional rolling was conducted up to the fourth pass, and from the fifth pass to the final pass, transverse rolling and unidirectional rolling were employed at the odd number and the even number of rolling pass, respectively. The hot-rolled sheets were annealed at 623K for 30 minutes in the electric furnace.

Table 1. Chemical composition of the used AZ91D magnesium alloy (mass%).

Mg	Al	Zn	Mn	Si	Cu	Fe	Ni
bal.	8.99	0.63	0.25	0.04	0.01	0.001	0.001

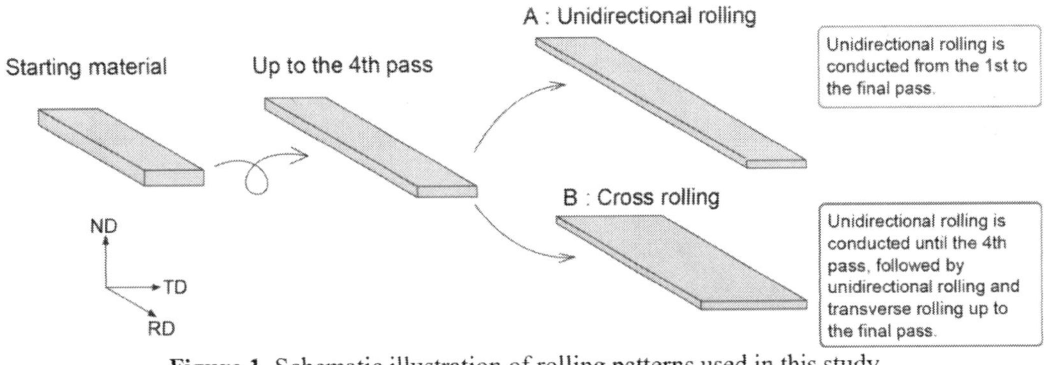

Figure 1. Schematic illustration of rolling patterns used in this study.

Tensile test and Vickers hardness test (results not shown in this paper) were performed in order to evaluate mechanical properties and planar anisotropy of as hot-rolled and 623K-annealed sheets. Dimensions and shape of tensile test pieces were conformed to the 1/5 scale of no.5 specimen JIS Z 2201. Tensile test pieces were spark-machined from the sheets, varying the angles 0°, 45°and 90° to the initial rolling direction (RD_0). The initial strain rate of tensile testing was $\dot{\varepsilon} = 8.33 \times 10^{-4}$ s^{-1}. Optical micrographic observation was conducted on TD planes of the as-rolled and annealed sheets. Macro texture measurement of mid-thickness planes of the as-rolled and annealed sheets was performed. For macro texture measurement, pole figure data were measured by the pseudo Schulz reflection method using Rigaku SmartLab multipurpose X-ray diffractometer system equipped with Cu-Kα radiation.

Incomplete (0001) pole figures were plotted from collected pole figure data using Mtex toolbox [9] in MATLAB 2019b software.

3. Results

3.1. Microstructures

The optical microstructures observed from the transverse direction (TD) section of the as-hot rolled sheets at 623K and 673K are shown in Figure 2. In the figure, there exist some etched pits at which second phase particles have presumably dropped off during immersion of chemical etching. Mechanical twins, subgrains and elongated recrystallized grains are observed in the 623K unidirectional rolled sheet (a). On the other hand, recrystallized grains and hot-band-like subgrain clusters are found in the 673K straight rolled sheet (b). In the cross rolled sheets of 623K (c) and 673K (d), mechanical twins do not appear in the observed area, and microstructures are covered with partially recrystallized grains.

Figure 3 shows optical microstructures of the sheets annealed at 623K. Microstructures in both annealed 623K- and 673K-unidirectional rolled sheets are covered by fully recrystallized grain and coarsened grains as seen in (a) and (b). Microstructures in annealed 623K- and 673k-cross rolled sheets are also covered by fully recrystallized grains, otherwise there are fewer coarsened grains found in the recrystallisation microstructures. The mean grain sizes measured by intercept counting method along the rolling direction are also shown in Figure 3. There is a tendency that aspect ratios of grain length over grain thickness of cross rolled sheets seem to be smaller than those of unidirectionally rolled sheets.

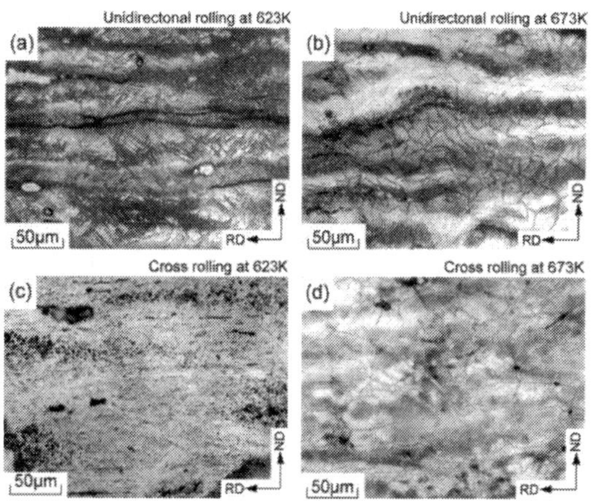

Figure 2. Optical microstructures of as-hot-rolled AZ91D sheets.

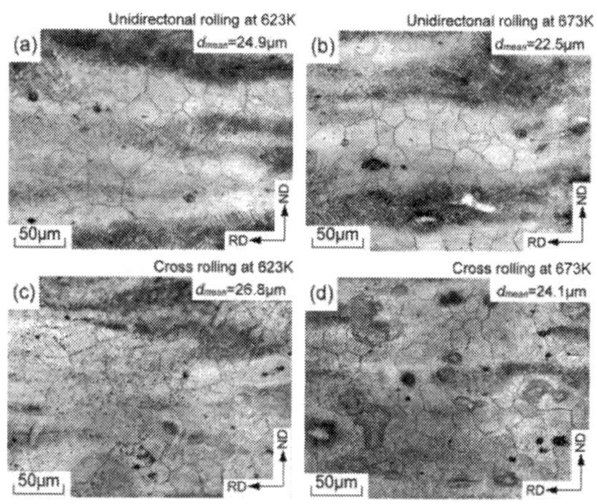

Figure 3. Optical microstructures of annealed AZ91D rolled sheets.

3.2. Mechanical properties

Nominal stress-nominal strain curves of the as-hot unidirectional (623K (a) and 673K (b)) and the as-hot cross rolled sheets (623K (c) and 673K (d)) are shown in Figure 4. According to the specifications of mechanical properties of as-cast commercial die-casting magnesium alloy AZ91, elongation to failure, 0.2% proof stress and ultimate tensile strength of are around 3%, 160MPa and 230MPa, respectively [10]. Ductility of both the as-unidirectional and the as-cross rolled sheets processed at 623K is enhanced by hot rolling process, showing passable elongation ranging from 4% to 15% at the maximum. Elongations along TD (90°) of both as-unidirectional and cross rolled sheets processed at 623K are distinctly less than 4% due to the early fracture during tensile test. Early fracture also occurs in RD (0°) of both as-hot rolled sheets, which results in 8% total elongation. Larger total elongations around 15% is obtained in the diagonal direction (45°) of both as-hot rolled sheets. Ultimate tensile strengths of the diagonal direction specimens are 350MPa for 623K-unidirectional rolling and 380MPa for 623K-cross rolling, respectively. At higher rolling temperature, 673K, as-hot-unidirectional rolled sheet shows comparatively uniform and larger elongation to failure, approximately 18%, especially in TD (90°). In contrast, as-cross rolled sheet processed at 673K shows there is a little difference among the three directions, RD (0°), diagonal direction (45°) and TD (90°) in nominal stress-nominal strain curves. It is attributed to that the effect of change in strain path and higher rolling temperature induce to restrain or minimize the planar anisotropy of rolled sheets. Nevertheless, total elongations are limited within a range of around 9~10%.

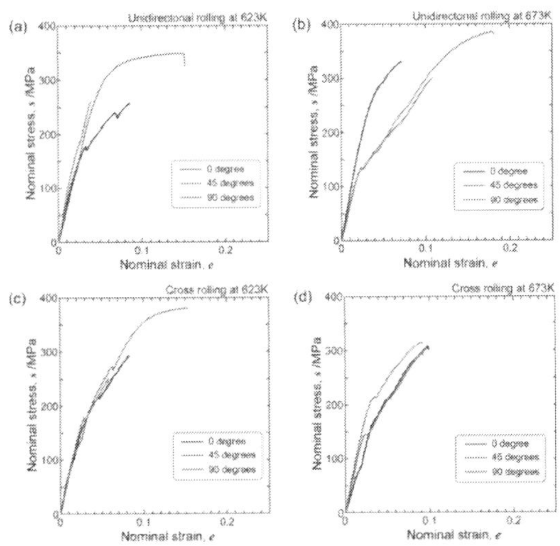

Figure 4. Nominal stress-nominal strain curves of as-hot-rolled AZ91D sheets.

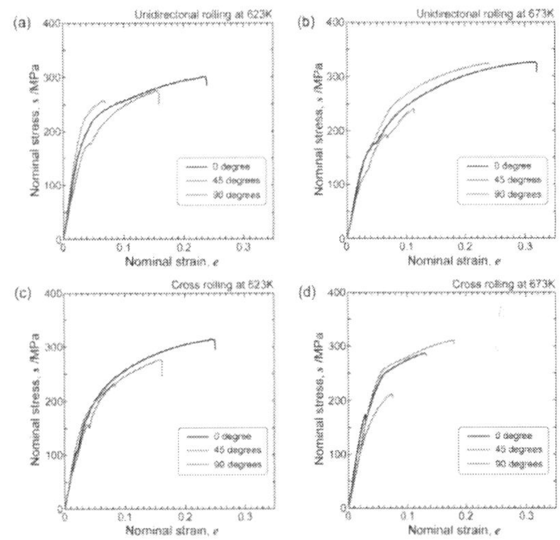

Figure 5. Nominal stress-nominal strain curves of hot rolled AZ91D sheets annealed at 623K.

Figure 5 demonstrates nominal stress-nominal strain curves of the unidirectional rolled and the cross rolled sheets annealed at 623K. As a consequence of recrystallisation annealing, total elongation under all the rolling conditions are well enhanced except for TD (90°) of 623K-unidirectional rolling, 623K- and 673K-cross rolling. Ultimate tensile strength varies from 300MPa to 325MPa in the specimens exhibiting considerably significant elongations. As for 673K-cross rolling, despite recrystallisation annealing, ductility of the annealed sheet does not develop well as compared with the other three rolling conditions, resulting in the total elongation range from 8 % to 19%.

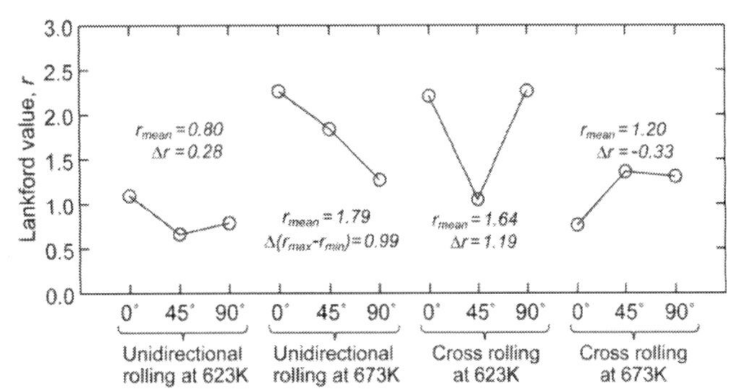

Figure 6. Variations of Lankford values of annealed AZ91D rolled sheets.

Figure 6 shows the variations of r-values (Lankford values or plastic strain ratio) of the annealed sheets. The r-values were calculated from width strain and thickness strain after 4% extension applied in tensile test in order to avoid a fracture. Except for 673K-unidirectional rolling, distributions of r-values show the V-shape or inverse V-shape. Mean r-values varying from 0.80 to 1.79 are generally lower as compared to AZ31. This is because an applied longitudinal strain (4% elongation) during tensile test is too smaller than 15~20% elongation in the other metallic materials such as steels, aluminum alloys and so on. Regarding to the index of planar anisotropy, 623K-unidirectional rolling is the lowest among the employed rolling conditions, although mean r-value of 623K-unidirectional rolling is also markedly the lowest among these rolling conditions. Accompanied with an increase in ductility, improvement of r-value may arise by applying higher annealing temperature, which may adversely lead to grain coarsening due to the secondary recrystallisation.

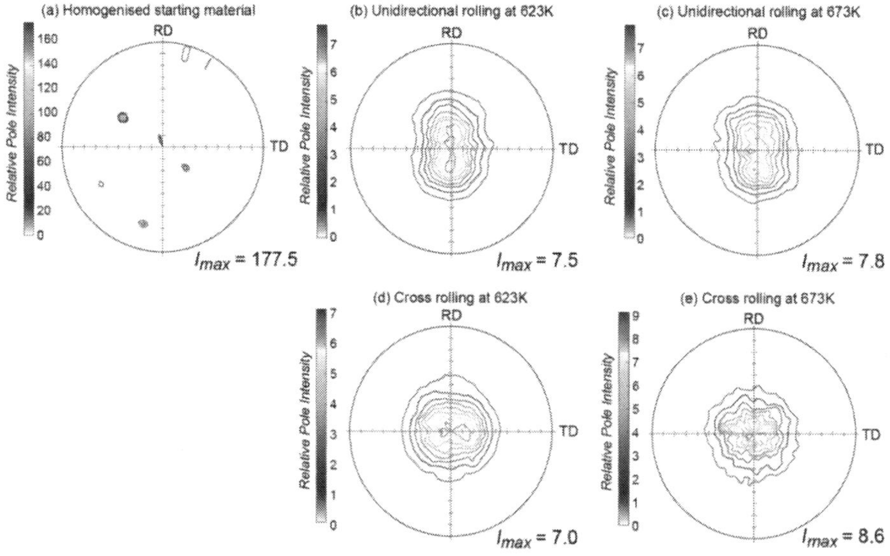

Figure 7. Incomplete (0001) pole figures of heat-treated cast AZ91D (starting material) and as-hot-rolled AZ91D sheets.

3.3. Macro textures

Figure 7 shows the incomplete (0001) pole figures of heat-treated cast starting material and as-hot-rolled AZ91D sheets. Orientation/pole densities in pole figures were normalised with each own X-ray diffraction raw data. Heat-treated starting material does not have an obvious (0001) basal texture because of cast ingot, and the maximum relative intensity lies in nearby the $(0\bar{1}12)$ pole in the pole figure. The pole figure of 623K-unidirectional rolled sheet shows the typical double-peak type (0001) basal texture with the peaks inclined towards ±15° in RD as seen in Figure 7 (b). 673K-unidirectional rolled sheet also shows substantially similar double-peak type (0001) basal texture (Figure 7 (c)). The double-peak type (0001) basal texture is formed in consequence of activation of pyramidal <c+a> slip system [11]. Contrastingly, macro texture of 623K-cross rolled sheet shows a significant (0001) basal texture with the peaks inclined towards ±10° in TD. Contours of lower relative intensity are concentrically broadened to around ±40° in both RD and TD. Macro texture of 673K-cross rolled sheet resembles that of 623K-cross rolled sheet, exhibiting higher relative intensity towards (0001) pole. This fact agrees with the findings of researches by Xi [7] and Sulkowski [8]. In cross rolling, crystal orientation change by rigid body rotation around ND axis in plane-strain compression imparts the tilt of basal pole in TD as a result of accumulation of strain path change.

Figure 8 depicts the incomplete (0001) pole figures of AZ91D sheets annealed at 623K. In unidirectional rolling at 623K and 673K, the strong (0001) basal textures appear while the inclined peaks towards RD almost vanish from the pole figures as seen in Figure 8 (a) and (b). In cross rolling at 623K and 673K, the strong (0001) basal textures also appear as the peaks inclined towards TD disappear due to dislocation rearrangement and grain growth during the static recrystallisation annealing. However, distributions of lower relative intensities remain moderately concentric in both RD and TD in the pole figures.

4. Conclusions

The following remarks are drawn;

1) The 4 mm thick cast ingot AZ91D materials were successfully rolled into 1mm thick sheets under four different rolling conditions. The as-hot unidirectional and cross rolled sheets demonstrate good ductility ranging from more than 5% up to 15% elongation in tensile test. It is confirmed that the effect of change in strain path and higher rolling temperature induces to restrain the planar anisotropy of cross rolled sheets. The total elongations of annealed sheets under all the rolling conditions are well enhanced.
2) Macro textures of the as-unidirectional rolled sheets exhibit the typical double-peak type (0001) basal texture with the peaks inclined towards ±15° in RD. In contrast to the as-unidirectional rolled sheets, macro textures of the as-cross rolled sheets have double-peak (0001) basal texture with peaks inclined towards ±10° in TD. Contours of lower relative intensity are concentrically broadened to around ±40° in both RD and TD. After recrystallisation annealing at 623K, evolution of (0001) basal texture becomes noticeably predominant under all the rolling conditions. Distributions of lower relative intensities remain moderately concentric in both RD and TD in the pole figures of the annealed cross-rolled sheets.

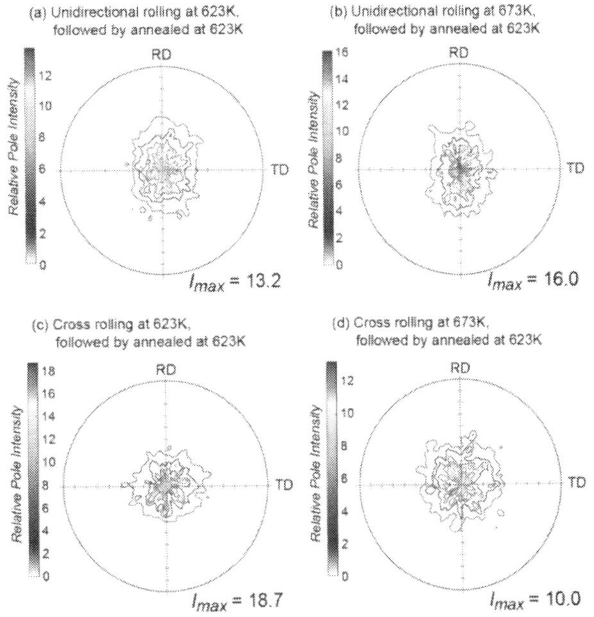

Figure 8. Incomplete (0001) pole figures of annealed AZ91D rolled sheets.

Acknowledgements

The authors are deeply grateful to Mr. Tsunayoshi Takahara of Comprehensive Analysis Center, Institute of Scientific and Industrial Research, Osaka University for the technical assistance of X-ray diffraction texture measurement.

References

[1] Mordike B L, Ebert T 2001 *Mat. Sci. Eng.* A, **302** 37-45
[2] Ren L, Fan L, Zhou M, Guo Y, Zhang Y, Boehlert C J, Quan G 2018 *Int. J. Lightweight Mater. Manuf.* **1** 81-88
[3] Al-Samman T, Li X 2011 *Mat. Sci. Eng.* A, **528** 3809-3822
[4] Kudo S, Yokoyama S, Shimoyama K, Kaneko S, Fujita F 2017 *Mat. Sci. Eng.* A, **680** 75-84
[5] Chino Y, Sassa K, Mabuchi M 2008 *Mater. Trans.* **49-12** 2916-2918
[6] Inoue R et al. 2017 *Japanese Patent Application Disclosure* P2017-160542A (in Japanese)
[7] Li X, Al-Samman T, Gottstein G 2011 *Mater. Des.* **32** 4385-4393
[8] Sulkowski B, Boczkal G 2015 *Metallurgy and Foundry Engineering*, **41-3** 143-151
[9] Bachmann F, Hielscher R, Schaeben H 2010 *Solid State Phenom.* **160** 63-68
[10] 1999 *ASM Specialty Handbook - Magnesium and Magnesium Alloys*, ed Michael M Avedesian and Hugh Baker (Materials Park: ASM International) 67
[11] Kocks U F, Tomé C N, Wenk H-R 1998 *Texture and Anisotropy* (Cambridge: Cambridge University Press) 204-207

IOP Conf. Series: Materials Science and Engineering 1121 (2021) 012005 doi:10.1088/1757-899X/1121/1/012005

Texture Evolution During Cold Forming of Rectangular Hollow Section

A Kaijalainen[1], V Javaheri[1], O Nousiainen[1], J Tulonen[2], P Steen[2] and J Kömi[1]

[1]Materials and Mechanical Engineering, Centre for Advanced Steels Research, University of Oulu, Oulu, Finland
[2]SSAB Europe, Hämeenlinna, Finland

Corresponding author email: antti.kaijalainen@oulu.fi

Abstract. This work aims to study the effect of cold forming on the texture evolution during the manufacturing of rectangular hollow sections. Conventional TMCP steel and a direct-quenched steel in 420 MPa strength level are compared. The texture was characterized at the centerline (S=0) and both surfaces (S=0.8) for base material, four flat side and one corner samples of the rectangular hollow section. The results show that the flat sides of both steels have the minor intensity of ~{554}<225> and ~{112}<110> texture components and an intense texture component of ~{001}<110> in the centerline. Generally, any significant difference between four flat size samples was not found and texture intensities of the conventional TMCP steel were slightly sharper compared to direct-quenched steel. The most important change is observed with the inner corner samples, where the randomly oriented texture in the base material and flat side samples changes to the {110}<111>/<112> shear texture components.

1. Introduction

Formed steel sections are widely used in building construction due to their relatively high strength and stiffness properties. The cold-formed and welded hollow sections which are an efficient low cost and environmentally friendly alternative for the hot-formed sections are the most popular structural steel products [1]. Cold-formed rectangular hollow sections can be fabricated out of the circular profiles in several forming stages introducing plastic deformation. The work hardening caused by plastic deformation during forming resulted in enhancing the strength and hardness although deteriorating the elongation and toughness.

Rolling texture and shear components of the bcc steels during hot rolling are broadly researched and established [2–5]. The main rolling texture components which are typically developed when austenite is deformed under plane strain conditions below its non-recrystallization temperature can be expressed as {112}<110>, {110}<110>,{111}<112> and {554}<225>, with minor amounts of {112}<131> and {100}<011>. While, shear components can be formed when austenite is deformed by rolling below its non-recrystallization temperature by developing their most popular orientations of {112}<111>, {110}<112> and {110}<111> [4].

The previous study of authors [6] showed that the impact toughness properties of a direct-quenched steel were really better than that which produced conventionally. As the continuation of that work, the aim of this study is to compare the microstructure and texture properties of that two steels which were produced with different production routes. The main focus is the characterization of textural evolution during cold deforming from base material to the rectangular hollow section. More detailed information about the effect of cold forming parameters on the mechanical properties and microstructural changes can be found elsewhere [6,7].

2. Experimental material and methods

Transformation texture properties of two cold-formed structural steels to rectangular hollow sections (RHS) are investigated. The studied hot-rolled strip steels were produced by i) a conventional thermomechanical controlled processing (TMCP) and by ii) a direct quenching (DQ) process. The chemical composition of the TMCP steel was 0.07C-1.4Mn-0.02Nb-0.016Ti and DQ sample was consisted of 0.06C-0.7Mn-0.03Nb-0.002Ti (in wt.%). Tensile properties in the hot-rolled stage were quite similar, the yield strengths were ~450 MPa, tensile strengths 530-550 MPa and total elongations were 24-27 %. The microstructure of base materials was mainly ferritic structure with a small fraction of carbon-rich areas as can be seen in figure 1.

Wall thickness of RHS materials was 8 mm and the cross-section dimension was 140 x 140 mm for the TMCP sample and 150 x 150 mm for the DQ material. After forming, the external corner radius was 20 mm, which is in the middle of EN 10219 tolerance range (16-24 mm for 8 mm thickness). As same as the hot rolled condition, after forming, tensile properties in rectangular hollow sections were quite close, the yield strengths were ~550 MPa and tensile strengths ~600 MPa. However, the Charpy V impact energies at -60 °C were significantly different such that for the TMCP it was 66 J compared to 90 J for the DQ sample. More detailed information on hot-rolled strips and rectangular hollow sections can be also found in Refs. [6,7] where microstructure, cold forming rate, and mechanical properties were investigated.

The macrotexture was characterized at the centerline (S=0) and both upper and lower surfaces (S=0.8) using Rigaku SmartLab X-ray Diffractometer (XRD) for four flat sides (FS1-4) and one corner (C) samples of the rectangular hollow section. The position of the XRD samples is illustrated in figure 2. The R_p value in all iterations was (conversion from measured pool graphs to computed pool graphs) less than five, therefore the results are reliable. Moreover, for the detailed investigations microtexture and microstructural characterization were studied using FESEM-EBSD acquisition and analysis (Zeiss UltraPlus FESEM and Oxford Aztec EBSD software). The EBSD measurements were performed at an accelerating voltage of 15 kV and a step size of 0.35 μm.

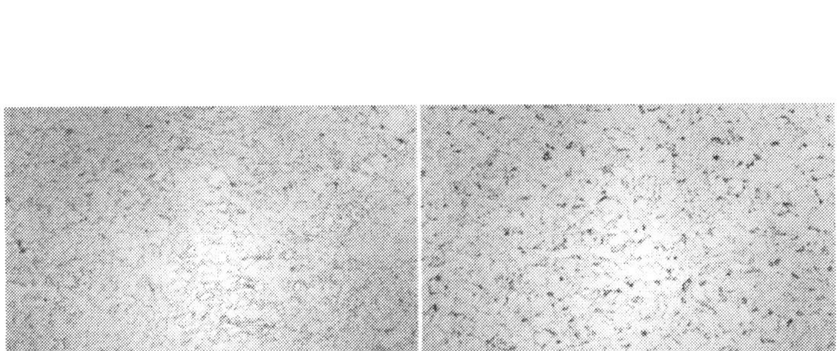

Figure 1. The microstructure of a) TMCP and b) DQ base material.

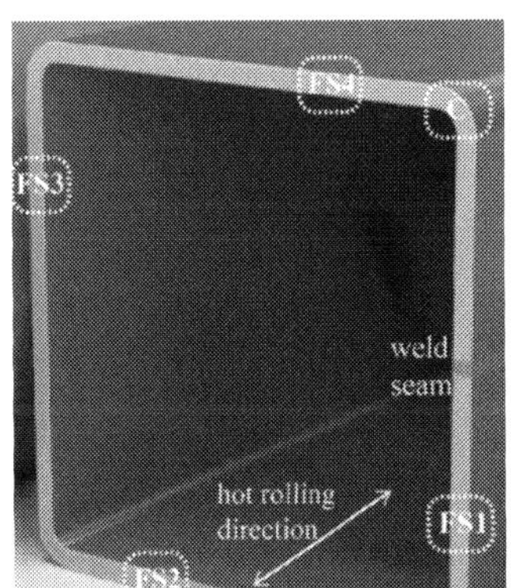

Figure 2. Schematic illustration of cut samples from four flat sides (FS1-4) and one corner (C) of the rectangular hollow section.

IOP Conf. Series: Materials Science and Engineering 1121 (2021) 012005 doi:10.1088/1757-899X/1121/1/012005

3. Results and discussion

3.1. XRD analysis

XRD transformation textures were determined at the surfaces (S=0.8) and centerlines (S=0) for base materials and flat side and corners of rectangular hollow section specimens (figure 2), except for the centerline of TMCP base material. As no significant difference between the four flat size specimens was found, only one flat side (FS3) ODF sections are shown in figures 3 (TMCP steel) and figure 4 (DQ steel). The overall texture of both steels was weak, which is a common feature of hot rolled carbon steels. In fact, the lower surface of the both steels have almost random grain orientation. It can be seen that the texture intensities of the conventional TMCP steel were slightly sharper compared to direct-quenched steel samples. Rolling texture components (i.e. ~{554}<225>, ~{112}<110>, ~{112}<131> and ~{001}<110>) were dominant of the investigated samples, except lower/inner surface samples. The XRD results showed that the more intense ~{112}<110> and ~{001}<110> texture components were developed on the flat sides of both steels rather than the base materials. At the TMCP outer corner sample, the intensity of ~{112}<110> texture component was the most and it was the dominant texture component such that other components were almost disappeared, especially at the centerline and inner corner. Especially, in the outer surface of TMCP steel can be seen that as deformation increases the intensities of the components are increasing. The texture of the lower surface of DQ steel consists of weak texture components {112}<111> and {110}<001>. In addition, a weak non-uniform {110}<uvw> -fibre was detected in this specimen. These findings were in consistent with the earlier observed textures in the surface of hot rolled DQ steel strips [8]. It was very interesting to notice that the effect of the deformation on the texture within the centreline of the sheet and the inner surface was comparable with the deformation induced textures of the TMCP steel. All the measurements showed very weak texture at the lower/inner surface, thus more detailed EBSD microstructural characterization performed to figure out the reasons, as discussed in the next section.

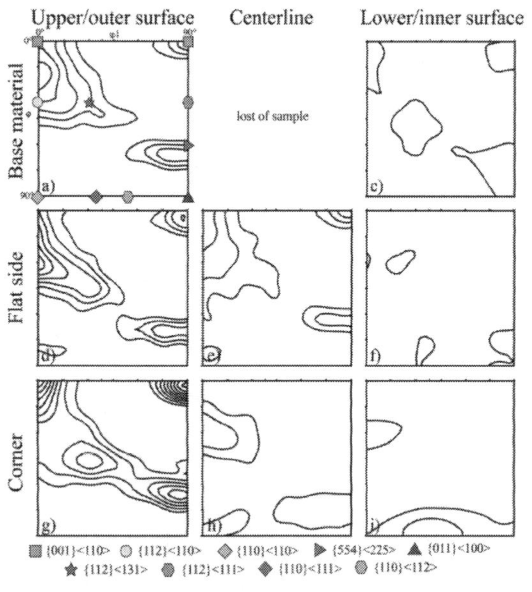

Figure 3. ϕ_2=45° sections of ODFs at the upper and lower surface (S=0.8) and centerline (S=0) positions in TMCP specimens. Base material (a,c), flat side (d-f) and corner (g-i) samples. Important orientations of the bcc structure in the ϕ_2=45° section are shown in figure a). (Levels: 1.5, 2.5,…)

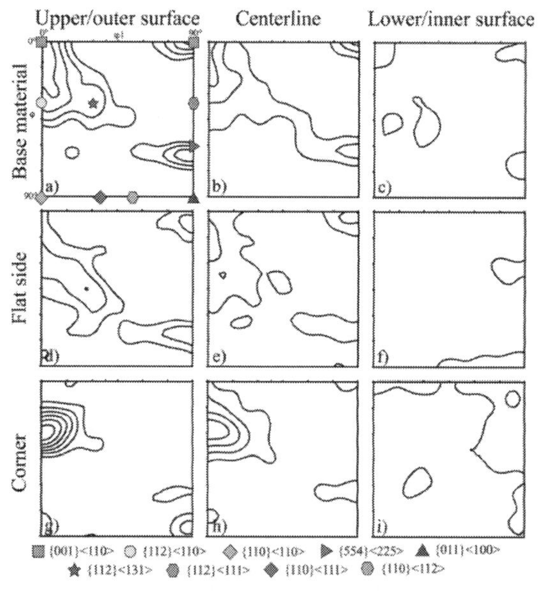

Figure 4. ϕ_2=45° sections of ODFs at the upper and lower surface (S=0.8) and centerline (S=0) positions in DQ specimens. Base material (a,c), flat side (d-f) and corner (g-i) samples. Important orientations of the bcc structure in the ϕ_2=45° section are shown in figure a). (Levels: 1.5, 2.5,…)

3.2. *EBSD microstructure and texture analysis*

Figure 5 shows the upper/outer, centerline, and lower/inner as-rolled and corner inverse pole figures map along with the low angle and high angle grain boundaries for the TMCP steel. It can be observed that the inner grain structure is compressed, and the outer is stretched. Detailed results for the base material and RHS materials are listed in Table 1. According to the grain boundaries analysis and figure 5, the inner corner areas experienced the smallest grain sizes where the highest compression occurred. Outer corner steels showed the second smallest grain structure while centerline of corner areas had the largest grain size. The highest fraction of low-angle grain boundaries (white color in figure 5) was measured for the inner corner areas. In the case of cold forming of strip materials in Ref. [7], it has been noticed that higher straining during cold forming increases the fraction of low-angle grain boundaries, however, a similar effect cannot be seen here from the EBSD measurements, except for those inner and outer corners. Therefore, it is notable that the base material has a lot of low-angle boundaries, and conversely more deformed flat side samples have less low-angle boundaries. As can be seen from the EBSD grain size results, there are no large differences in grain sizes between investigated steels.

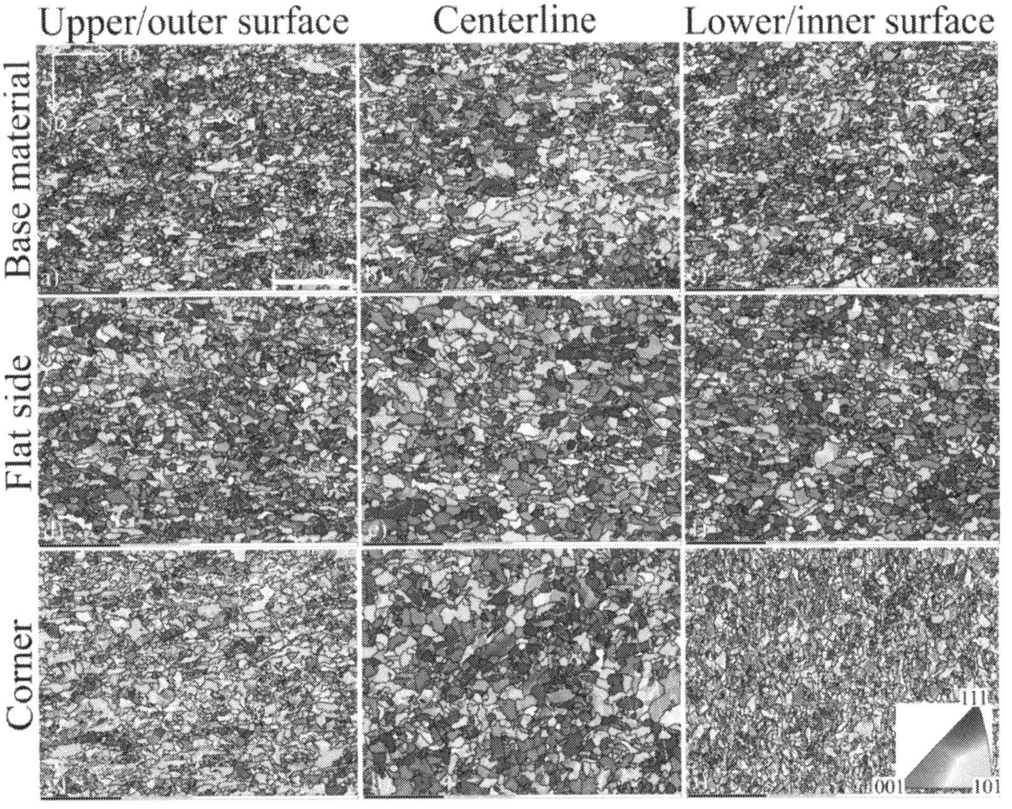

Figure 5. EBSD inverse pole figures (coloring in RD direction) with low- (>2.5°, white) and high-angle (15°-62.7°, black) boundaries. Microstructures of (a-c) base material, (d-f) flat side and (g-i) corner of TMCP steel. The scale bar is 50 μm. (Indexing of the patterns were between 89-95 % before clean-up)

Table 1. EBSD grain size of high-angle grains and fraction of low-angle boundaries.

Material	High-angle grain size (μm)			Fraction of the low-angle boundaries (2.5°-15°)		
	outer	center	inner	outer	center	inner
TMCP base	3.09	3.91	3.18	0.28	0.29	0.24
TMCP flat side	3.80	4.49	3.68	0.24	0.18	0.12
TMCP corner	3.74	4.48	3.28	0.56	0.21	0.64
DQ base	4.52	4.83	4.04	0.14	0.16	0.36
DQ flat side	3.91	4.75	4.52	0.29	0.21	0.29
DQ corner	4.82	5.04	3.17	0.21	0.28	0.70

*Note: Grains below 0.78 μm are excluded from the calculation.

From the EBSD data of TMCP steel, ϕ_2=45° sections of ODFs are calculated and results are presented in figure 6. Pole figures results are plotted in figure 7. The results were in good agreement with the XRD macrotexture indicating that the centerline of the base material has mainly the rolling texture where it increases by increasing the amount of deformation. Outer/upper surface texture intensities are weaker than centerline and also weaker than those intensities measured from the XRD data owing to the smaller investigated region. XRD is measuring a larger area than the EBSD where acquisitions are from a quite small area (200 x 150 μm). Similarly, very weak or randomly orientated texture was found for lower/inner EBSD samples compared to the XRD results.

Since the EBSD acquisitions (upper, centerline, and lower) are from the same sample, the acquisitions are obtained from the same plane which makes the job easier to determine the differences in texture between the different positions in one material. Hence, assuming only the typical bcc rolling texture at the centerline, the pole figures can clearly show the texture rotation during RHS forming. As regards, at the outer surface samples (in figures 7a, d, and g), texture shifting 10 degrees down from ~{112}<110>, which is transformed component during hot-rolling of the material. Therefore, during the cold forming process texture is sharpening and slightly increase at the centerline and outer surface of the material. However, the most significant change is observed with the inner corner samples (figure 7i), where in the base material and flat side samples the randomly oriented texture evolves to the {110}<111>/<112> and minor {112}<131> shear texture components.

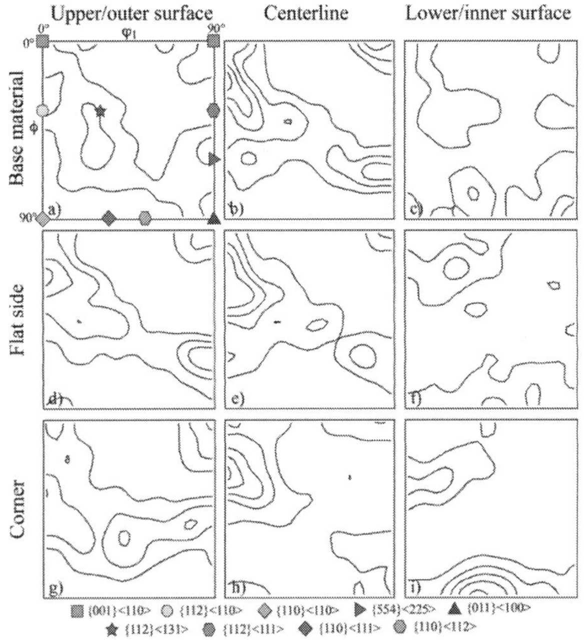

Figure 6. ϕ_2=45° sections of ODFs at the upper and lower surface and centerline positions in TMCP specimens. Base material (a,c), flat side (d-f) and corner (g-i) samples. Important orientations of the bcc structure in the ϕ_2=45° section are shown in figure a). (Levels: 1, 2,...)

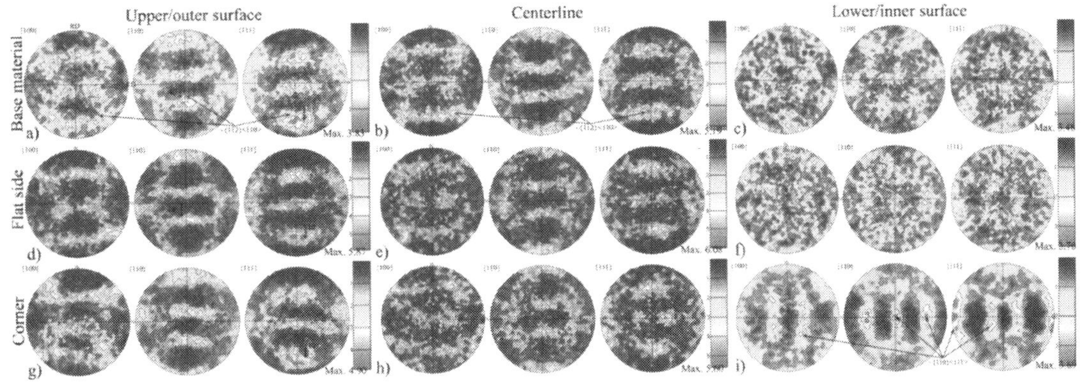

Figure 7. Pole figure (upper hemispheres) of the investigated material. Base material (a-c), flat side (d-f) and corner (g-i) samples.

4. Conclusions

The evolution of transformation texture from the base material to cold deformed rectangular hollow section during the cold forming process has been investigated. The main results can be summarized as follows:

- Inner corner areas had the smallest grain sizes with the highest compression, and the centerline areas had the largest grain size. The inner corner areas have the highest fraction of low-angle grain boundaries.
- Typically texture intensities increased as deformation increased.
- Outer surface samples texture shifted 10 degrees from ~{112}<110>, which was probably initiated during the hot rolling process.
- The most significant change was observed with the inner corner sample, such that in the base material and flat side samples the randomly oriented texture changes to the shear texture.

References

[1] Puthli R and Packer J A 2013 Structural design using cold-formed hollow sections *Steel Constr.* **6** 150–7

[2] Ray R K and Jonas J J 1990 Transformation textures in steels *Int. Mater. Rev.* **35** 1–36

[3] Kestens L and Jonas J J 2005 Transformation and Recrystallization Textures Associated with Steel Processing *ASM Handbook vol. 14A, Metalworking: Bulk Forming* ed S L Semiatin (Materials Park: ASM International) pp 685–700

[4] Wittridge N J and Jonas J J 2000 The austenite-to-martensite transformation in Fe–30%Ni after deformation by simple shear *Acta Mater.* **48** 2737–49

[5] Kaijalainen A, Javaheri V, Lindell D and Porter D A 2018 Development of crystallographic texture under plane and shear strain in ultrahigh-strength strip steels *IOP Conf. Ser. Mater. Sci. Eng.* **375** 012026

[6] Kaijalainen A, Mourujärvi J, Tulonen J, Steen P and Kömi J 2020 Effect of direct quenching on the mechanical properties of cold formed S500 rectangular hollow section *Procedia Manuf.* **50** 777–83

[7] Kaijalainen A, Mourujärvi J, Tulonen J, Steen P and Kömi J 2021 Improvement on Impact Toughness of Cold Formed S420 Steel by Direct Quenching *Mater. Sci. Forum* **1016** 648–53

[8] Saastamoinen A, Kaijalainen A, Porter D and Suikkanen P 2017 The effect of thermomechanical treatment and tempering on the subsurface microstructure and bendability of direct-quenched low-carbon strip steel *Mater. Charact.* **134** 172–81

IOP Conf. Series: Materials Science and Engineering 1121 (2021) 012006 doi:10.1088/1757-899X/1121/1/012006

Crystallographic orientation on raft-like structure developed by tensile deformation in Cu-Fe dual phase alloy sheet

N. Koga[1], S. Tomono[2] and O. Umezawa[3]
[1] Division of Mechanical Science and Engineering, Kanazawa University, Kakuma-machi, Kanazawa, 920-1192 Japan.

[2] Graduate School of Engineering, Yokohama National University, 79-5 Tokiwadai, Hodogaya, Yokohama, 240-8501 Japan.

[3] Faculty of Engineering, Yokohama National University, 79-5 Tokiwadai, Hodogaya, Yokohama, 240-8501 Japan.

E-mail: koga-norimitsu@se.kanazawa-u.ac.jp

Abstract. The crystallographic orientation of a raft-like structure developed by tensile deformation in Cu-40 mass%Fe dual phase alloy sheet was investigated. The sheet exhibited Cu and Fe layer structure aligned along the rolling direction (RD). The tensile tests were carried out parallel to the RD. The rearrangement of the layer structure was observed in a necked region, where the layers were distorted and aligned along the normal direction (ND). The layered structure perpendicular to the tensile direction is similar to the raft structure developed by creep deformation in a nickel-based super alloy. The bending of layers in the raft-like structure and shear fracture were detected in the cross-section of the samples. The raft-like structure in Cu-Fe dual phase alloy displayed a specific crystal orientation such as $<111>_{Cu}$//ND, $<101>_{Cu}$//RD, $<101>_{Fe}$//ND, and $<111>_{Fe}$//RD. The orientations are matched to those rotated 90 degrees around the transverse direction of the layer structure. Therefore, the bending of the layer structure in a necked part and/or local shear deformation may be responsible for the raft-like structure development in Cu-Fe dual phase alloy.

1. Introduction

The crystallographic orientation in a metal continuously rotates during tensile deformation because an active slip direction moves in the direction parallel to the tensile axis [1]. The crystallographic orientation rotation develops the deformation texture of the metal, depending on its crystal structure. Generally, bcc and fcc metals develop <110> and <111> textures along the tensile direction, respectively, owing to those slip systems [2]. In addition, a local deformation, i.e. necking, also occurs during a tensile test. Within a necking region, the stress state becomes triaxial; however, the texture within necking regions has not been investigated thoroughly.

The binary system of copper and iron exhibits low mutual solubility in both matrix phases and, therefore, Cu–Fe alloy forms a copper (fcc) and iron (bcc) dual phase structure at room temperature. Cu-Fe alloy has been reported to exhibit excellent tensile properties at cryogenic temperatures, compared to those of single-phase materials [3-4]. In this study, we discovered the characteristic deformation structure within the tensile necking region of a Cu-Fe binary alloy, and the formation mechanism of the characteristic deformation structure was discussed through analysis of the crystallographic orientation.

2. Experimental procedure

The material used in this study was a commercial cold-rolled Cu-40 mass%Fe alloy. The specimen was heat-treated at 1123 K for 1.8 ks and subsequently followed by water cooling. The microstructure was observed by an optical microscope (OM) and scanning electron microscope (SEM), while the crystal orientation was analyzed with the electron backscattered diffraction (EBSD) method. Tensile test specimens of 20 mm in gage length and 4 mm in width were cut from the plates along the RD. The tensile test was carried out at initial strain rate of approximately 5.2 $\times 10^{-4}$ s^{-1} at 293 K. After tensile test, EBSD analysis was conducted on normal direction (ND) planes within the necking region in the fractured specimen. Crystallographic orientation in the rolling direction (RD) and transverse direction (TD) planes were evaluated from the obtained data by using OIM™ analysis 7.0.1. Additionally, the Cu-50 mass%Fe alloy was tensile tested in liquid nitrogen (77 K), and the microstructure within the necking region in the fractured specimen was observed by using SEM.

3. Results and discussion

3.1. Initial microstructure

Figure 1 shows OM images of the RD, TD, and ND planes after heat-treatment in the Cu-40 mass%Fe alloy. Fe and Cu layers were linearly aligned along the RD. The layer structure included some defects, i.e. there were many interruptions and bends of the layer. Individual layer thickness was approximately 10 μm. Figure 2 presents the inverse pole figure (IPF) maps depicting the crystal orientation of the ND, RD, and TD in the Cu and Fe phases in the Cu-40 mass%Fe alloy. The intensity distribution of crystal orientation plotted on the standard stereographic triangle is also displayed in Figure 2. The crystal orientation rotation within a grain was gradually developed in both the Cu and Fe phases from line profile analysis, indicating that strain introduced during cold rolling remained even after annealing. The Fe phase exhibited a general rolling texture [5] such as $<111>_{Fe}$//ND or $<001>_{Fe}$//ND, while the crystal orientation in the Cu phase was $<111>_{Cu}$ //ND, which did not match with the general rolling texture [6] such as $<110>_{Cu}$//ND, $<211>_{Cu}$//ND, and $<123>_{Cu}$//ND. As the part of Cu phase was finely recrystallized grain and twinned. These features may affect the texture of the Cu phase after annealing.

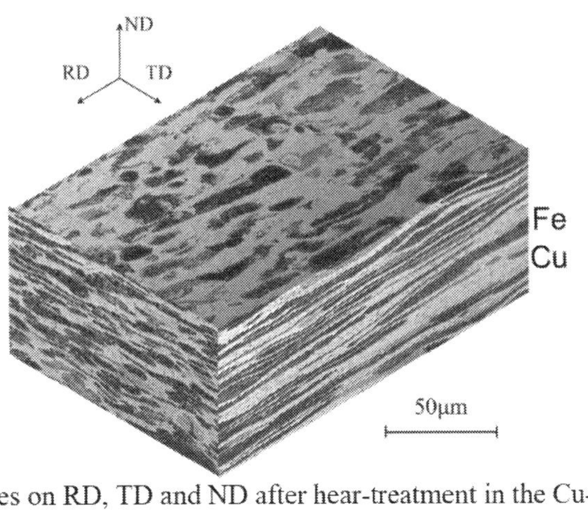

Figure 1 OM images on RD, TD and ND after hear-treatment in the Cu-40 mass%Fe alloy.

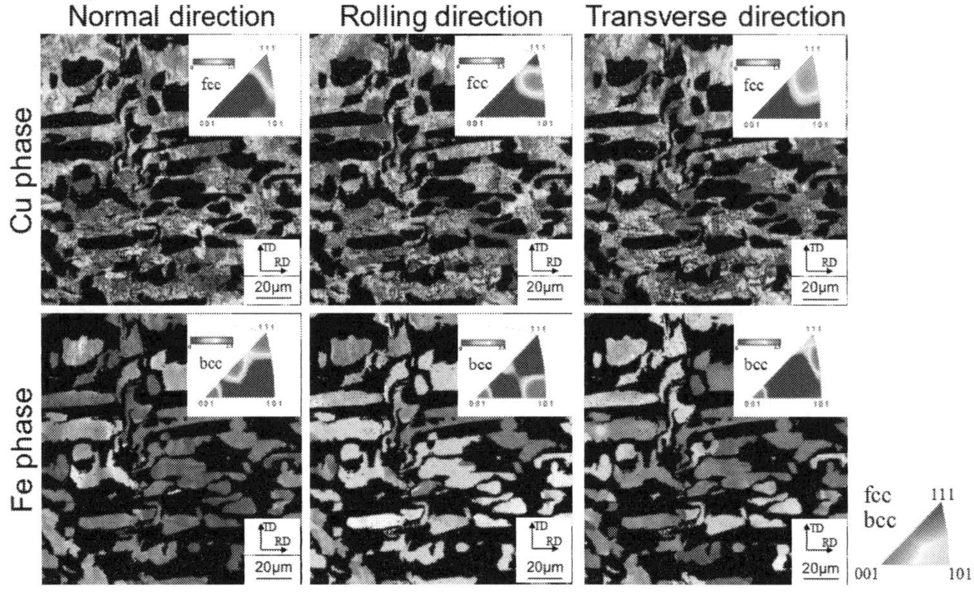

Figure 2 Inverse pole figure maps of ND, RD and TD in Cu and Fe phases after heat-treatment in the Cu-40 mass%Fe alloy. The intensity distribution of crystal orientation is plotted on the standard stereographic triangle.

3.2 Deformation structure within necking

Figure 3 (a) shows an SEM image of the fractured specimen in the Cu-40 mass%Fe alloy. Since both the Cu and Fe phases exhibit high ductility at room temperature, the necking region appeared clearly in the Cu-Fe alloy. Figures 3 (b) and (c) are enlarged SEM images within the white squares in (a) and (b). Within the necking region, part of the layer structure was rearranged perpendicular to the tensile direction as shown in Figure 3 (c). This characteristic deformation structure is similar to the layer structure developed by creep deformation in a nickel-based super alloy [7]. The nickel-based super

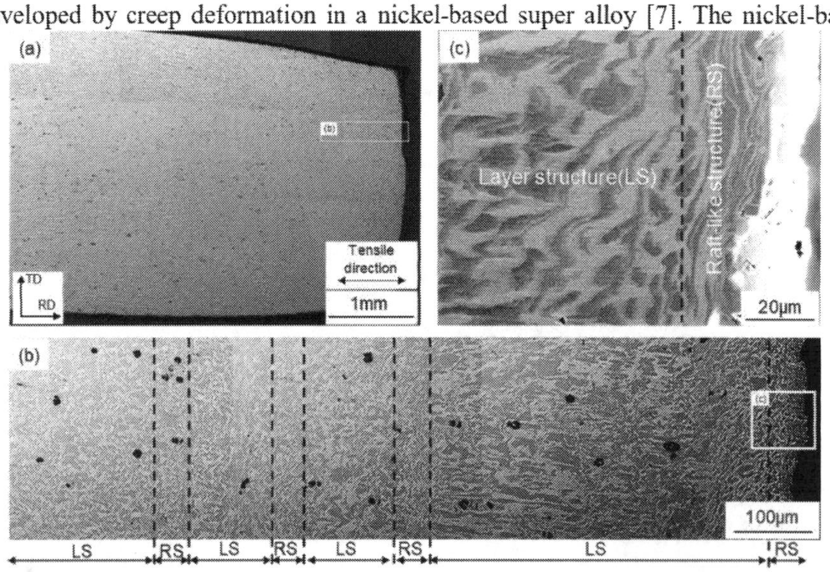

Figure 3 (a) Whole SEM image of fractured specimen in the Cu-40mass%Fe alloy. SEM images (b) (c) are enlarged within white squares in (a) and (b), respectively.

alloy consists of a Ni matrix and cubic $Ni_3(Al+Ti)$ (γ'). After creep test, the γ' elongates along a direction perpendicular to the loading direction, which is defined as the raft structure. This raft structure is formed through a diffusion process by using the lattice misfit between the Ni matrix and γ' precipitations as a driving force. Therefore, the raft structure in the nickel-based super alloy does not form under deformation at room temperature, where Ni and Al atom diffusions are negligible. Both Cu and Fe atoms also hardly diffuse at room temperature, and the formation mechanism of the characteristic deformation structure in Cu-Fe alloy differs somewhat from that in the nickel-based super alloy. Thus, we called the characteristic deformation structure a raft-like structure. The raft-like structure was intermittently developed within the necking region as shown in Figure 3 (b).

Figure 4 shows SEM images of the fractured specimen seen in Figure 3 with tilted at 70 degrees. The fracture surface lies approximately 45 degrees from Figure 4(a), indicating that the shear fracture occurred after necking in the Cu-Fe alloy. The layer structure within the raft-like structure bent to the ND as indicated by arrows in Figures 4 (b) and (c). Moreover, the SEM images observed from the RD plane in the fracture specimen (Figure 5) revealed that part of the layer widens along the ND. However, the bending of the layer structure to the ND was not observed from the RD plane (Figure 5). According to these observation results, it can be concluded that the raft-like structure forms by the bending of the layer to the ND around the TD axis.

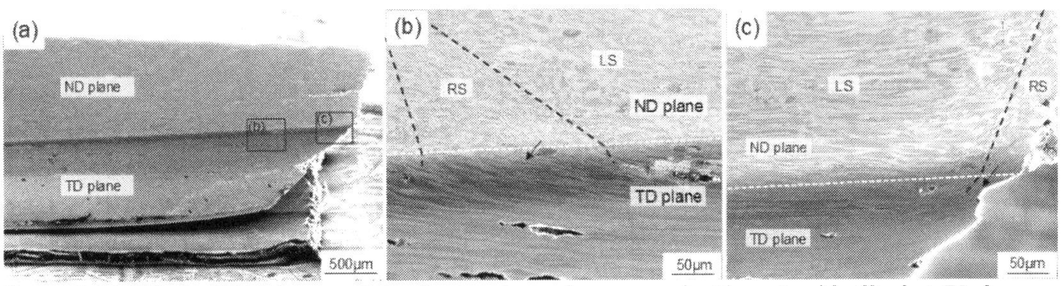

Figure 4 (a) Whole SEM image of the fractured specimen seen in Figure3 with tilted at 70 degrees. SEM images (b) and (c) are enlarged within black squares in (a).

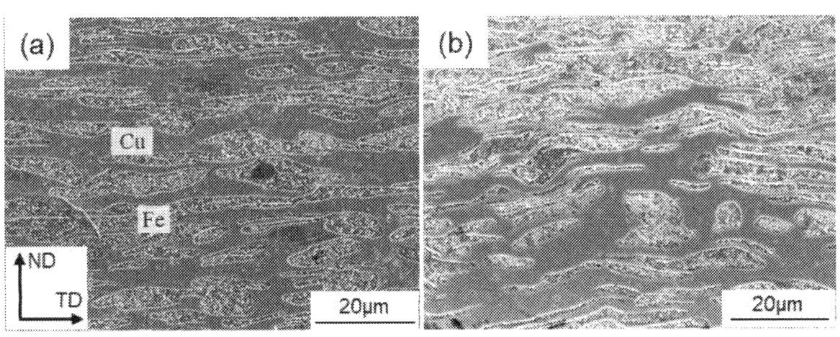

Figure 5 SEM image observed from RD plan in (a) as annealed and (b) fractured specimens in the Cu-40 mass%Fe alloy.

3.3 Crystallographic orientation in raft-like structure.

Figure 6 shows IPF maps of the Cu and Fe phases in the ND, RD, and TD in the same region as Figure 3 (c). The intensity distributions of crystal orientation within the layer structure (A) and raft-like structure (B) are displayed below the IPF maps. Within the layer structure (A), typical deformation textures of Cu and Fe were developed by tensile deformation, i.e. $\langle 101\rangle_{Cu}$//ND, $\langle 111\rangle_{Cu}$//RD, $\langle 111\rangle_{Fe}$//ND, and $\langle 101\rangle_{Fe}$//RD. In contrast, within the raft-like structure (B), specific crystal orientations such as $\langle 111\rangle_{Cu}$//ND, $\langle 101\rangle_{Cu}$//RD, $\langle 101\rangle_{Fe}$//ND, and $\langle 111\rangle_{Fe}$//RD were developed.

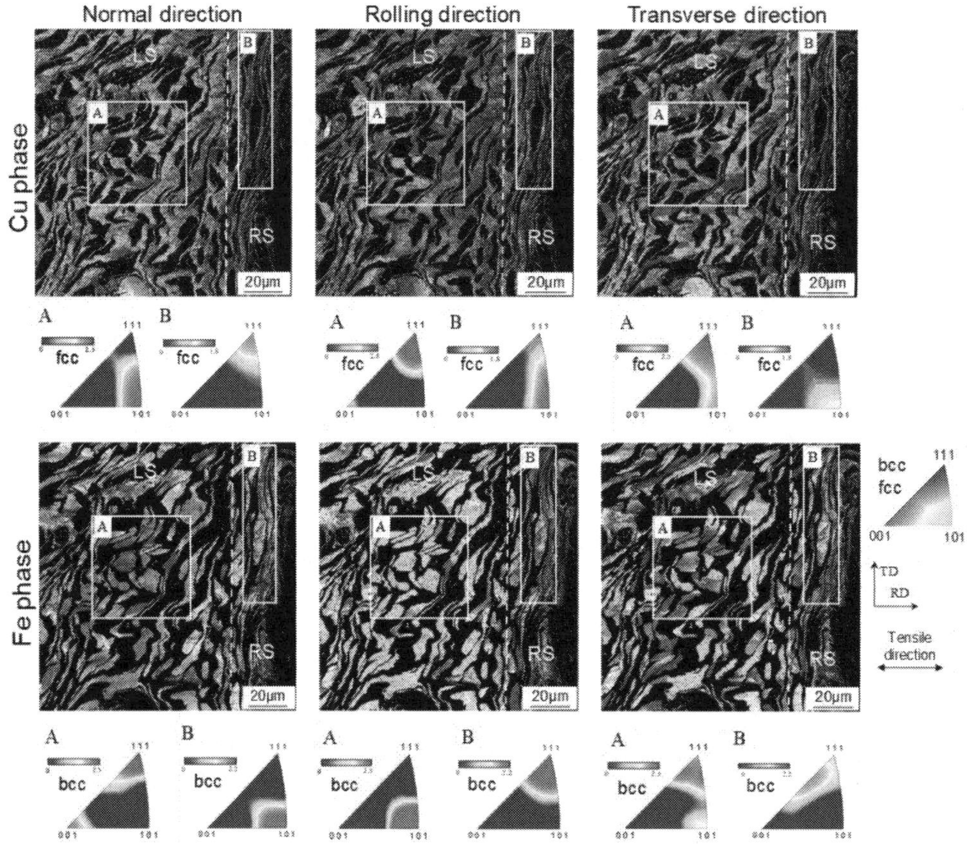

Figure 6 Inverse pole figure maps of Cu and Fe phases on ND, RD and TD in the same region as Figure 3 (c). The intensity distributions of crystal orientation within the layer structure (A) and raft-like structure (B) were plotted on the standard stereographic triangle.

Therefore, the deformation texture and three-dimensional morphologies within the raft-like structure are possibly explained from the following formation mechanism, as depicted in Figure 7. Initially, the typical tensile deformation texture is uniformly developed in the specimen until necking. The layer structures then bend by necking as shown in Figure 7, and the crystal orientation within the necking region rotates from the typical tensile texture around the TD axis. Moreover, shear deformation occurs near the fracture region and also bends the layer structures to the ND, as seen in Figure 7. In the region where the layer completely rotates to the ND, the specific crystal orientation of the raft-like structure is developed. The raft-like structure intermittently observed in Figure 3 (b) may be due to defects of

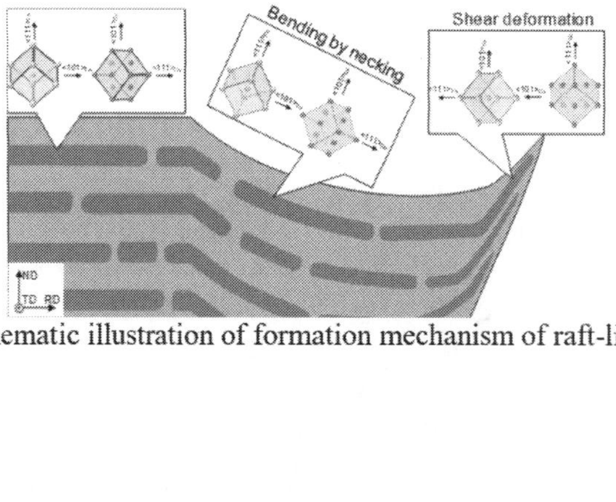

Figure 7 Schematic illustration of formation mechanism of raft-like structure

layer structure and local shear deformation. In the Cu-50mass%Fe alloy which was tensile-deformed at 77 K (Figure 8), the raft-like structure appeared. The covered by the raft-like structure in this specimen was much larger than that in the Cu-40mass%Fe alloy, as the raft-like structure appeared in the entire necking region in Cu-50mass%Fe. Thus, the development of the raft-like structure should depend on tensile test conditions, volume fractions and distribution of each phase, although its formation factor is still unclear. Nevertheless, it appears that the raft-like structure in Cu-Fe alloy is developed through a deformation process, which completely differs from the raft structure developed in the creep deformation of nickel-based super alloy. Therefore, further study about the raft-like structure in Cu-Fe alloy, such as determining the formation factors of raft-like structure and its contribution to the mechanical properties, is necessary.

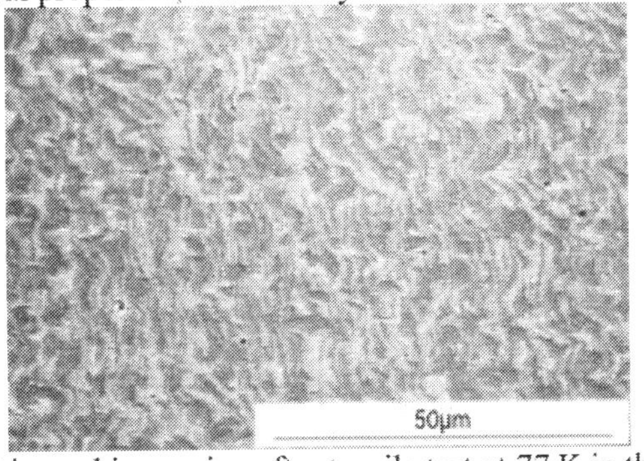

Figure 8 SEM image within necking region after tensile test at 77 K in the Cu-50 mass%Fe alloy.

4. Conclusions

The characteristic deformation structure within the necking region of tensile deformed Cu-Fe binary alloy was investigated, and the formation mechanism of the deformation structure was discussed through the analysis of crystallographic orientation. The major results are summarized as follows:

The layer structure of the alloy consisting of copper and iron phases, was partly rearranged perpendicular to the tensile direction within the necking region after tensile test. The resulting structure was similar to a raft structure developed during creep test of a nickel-based super alloy. Hence, the characteristic deformation structure in Cu-Fe alloy was labeled a raft-like structure.

Layer bending to the normal direction in the raft-like structure was observed in the cross-section of the samples. Moreover, shear fracture occurred, and the layers bent in the normal direction near the fracture surface.

The raft-like structure displayed specific crystal orientations such as $<111>_{Cu}$//ND, $<101>_{Cu}$//RD, $<101>_{Fe}$//ND, and $<111>_{Fe}$//RD. The orientations were matched to those rotated 90 degrees around the transverse direction of the layer structure. Therefore, the bending of the layer structure in a necked region and/or local shear deformation may be responsible for the raft-like structure development in the Cu-Fe dual phase alloy.

References

[1] Sevillano J.G *et al* 1980 *Prog. Mater. Sci.,* **25** 69.
[2] Hosford W.F 1993 *The Mechanics of Crystals and Textured Polycrystals* (Oxford University Press) pp 128-138.
[3] Koga N *et al* 2018 *IOP Conference Series: Materials Science and Engineering* **879** 012004.
[4] Koga N *et al* 2020 *J. Jpn. Res. Ins. Adv. Copper-Base. Mater. Tech.,* **59** 289.
[5] Holscher M *et al* 1991 *Steel Research* **62** 567.
[6] Kestens L *et al.* 2016 *Materials Science and Technology* **32** 1303.
[7] Sato A *et al* 2006, *J.Japan Inst.Met. Mater* **70** 666.

IOP Conf. Series: Materials Science and Engineering 1121 (2021) 012007 doi:10.1088/1757-899X/1121/1/012007

Adiabatic shear bands formation in polycrystalline aluminium

I Mania[1], H Paul[1,2], R Chulist[1] and P Petrzak[1]

[1]Institute of Metallurgy and Materials Science, Polish Academy of Sciences, 25 Reymonta St. 30-059 Krakow, Poland

Corresponding author (H.P.): e-mail: h.paul@imim.pl

Abstract. The microstructure and texture evolutions during dynamic (or high strain rate) deformation of commercially pure AA1050 alloy have been studied to elucidate the mechanisms of shear band (SB) formation and its propagation across the flattened grains arranged in layers with special attention to texture evolution. The hat-shaped samples were compressed using drop hammer at a strain rate of 5.3 x 10^2 s^{-1}. Detailed microstructure and texture characterizations were carried out using SEM equipped with EBSD facility. The shear displacement moves the upper part of the hat-shaped sample towards the bottom one leading to a strain localization in the form of SB. It was found that the strain localization occurs *via* deflection of flattened grains within narrow areas leading to kink-type bands that are considered to be the precursors of SB. The strain-induced crystal lattice rotation led to the formation of new texture components, different from those identified inside the undeformed matrix. It also facilitates slip propagation across the grain boundaries. The mechanism of macro-SB formation is essentially crystallographic in nature since in all grains of the sheared zone, the crystal lattice rotated in such a way that one of the {111} slip planes became nearly parallel to the shear plane and the <011> direction became parallel to the direction of maximum shear.

1. Introduction

The occurrence of shear bands (SB) and their compact clusters called macroscopic shear bands (macro-SB) constitutes an important scientific and technological problem concerning metal forming, e.g. [1-3]. Nevertheless, fundamental studies regarding SB formation in materials deformed at high strain rates are still relatively limited. The so-called adiabatic shear bands (ASB) are areas of localized intense shear that appear very quickly during deformation especially for metals of lower density and lower heat capacity, e.g. Ti and its alloys [4]. A widespread conviction persists that the competition between strain rate hardening and thermal softening determines the onset of SB, as it has been initially proposed by Zenner and Hollomon [5]. When thermal softening prevails over strain hardening, an abrupt loss of homogeneity of plastic deformation occurs and then material falls in the shear banding deformation mode. Rittel et al. [6] revealed that the specimen temperature rise prior to strain localization has almost no effect on the onset of ASB formation. Therefore, Rittel et al. [6] and Ossovski et al. [7] modified the Zenner-Hollomon concept, assuming a microstructural softening due to dynamic recrystallization, where the dynamically stored energy of cold work is used as a quantitative criterion of the onset of ASB.

The descriptions of initial stage of strain localization at high strain rates are to a large extent based on models which do not account for the crystallographic nature of metals or include the crystallographic determinations only partially, e.g. [8]. This is despite the residual microstructure and crystallographic texture have been identified as important and related aspects to shear localization during deformation at conventional strain rates [3,9-13]. In this context there is lack of clear answer to the fundamental question - *what are the conditions for initiating an ASB*? It indicates that the real elementary mechanism of band nucleation, its thickening and propagation across the boundaries in polycrystalline aggregate, is not fully understood. The same applies to the formation of deformation texture where strain localization leads to local softening and specific texture components.

In face centred cubic (fcc) metals or alloys ASB has been rarely reported, even though the formation of SB in such metals is one of the most commonly observed phenomenon accompanying the plastic deformation. Generally, two groups of SBs deformed at 'conventional strain rates' can be distinguished in fcc metals according to the stacking fault energy (SFE). In metals with a low SFE, brass-type SB can be readily observed after medium deformations, e.g. [3,9-11]. They develop within the microstructures characterized by thin twin-matrix lamellae. In metals of a medium-to-high SFE, copper-type SBs are formed against the background of band-like dislocation structures of elongated cells (microbands), e.g. [12,13]. Shear banding tends to become increasingly difficult in metals of very high SFE under plane strain deformation, and therefore have not always been observed in high purity aluminium. However, SB formation in Al and Al-based alloys is feasible when using hat-shaped samples.

The present work was undertaken to establish the effect of structure of flattened grains on the macro-SB formation during impact loading in technical purity aluminium (AA1050 alloy). The boundaries between grains of initial materials were used as markers of morphological changes during band formation. The deformation of hat-shaped samples leads quickly to well-defined macro-SB and corresponding texture changes. This opens the possibility to track carefully the crystal lattice reorientation within particular grains and the slip propagation across the grain boundaries (GB). Since shear banding strongly affects texture, electron backscattered diffraction (EBSD) in a scanning electron microscopy (SEM) was used.

2. Experimental

Hat-shaped specimen presented in Figs. 1a, d were machined from the hot-rolled sheet maintaining the axis of cylindrical sample perpendicular to the rolling plane of the initial sheet. The samples were deformed using a drop-hammer to logarithmic strains of ~ 0.61, under an applied energy of 600 J and an initial strain rate close to 530 s^{-1}. The grain structure of initial sheet and the as-deformed samples were characterised by SEM/EBSD. In the case of hot-rolled material the orientation maps were measured along the ND-RD and ND/TD sections, where: ND, RD and TD are normal, rolling and transverse directions, respectively. The microstructure of samples after impact deformation were characterized along section parallel to main sample axis (SA) using light microscopy and SEM/EBSD system. In the case of hat-shaped samples the indices *{hkl}<uvw>* always represent the texture components that have the normal of *{hkl}* plane perpendicular to SA-RA section, whereas the *<uvw>* direction parallel to radial axis (RA). (The hat shaped sample section is 60° || SA rotated with respect to ND-RD section of the initial sheet). The SEM orientation maps were measured using a FEI Quanta 3D equipped with a high resolution EBSD facility, typically at 15-20 kV and a working distance of 7 - 10 mm. The step sizes were ranged between 70 and 500 nm. Smaller step sizes (<100 nm) were selected to capture detailed microstructural features, whereas larger ones were used in the analyses of the textural changes during macro-SB formation.

3. Results and discussion

3.1. Microstructure and texture of initial material

The microstructure of the initial material was characterized in two sections perpendicular to the rolling plane by light microscopy and SEM/EBSD. The microstructure images reveal layers of very large flat grains (Figs. 1a, b) aligned along the rolling plane. The grain size in ND ranged between 20 μm and 60 μm. The grain dimensions in TD and particularly along RD were significantly larger at level of a few hundred of microns. The hot-rolled AA1050 alloy is characterized by some components of the copper-type rolling texture, i.e. two variants of brass {110}<112> and four of S{123}<634>, but no C{112}<111> component was observed, as shown in the {111} pole figures (PFs) in Fig. 1c.

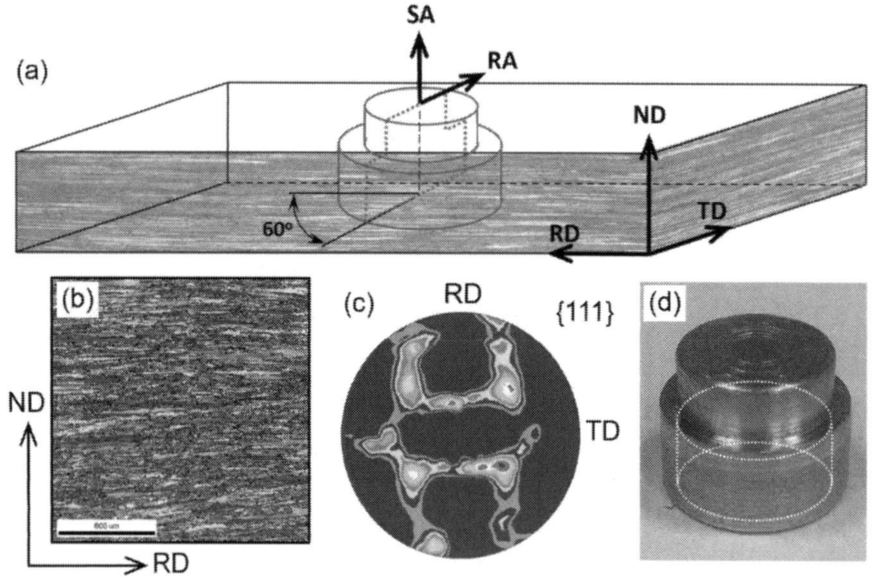

Figure 1. (a) Schematic showing of the sample sectioning. (b) Initial microstructure in longitudinal section and (c) corresponding texture. (d) Hat shaped sample. Optical microscopy observation and SEM/EBSD measurements with step size of 1 μm.

3.2. Morphological changes due to shear banding

The microstructural features of the macro- shear banding were analysed by optical microscopy on the anodized sample sections. The SA - RA section shows formation of two almost symmetrically situated families of macro-SB: positively (macro-SB^1) and negatively (macro-SB^2) inclined at 55 - 85° with respect to RA. The axisymmetric SBs are occurring due the hat-shaped geometry of the sample and are in fact the same microstructural elements but mirror-reflected. The very first plastic instability, with which the shear banding starts, was due to their double kinking, as observed in the SA-RA section. The macro-SB were initiated near the sample free surfaces, where the grain boundary kinking was the greatest. In the next step SB propagates towards sample centre. The obtained contrast revealed changes in the grain boundary inclination during macro-SB formation. A rigid rotation of the lamellae by ~ 75 - 85° near the sample free surfaces was observed as well as their relative translation in the areas outside the band (Figs. 2a, b). In the areas near the central part of the sample, the GB inclination angle gradually decreases to ~ 30°. This suggests that the MSB propagated from the sample free surfaces towards the sample centre [12]. At the macro-SB boundary, the traces of GB show diverse inclinations, varying from 0° to about 85° to RA forming very broad transition layers which separate the core of the macro-SB from the matrix, as earlier observed at TEM scale in twinned structures of Cu-Al alloy, e.g. [3, 9-11]. The core region of each macro-SB is surrounded by two transition layers, in which the boundaries between the flattened grains are progressively bent (Fig. 2a). For this specific case of macro-SB formation the transition layers have a significantly larger thickness than in the core region. The GB traces revealed a well-defined rotation of opposite sign within the symmetrically situated bands (Figs. 2a, b). Therefore, it is deduced that the textures in the macro-SB^1 and macro-SB^2 areas are essentially different and stems from two opposite rotations. The sense of the rotation is to increase the inclination of the flattened grains with respect to RA. This locates the traces of the GB closer to the shear plane.

3.3. Orientation changes as a result of macro-SB formation.

The local orientation measurements with a high spatial resolution provide information about the mechanisms of band formation by following the subtle orientation changes in the areas of macro-SB. To a first approximation, the orientation maps confirm that the traces of GBs (in analysed area of given macro-SB) increase their inclination angle with respect to RA *via* rotation by ~45° around the axis perpendicular to the analysed section. However, this simple rotation cannot explain alone the mechanism responsible for 'transformation' of the matrix texture components into the one identified inside the band. This leads to the conclusion that an accurate crystal lattice rotation is more complicated than described above rigid body rotation.

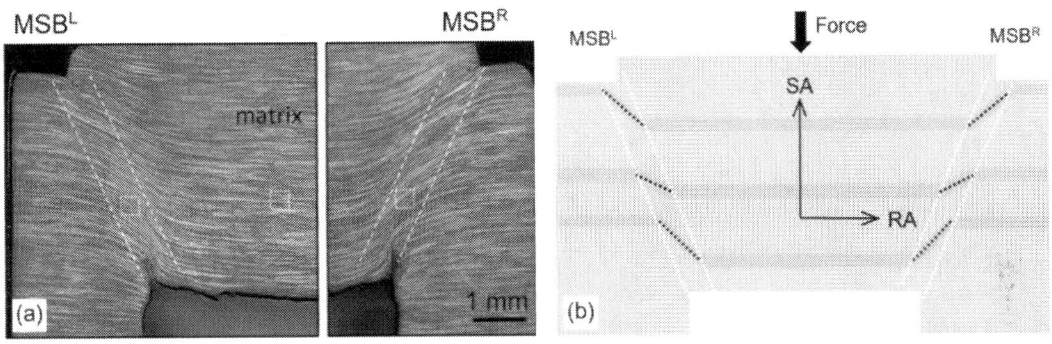

Figure 2. (a) Optical micrograph showing the structure of MSB on sample scale (sample axial section), and (b) schematic presentation of the rotations inside the MSB; reorientation of the structure elements inside the MSB and displacement of the layers outside the band.

It is apparent that the experimentally observed texture of the matrix was composed of three scattered groups of orientations. Since the scattering of each component group often exceeds 30° each group can be represented by an 'average' orientation and described as follows: M^1 - (-110)[-1-12], M^2 - (05-3)[-535] and M^3 - (-110)[-5-5-2]. The texture image measured inside each macro-SB is composed of two main groups of components. For macro- $SB^{R\ or\ L}$ the texture components can be defined as: MSB^{R1} - (-110)[-1-13] and MSB^{R2} - (02-3)[-532] (for the right side), whereas for MSB^{L1} - (-110)[115] and MSB^{L2} - (-12-1)[-101] (for the left side).

The orientations of the matrix undergo different but not accidental rotations during their incorporation into the given macro-SB area (Figs. 3a-c). Therefore, the rotation axes between the matrix and macro-SB provide essential information to understand the mechanisms responsible for SB formation. It is assumed here that the crystal lattice rotation results from the activity of specific slip system(s) and the rotation axis is perpendicular to the active slip plane normal and slip direction. During strain localization, the orientations identified in the matrix undergo rotations around the selected <112> or <011>-type axes due to the dominance of given {111}<011>-type slip system(s). All the identified rotations always align with one of the {111} plane (in each orientation groups), towards position parallel to the SB plane. It is clear that the rotation tendencies described above are also crucial for understand the mechanism of slip propagation across the GB since the {111} slip plane (which is parallel to the shear band plane) is common for neighbouring layers characterized by two main groups of orientations identified inside macro-SB areas.

The proposed scenario of the crystal lattice re-orientation during the matrix structure incorporation to the macro-SB region is as follows. In the early stages of macro-SB formation, the highly stressed slip system leads to the crystal lattice rotation of the grains inside the matrix towards their position inside sheared zone. In the case of all three orientation groups (forming texture of the matrix) the rotation occurs around one of the <112>-type axis (or in the case co-planar slip system around summary the <011>-type axis) leading to formation of two main groups of orientations inside sheared zone with common the {111} plane parallel to the shear band plane. The identified rotations that lead to transformation of matrix components into the MSB^R one can be defined as follows:

M^1(-110)[-1-12] + 15° rotation around [-110] → MSB^{R2} (-110)[-1-13]
M^2(04-3)[-534] + 40° rotation around [-21-1] → $MSB^{R1(b)}$ - (02-3)[-532]
M^3(-110)[-5-5-2] + 30° rotation around [-110] → $MSB^{R1(a)}$ - (-551)[-4-3-5]

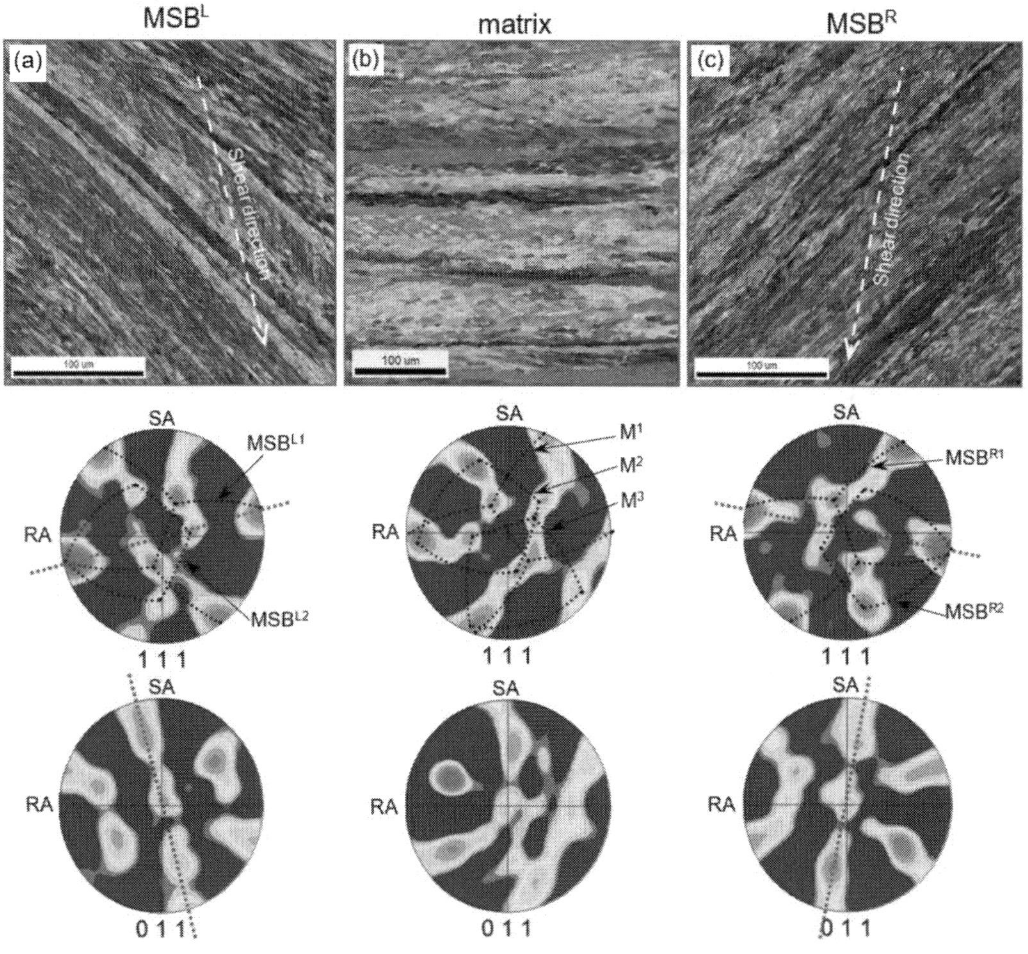

Figure 3. Orientation changes due to (a) MSB^L, (b) matrix and (c) MSB^R formation. SEM/EBSD orientation maps measured in SA-RA plane with step size of 70 nm .

Similar rotations can be identified for transformation of matrix components into the MSB^L. If the orientation group of the matrix layers is denoted 'M^{2}' only a simple rotation around axis parallel to [-21-1] is needed for the coincidence of one of the {111} plane with the shear plane and <110> direction with the close proximity of the shear direction. If the orientation groups of the matrix are denoted 'M^1' and 'M^3' a rotation around axis parallel to [-110] is needed (the co-planar slip can take place along a compound <112> direction). Rotation around the [-110] axis is in fact the superposition of two rotations around the axes lying on the same the (11-1) plane, i.e. [-121] and [-21-1]. According to this, the majority of the grain orientations inside the macro-SB are rotated around the <110> axis lying in the shear plane. However, both cases enable shear (on double or single slip system(s)) along the SB plane. These rotations lead to the coincidence of the shear direction with the <110> direction. In each case the rotations inside macro-SB occur in such a way that one of the {111} plane became (nearly) parallel to the shear plane, despite different initial grain orientations. Additionally, one of the <011>-type directions lying in these planes, systematically tends to coincide with the shear direction.

In this polycrystalline aggregates the macroscopically observed shear plane, in fact, consists of small segments limited to the particular grains or their fragments (Figs. 3a, c). These parts are only slightly deviated from the macroscopic shear plane. Finally, one of the {111} slip planes (~ common for the all neighbouring layers) becomes nearly parallel to the maximum shear stress plane. The re-orientation of the {111} planes towards the macro- SB plane facilitates further dislocation slip in the <110> shear direction. In this way, the mechanism of band nucleation and development is strictly crystallographic and connected with a single slip or double co-planar slips operation. A natural consequence of this rotation is that the inclinations of the {111} planes within and outside the band are different.

4. Conclusions

This study on AA1050 aluminium alloy clarifies the mechanisms responsible for the microstructure and texture evolution resulting from macro-SB formation during high strain rate deformation. The most important features may be summarized as follows. (i) In the layered structure of flattened grains the shear banding occurs *via* deflection of flattened grains within some narrow areas leading to kink-type bands that are the precursors of SB. (ii) The mechanism of macro- SB formation is strictly crystallographic in nature since in all the grains of the sheared zone, the crystal lattice rotated in such a way that one of the {111} slip planes became nearly parallel to the shear plane and the <011> direction became parallel to the direction of maximum shear. (iii) This strain-induced crystal lattice rotation led to the formation of new texture components, different from those identified inside non-deformed matrix, that facilitate slip propagation across the grain boundaries. (iv) The macroscopically observed macro-SB plane consists of small segments limited to the particular grains or their fragments. These segments were only slightly deviated from the macroscopic shear plane.

Acknowledgments

This work was supported partially by the National Science Centre (Poland), under grant no: UMO-2018/31/B/ST8/00942.

References

[1] Gill Sevillano J, Van Houtte P, Aernoudt E 1977 *Scripta Metall* **11** 581
[2] Hatherly M, Malin A S 1984 *Scripta Metall* **18** 449
[3] Paul H, Morawiec A, Driver J H, Bouzy E 2009 *Int J Plast* **29** 1588
[4] Walley S, 2007 *Metal Mater Trans* **A 38A** 2629
[5] Zener C, Hollomon J 1944 *J Appl Phys* **15** 22
[6] Rittel D, Osovski S 2010 *Int J Fract* **162** 177
[7] Ossowski S, Rittel D, Landau P, Venkert A 2012 *Scripta Mater* **66** 9
[8] Wright T Physics and mathematics of adiabatic shear bands, Cambridge University Press, Cambridge 2002
[9] Paul H, Driver J H, Maurice C, Jasieński Z 2003 *Mat Sci Engn* **A 359** 178
[10] Paul H, Morawiec A, Bouzy E, Fundenberger J J, Piątkowski A 2004 *Metal Mater Trans* **35A** 3775
[11] Hong C S, Tao N R, Huang X, Lu K 2010 *Acta Mater* **58** 3103
[12] Paul H, Driver J H, Tarasek A, Wajda W, Miszczyk M M 2015 *Mat Sci Engn* **A 642** 167
[13] Wagner P, Engler O, Lücke K 1995 *Acta Metall Mater* **43** 3799

IOP Conf. Series: Materials Science and Engineering 1121 (2021) 012008 doi:10.1088/1757-899X/1121/1/012008

Observation of Inhomogeneous Deformation in a Cold-Rolled Ti-added Ultra-Low Carbon Steel using High-Precision Markers Drawn by Focused Ion Beam

T Morikawa[1], R Kurosaka[1], M Tanaka[1], T Ichie[2] and K Murakami[3]

[1]Department of Materials Science and Engineering, Kyushu University, 744 Motooka, Fukuoka 819-0395, Japan
[2]Nippon Steel Corporation, 1-1 Tobihata-cho, Tobata-ku, Kitakyushu 804-8501, Japan
[3]Nippon Steel Corporation, 20-1 Shintomi, Futtsu 293-8511, Japan

morikawa@zaiko.kyushu-u.ac.jp

Abstract. The development of deformation inhomogeneities in ultra-low carbon steel due to cold rolling has been investigated by observation of the longitudinal plane at chosen sites of a rolled sheet using SEM and SEM-EBSD techniques. Particular attention has been paid to the development of strain distribution in the crystals. The microstructures and the orientation distribution in the longitudinal plane of a sheet rolled to a 60% reduction in thickness were observed, and some grains with preferred orientation such as α-fiber and γ-fiber were selected. In order to examine the local strain distribution of these grains due to cold rolling, high-precision dot markers, 0.3μm in diameter, were drawn using a focused ion beam. Then, before being subjected to additional rolling, the sheet was fitted into a frame made of the same steel under a plane strain condition. Using the marker method, the local displacement of the grains due to cold rolling has been directly measured.

1. Introduction

The development of preferential orientation distribution in steel sheets significantly influences its mechanical and electrical properties. It is possible to measure the crystal orientation of a steel plate through diffraction methods such as X-ray diffraction and SEM-EBSD, and much is known about the conditions that cause the formation of the macroscopic and average orientation distribution on such plates. Dislocation substructures are often observed in rolled plates, and the crystal orientation varies locally with the formation of individual substructures [1-3]. It is well known that these micro-regions have a relatively large orientation difference than in the surrounding regions and are the initiation sites for recrystallization by heat treatment after rolling. To elucidate the formation mechanism of these recrystallized microstructures, it is important to understand the occurrence of inhomogeneous deformation in the cold-rolled plates, especially during early stage of deformation.

In our laboratory, to investigate the formation process of inhomogeneous deformation structures, a method to follow the crystal orientation distribution of a particular region before and after the rolling process was developed. So far, we have studied how the local orientation changes across the entire length of the longitudinal plane on a rolled plate with intermediate thickness reduction (approximately 70%) [4-5]. It was found that in addition to grains whose orientation changed almost simultaneously throughout the grain and developed a preferred orientation, there were grains whose interior was divided into several regions, each of which developed its own different orientation. In some of the grains of this type, submicron-sized fine structures were observed to be formed on the newly generated misorientation boundaries. These grains are expected to become the initiation sites for recrystallization during heat treatment.

In this study, to understand the inhomogeneous deformation state caused by cold rolling, we constructed nano-order markers regularly along the longitudinal plane of the rolled plate using a focused ion beam (FIB), measured the displacement of those markers by observing the same area, and estimated the strain distribution. In particular, the changes in orientation and strain distribution of grains with a preferential orientation in the rolling process and grains with a certain degree of grain subdivision in the middle of the process were traced.

2. Experimental Procedure

Ti-added ultra-low carbon steel was employed; it had an initial grain size of approximately 50 μm after heat treatment. The plate was cold-rolled without lubrication until its thickness had reduced by 60%, and was then cut out. The longitudinal plane was polished for observation; the deformation structure was observed by SEM, and the crystal orientation distribution was identified by SEM-EBSD.

Several preferential orientation grains (α-fiber: rolling direction(RD)//<110> in the rolling direction, γ-fiber: normal direction(ND)//<111> in the normal direction of the plate, Cube: parallel to <100> in both RD and ND) were selected, and carbon dots with a diameter of 0.3 μm were deposited by focused ion beam (FIB) to be used as markers. The markers, which were arranged in a square structure, had intervals of 0.7 μm. To re-inspect the marked longitudinal plane after additional rolling, the specimen was inserted into a mold frame, which has same thickness as the specimen, before being rolled again, to protect the observation surface. Additional rolling was performed to attain a 70% thickness reduction, and plastic strain distributions were obtained by tracing the displacement of the markers, as well as capturing the changes in crystal orientation in chosen regions.

3. Results and discussion

Figure 1(a) is an SEM image of the longitudinal plane of a rolled plate at a 60% reduction in thickness, which was marked by carbon deposition using FIB. Figure 1(b) is an SEM image of the same area after

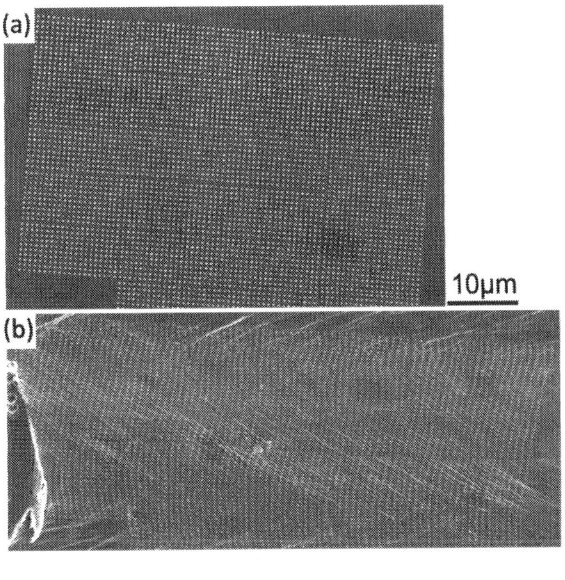

Figure 1 SEM images obtained from the same area in longitudinal plane, (a) 60% reduction in thickness. (b) 70% reduction in thickness.

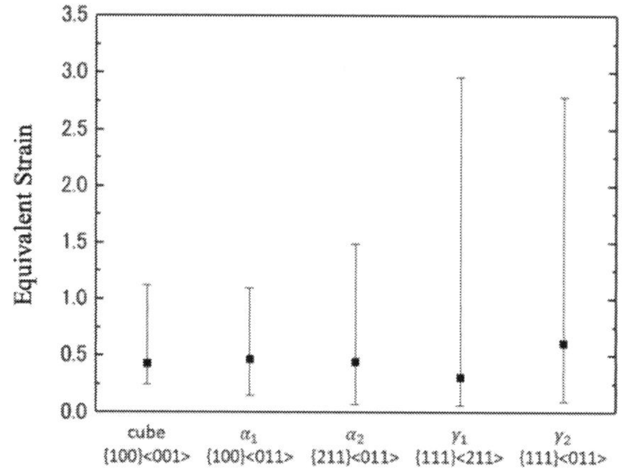

Figure 2 Equivalent strain distribution of grains with preferred orientation.

additional rolling has been applied to deform the plate to a 70% reduction. After rolling, the markers remained attached to the longitudinal plane, although their positions changed due to deformation. From the displacement of the markers, the equivalent plastic strains in the squares formed by these points were estimated.

Equivalent plastic strain distributions were also calculated for the grains with the major preferred orientations grain. Figure 2 shows the equivalent plastic strain distributions within the five preferred orientation grains at a 70% reduction in thickness, which are cumulative for zero strain at 60% reduction in thickness. The bars in the figure correspond to the widths of the maximum and minimum values, and the black squares represent the average values in each grain. The mean strain value of each orientation grain is almost the same regardless of the orientation, while the variation of strain for γ-fiber grains is approximately twice as large as those for the other orientations. These results indicate that the inhomogeneity of deformation in grains of γ-fiber is more pronounced than in other orientations, and inhomogeneous structures such as shear bands were noticeably developed in the SEM images of the grains.

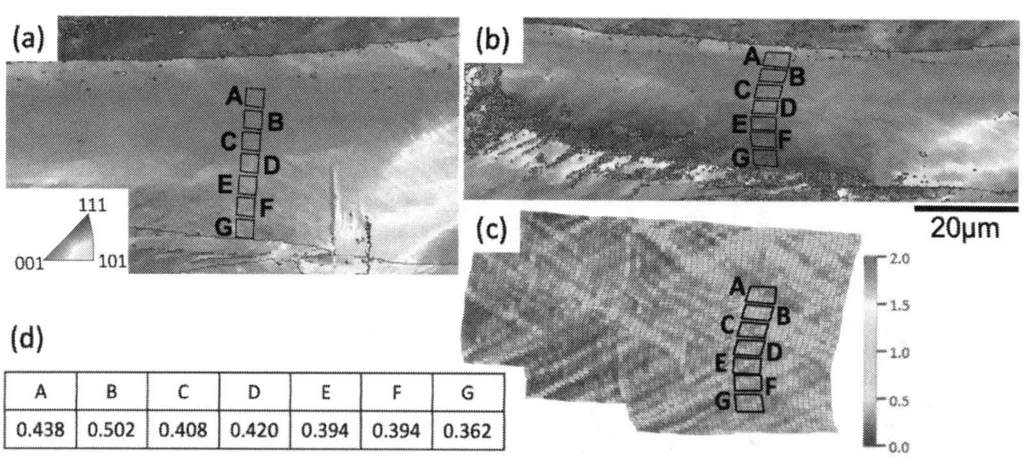

A	B	C	D	E	F	G
0.438	0.502	0.408	0.420	0.394	0.394	0.362

Figure 3 OIM images(ND) obtained from same area in longitudinal plane, (a)60% reduction in thickness, (b)70% reduction in thickness, (c)equivalent strain distribution at 70% reduction in thickness, (d)average equivalent strain of the areas A-G in the figures.

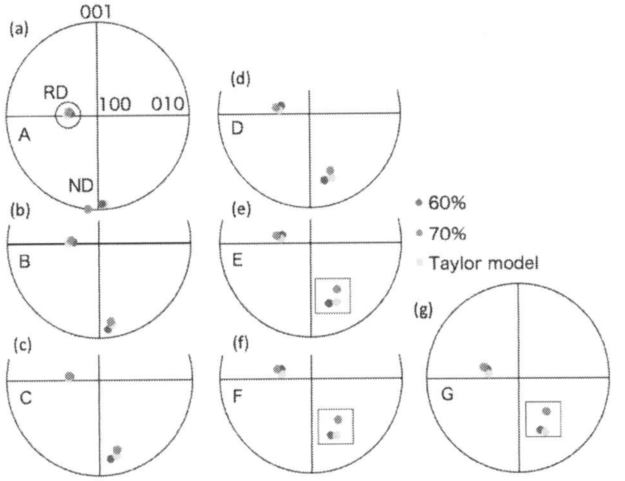

Figure 4 Orientation changes from 60% to 70% reduction in thickness in the areas A-G in figure 3.

Figures 3(a) and (b) show the crystal orientation images parallel to the ND at 60% and 70% thickness reduction. The horizontal direction corresponds to RD. The orientation of the top and bottom regions inside the central grain in figure 3(a) differs slightly, and the color of the lower area of the grain changes more across the images, indicating higher misorientation between the top and bottom regions. Figure 3(c) shows the equivalent plastic strain distribution calculated from marker displacement at 70% thickness reduction. A region of strain concentration inclined toward the rolling direction can be seen. In figure 3(b), the top of the grain is red and the bottom is blue, and the orientation parallel to the normal direction of the plate changes gradually near the boundary. Despite the occurrence of such a change in orientation, the strain distribution shown in figure 3(c) is relatively uniform, with no significant variation between the top and bottom regions of the grains.

We investigated the relationship between the observed strain distribution and the change in orientation of the grains due to cold rolling. As shown in figures 3(a) and (b), seven locations (A-G) were selected, including a region with a significant change in orientation along the ND, and the average crystal orientation at each of these locations was calculated from the OIMs. In addition, these areas are indicated in figure 3(c). The average strains at these locations are summarized in figure 3(d). The areas where crystal orientation changes significantly with increasing thickness reduction correspond to the areas E-G; however, the average strains in these areas (<0.4) are less than the average strain at locations A-D (0.4-0.5), where the ND orientation in the grain is nearly maintained at almost <100>. Although the area G is very close to the grain boundary, the crystallographic orientation change within the region is small, and the measured strain is not large.

Based on the average strains obtained at 70% thickness reduction and the average crystal orientations at 60% thickness reduction at each locations A-G (figure 3), the crystal orientations at a thickness reduction of 70% were predicted using the Taylor model assuming a pencil glide. The predicted orientations were compared with the results obtained experimentally. As a method of orientation prediction, the Taylor model gives a unique orientation for any given strain, assuming a deformation that minimizes the sum of shear strains due to slip in the four <111> directions. The results are summarized in the 100 standard stereo projections shown in figure 4. Figures 4(a)-(g) show the average crystal orientation, ND, and RD for each crystal orientation at both 60% and 70% of thickness reductions at locations A-G (figure 3), as well as those at 70% thickness reduction, predicted by the Taylor model. Average crystal orientations of RD predictions at each location agree well with results. On the other hand, although average crystal orientations of ND are similar for locations A-D, the measured ND at a 70% reduction is rotated by approximately 15 degrees than that at 60% reduction, while the Taylor model predicts only a few degrees of change in orientation for E-G. As shown in figure 3(d), the equivalent plastic strains across locations of E-G are smaller than those across A-D. Therefore, it can be assumed that the crystal rotation caused by the large deviation from the Taylor model occurred in these areas, suggesting that <111> slips were activated inhomogeneously in the locations of E-G.

4. Summary

Carbon deposition markings were applied to the longitudinal plane of a rolled sheet using a focused ion beam system, and the equivalent plastic strain distributions of the grains with the preferred orientation were investigated after reducing thickness from 60% to 70% through cold rolling. The inhomogeneity of strain in the grain oriented γ-fiber was more pronounced than in the oriented α and Cube fibers. The division of grains inside the initial grains during additional rolling was observed, and the orientations of these grains after additional rolling were predicted from based on the strains generated and the orientations before rolling. A comparison of the estimated and measured orientations after additional rolling suggests that inhomogeneous activation of slip that deviates from the Taylor model occurs in regions where significant orientation changes occur.

Acknowledgment

This work was supported by JSPS KAKENHI Grant Number JP18K04751.

References

[1] Bay B, Hansen N, Hughes D A and Kuhlmann-Wilsdorf D 1992 *Acta Metall.Mater.* **40** 205
[2] Hansen N 1990 *Mater.Sci.Tech.* **6** 1039
[3] Li B L, Godfrey A, Meng Q C, Liu Q and Hansen N 2004 *Acta Mater.* **52** 1069
[4] Tsukamoto G, Morikawa T, Higashida K, Kimura K and Ushioda K 2017 *ISIJ Int.* **57** 1476
[5] Kurosaka R, Morikawa T, Tanaka M, Ichie T and Murakami K 2019 *CAMP-ISIJ* **32** 192

IOP Conf. Series: Materials Science and Engineering 1121 (2021) 012009 doi:10.1088/1757-899X/1121/1/012009

Texture and mechanical properties of Cu alloy by cryogenic high-speed rolling

S Lee[1), 2)], R Muchime[1)], R Matsumoto[1)] and H Utsunomiya[1)]

[1)] Division of Materials and Manufacturing Science, Graduate School of Engineering, Osaka University, 2-1 Yamada-oka, Suita, Osaka 565-0871, Japan
[2)] Microstructure Analysis Technology Group, Research Center for Structural Materials, National Institute for Materials Science (NIMS), 1-2-1 Sengen, Tsukuba, Ibaraki 305-0047, Japan

aitam0408@gmail.com

Abstract. Cryogenic high-speed rolling (CHSR), where the sheet cooled in liquid nitrogen is supplied to rolls rotating at 1500 m/min at room temperature, was applied to several Cu alloys. After the CHSR, mechanical strength was improved with texture transition from the 'copper-type' to the 'brass-type' components. This trend was clearly observed in the case of Cu alloys with intermediate SFE. It is considered that the deformation mode changed from the dislocation slip to deformation twinning and shear banding under high Z parameter conditions of CHSR. It is also found that CHSR can improve the strength of Cu alloys with less decrease in electrical conductivity.

1. Introduction

Copper and copper alloys have been studied to investigate the effects of stacking fault energy (SFE) on the deformation behavior of FCC metals because deformation twinning is known to the dominant deformation mode when SFE is less than 25 mJ/m^2 [1]. SFE of Cu (=78 mJ/m^2) decreases with the addition of alloy components, such as Zn and Al. The change in SFE significantly affects the microstructure change by plastic deformation, which is an important factor in determining the mechanical and electrical properties of copper and copper alloy.

Deformation mode is mainly determined by the SFE of material, but it also varies with deformation temperature and strain rate [2, 3]. The effects of these extrinsic factors are not significant, but if they have huge changes, deformation mode can be made enough to change from crystallographic slip to deformation twinning.

The authors reported researches rolling with a severe operating condition, named cryogenic high-speed rolling (CHSR). In CHSR, rolling specimen only cooled in liquid nitrogen with rolls at room temperature and supplied to high-speed rolling [4,5]. In the process, heat transfer from the rolls to the specimen is limited because of the short rolling duration. The low initial temperature (~100 K) and high strain rate (~1500 s^{-1}) could realize the high Zener-Hollomon parameter (Z), leading to the change deformation mode from crystallographic slip to twin. Evolution in microstructures and change in mechanical properties by CHSR were studied in Cu-Zn [4] and Cu-Al [5] alloys. However, the evaluation of CHSR in pure Cu and analysis of texture evolution has not been studied yet.

In this study, CHSR was applied to Cu and Cu alloys. After the rolling, texture evolution was observed. In addition, change in mechanical strength and electrical conductivity was measured to identify the improvement of balance of strength – conductivity after CHSR.

Table 1. Chemical composition and stacking fault energy of the materials used.

	Al	Zn	Fe	Si	Cu	SFE [1,6]
OFC	-	-	-	-	bal.	78 mJ/m^2
Cu-5Zn	-	5.1	-	0.02	bal.	50 mJ/m^2
Cu-3Al	3.11	-	0.31	0.01	bal.	25 mJ/m^2
Cu-7Al	6.79	-	0.03	0.006	bal.	7 mJ/m^2

Table 2. Rolling conditions employed in this study

	Low speed cold rolling (LSR)	Cryogenic high-speed rolling (CHSR)
Roll diameter	Ø 310	Ø 530
Rolling speed	5 m/min	1500 m/min
Temperature	RT	77 K
Reduction in thickness	Up to 60~80 %	

*Specimens for CHSR were soaked in liquid nitrogen for 900 s before the rolling

2. Experimental Procedure

Oxygen-free copper (OFC), Cu-5Zn [4], Cu-3Al [5], and Cu-7Al [5] alloy were used in this study. The chemical compositions and stacking fault energy [1,6] of the sheets are shown in table 1. The mean grain size of the alloys was 6.5 μm at OFC, 13.5 μm at Cu-5Zn, 19.9 μm at Cu-3Al, and 23.7 μm at Cu-7Al, respectively.

Rolling with two different conditions were carried out, as shown in table 2. CHSR was carried out on a 2-high, high-speed rolling mill with a roll diameter of 530 mm at 1500 m/min. Before the CHSR, specimens were soaked in liquid nitrogen for 900 s and then supplied to the rolls within 3 s. The sheet temperature before the CHSR was around 100 K, while that after the CHSR was still under room temperature. Conventional low-speed cold rolling (LSR) with a roll diameter of 310 mm at 5 m/min was also carried out at room temperature as the control group. The thickness was reduced up to 60-80 %.

Microstructure and texture after the rolling were observed on the plane perpendicular to the transverse direction (TD) by a Scanning Electron Microscope with electron backscatter diffraction (SEM-EBSD) analysis in the cases of OFC and Cu-5Zn. The specimens were prepared by mechanical polishing until #2000 of SiC paper and 0.3 μm of Al_2O_3 powder, followed by electro-polishing in a solution (H_3PO_4 : C_2H_5OH : H_2O = 50 ml : 50 ml : 100 ml), with a voltage of 5 V at 273 K. The operation voltage of the SEM was 15 kV. The step size in the Kikuchi-pattern scanning was 0.1-1 μm. The points with a confidence index (CI) less than 0.1 were excluded from the analysis. ND-IPF maps and (111) pole figures were plotted using TSL OIM Analysis 7 software.

In the cases of Cu-3Al and Cu-7Al, pole figure data were measured by the pseudo-Schulz reflection method using Rigaku SmartLab multipurpose X-ray diffractometer system equipped with Cu-Kα radiation. (111) pole figures were plotted using Smartlab Studio II software.

Vickers hardness test was conducted with an indentation load of 0.98 - 1.96 N (0.1 - 0.2 kgf) with a holding time of 15 s. The electrical conductivity of the specimen was measured using the four-probe method and expressed as a percent of International Annealed Copper Standard (%IACS), which is following,

$$\%IACS = \frac{\kappa_{specimen}}{\kappa_{annealed\ Cu}} = \frac{R_{annealed\ Cu}}{R_{specimen}} \quad (1)$$

IOP Conf. Series: Materials Science and Engineering 1121 (2021) 012009 doi:10.1088/1757-899X/1121/1/012009

where $\kappa_{specimen}$ and $\kappa_{annealed\ Cu}$ is the conductivity of the specimen and that of the standard annealed copper, respectively. $R_{specimen}$ is the electrical resistivity of the specimen measured by the four-probe method, and $R_{annealed\ Cu}$ is the electrical resistivity of the annealed copper (=1.7241 × 10^{-8} Ω·m, ASTM standard B193-02), respectively. The electric current was applied parallel to the rolling direction.

3. Results and discussions

3.1. Microstructure

Figure 1 shows the inverse pole figure (IPF) map showing ND orientation on the longitudinal section of the rolled sheets. As the reduction in thickness increased, elongated grains were observed parallel to the rolling direction. In the case of 30 % and 70 % LSRed, ND//<111> orientation and ND//<112> orientation were mainly observed. On the other hand, in the case of CHSR, although the ND//<110> orientation was mainly observed, a little amount of ND//<111> orientation was observed. In addition, grains that were not elongated parallel to the rolling direction but diagonally developed were also observed, in the case of 70 % CHSR. It would be the twin deformation was locally occurred due to the high Zener-Hollomon parameter (Z) of CHSR.

Figure 2 shows the inverse pole figure (IPF) map on the longitudinal section of the rolled sheets showing ND orientation. Grains elongated in the rolling direction were observed. Deformation twins were formed in the inlined direction about 35 degrees to the rolling direction. Remnant grains are coarse and elongated in the rolling direction showing the ND//<110> orientation, while inlined and twinned grain showed ND//<111> orientation. CHSR showed a higher fraction of ND//<111> orientation than that of LSR.

Figure 3 shows the microstructures of the rolled Cu-3Al obtained by the EBSD analysis. Twin boundaries appeared locally with a narrow width in elongated grains in the 30 % rolled 3Al. After the 67 % rolling, shear bands appeared near the grains where the deformation twinning has occurred. The CHSRed specimen showed a higher fraction of shear bands than that of the LSR, as shown in figure 3(c) and (e). The fragmentation of grains by shear banding was also observed after the 67 % rolling, which contributes to the grain refinement. In the case of CHSR, the intersections of shear bands turn into rhomboidal prisms observed in the microstructure.

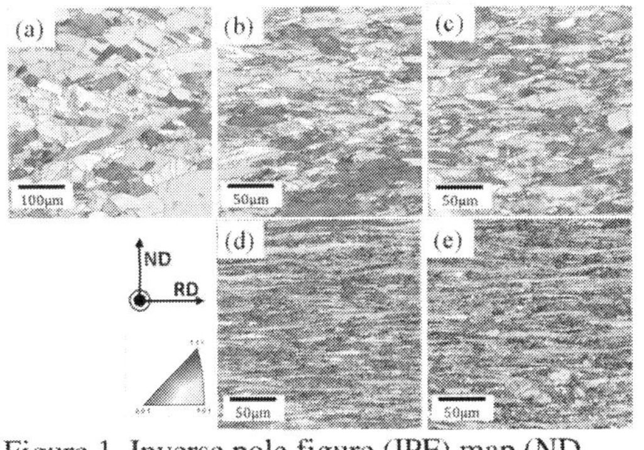

Figure 1. Inverse pole figure (IPF) map (ND orientation) of oxygen free copper (OFC) after cryogenic high speed rolling (CHSR) and conventional cold low-speed rolling (LSR). (a) Initial specimen, (b) After 30 % LSR (c) After 30 % CHSR, (d) After 70 % LSR, and (e) After 70 % CHSR

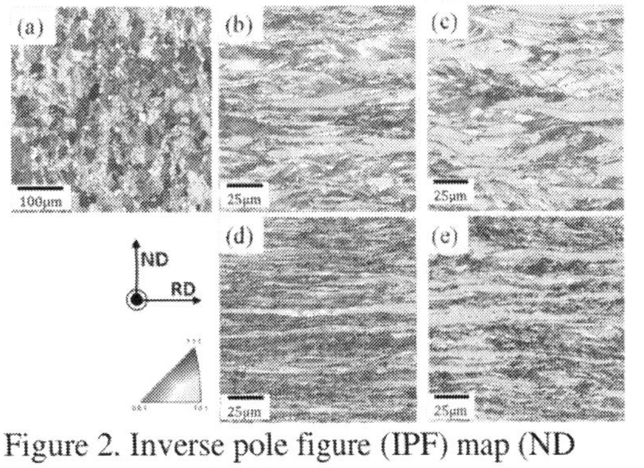

Figure 2. Inverse pole figure (IPF) map (ND orientation) of Cu-5Zn after cryogenic high speed rolling (CHSR) and conventional cold low-speed rolling (LSR). (a) Initial specimen, (b) After 60 % LSR (c) After 60 % CHSR, (d) After 80 % LSR, and (e) After 80 % CHSR [4]

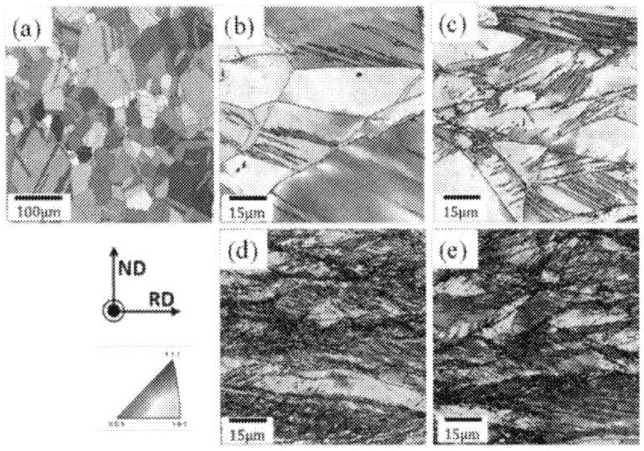
Figure 3. Inverse pole figure (IPF) map (ND orientation) of Cu-3Al after cryogenic high speed rolling (CHSR) and conventional cold low-speed rolling (LSR). (a) Initial specimen, (b) After 30 % LSR (c) After 30 % CHSR, (d) After 67 % LSR, and (e) After 67 % CHSR [5]

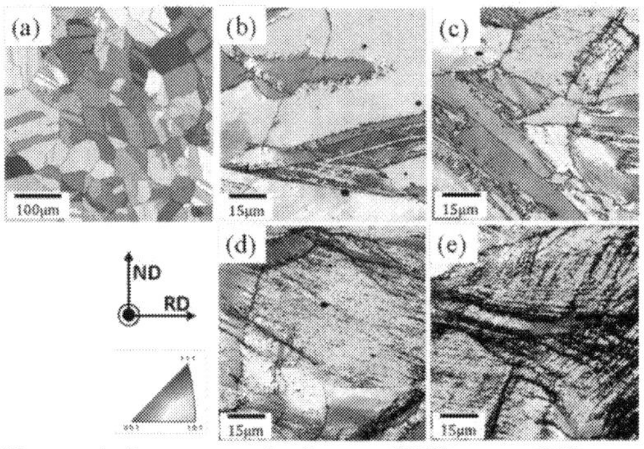
Figure 4. Inverse pole figure (IPF) map (ND orientation) of Cu-7Al after cryogenic high speed rolling (CHSR) and conventional cold low-speed rolling (LSR). (a) Initial specimen, (b) After 30 % LSR (c) After 30 % CHSR, (d) After 60 % LSR, and (e) After 60 % CHSR [5]

Figure 4 showed the EBSD maps of the Cu-7Al. In contrast to other Cu alloys, the LSR and the CHSR showed similar microstructures in the case of the Cu-7Al. After 60 % rolling, the deformation twins and shear bands appeared within selected elongated grains, which were narrower than those of Cu-3Al.

3.2. Textures after the rolling
{111} pole figures were drawn based on EBSD data in the case of OFC and Cu-Zn, as shown in figure 5. The LSRed OFC and Cu-5Zn showed typical 'copper-type' texture, which is {112}<111> orientation developed with a very sharp peak. On the other hand, in the case of CHSR, the less significant {112}<111> orientation and the peak spread toward the {110}<112>. In addition, as shown in figure 5(d), 80 % CHSRed Cu-5Zn showed evidence of a typical brass-type texture, where two spread poles at the top and bottom are connected at the center.

In the cases of Cu-3Al and Cu-7Al, the formation of shear bands leads to the low confidence index (CI) in EBSD analysis. {111} pole figures were obtained using XRD because of the limited observing area and low CI in EBSD. Figure 6 shows the incomplete {111} pole figures after 60 – 67 % rolled Cu-Al alloys. Intensities in pole figures were normalized with each own X-ray diffraction raw data. In these cases, typical 'brass-type' texture was observed, which was shown widely spread peak around at {110}<112> and {112}<111> orientation, connected at the center, regardless of the rolling method. In contrast to OFC and Cu-5Zn, the maximum intensity of CHSR was higher than that of LSR. It is considered that the conflict between 'copper-type' deformation due to high SFE and 'brass-type' deformation due to high Z in CHSR induced to decrease the maximum intensity. On the other hand, twin deformation occurs at room temperature with a low strain rate in Cu-Al with intermediate and low SFE alloys. In these cases, the increased maximum intensity could be thought of as the promoted 'brass-type' deformation by CHSR.

3.3. Mechanical and electrical properties after the rolling
Figure 7 shows the Vickers hardness of Cu and Cu alloys before and after the rolling. All of the initial specimens of Cu and Cu alloys were shown the Vickers hardness less than 100 HV. OFC showed the highest hardness (89 HV), which is the lowest initial mean grain size. However, the increase in hardness changes depending on the SFE of the alloys after the rolling. The tendency with the lower SFE, the higher hardness was observed. The 60 % CHSRed Cu-7Al showed the highest hardness, which was 256 HV.

The CHSRed specimens showed higher Vickers hardness than those of LSRed specimens, regardless of the alloy system. However, the increased amount of hardness after CHSR was dependent on the alloy system, compared to LSR. For example, in the case of 30 % CHSRed OFC, only 7 HV improved, which was 5 % increasing. On the other hand, the 30 % CHSRed Cu-3Al showed 11 % improved hardness (217 HV). As the reduction in thickness increases, the effect of CHSR appears to be less effective. The 60 % CHSRed Cu-5Zn and Cu-7Al showed 6 % and 3 % hardness improvement, respectively. As the SFE decreases, the accumulation of dislocation density at each strain and accumulation limit of the dislocation density increases [6]. The higher Z parameter in CHSR affected a similar effect with the decrease in SFE [7]. It is considered that CHSR inhibited recovery and lead to rapid work hardening at the early stage of rolling, and reached the accumulation limit of dislocation density faster. However, Cu-7Al with 60 % CHSR showed a similar hardness compare to that of LSR. This is thought to be because too low SFE is dominant to induce insensitive to the changes in temperature and strain rate.

The electrical conductivity decreased with an increasing reduction in thickness, as shown in Figure 8. Decreasing SFE decreased conductivity remarkably. The CHSRed Cu-5Zn and Cu-3Al, which were intermediate SFE alloys, showed a similar (or slightly higher) conductivity than those of the LSRed specimens. Meanwhile, the conductivities after CHSR were less than those after LSR, in the cases of OFC and Cu-7Al. However, it is notable that CHSR improved to the high strength compare to LSR; the electrical conductivities of both specimens are comparable.

3.4. *Effect of cryogenic high-speed rolling on Cu alloys*

The balance between Vickers hardness and electrical conductivity is shown in Figure 9. It was found that the balance of CHSR improved compare to that of LSR; the details are as followed.

In the case of OFC with high SFE, it was confirmed that the electrical conductivity also decreased with the improvement of the hardness. Therefore, the balance has improved but is less effective than other alloy systems. Although CHSR induced twin deformation and development of brass-type texture, slip deformation and development of copper-type texture was found to be dominant.

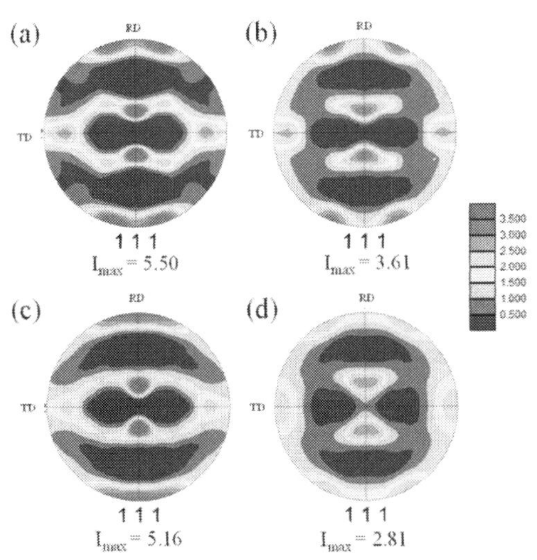

Figure 5. {111} pole figures after cryogenic high speed rolling (CHSR) and conventional cold low-speed rolling (LSR). (a) 70 % LSR, OFC, (b) 70 % CHSR, OFC (c) 80 % LSR, Cu-5Zn, and (d) 80 % CHSR, Cu-5Zn

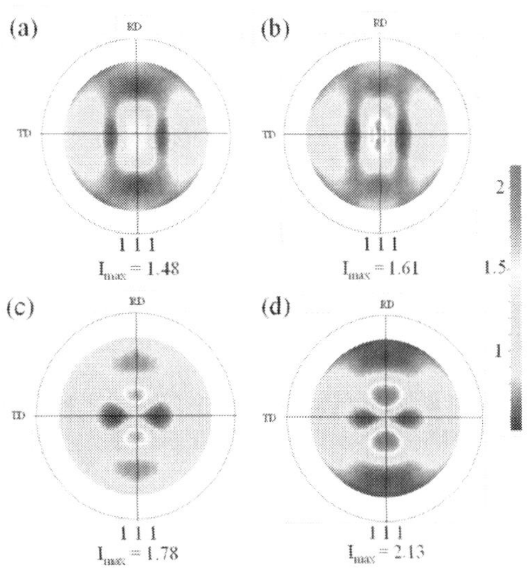

Figure 6. Incomplete {111} pole figures after cryogenic high speed rolling (CHSR) and conventional cold low-speed rolling (LSR). (a) 67 % LSR, Cu-3Al, (b) 67 % CHSR, Cu-3Al (c) 60 % LSR, Cu-7Al, and (d) 60 % CHSR, Cu-7Al

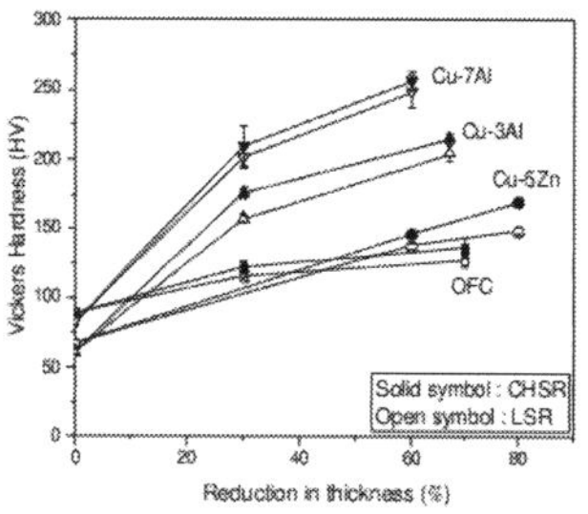

Figure 7. Change in Vickers hardness of Cu and Cu alloys after cryogenic high speed rolling (CHSR) and conventional cold low-speed rolling (LSR) as a function of reduction in thickness

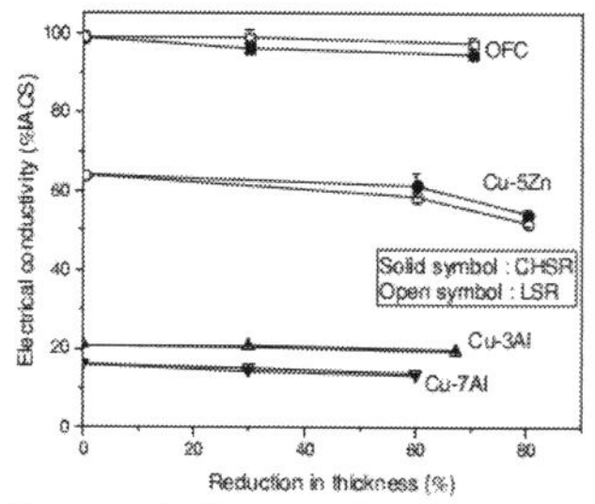

Figure 8. Change in electrical conductivity of Cu and Cu alloys after cryogenic high speed rolling (CHSR) and conventional cold low-speed rolling (LSR) as a function of reduction in thickness

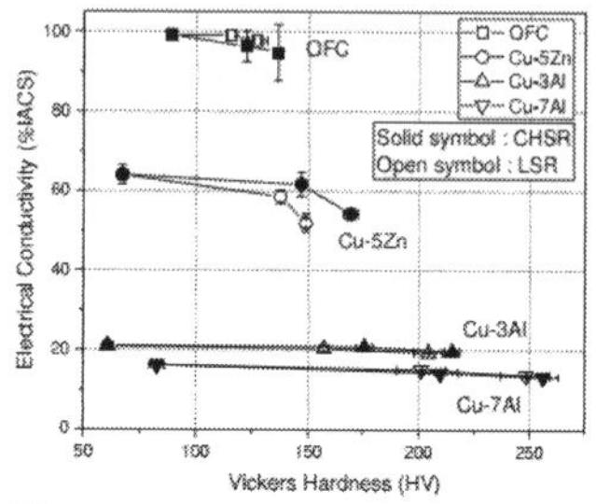

Figure 9. Balance of Vickers hardness and electrical conductivity of Cu and Cu alloys after cryogenic high speed rolling (CHSR) and conventional cold low-speed rolling (LSR)

On the other hand, in the case of Cu-7Al with very low SFE, the effect of improving the hardness and electrical conductivity of CHSR was not significant compared to LSR. In this case, the twin deformation and the development of brass-type texture are too dominant, and CHSR is less effective.

It is found in the cases of Cu-5Zn and Cu-3Al, the balance was significantly shifted to the right, which promoted twin deformation, leading to improvement in properties and development of the brass-type texture. Therefore, it was confirmed that CHSR improves the strength-conductivity balance in the copper alloy, and it was more clearly observed when SFE was intermediate range 25 – 50 mJ/m^2.

4. Conclusion

Cryogenic high-speed rolling (CHSR), where the specimen is cooled in liquid nitrogen and supplied to high speed rolling with rolls at room temperature, of the Cu and Cu alloys (OFC, Cu-5Zn, Cu-3Al, and Cu-7Al) was carried out to investigate the mechanical and electrical property and microstructure and macrotexture evolution. The remarks obtained are as follows,

1. CHSR promoted twin deformation and the development of brass-type texture.
2. CHSR is more effective to Cu-5Zn and Cu-3Al with intermediate SFE in the balance of Vickers hardness and electrical conductivity. In other words, it is less sensitive in the case of OFC with high SFE and Cu-7Al with extremely low SFE.

Acknowledgments

This study was financially supported in part by Japan Institute of Copper.

References

[1] Hatherly F J, Humphreys M 2004 *Recrystallization and Related Annealing Phenomena 2nd edition* (Oxford : Pergamon Press) pp. 26-35
[2] An X H, Wu S D, Wang Z G, Zhang Z F 2019 *Prog. Mater. Sci.* **101** 1
[3] Wang P, Jie J, Liu C, Guo L, Li T 2018 *Mater. Sci. Eng. A.* **715** 236
[4] Lee S, Matsumoto R, Utsunomiya H, Fujiwara H, 2019 *J. Jpn. Ins. of Copper* **58** 52
[5] Lee S, Im Y D, Matsumoto R, Utsunomiya H, 2021 *Mater. Sci. Eng. A* **799** 139815
[6] Rohatgi A, Vecchio K S, Gray III G T 2001 *Acta Mater.* **49** 427
[7] Zhang Y, Tao N R, Lu K 2011 *Acta Mater.* **59** 6048

IOP Conf. Series: Materials Science and Engineering 1121 (2021) 012010 doi:10.1088/1757-899X/1121/1/012010

Suppression of serration of Al-Mg sheet by periodic indentation

H Utsunomiya[1], N Ochi[1], S Koshi[1], K Natori[1] and R Matsumoto[1]

[1] Division of Materials and Manufacturing Science, Graduate School of Engineering, Osaka University, 2-1 Yamadaoka, Suita, 565-0871, Japan

uts@mat.eng.osaka-u.ac.jp

Abstract. Al-Mg alloy sheets often exhibit surface defects, e.g., stretcher strain, after sheet metal forming. The surface defects are formed by nonuniform deformation due to the dynamic strain aging where serrations appear on stress-strain curves in tensile test. In order to suppress the nonuniform deformation, the authors propose periodic micro indentation on sheet surface in this study. Four Al-Mg alloy sheets were subjected to the tensile test after the indentation. Strain gauges on specimen surface were used to investigate the evolution of local strain. It is concluded that the periodic indentation can suppress nonuniform deformation.

1. Introduction

Al-Mg alloy sheets often exhibit nonuniform deformation at room temperature. Surface defects, i.e., ridging/roping or stretcher strain are caused by the nonuniform deformation. They are industrial problems in sheet metal forming process because the defects deteriorate deformability of the sheets as well as surface quality of the formed products. Various investigations were conducted to reveal the formation mechanism of the surface defects [1-3] and forming conditions, e.g., temperature [4], strain rate [5] and microstructure [6]. It was reported that the dynamic strain aging or Portevin-LeChatelier effect of Mg atoms is a metallurgical mechanism and that the nonuniform deformation appears by the intermittent propagation of deformation bands. Accordingly, stress oscillation, i.e., serrations appear on stress-strain curve in tensile tests. This paper reports that periodic micro indentation on sheet surface induces uniform deformation and reduces the serrations.

2. Experimental

AA5182-O aluminum alloy (Al-4.55mass%Mg) sheets with a thickness of 1.00 mm were mainly used in this study. The sheets showed fully recrystallized microstructure with mean grain size of 16.6 μm. In order to investigate the effects of Mg content, three other Al-Mg alloy, i.e., AA5052-O (Al-2.5mass%Mg), AA5154-O (Al-3.5mass%Mg), and AA5022-O (Al-4.2mass%Mg), sheets were also used. The thicknesses of the alloy sheets were 0.93 mm, 1.60 mm, and 1.00 mm, respectively. Dumbbell-shaped tensile specimens with a parallel part of 24 mm in length and 10 mm in width were prepared by an electric discharge wire-cutting machine. The gauge length (GL) of 20 mm was marked in the parallel part.

Micro indentation with a grid spacing of λ=283, 400, 566 or 800 μm was applied to the specimen surface as shown in figure 1 using an automatic micro Vickers hardness tester, Mitutoyo Corp., HM-200, at a load of 19.6 N. For the AA5182-O alloy sheets, the diagonal length of the square impressions

IOP Conf. Series: Materials Science and Engineering 1121 (2021) 012010 doi:10.1088/1757-899X/1121/1/012010

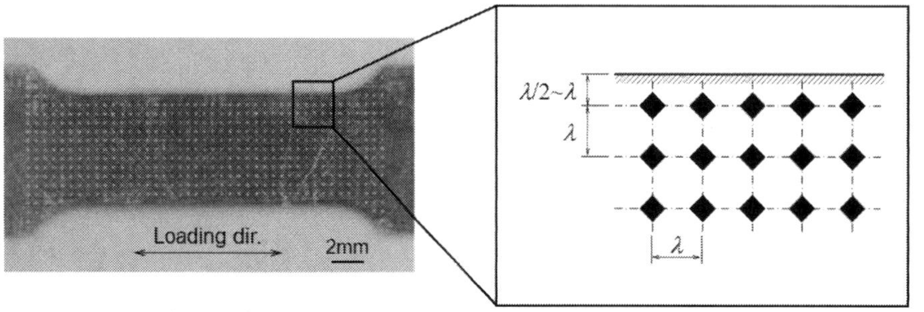

Figure 1. Tensile specimen after indentation (λ=800 μm) with schematic illustration of impression pattern (right figure).

was 235.7±2.4 μm; the areal fractions of the projected impressions of λ=283, 400, and 566 μm were 33.8%, 16.9%, and 8.7% of the parallel part, respectively. Normally, the indentation were applied on single side (S), however, it was applied on double sides (D) under limited conditions for comparison.

Uniaxial tensile test was conducted at a constant crosshead speed of 2.5 mm/min at room temperature on an Instron-type machine. At the same time, local deformation behavior of the tensile specimen was measured by strain gauges with a gauge length GL=1, 2, or 5 mm adhered on specimen surface at the center of the parallel part.

3. Results

3.1. Change in tensile properties by indentation

Tensile properties of the initial and the indented sheets are shown in table 1. Proof stress and tensile strength increased with an increase in magnesium content, AA5052 (Al-2.5%Mg) < AA5154 (Al-3.5%Mg) < AA5022 (Al-4.2%Mg) < AA5182 (Al-4.55%Mg). The indentation had little effect on tensile strength and total elongation. Figure 2 shows enlarged stress-strain curves of the AA5182 alloy sheet. Nominal strain e in figure 2 was estimated from the displacement of the crosshead, i.e., tensile speed and duration. The initial sheet without impressions showed large yield elongation and serrated stress-strain curve. The yield elongation was clearly reduced by the indentation, however, it changed stress amplitude of the serrations little.

Table 1. Mechanical properties of specimen with/without indentation.
(S: single-sided indentation, D: double-sided indentation.)

Test material	λ /μm	0.2% proof stress /MPa	UTS /MPa	Uniform elongation	Total elongation
AA5182-O	Initial	137	274	0.265	0.294
	400 (S)	133	272	0.255	0.292
	400 (D)	129	285	0.250	0.291
	283 (S)	136	276	0.255	0.293
AA5052-O	Initial	101	198	0.249	0.318
	400 (S)	106	199	0.236	0.308
AA5154-O	Initial	104	227	0.260	0.299
	400 (S)	105	228	0.248	0.311
AA5022-O	Initial	132	275	0.267	0.289
	400 (S)	127	277	0.260	0.280

3.2. *Change in local strain by strain gauges*

All Al-Mg alloy sheets showed serrations on stress-strain curve. It is known that not the stress but the strain increases in a stepwise manner [3, 4]. Evolution of local strain, e^*, measured by the strain gauges adhered on specimen surface is shown in figure 3. It is clear that local strain increases in a stepwise manner. Nominal strain e^* increases more smoothly when the density of applied impressions is higher, e.g. (d) λ=283μm, especially in case of the longer gauge GL=5mm.

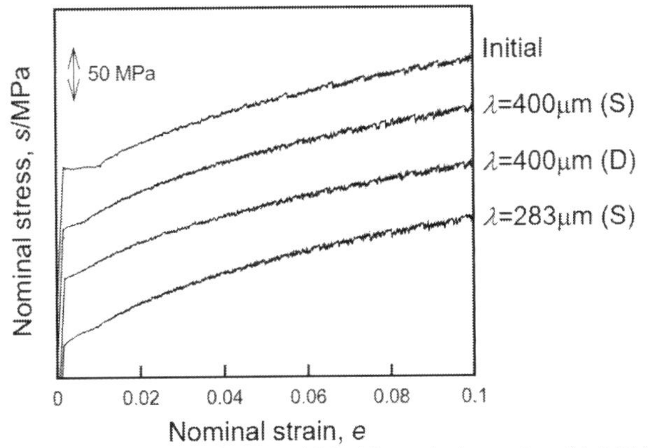

Figure 2. Stress-strain curve of specimen with/without indentation (AA5182-O curves are shifted vertically. Nominal strain, *e*, was estimated from the displacement of crosshead on tensile test machine.

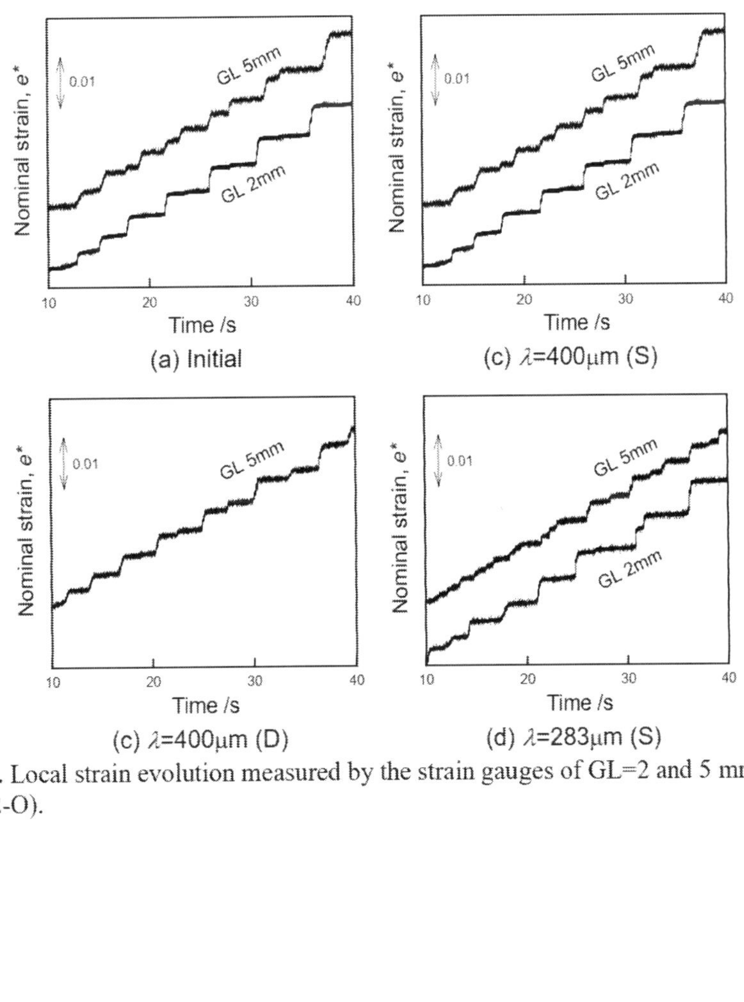

Figure 3. Local strain evolution measured by the strain gauges of GL=2 and 5 mm (AA5182-O).

In figure 4, outputs of the two strain gauges are compared. One strain gauge was adhered on front surface of the specimen, while the other strain gage was adhered on the back surface. Outputs of the two strain gauges were approximately equal so that the presence of the impressions on the adhered surface was not important. In other words, the deformation is uniform through the thickness of the specimen, while the deformation is not uniform in the tensile direction. In figure 3, gradient of stepwise strain measured by GL=2 mm was steeper than by GL=5 mm. The gradient difference can be explained by the fact that the shorter the gauge length, the shorter the duration required for deformation bands to propagate through the strain gauge.

The increase in step height of stepwise strain indicates that the ratio of (band propagation distance) / (gauge length) is higher and the deformation is more concentrated and nonuniform. To evaluate

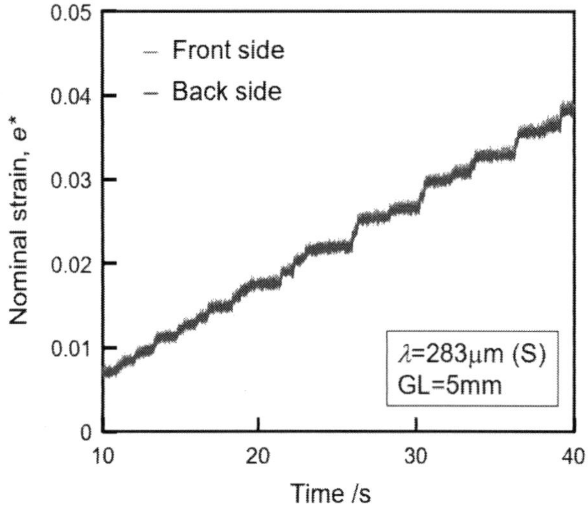

Figure 4. Comparison of local strains measured on both side of the specimen (AA5182-O).

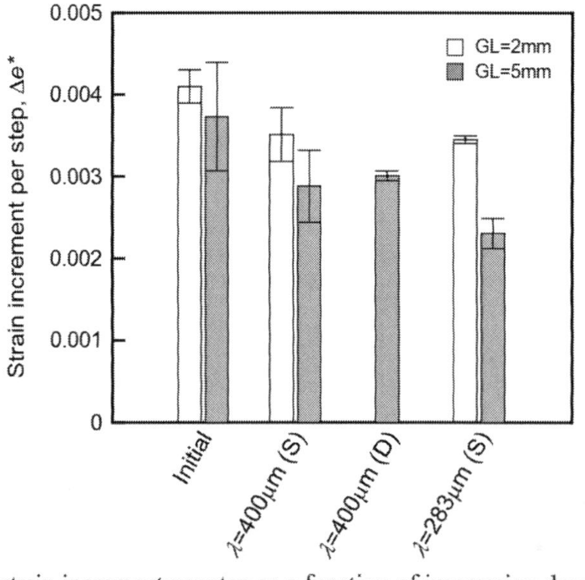

Figure 5. Local strain increment per step as a function of impression density (AA5182-O).

quantitatively, average local strain increment per step, Δe^*, was calculated by dividing strain increase by the number of steps appeared in the testing time from 10s to 40s. The calculated strain increments per step Δe^* for two gauge length (GL=2mm and 5mm) are compared in figure 5. Δe^* decreased, i.e., the deformation became more uniform with increasing impression density. The uniformity depended on the density of impressions instead of the number, because no significant differences was observed between the single-sided (S) and the double-sided (D) specimens. For the specimens after the indentation, it was found that propagation distance of deformation bands is less than 5 mm because Δe^* measured by GL=5 mm was smaller than by GL=2 mm. On the other hand, Δe^* of the specimen without indentation show weak dependence on gauge length. The results suggest band propagation distance for the specimen with the indentation is shorter than the specimens without the indentation. In other words, nonuniform deformation associated with concentrated deformation bands is suppressed by the periodic indentation.

Figure 6 shows the effects of the indentation on Δe^* for four Al-Mg alloys. The indentation

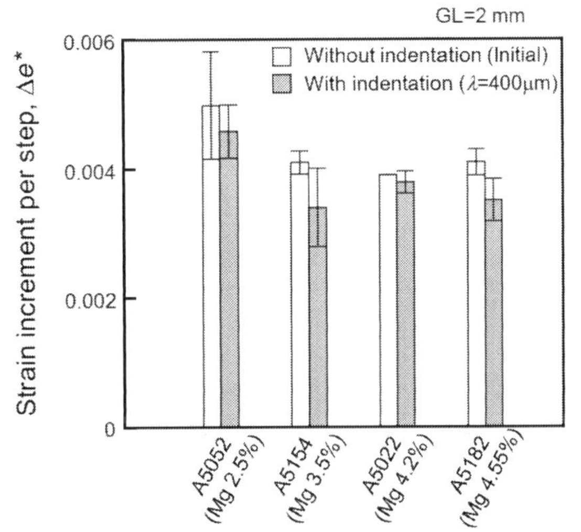

Figure 6. The influence of Mg content on local strain increment per step.

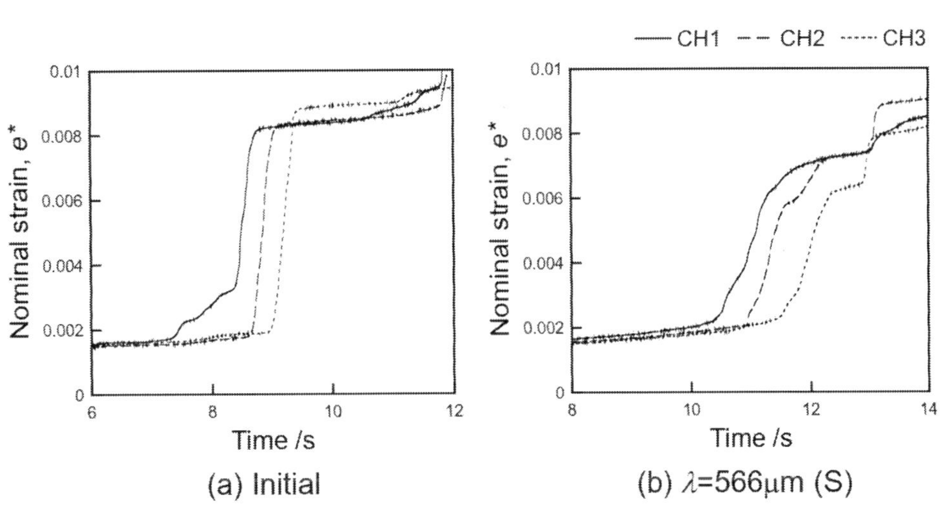

Figure 7. Local strain evolution measured by adjacent three strain gauge of GL=1 mm (AA5182-O).

reduced Δe^*, i.e., stepwise strain evolution became smooth for all test materials. Suppressing effect by indentation does not strongly depend on Mg content, however, Δe^* may decrease with increasing Mg content [7, 8].

4. Discussion

To observe the propagation of deformation bands, five strain gauges with GL=1 mm arranged with 2 mm interval in a loading direction were used. Adjacent three strain gauges showed same strain behavior with time lag as shown in figure 7. The behavior can be explained aforementioned discussion: propagation distance of deformation bands is less than 5 mm. Mean propagation speed of deformation bands calculated from the time interval and the distance between strain gauges was 5.9 mm/s for the specimen without the indentation, and 4.0 mm/s for the specimen with the indentation of λ=566 μm. The propagation speed in the initial sheet 5.9mm/s is closed to 6.2mm/s reported for AA5052 alloy sheets [9]. It is obvious that strain concentration occurred in units of a few millimeters as the propagation speed was about a hundred times faster than the crosshead speed of tensile test machine.

It is supposed that yield elongation decreases, and the band propagation is shortened and slowed since a large number of deformation bands are generated from the impressions. As a result, the indentation suppresses the strain concentration and the nonuniform deformation. The method using the indentation can be introduced locally without doping alloying elements and is expected to be used in sheet metal forming process. As the indentation can be applied only on single side, surface quality of the other side maintains. If the sheet was used for bodies and cups, decrease in outer surface quality by the indentation may not be a drawback.

5. Conclusion

In order to suppress the serrations on stress-strain curve, this study proposed application of periodic micro indentations on specimen surface to induce uniform deformation. Four Al-Mg alloy sheets were investigated by tensile test after lattice-pattern indentations. The following remarks were found.

(1) Serrations on stress-strain curve are caused by nonuniform deformation associated with concentrated deformation bands. The nonuniform deformation is more obvious in Al-Mg alloy with increasing magnesium content. The periodic indentation suppresses serrations on stress-strain curves, while shows little effect on tensile properties.
(2) High-density impressions are more effective to suppress serrations.

Acknowledgement
This study was financially supported in part by the Light Metal Educational Foundation, Inc.

References

[1] Sutoh E 1970 *Strecher Strain* (Sendai: The Japan Inst. of Metals and Materials)
[2] Pink E and Grinberg A 1984 *Aluminum* **60** 687-691 764-768
[3] Curtin WA, Olmsted DL and Hector LG 2006 *Nature Materials* **5** 875-880
[4] Nakayama Y, Nomura K and Furuta M 2006 *J. Japan Inst. Light Metals* **56** 1 39-44
[5] Onodera R, Nonomura M, Aramaki M 2000 *J. Japan Inst. Metals* **64** 12 1162-1171
[6] Ikeno S, Uetani Y and Tada S 1984 *J. Japan Inst. Metals* **48** 12 1163-1167
[7] Yanagawa M and Oie S 1991 *J. Japan Inst. Light Metals* **41** 2 119-125
[8] Kami T, Yamada H and Ogasawara N 2017 *Abstracts of 132th Congress of J. Japan Inst. Light Metals* 331-332
[9] Shimo K, Obata Y and Mori Y 2007 *Abstracts of 40th Meeting in College of Industrial Technology, Nihon University.*

IOP Conf. Series: Materials Science and Engineering 1121 (2021) 012011 doi:10.1088/1757-899X/1121/1/012011

New Insight into the development of deformation texture in face-centered cubic material

Gyan shankar[1], Deepak Kumar[1], Satyam Suwas[1]

[1] Department of Materials Engineering, Indian Institute of Science, Bangalore, India

Email: gyanshankar@iisc.ac.in

Abstract. Despite a tremendous amount of research to understand the evolution of microstructural and texture changes during deformation, there is still a need for further deep insight into it. The most used deformation process underuse in industries is the rolling of material. Stacking fault energy is the most critical material property, which governs the deformation behavior. In the present study, the microstructure and texture changes of a high SFE material (pure nickel) during cold rolling was investigated. The objective is to find criteria for the change of orientation of a particular grain as rolling proceed. Pseudo-in-situ rolling was done through which the shape, orientations, and neighbors of each grain could be tracked as a function of rolling reductions. It was found that orientations of some grains remain stable after a large reduction and do not develop sub-grains within it, whereas orientations of some grains change drastically at a very low deformation level along with the evolution of a large number of sub-grains.

1. Introduction

The underlying deformation mechanisms and the corresponding development of microstructure and texture in face-centered cubic (FCC) material have been the subject of interest for several decades [1–4]. Plastic deformation in materials takes place mostly by either of two mechanisms, slip or twinning. After large deformation, when dislocation density in the material becomes very high, the mobility of these dislocations becomes difficult, which produces deformation heterogeneities like micro-bands, shear bands, etc. [1-3]. Along with it, as the deformation proceeds, the material attains a certain unique crystallographic texture through grain rotation and to accommodate the strain incompatibility developed during deformation [4]. Dislocation mobility and texture formation are inter-related and affected by the stacking fault energy (SFE) of material, the initial orientation of grains, type of deformation (Schmid factor of the grain), and misorientation across its neighbors to maintain strain incompatibility [4-7].

Rolling texture in high SFE FCC material such as Al, Ni etc. shows Cu-type texture having majorly Cu {112}<111>, Bs {110}<112> and, S {123}<634> components [4,8]. The texture of low SFE materials, known as Brass type texture, is characterized by the absence of Cu {112}<111> and presence of strong Bs {110}<112> and Goss {110}<001> components [4,8]. However, even in the case where deformation texture is considered to be very strong, more than 50% of grains belong to some random orientation. Most of the existing theory deals only with the formation of overall bulk texture and does not clearly explain the probability and the amount of rotation of a particular grain as a function of deformation. There exist certain criteria for such as the Schmid factor and Taylor factor, which deals with the probability of occurrence of plastic deformation in grain [9, 10]. However, it fails to explain the role of the neighboring grain orientation.

The earliest model that exists to predict the deformation texture is the Sachs model [9], which assumes that each grain of a polycrystalline material will behave as an unconstrained single crystal of the same orientation, i.e., independent of its neighboring grains. It also assumes a single slip operating in each grain. Because of all these assumptions, this model fails to predict the amount of rotation of each grain during deformation. The other model that exists is the full constraint Taylor model [10], which assumes that, during deformation, all the grains will undergo the same shape change as the entire polycrystal. The other assumption of this model is that critical resolved shear stress for slip is the same for all the active slip systems, which strain harden at the same rate. The main shortcomings of Taylor's model are that it neglects elastic strains and strain heterogeneities and that its prediction of the existence of at least five slip systems, which may not be true. Due to these assumptions, this model fails to predict texture changes in low SFE material. Recently developed, visco-plastic self-consisted (VPSC) model predicts deformation texture in large no. of cases [11, 12]. However, it does not incorporate intra-granular misorientation, different microstructural features, and predicts overall bulk-texture.

The aim of the present work is to understand the probability and the amount of rotation at the individual grain level as a function of deformation. Pseudo-in-situ rolling was performed through which the shape, orientations, and neighbors of each individual grain could be tracked as a function of rolling reductions. The role of initial grain orientation, Schmid factor, and neighbor grain orientation during deformation have been investigated.

2. Experimental details

Pure nickel of 99.99% purity granules was melted in a vacuum arc melting furnace. To break the as-cast dendritic structure and to randomize the initial solidification texture, materials were 50% cross-rolled and further annealed in vacuum at 800 °C for 6 hours. It produced a homogenized microstructure having strain-free equiaxed grains and a weak texture. Further, cold rolling of the material was done till 30% cold-rolling reduction. EBSD scan of initial and 10%, 20%, and 30% cold-rolled (CR) material were done at the same region in the material without intermediate polishing so that the same grain as a function of deformation could be tracked, called pseudo-in-situ rolling. EBSD scan was taken on the transverse plane (RD-ND) of the specimen in a field emission scanning electron microscope (SEM), equipped with electron backscattered diffraction (EBSD) system. Samples for EBSD scans were metallographically polished and then electro-polished using A2 solution. For EBSD scans, the SEM was operated at 25 kV, and a step size of 200 nm was used throughout for all the samples. TSL OIM 8.1 software was used for data analysis.

3. Results and discussions

Figure 1a-1d shows the IPF map of initial pure nickel and differently rolled materials scanned in the same region. The change in shape and orientation of some grains are shown by the arrow.

IOP Conf. Series: Materials Science and Engineering 1121 (2021) 012011 doi:10.1088/1757-899X/1121/1/012011

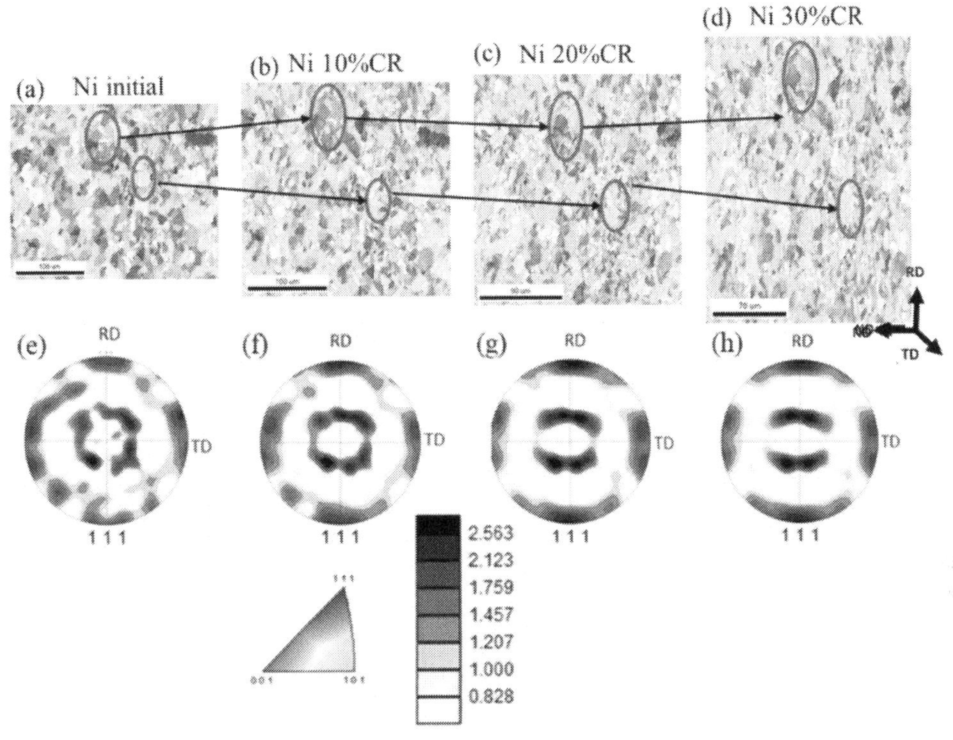

Figure 1: Inverse pole figure (IPF) map of pure nickel (a) Initial, (b) 10% CR, (c) 20% CR, (d) 30% CR, material, and corresponding (111) pole figure of (e) Initial, (f) 10% CR, (g) 20% CR, (h) 30% CR, material. Same regions were tracked during rolling without intermediate polishing so that change in morphology and orientation of individual grain could be captured. Tracking of some grains circled in red color is shown by the arrow. The IPF color coding refers to a direction parallel to ND.

It can be seen that some of the grains (region 1) have shown a negligible change in orientation (2°/<0 1 -5>) even after 30% cold-rolling, whereas some grains (region 2) have shown a significant change in orientation (7°/<1 1 3>) just after 10% CR. Similarly, the change in orientation of each grain can be calculated as a function of cold-rolling reduction. Figure 1e-1h shows (111) pole figure of initial and cold rolled material. It can be seen that as rolling proceeds, the Cu-type rolling texture is developing. However, the maximum intensity is quite low after 30% CR showing a value of 2.6.

IOP Conf. Series: Materials Science and Engineering 1121 (2021) 012011 doi:10.1088/1757-899X/1121/1/012011

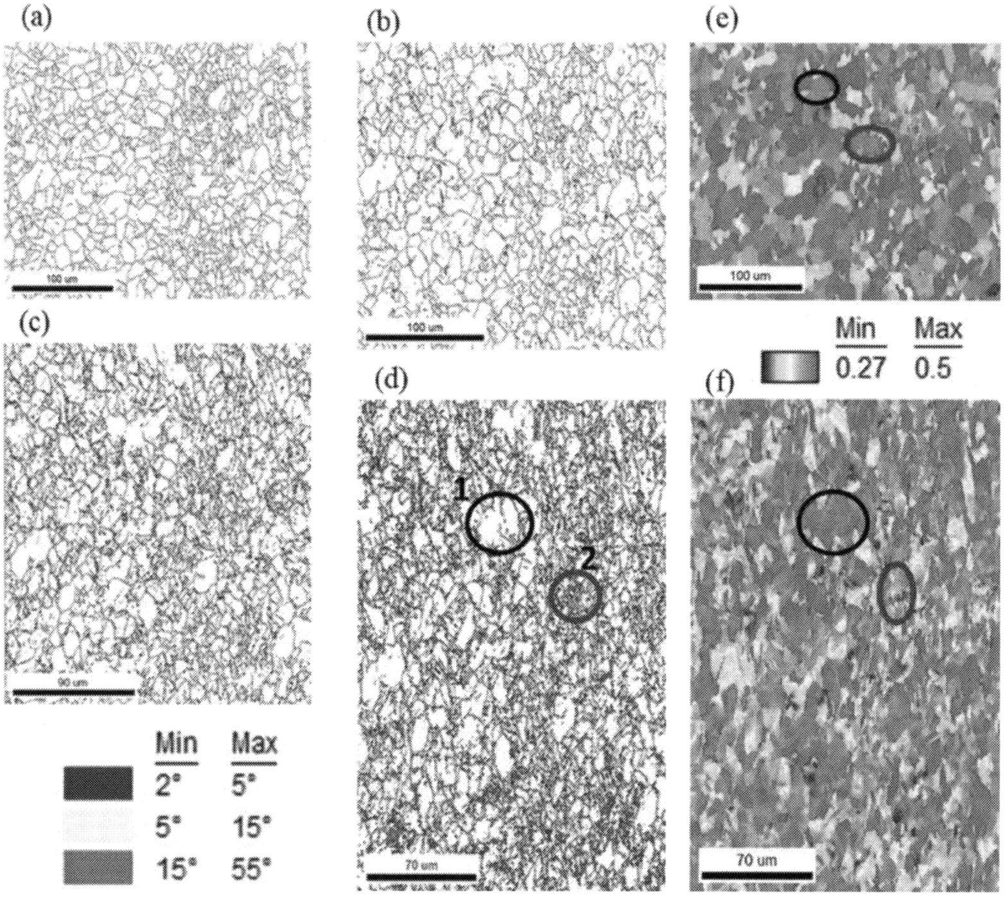

Figure 2: Grain boundary character distribution (GBCD) map of pure nickel (a) Initial, (b) 10% CR, (c) 20% CR, (d) 30% CR, material, and schmid factor map of (e) Ni initial, (f) Ni 30% CR, material. The black circle shows a region of sparse LAGB, and the blue circle shows a region of dense LAGB.

For a better understanding of the change in orientation in different grains, grain boundary character distribution was plotted. Figure 2a-2d shows the GBCD map of initial and cold-rolled nickel. Initial material has shown mostly high angle grain boundaries (HAGB) (red) and having a grain size of about 15-20 μm. As the rolling proceeds, the fraction of low angle grain boundaries (LAGB) (blue) increases, and it shows the highest fraction in 30% CR material. However, it can be seen that the distribution of LAGB is not homogeneous. Some grains (region 1) do not show any sub-grain, and some grains (region 2) show dense sub-grains within the grain. It can be attributed to the ease of deformation of a particular grain, i.e., initial orientation and the Taylor/Schmid factor of the grain. Figure 2e and 2f show the Schmid factor map of initial and 30% CR material. Region 1 shows a higher Schmid factor (black circle) compared to region 2 (blue circle), indicating easier deformation in the former case and thereby less dislocation accumulation, which results in a small change in orientation as a function of deformation.

To further analyze the data, grain 1 and grain 2 was partitioned and shown in figure 3. Figure 3b and 3c clearly shows that grain 1 has developed negligible sub-grain and have orientation {001}<uvw>, whereas grain 2 has developed very dense sub-grain and have orientation {110}<uvw>. It was also observed that other grains of this family have also shown similar trends. However, a deeper insight of grain 1 shows that it has also shown some amount of sub-grains mostly near the edge of the grains, which indicates that formation of sub-grain within a grain does not only depend on its own orientation or Schmid factor but also depends on its neighboring grains orientation or misorientation across the grain boundaries. So, it can be concluded that the formation of sub-grain within the grain depends on its own orientation, i.e., Schmid factor of grain. However, the formation of sub-grain at the edge of grain may results from strain incompatibility at the grain boundary due to high misorientation across the interface [4-5].

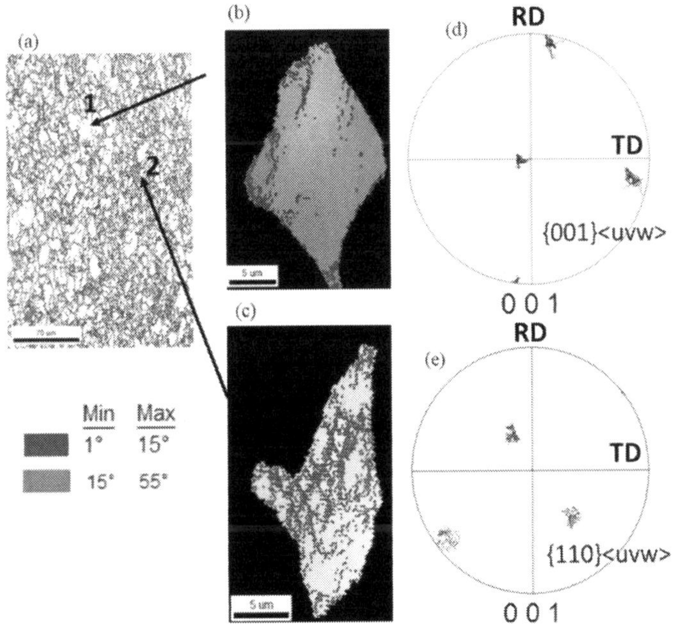

Figure 3: Grain boundary character distribution (GBCD) map of (a) Ni 30%CR (b) grain having sparse LAGB, (c) grain having dense LAGB, (d) (001) pole figure of grain 1 showing {001}<uvw> orientation, and (e) (001) pole figure of grain 2 showing {110}<uvw> orientation.

To further investigate the role of neighboring grain orientation, misorientation across all the neighbors of grain 1 and grain 2 is plotted for initial material before rolling, in figure 4a and 4b, respectively. Grain 1 has five neighboring grains having an average misorientation of 54.6° across all of its neighbors. Grain 2 has eight neighboring grains having an average misorientation of 51.2° across all of its neighbors, which is almost the same as grain 1. It was seen earlier that grain 2 had shown a significant change in orientation along with the development of sub-grains within it, compared to grain 1. It can be concluded that numbers of neighboring grains are a more important factor than average misorientation across all the grain boundaries. Figures 4c and 4d show the Schmid factor map of grain 1 and grain 2, along with all of its neighbors, before rolling. It can be seen that grain 1 has a higher Schmid factor compared to grain 2. However, the Schmid factor difference in grain 1 across all of its neighbors is less compared to grain 2, which can also play an important role during the rotation of grain during deformation. High Schmid factor difference across the grain boundary may result in high strain incompatibility at the interface and it can promote more rotation of the grain, which can be seen in case of grain 2.

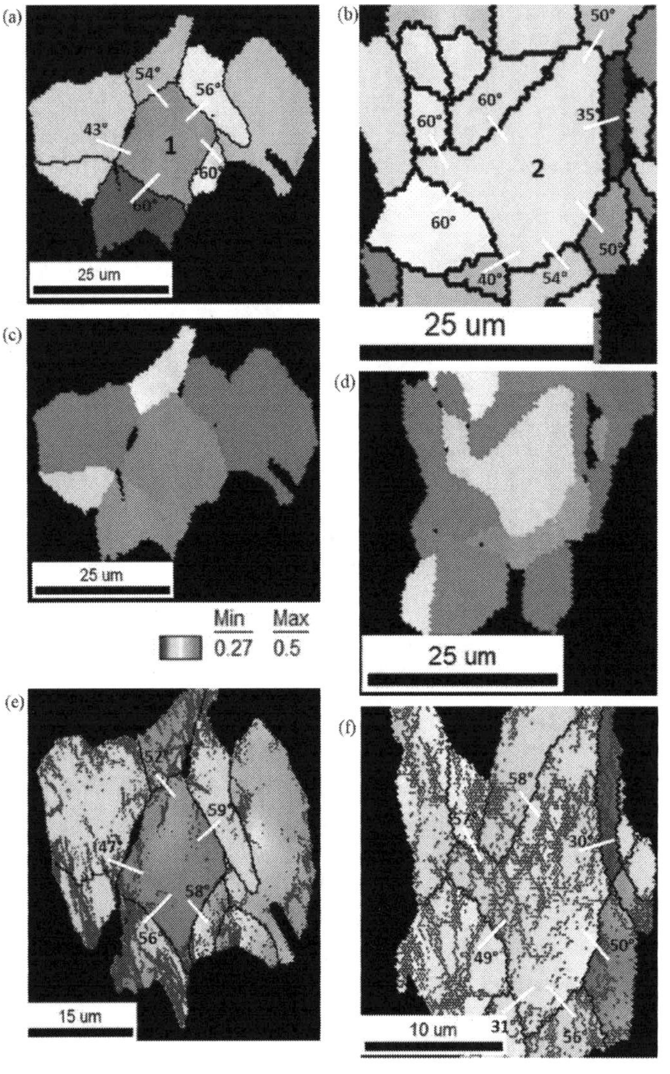

Figure 4: IPF map of two selected grain in nickel before rolling (a) grain 1 along with its neighbors, (b) grain 2 along with its neighbors, (c), (d) corresponding Schmid factor map of the same region, respectively. (e), (f) IPF map of the same region through tracking all the grains after 30% cold rolling, respectively. The white line shows a misorientation angle across the grain with all of its neighbors.

4. Conclusions

Pseudo-in-situ rolling of pure nickel was performed to investigate the role of different factors in the change of orientation of individual grain as a function of rolling. The following conclusion could be drawn from this study.

- {110}<uvw> orientation has shown a greater change in orientation and development of sub-grain within it compared to {100}<uvw> orientation.
- The number of neighboring grains and Schmid factor of grain along with the Schmid factor of neighboring grain play an important role in the rotation of grain during deformation.

References

[1] Duggan BJ, Hatherly M, Hutchinson WB and Wakefield PT 1978 Deformation structures and textures in cold-rolled 70:30 brass, *Met. Sci.* **12** 343–351.

[2] Hutchinson B 1999 Deformation microstructures and textures in steels, *Philos. Trans. R. Soc.* A, **357** 1471–85.

[3] Hirsch J and Lücke K 1988 Mechanism of deformation and development of rolling textures in polycrystalline FCC metals I. description of rolling texture development in homogeneous CuZn alloys, *Acta Metall.* **36** 2863–82.

[4] Lücke K, Hatherly M and HIRSCH J 1988 Overview no. 76: Mechanism of deformation and development of rolling textures in polycrystalline fcc metals- III the influence of slip inhomogeneities and twinning, *Acta Metall.* **36** 2905–27.

[5] Madhavan R, Ray RK and Suwas S 2014 New insights into the development of microstructure and deformation texture in nickel-60 wt.% cobalt alloy, *Acta Mater.* **78** 222–235.

[6] Hutchinson WB, Duggan BJ and Hatherly M 1979 Development of Deformation texture and microstructure in cold-rolled Cu-30Zn, *Met. Technol.* **6** 398–403.

[7] Shankar G and Suwas S 2018 Effect of strain path change on the texture evolution after cold rolling and recrystallization of Nickel-40 wt. %Cobalt alloy, *IOP Conf. Ser. Mater. Sci. Eng* **375**, 012018.

[8] Ray RK 1995 Rolling textures of pure nickel, nickel-iron and nickel-cobalt alloys, *Acta Metall. Mater.* **43** 3861–3872.

[9] Sachs G 1928 Zur Ableitung einer Fliessbedingung. *Z Verein Deut Ing* **72** 769–774

[10] Taylor GI 1938 Plastic strain in metals. *J Inst Met* **62** 307–324

[11] Molinari A, Canova GR, Ahzi S 1987 A self-consistent approach of the large deformation polycrystal viscoplasticity. *Acta Metall.* **35** 2983–2994

[12] Shankar G, Madhavan R, Kumar R, Sahoo B, Ray RK and Suwas S 2020 Micro-mechanism of evolution of microstructure and texture in Ni-Fe alloys, *Materialia* **13**, 100811.

Acknowledgement

The authors are thankful to the Dept. of Materials Engineering and Advanced Facility for Microscopy and Microanalysis (AFMM), Indian Institute of Science Bangalore, for providing easy access to instruments to conducts experiments.

IOP Conf. Series: Materials Science and Engineering 1121 (2021) 012012 doi:10.1088/1757-899X/1121/1/012012

Recrystallization behaviour of IF steel at the interface of Al junction

K Okuda[1,2]、 **K Han**[2,3]、 **R Kainuma**[2]

1) JFE Steel Corporation, Steel Research Laboratory, 1-1, Minamiwatarida-cho, Kawasaki-ku, Kawasaki 210-0855, JAPAN

2) Department of Materials Science, Graduate School of Engineering, Tohoku University, Aoba-yama 02, Aoba-ku, Sendai 980-8579, JAPAN

3) National Institute for Materials Science (NIMS), 1-2-1 Sengen, Tsukuba, Ibaraki, 305-0047 JAPAN

e-mail: kan-okuda@jfe-steel.co.jp

Abstract. The recrystallization behavior of an IF steel was investigated at the interface with aluminum junction, using cold-rolled IF steel sheets with high recrystallization temperature. In the region surrounded by the tongue-like η phase, recrystallization of the steel was fast at first glance, and the equiaxed structure was formed, but actually, it had a subgrain structure. The η phase grew preferentially to the c axis, and the growth of the η-Fe_2Al_5 phase distorted the surrounding iron due to the difference in the molar volume; compressive deformation was expected in the a-axis and b-axis directions, and tensile deformation was expected in the c-axis. The growth of η phase obviously changed the recrystallization behavior of the IF steel. The development of γ-fiber crystalline texture (<111>/ND), which was a typical recrystallization texture of IF steel, was not observed in the region surrounded by η phase.

1. Introduction

In view of environmental problem of global warming and safety regulations for collision, automobile steel sheets are becoming increasingly higher in tensile strength to reduce the thickness [1,2]. CO_2 emission regulations are expected to become more stringent. There is a trend of multi-material to replace some parts with lighter materials such as aluminum, magnesium and carbon fiber reinforced polymer (CFRP). Since it is necessary to join parts together when assembling automobile parts, joining technology of dissimilar materials has been studied. Friction stir welding (FSW) is one of the candidates for bonding of dissimilar metals [3-5]. In this method, a rotating heat-resistant pin is inserted by a high pressure in the cladding part and moved along the interface. Then the materials are bonded by the plastic flow. Fe is subjected to very strongly deformed, increasing the temperature, so that deformation and recrystallization may occur simultaneously. In the case of Al/Fe joints, among the several intermediate compounds in Al-Fe systems, the η-Fe_2Al_5 phase is known to grow preferentially toward the C axis, which could give some constrain to the iron matrix [6,7]. In this paper, the recrystallization behavior of an IF steel was investigated at the interface with steel-aluminum junction, using cold-rolled IF steel sheets with high recrystallization temperature.

2. Experimental procedures

A steel with chemical composition of Fe -0.007% C -0.6% Mn -0.068% Nb (mass%) was used for examination, expected to have a higher recrystallization temperature due to Nb and C contents higher than those in general IF steels. The steel having this composition was melted by vacuum melting and then hot-rolled into a thickness of 3.5 mm. After grinding the both sides, the steel sheet was cold-rolled in one direction to a reduction ratio of 90% with no intermediate annealing in order to obtain a deformed sheet with a thickness of 0.28 mm. In the condition that a cold-rolled Al plate of 0.54 mm were sandwiched with the two steel sheets, the samples were heat-treated at 650 and 700 ° C for 2 to 10 minutes. After heat treatment, the sandwich samples were embedded in a conductive mold, and the surface in the cross section was examined by FE-EPMA/WDS and SEM-EBSD after polishing.

3. Results and discussions

Figure 1 shows microstructures of the specimen annealed at 700 ° C for 10 min. A needle or rectangular crystal in the Al phase observed here is considered to be the θ-Fe_4Al_{13} phase, formed during solidification. In the joined parts, two different contrast layers were observed between IF steel and pure Al, and these two layers can be confirmed by FE-EPMA/WDS analysis to be η and θ phases. As well known, the η phase preferentially grows into the steel side with a tongue shape.

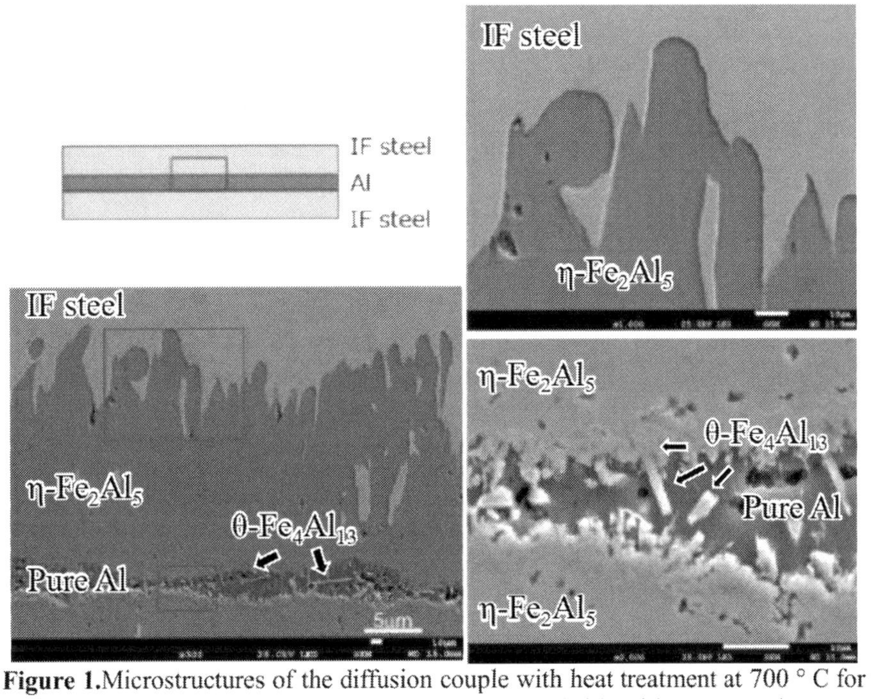

Figure 1. Microstructures of the diffusion couple with heat treatment at 700 ° C for 10 min. The η phase preferentially grows into the steel side with a tongue shape.

Figures 2 shows the result of EBSD analysis obtained from a specimen annealed at 700 ° C for 10 min. In the microstructure of the Fe phase far from the tongue structure region, subgrain structures, which have not been eroded by recrystallized grains, remain a little in an elongated shape, and it can be seen that recrystallization is about to complete. On the other hand, in the Fe region surrounded by tongue-like η phases, the grains seem to be fine; a part of the grains is equiaxed. The crystal orientation is close to <110>/ND, which is not seen in conventional recrystallization of steel sheets, especially in the vicinity of the part facing to the side plane of the η tongues. The KAM value, which is related to the

IOP Conf. Series: Materials Science and Engineering 1121 (2021) 012012 doi:10.1088/1757-899X/1121/1/012012

local strains, or geometrically necessary dislocations, was especially high in the steel area embedded in η phases. Figure 3 shows the misorientation profile along the line in the figure, which is in the steel area surrounded by η phase. The crystal orientation is rotated within the grains in the valley region of the tongue shape. On the other hand, on the crystal orientation of the η phase, the C axis grows to the direction perpendicular to the junction plane (steel sheet plane normal), and especially, in the tip region of the tongue. The orientation in the root part is slightly different from the C-axis; it is fine-grained. Hence, in the η phase, crystals with the growth direction oriented to the C axis grow preferentially, and those with other orientations appear to be stranded.

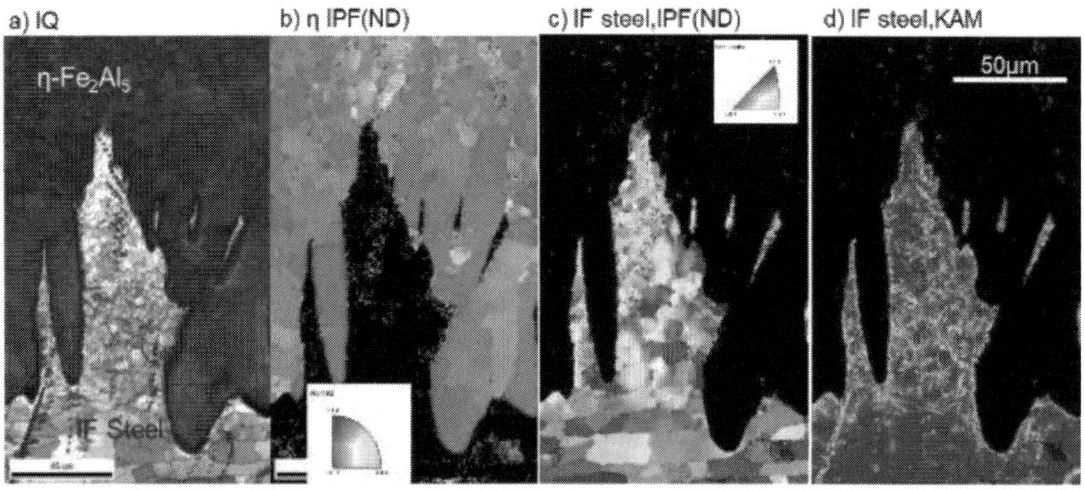

Figure 2.EBSD analysis measured for specimen at 700 ° C for 10 min, (a) Image quality map, (b) Inverse pole figure map (ND) of the η phase, (c) Inverse pole figure map (ND) of the steel, and (d) KAM map of the steel.

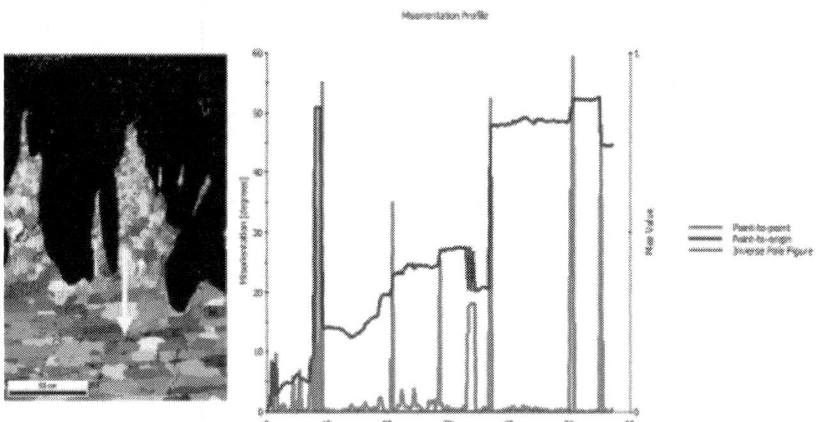

Figure 3. Misorientation profile along the line in the figure, which is in the steel area surrounded by η phase. The specimen was heat-treated at 700 ° C for 10 min.

Since the recytallization of the IF steel just completed at 700 ° C for 10 min, the measurement at the lower temperature is conducted to study the behaviors at earlier stage of recrystallization. Figure 4 shows the result of EBSD analysis around the interface of sample annealed at 650 ° C for 2 min. Partial recrystallization is observed on the steel side away from the η phase tip, while the region surrounded by the η phase has relatively equiaxed grains. In the inverse pole figure map of the BCC phase, there is a crystal orientation different from that of α-fiber and γ-fiber, which are the textures of conventional partial recrystallization of IF steel, in the region surrounded by η phase [8]. Due to the partial recrystallization structure, there is a high KAM value in the area on the steel side away from the η phase tip. On the other hand, in the region sandwiched by two η tongues, the KAM value is not constant, becoming higher near the interface between η phase and α phase.

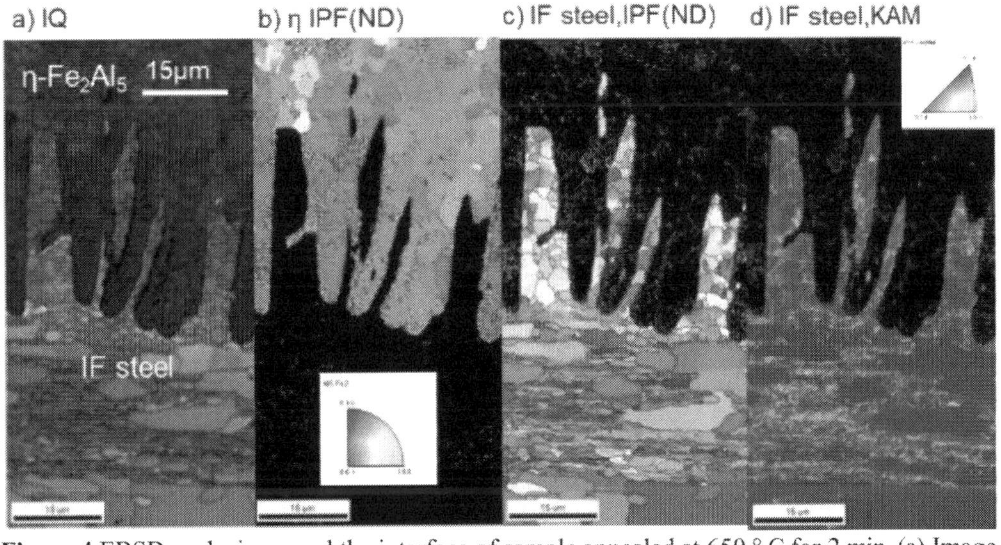

Figure 4.EBSD analysis around the interface of sample annealed at 650 ° C for 2 min, (a) Image quality map, (b) Inverse pole figure map (ND) of the η phase, (c) Inverse pole figure map (ND) of the steel, and (d) KAM map of the steel.

Figure 5 shows the ODF maps taken from the steel regions on the outside and inside of the tongue structure zone in the sample annealed at 650 ° C for 2 min. The typical α-fiber and γ-fiber texture in conventional cold-rolled steel sheets appear in the $\varphi_2 = 45$ ° section in the region not affected by η phase. The steel adjacent to η has the crystal orientation rotated from the conventional texture. The orientation relationships of the main orientation components between the outside and the inside of the tongue structure zone are as follows: misorientation 21°, rotation axis [-5 29 7] in $\varphi_2 = 45$ ° section; misorientation 19 °, rotation axis [-5 18 -1] in $\varphi_2 = 75$ ° section. (Rotation axis is crystal axis coordinate.) In this way, the grain orientations of the steel affected by the growth of η phase are rotated approximately 20 degrees from the normal condition.

BCC iron contains 2 iron atoms in a unit cell with a lattice parameter of 0.286 nm. The unit cell volume is 0.0234 nm^3, and the volume per 1 iron is 0.0117 nm^3. The η phase has an orthorhombic oC_{24} structure with lattice parameters a = 0.766, b = 0.642, c = 0.422 nm and a slightly shorter c-axis and 15.2 atoms in the unit cell. The unit cell volume is 0.2075 nm^3, and the volume per 1 metal atom is 0.01365 nm^3. Since the volume per atom changes in this way, the growth of η phase distorts the surrounding iron, especially compressive deformation is applied in the a-axis and b-axis directions; rather tensile deformation is expected for the c-axis [9].

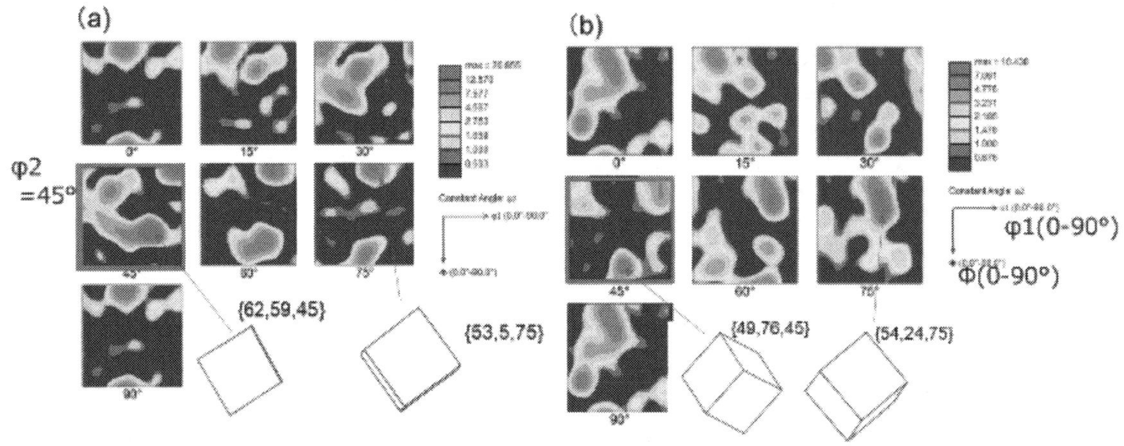

Figure 5.Comparison with ODF between (a) in the region not affected by η phase, and (b) in the region surrounded by η phase at 650 ° C for 10 min.

Thus, the texture of the steel surrounded by the η phase could dramatically change, when η phase grows in to the steel matrix in which the recrystallization proceeds. In order to quantitatively study the evolution of the recrystallization texture of steels surrounded by η phase, further examination is necessary.

4. Conclusions

We investigated the relationship between the growth of η phase on the Fe-Al interface and recrystallization of steel using Nb-added IF steel. The growth of η phase apparently changed the recrystallization texture of the steel, and the development of γ-fiber obtained in IF steel did not appear in the region surrounded by η phase. The further detailed experimental analysis will be necessary for clarifying the recrystallization mechanism.

References

[1] A R. Kuziak, R. Kawalla, S. Waengler: Arch. Civil & Mech. Eng.: 8,(2008), 103-117
[2] O. Grässel, L. Krüger, G. Frommeyer, L.W. Meyer : Int. J. Plast.:16,(2000),1391-1409.
[3] WB.Lee, M.Schmuecker, UA.Mercardo, G. Biallas, S-B. Jung: Scri. Mater.,55,(2006),355-358.
[4] A. Elrefaey, M. Gouda, M. Takahashi and K. Ikeuchi: J. Mater. Eng. & Perform.:14,(2005),10–17.
[5] W.M. Thomas, P.L. Threadgill and E.D. Nicholas: Sci. & Tech. Weld. & Joining:4,(1999) 365-372.
[6] N.Takata et al.:Intermat.67,(2015),1.
[7] K.Han, I.Ohnuma, R.Kainuma: J. Alloys & Comp.,668,(2016), 97-106.
[8] R.K.Ray, J.J.Jonas, and R.E.Hook: Int. Mater. Rev.,39,(1994),129-172.
[9] T.S.Shih,S.H.Tu:Mater. Sci.Eng.A, 454 (2007) 349.

IOP Conf. Series: Materials Science and Engineering 1121 (2021) 012013 doi:10.1088/1757-899X/1121/1/012013

A phase-field investigation of recrystallization boundary migration into heterogeneous deformation energy fields: Effects of dislocation boundary sharpness

R Li[1], V Yadav[2], N Moelans[2], Y Zhang[1] and D Juul Jensen[1]

[1] Department of Mechanical Engineering, Technical University of Denmark, 2800 Kgs. Lyngby, Denmark
[2] Department of Materials Engineering, KU Leuven, Kasteelpark Arenberg 44 Bus 2450, Leuven 3001, Belgium

E-mail: rulia@dtu.dk

Abstract. The migration of recrystallization boundaries into spatially varying deformation energy fields are simulated based on a two-dimensional phase-field model. The energy fields are chosen as idealized versions of deformation microstructures subdivided by two sets of intersecting geometrically necessary dislocation boundaries (GNBs), and effects of the sharpness of the GNBs are investigated. The simulations show that the shape of the recrystallizing grain as well as the recrystallization kinetics are considerably affected by the wall characteristics of the GNBs. Recrystallization occurs faster in the deformed matrix with "sharper" walls. The simulation results highlight the importance of the deformation microstructure characteristics on the recrystallization kinetics, and as the deformation microstructures depend on the initial grain orientations, the results also indicate tight relations between initial, deformation and recrystallization textures.

1. Introduction

Annealing of a deformed metal typically leads to recrystallization by which the deformed grains are replaced by new almost perfect grains: A recrystallized grain has a much lower density of dislocations than that in the deformed matrix [1]. The driving force for recrystallization is generally assumed to be the energy stored in the matrix in the form of defects and dislocations created by plastic deformation [1,2]. Only recently has it been demonstrated that curvature driving and dragging forces related to sharp retrusions and protrusions on migrating recrystallization boundaries may be of the same order of magnitude [3]. Important for both the local stored energy distribution and the curvature forces is how the dislocations are arranged in the matrix. This distribution is, in almost all cases, heterogeneous, as the dislocations arrange to minimize their energy as much as possible into low energy dislocation structures [4]. On the grain scale, the common framework is that the dislocations tend to form structures with a high dislocation density in geometrically necessary boundaries (GNBs) separating regions with much lower dislocation densities from each other. For an overview, see [5]. The driving force for recrystallization thus varies along the recrystallization boundaries, and the boundary profile may change, reflecting how the local dislocation structures are absorbed [6–8]. An important insight

IOP Conf. Series: Materials Science and Engineering 1121 (2021) 012013 doi:10.1088/1757-899X/1121/1/012013

from a texture perspective is that grains with different crystallographic orientations deform following this common framework but with different arrangements and types of dislocation boundaries, for example some being on {111} planes, others not [9].

The growth of recrystallized grains has been well characterized by three-dimensional X-ray microscopy in the bulk of commercially pure aluminum [8,10–12], revealing a heterogeneous growth pattern, with irregular protrusions and retrusions of different amplitudes and widths. It has been suggested that the size and shape of the protrusions and retrusions are correlated in a relatively complex way to the spatial variations in stored energy [11]. A serious complication when interpreting the experimental results is the large number of parameters affecting the recrystallization boundary migration, many of which are correlated to each other, and many of which are not known. Numerical simulations provide potent tools to investigate effects of all these parameters *individually*. As a very general technique, the phase-field method introduces order parameters to track the microstructure evolution in specific phase fields. The method has proved very suitable for modeling complex morphological processes, *e.g.*, grain growth [13], solidification [14], and precipitation [15]. As to the study of recrystallization, it is also possible to introduce specific deformation microstructures into a phase-field model. The movement of an initially planar boundary during recrystallization was simulated using a relatively simple 1D deformation field [6], and most recently, Yadav *et al.* [7] studied effects of the 2D geometrical alignment of dislocation boundaries on the recrystallization boundary migration, revealing the complexity of recrystallization in heterogeneous energy fields. In these papers, a sinusoidal function was used to represent the microstructural variations. This corresponds to relatively broad dislocation boundaries and a smoothly varying deformation field. Experimentally the GNBs are often seen as sharp, narrow boundaries, and the dislocation density variations may thus in reality be more abrupt. The aim of the present work is to study effects of this on recrystallization by stimulating the growth of an initially circular nucleus in three deformation fields with the same average stored energy but with the majority of the energy concentrated in more or less sharp boundaries.

2. Simulation details

The phase-field model employed in this paper is inspired by the simulation works of Moelans [6,16]. The primary strategy is introducing two order parameters $\eta_{\mathrm{rex}}(x,y,t)$ and $\eta_{\mathrm{def}}(x,y,t)$, which are continuous functions of the spatial coordinates and time, to distinguish different states of the system, with $\eta_{\mathrm{rex}},\eta_{\mathrm{def}} = 1,0$ and $\eta_{\mathrm{rex}},\eta_{\mathrm{def}} = 0,1$ in the recrystallizing grain, and deformed matrix, respectively. The thermodynamic free energy (F) is assumed to consist of contributions from the grain boundary energy (F_{gb}) and the stored energy (F_{def}), which can be described as

$$F_{gb} = \int M\left(\frac{\eta_{rex}^4}{4} + \frac{\eta_{def}^4}{4} - \frac{\eta_{rex}^2}{2} - \frac{\eta_{def}^2}{2} + 1.5\eta_{rex}^2\eta_{def}^2 + 0.25\right) + \frac{\mathrm{k}}{2}((\nabla\eta_{rex})^2 + (\nabla\eta_{def})^2)\,\mathrm{d}\Omega \quad (1)$$

$$F_{def} = \int f_{def}(x,y)\frac{\eta_{def}^2}{\eta_{rex}^2+\eta_{def}^2}\mathrm{d}\Omega \quad (2)$$

where f_{def} is the local stored energy density. Model parameters κ, and M are related to the grain boundary energy and the diffuse interface width (ℓ_{gb}).

A Fourier-spectral method with semi-implicit time-stepping was employed to update the order parameters based on the assumption of periodic boundary conditions [17]. Simulations parameters used in this paper are as follows: time-step $\Delta t = 0.01$, grid spacing $\Delta x = 1$, model parameters $L = 5$, and $M = 1$, which are chosen empirically for a good balance between accuracy and computing efficiency. More details about the model can be found in [6,7].

We here idealize typical deformation microstructures by two sets of equispaced GNBs lying at equal but opposite angles of π/12 and -π/12, respectively, to the vertical axis, which for rolled samples corresponds to the rolling direction. Three kinds of f_{def} are used for the simulations:

$$f_{def,1}(x,y) = \max\left\{A_1\left[1 + \sin\left(\frac{\pi}{64}\left(y - \frac{x}{\tan(\pi/12+\pi/2)}\right)\right)\right], A_1\left[1 + \sin\left(\frac{\pi}{64}\left(y - \frac{x}{\tan(-\pi/12+\pi/2)}\right)\right)\right]\right\} \quad (3)$$

$$f_{def,2}(x,y) = \max\left\{A_2\left[\sin\left(\frac{\pi}{128}\left(y - \frac{x}{\tan(\pi/12+\pi/2)}\right)\right)\right]^4, A_2\left[\sin\left(\frac{\pi}{128}\left(y - \frac{x}{\tan(-\pi/12+\pi/2)}\right)\right)\right]^4\right\} + C \quad (4)$$

$$f_{def,3}(x,y) = \max\left\{A_3\left[\sin\left(\frac{\pi}{128}\left(y - \frac{x}{\tan(\pi/12+\pi/2)}\right)\right)\right]^{10}, A_3\left[\sin\left(\frac{\pi}{128}\left(y - \frac{x}{\tan(-\pi/12+\pi/2)}\right)\right)\right]^{10}\right\} + C \quad (5)$$

where $A_1 = 0.04$, $A_2 = 0.0953$, $A_3 = 0.1325$, $C = 0.001$. Figure 1a-c show the representation of $f_{def,1}$, $f_{def,2}$ and $f_{def,3}$. Cross-sectional plots of the three stored energy fields at vertical and horizontal directions are shown in figure 1d-i, which corresponds to the red and purple traces in figure 1a-c, visualizing the wall profiles. The average stored energy density values of the employed fields are the same and equal to 0.0561 in all three cases. We assumed that the spatial variations in stored energy are constant irrespective of annealing time, meaning that recovery is not considered in the simulations.

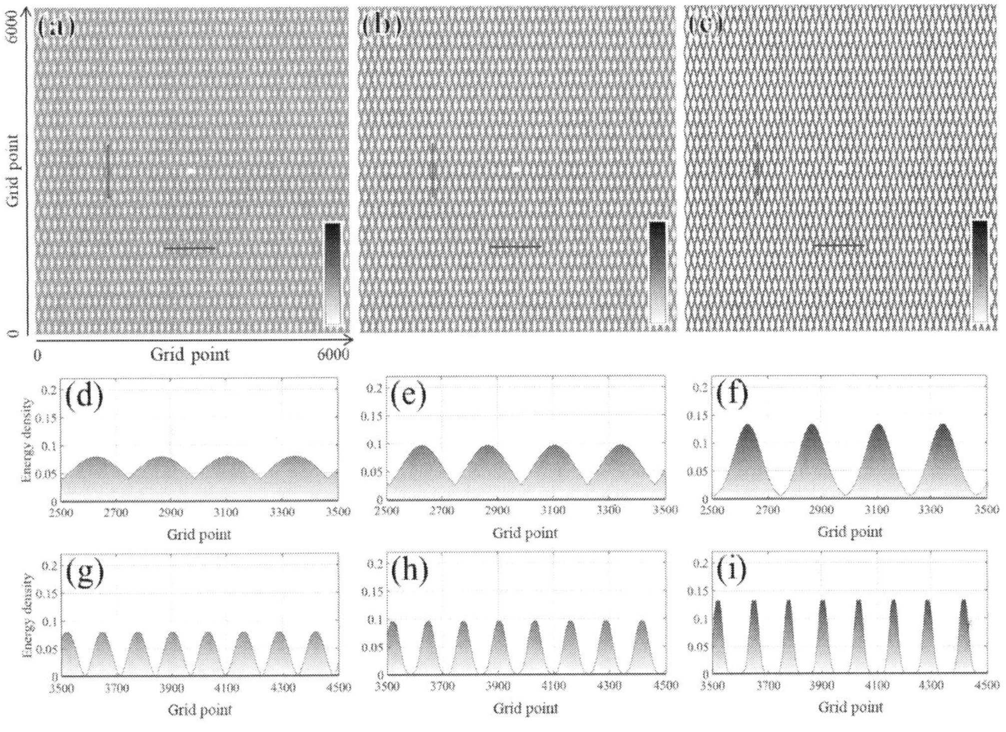

Figure 1. Representation of the employed stored energy fields and cross-sectional plots at vertical/horizontal directions. (a, d, g) $f_{def,1}$. (b, e, h) $f_{def,2}$. (c, f, i) $f_{def,3}$. The black-white scale range is here chosen to be from 0 to 0.18, with black representing the highest stored energy density. The center-positioned white circle in (a-c) represents the original nuclei (see section 3).

The system size was 6000×6000 grid points. The code was written in Julia programming language [18], which allows an efficient implementation of the Fourier-spectral method by calling a GPU (NVIDIA Quadro P5000) on an HP Z4 workstation.

3. Results and discussion

One circular nucleus/grain of radius 50 grid points were center-positioned in each of the three simulation boxes to grow (*i.e.*, recrystallize) into the different stored energy fields. Figure 2 shows the positions of the recrystallization boundary traces starting from the time-step 60000 to 260000 with an interval of 5000 time-steps. Note that only the top-right part of the simulation box is plotted, and we highlight the migration traces at the time-step of 60000, 160000, and 260000 with red lines. Figure 2a, as a reference, shows the migration traces in a uniform stored energy field, which are all perfect circles. While as seen in figure 2b-c, the original circular boundaries migrate and change shapes while absorbing the GNBs, yielding hexagon-shaped grains in the three heterogeneous fields.

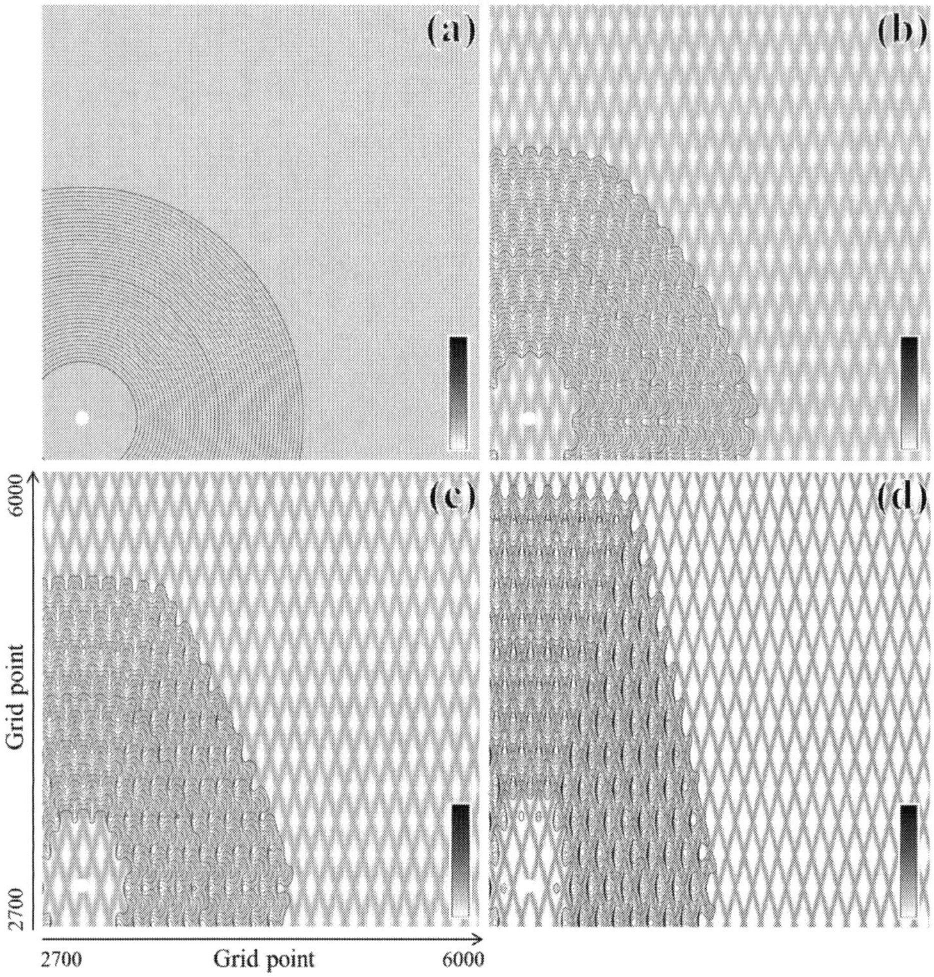

Figure 2. Recrystallization boundary traces as a function of time obtained in the simulations. (a) Uniform field. (b) $f_{def,1}$. (c) $f_{def,2}$. (d) $f_{def,3}$. The filled white circle area represents the original nuclei. The traces are plotted every 5000 time-steps starting from the time-step of 60000 to 260000. The black-white scale range is here 0 to 0.4, with black representing the highest stored energy density.

Specifically, figure 3 shows the simulated shapes of the recrystallizing grains after annealing for 260000 time-steps. It is noteworthy that while the wall-spacing, angle, and average stored energy density are the same for all the employed fields, the resultant grain shapes differ significantly, showing GNB-dependent anisotropic recrystallization behavior. Most obvious, the shape of the growing grain becomes closer to a narrow hexagon when the GNB sharpness increases as the differences in the horizontal and vertical migration rates become more apparent. The overall boundary velocities in the horizontal and vertical yield ratios of 1:1.2, 1:1.4, and 1:2.1 in $f_{def,1}$, $f_{def,2}$ and $f_{def,3}$, respectively. In all cases, the boundary positions coincide in the ~48° direction.

The migrating boundary profile is highly dynamic while moving into the heterogeneous deformation fields: protrusions transform into retrusions and vice-versa continuously, and the boundary experiences a stop-and-go type movement (boundary segments remain for a longer period at

IOP Conf. Series: Materials Science and Engineering 1121 (2021) 012013 doi:10.1088/1757-899X/1121/1/012013

positions with low stored energy density and then advance suddenly to the next position of similar low stored energy), which is similar to what has been observed experimentally, *e.g.*, [7]. This is more evident in the field with "sharper" walls. As the stored energy density gradient is very high in $f_{def,3}$, the curvature related driving force cannot balance the stored energy gradient. Therefore some moving boundary segments can quickly bow out, and parts of the moving boundary on both sides of the stagnated part can join thereby pinching off a part of the boundary, leaving behind isolated unrecrystallized islands of the deformed matrix. These isolated islands recrystallized upon further annealing.

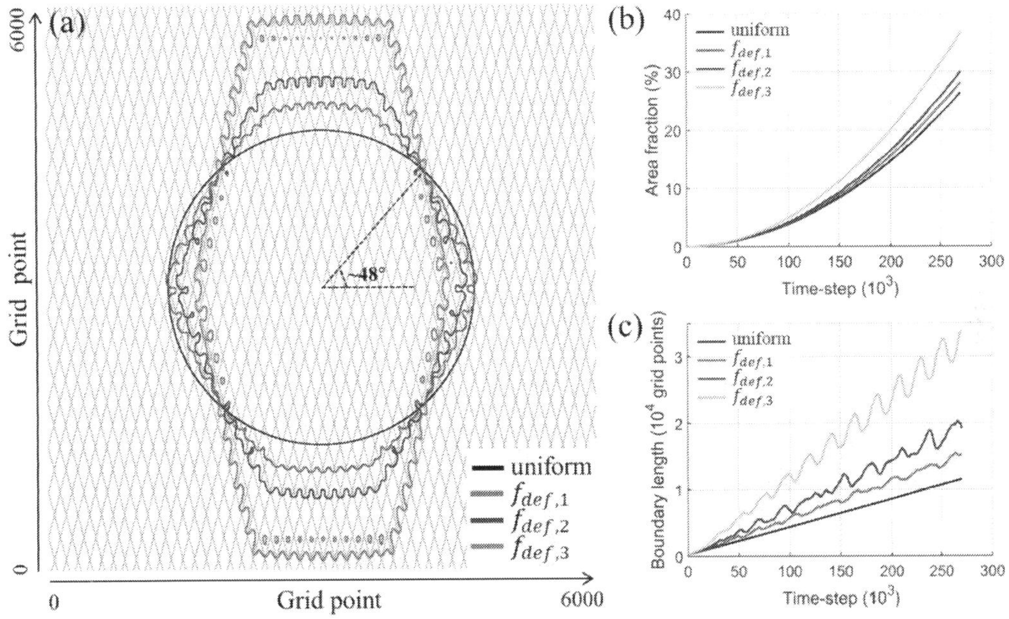

Figure 3. (a) The simulated shapes of the recrystallizing grain at the time-step of 260000 in the different stored energy fields (taken from figure 2). The simulated area fraction (b) and boundary length (c) of the recrystallizing grain in the different stored energy fields as a function of annealing time.

Figure 3b and c show the recrystallized area fraction and boundary length of the recrystallizing grain as a function of annealing time. Both values are always the largest in $f_{def,3}$ and smallest in the uniform field at any time-step, and the difference becomes more and more evident with annealing, suggesting that recrystallization occurs faster in the field with "sharper" GNBs ($f_{def,3}$). Note that the boundaries of the left behind isolated islands of deformed material are also included in both figure 3b and c. As shown in figure 3b, the increasing rate of recrystallized area fraction in $f_{def,3}$ is 40% higher than that in the uniform field after 260000 time-steps.

The simulation results also demonstrate the anomalous scenario where the recrystallization boundary length (corresponding to the grain surface area in 3D) may not always monotonously increase with annealing time but is significantly influenced by the change in boundary roughness and boundary pinch-off events, which occur when the migrating boundary meets the "sharper" GNBs (see figure 3c).

4. Conclusions

The *sharpness* of the geometrically necessary boundaries in the deformation microstructure is a dominating factor affecting the morphology of recrystallizing grains and the boundary migration velocity during annealing. Recrystallization occurs faster in deformed microstructures with "sharper" walls. More generally, with the aid of simulations, we have demonstrated the opportunity to quantify effects of specific deformation microstructure parameters on recrystallization kinetics by introducing various microstructures into the phase-field model. Thereby effects of different parameters can be investigated *separately*, and the simulations may suggest critical experiments.

Acknowledgments
The financial support from the European Research Council (ERC) under the European Union's Horizon 2020 research and innovation programme (M4D-grant agreement No. 788567 and grant agreement No. 714754 INTERDIFFUSION ERC-2016-STG) is gratefully acknowledged.

References
[1] Humphreys F J and Hatherly M 2004 *Recrystallization and Related Annealing Phenomena* (Elsevier)
[2] Ashby M F 1980 Recrystallization and grain growth of multi-phase and particle containing materials *1st Risø international symposium on metallurgy and materials science, Risø* p 325
[3] Zhang Y, Godfrey A and Juul Jensen D 2014 In-situ investigation of local boundary migration during recrystallization *Metall Mat Trans A* **45** 2899–2905
[4] Kuhlmann-Wilsdorf D 1989 Theory of plastic deformation-properties of low energy dislocation structures *Mater Sci Eng A* **113** 1–41
[5] Hansen N and Juul Jensen D 2011 Deformed metals–structure, recrystallisation and strength *Mater Sci Technol* **27** 1229–1240
[6] Moelans N, Godfrey A, Zhang Y and Juul Jensen D 2013 Phase-field simulation study of the migration of recrystallization boundaries *Phys Rev B* **88** 054103
[7] Yadav V, Moelans N, Zhang Y and Juul Jensen D 2021 Influence of geometrical alignment of the deformation microstructure on local migration of grain boundaries during recrystallization: A phase-field study *Scripta Mater* **191** 116–119
[8] Zhang Y, Budai J, Tischler J, Liu W, Xu R, Homer E R, Godfrey A and Juul Jensen D 2017 Boundary migration in a 3D deformed microstructure inside an opaque sample *Sci Rep* **7** 1–8
[9] Huang X and Winther G 2007 Dislocation structures. Part I. Grain orientation dependence *Philos Mag* **87** 5189–5214
[10] Schmidt S, Nielsen S, Gundlach C, Margulies L, Huang X and Juul Jensen D 2004 Watching the growth of bulk grains during recrystallization of deformed metals *Science* **305** 229–232
[11] Zhang Y, Godfrey A and Juul Jensen D 2011 Local boundary migration during recrystallization in pure aluminium *Scripta Mater* **64** 331–334
[12] Juul Jensen D and Zhang Y 2020 Impact of 3D/4D methods on the understanding of recrystallization *Curr Opin Solid State Mater Sci* 100821
[13] Moelans N, Spaepen F and Wollants P 2010 Grain growth in thin films with a fibre texture studied by phase-field simulations and mean field modelling *Philos Mag* **90** 501–523
[14] Wang N, Smith N and Provatas N 2017 Investigating gas-phase defect formation in late-stage solidification using a novel phase-field crystal alloy model *Phys Rev Mater* **1** 043405
[15] Chang K and Moelans N 2015 Phase-field simulations of the interaction between a grain boundary and an evolving second-phase particle *Philos Mag Lett* **95** 202–210
[16] Moelans N, Zhang Y, Godfrey A and Juul Jensen D 2015 A phase-field simulation study of irregular grain boundary migration during recrystallization *IOP Conf Ser: Mater Sci Eng* **89** 012037
[17] Chen L Q and Shen J 1998 Applications of semi-implicit Fourier-spectral method to phase field equations *Comput Phys Commun* **108** 147–158
[18] Bezanson J, Edelman A, Karpinski S and Shah V 2017 Julia: A fresh approach to numerical computing *SIAM Rev* **59** 65–98

IOP Conf. Series: Materials Science and Engineering 1121 (2021) 012014 doi:10.1088/1757-899X/1121/1/012014

Growth of Grains in the Third Orientation in an Inhomogeneous Matrix Consisting of Two Orientation Groups - A Modified Potts–Monte Carlo Simulation -

Kunio Ito

Department of Materials Engineering, The University of Tokyo, Bunkyo-Ku, Tokyo, 113-8656 Japan

E-mail: ito_e-prof@material.t.u-tokyo.ac.jp

Abstract. The growth of a C-grain embedded in the matrix of A- and B-grains has been simulated. A, B, and C denote orientation groups. Boundaries were defined as "specified" if they consisted of A and C grains, else they were defined as "unspecified". The edges of an embedded grain were named according to component grains as CAA, CAB, and CBB triple lines. The inhomogeneity of the matrix structure was presented as the ratio between their numbers. When the mobility of specified boundary is higher than that of unspecified boundary, the volume fraction of the C-grain increases with grain coarsening, which is affected by the ratio between triple lines. The results suggest that the development of the grain growth texture is affected by the orientation distribution in a specimen and that the influence must be bigger when the mobility of the triple line depends on the combination of relevant grains.

1. Introduction

Changes in crystallographic textures have been examined by simulating the grain coarsening process[1]–[3] using the grain embedding method[3],[4]. Boundary energy and boundary mobility were controlled as a function of orientation relations between adjusting grains. In the embedding method, the orientations of grains are classified into three groups, i.e., A, B, and C. An increase in the volume fraction of grains in the orientation group C through the grain coarsening process was studied. Thus far, similar to other studies[5], grains in the orientation group A and those in the orientation group B were homogeneously distributed in the matrix.

In this paper, the growth of grains in the orientation group C in the matrix of inhomogeneous distribution of grains in the two orientation groups is reported.

2. Modelling

2.1. Preparation of the matrix structure

First, structures similar to those in the previous report[3] were prepared, where the grains in the two matrix orientation groups A and B were identical in both volume fractions and grain size distributions. Then, the specimen was divided into 8 (=2 × 2 × 2) subdivisions of categories I and II so that they were three-dimensionally alternatingly located. In the subdivision of category I, the orientations of grains of group B were changed to the orientations of group A and vice versa in the subdivision of category II. The orientations of grains lying over the two categories were unaltered. The specimens made from this type of the matrix structure are called the 222 specimen, and those made by a similar process through 512 (=8 × 8 × 8) subdivisions are called the 888 specimen. The 888 specimen corresponds to the specimen with a random orientation distribution[3](figure 1).

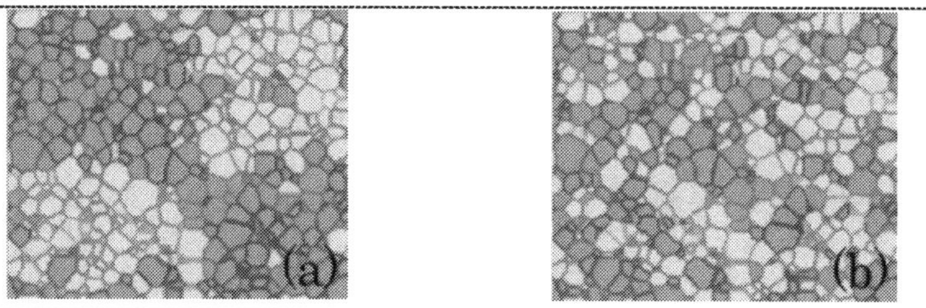

Figure 1. Sections of initial matrix structures prior to embedding a grain in orientation group C. (a) 222 and (b) 888 specimens. Grains in the orientation groups A and B are, respectively, colored as ■ and ■.

2.2. *Algorithm for coarsening*

A grain belonging to the orientation group C was embedded at the center of the matrix structure, and the coarsening process was simulated by the same algorithm as that reported in[3],[4]. Boundaries between the embedded grain and matrix grains in the orientation group A are defined as "specified," and the other boundaries are defined as "unspecified". The energy of cell i in orientation O_i was given by equation (1). f_{in} represents the dependence of boundary energy on orientation difference. The orientation change from O_i^b to O_i^a was accepted by probability p . $R_{O_i^a O_i^b}$ represents the dependence of boundary mobility on orientation difference.

$$E_i(O_i) = (\sum_{n=1}^{26} f_{in}\overline{\delta_{in}})/100 \quad (1)$$

$$\Delta E = E_i(O_i^a) - E_i(O_i^b) \quad (2)$$

$$p = p(\Delta E)/R_{O_i^a O_i^b} \quad (3)$$

In the case of discrimination of boundary energy, if the combination of O_i and O_n corresponded to a specified boundary, then f_{in} was set to 65, else to 100, and $R_{O_i^a O_i^b}$ was fixed to 1. In the case of discrimination of boundary mobility, if the combination of O_i^a and O_i^b corresponded to the migration of specified boundary, then $R_{O_i^a O_i^b}$ was set to 1 else to 3, and f_{in} was fixed to 100. In the following figures, the former and the latter cases are, respectively, designated as F065R100 and F100R033.

3. Statistical results of the grain growth of embedded grain

3.1. *Parameters concerning the grain growth*

$<V>(t)$; mean volume of matrix grains at time t, $<V>(t_0) = 2900$ in the initial matrix structure

$V_0(t)$; volume of an embedded grain at time t

$<V>(t_1)$; mean volume of matrix grains when $<V>(t_1)/<V>(t_0) = 1.1$

$C_r = <V>(t_r)/<V>(t_1)$; matrix coarsening ratio at time t_r

t_2, t_4, t_8, t_{16}; time for $C_r = 2, 4, 8, 16$

$R_{growth(t_r/t_1)} = (V_0(t_r)/V_0(t_1))/C_r$; relative coarsening ratio of an embedded grain at time t_r.

$R_{growth(t_r/t_1)} > 1$ means an increase in the volume fraction of the embedded grain in a specimen[4].

$r_{eq}(t)$; equivalent radius of an embedded grain, $V_0(t) = 4\pi r_{eq}(t)^3/3$

$R_{eq}(t) = r_{eq}(t)/\,half\ length\ of\ specimen$; relative equivalent radius of an embedded grain

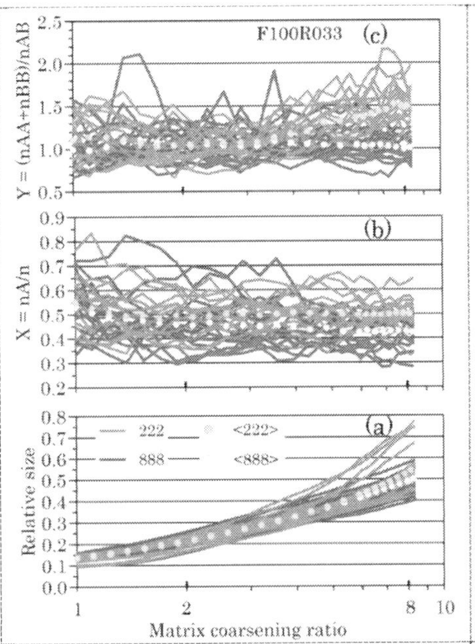

Figure 2. Coarsening process in the case of mobility discrimination

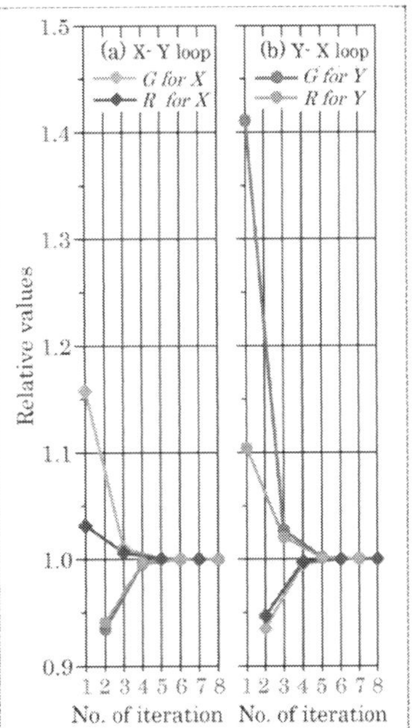

Figure 3. Iteration processes of correlation analysis (mobility discrimination case)

3.2. Parameters concerning boundaries and triple lines surrounding an embedded grain

n_A ; number of specified boundaries

n_B ; number of unspecified boundaries

$X = n_A/(n_A + n_B)$; "fraction of specified boundaries"

n_{AA} ; number of triple lines that include two neighboring grains belonging to the orientation group A.

n_{AB} ; number of triple lines including one neighboring grain belonging to the orientation group A and another one belonging to the orientation group B

n_{BB} ; number of triple lines including two neighboring grains belonging to the orientation group B

$Y = (n_{AA} + n_{BB})/n_{AB}$; "ratio of mixed triple lines"

Coarsening processes are exemplified in figure 2. The ordinate axis "Relative size" represents $R_{eq}(t)$. Plural specimens were made using randomly made matrix structures by changing sizes of embedded grains[2],[3]. One kinked line shows a process of one specimen, and round-shaped marks represent the means of 222 and 888 specimens.

3.3. Parameters concerning correlations between the growth of embedded grain and the degree of inhomogeneity of matrix grains

$R_{growth(t_e/t_b)} = R_{growth(t_e/t_1)} / R_{growth(t_b/t_1)}$; relative coarsening ratio of an embedded grain during the time interval between t_b and t_e. In the case of different boundary mobilities, $t_b = t_2$ and $t_e = t_8$. For different boundary energies, $t_b = t_4$ and $t_e = t_{16}$. Thus, the two conditions were compared under similar matrix grain sizes.

$<X>(t_b,t_e)$; the mean of X from t_b to t_e along a kinked line (e.g., figure 2 (b)).

$<Y>(t_b,t_e)$; the mean of Y from t_b to t_e along a kinked line.

3.4. Method for calculating correlation coefficients

Let X_i, Y_i, and Z_i represent $<X>(t_b,t_e)$, $<Y>(t_b,t_e)$, and $R_{growth(t_e/t_b)}$ of the i th specimen. The data pooled over 222 and 888 specimens are expressed as $\{X_i\}$, $\{Y_i\}$,and $\{Z_i\}$.

X–Y iteration loop; analysis between $\{X_i\}$ and $\{Z_i\}$ followed by the analysis of the residue

1) get correlation coefficient R_{x1} and approximate equation $Z_{i1}^{apr} = a_{x1}X_i + b_{x1}$ from $\{X_i\}$ and $\{Z_i\}$

2) get correlation coefficient R_{y1} and approximate equation $Z_{i2}^{apr} = a_{y1}Y_i + b_{y1}$ from $\{Y_i\}$ and $\{\Delta Z_{i1} = Z_i - Z_{i1}^{apr}\}$

3) similarly, get R_{x2} and $Z_{i3}^{apr} = a_{x2}X_i + b_{x2}$ from $\{X_i\}$ and $\{\Delta Z_{i2} = Z_i - Z_{i2}^{apr}\}$

4) get R_{y2} and $Z_{i4}^{apr} = a_{y2}Y_i + b_{y2}$ from $\{Y_i\}$ and $\{\Delta Z_{i3} = Z_i - Z_{i3}^{apr}\}$ and return to 3)

get $(R_{x\infty}, a_{x\infty})$ and $(R_{y\infty}, a_{y\infty})$ by iterating 3)–>4)

Y–X iteration loop; analysis between $\{Y_i\}$ and $\{Z_i\}$ followed by the analysis of the residue

get $(R_{x\infty}, a_{x\infty})$ and $(R_{y\infty}, a_{y\infty})$ by iteration that is similar to the X–Y iteration

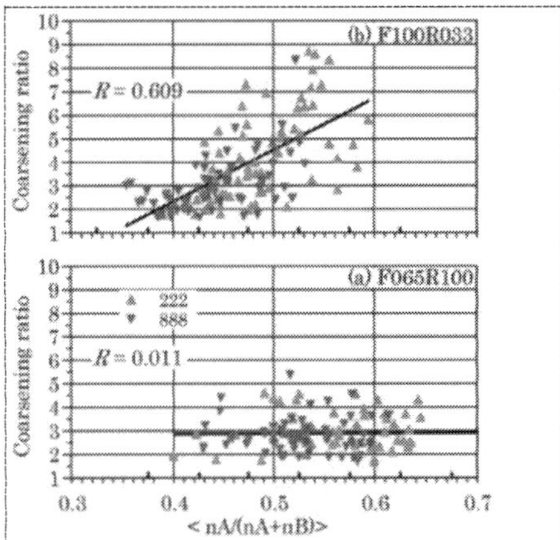

Figure 4. Correlation between the fraction of specified boundaries and the relative coarsening ratio of an embedded grain

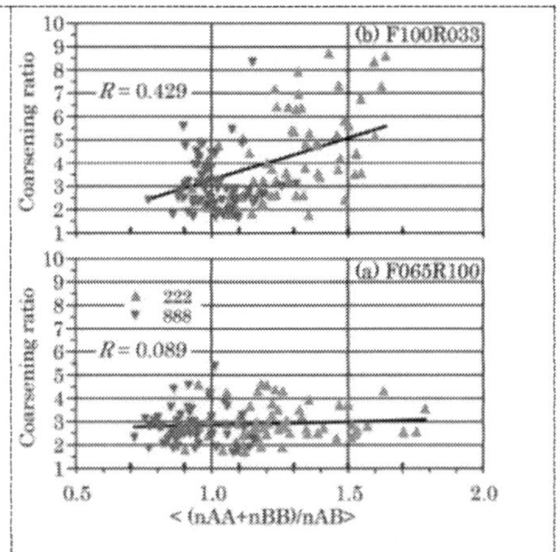

Figure 5. Correlation between the ratio of mixed triple lines and the relative coarsening ratio of an embedded grain

IOP Conf. Series: Materials Science and Engineering 1121 (2021) 012014 doi:10.1088/1757-899X/1121/1/012014

As shown in figure 3, where G and R, respectively, represent a_x or a_y and R_x or R_y, both loops give the same convergent values. Plotted points are normalized with respect to them.

$\{Z_i\}$ are plotted against $\{X_i\}$ (figure 4) and against $\{Y_i\}$ (figure 5). The values of R_x and R_y after convergence are given in the figures, and the lines correspond to G.

4. Observation of shapes of embedded grain

Three-dimensional shapes of embedded grain are shown by its surfaces in figures 6 and 7.

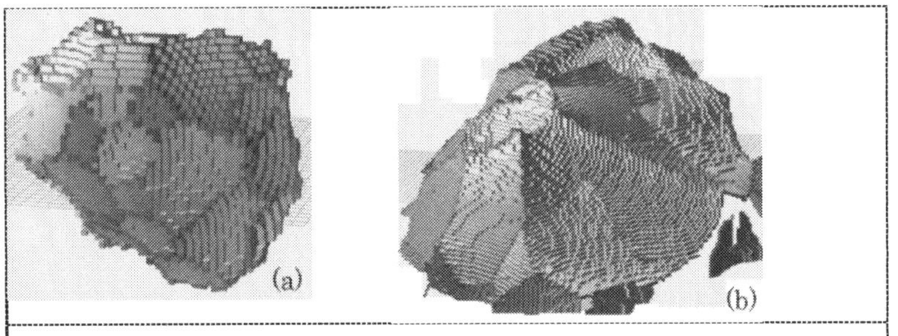

Figure 6. Embedded grain in the 222 specimen; energy discrimination case, matrix coarsening ratio =16. (a) Whole grain; one cell in the figure represents 64 (= $4\times4\times4$) cells in the original structure. (b) Part of the grain; the cell size is the same as the original one. The colors of the cells show the orientation groups of neighboring grains.

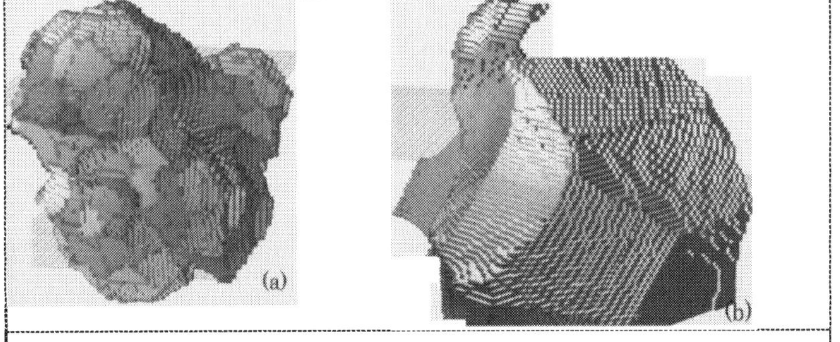

Figure 7 Grain embedded in a 222 specimen; mobility discrimination case, matrix coarsening ratio = 8. Differences in (a) and (b) are the same as those in figure 6.

5. Discussion

5.1. Expression of the inhomogeneity of the matrix structure by the "ratio of mixed triple lines" parameter

This triple-lines-based parameter is expected to be equal to unity under the present condition that the numbers and sizes of grains in two orientation groups are identical, when grains in the two groups are randomly distributed, and expected to become bigger than unity when grains in the same group are clustering to make colonies. With the growth of embedded grain, the difference in this parameter increases between 222 and 888 specimens (figure 2). The increase corresponds to the inhomogeneity of 222 specimens in their internal structures (figure 1(a)). By responding to the intentional design of matrix structures, the triple-lines-based parameter of 222 specimens was bigger than that of 888 specimens at the time when the growth rates of embedded grains were compared (see the axis of abscissa in figure 5).

Triple lines and quadruple points have been pointed out to affect the grain growth process[5]–[7]. The ratio of mixed triple lines represents the composition of orientations of grains surrounding an embedded grain. Hence, it is suggested that the degree of inhomogeneity in orientation distribution in a specimen will yield a stronger influence on textural development by grain coarsening, if the mobility of triple lines and quadruple points depend on the combination of related orientations.

5.2. Comparison of boundary energy discrimination with boundary mobility discrimination

Embedded grains in 222 specimens grow anisotropically corresponding to the inhomogeneity of the matrix structure (figures 6 and 7). This trend appears more distinctly under condition of mobility discrimination than under condition of energy discrimination (figure 7). When the mobility was different, grains in the orientation group B interfere with the potential rapid growth of the embedded grain into grains in the orientation group A. Under the condition of boundary energy discrimination, an embedded grain grows by wetting into the space between two grains in the orientation group A. Grains in the orientation group B do not essentially obstruct this growth.

The effect of ratio of mixed triple lines on the growth of embedded grain is bigger in the case of mobility discrimination than in the case of energy discrimination (compare (a) with (b) in figure 5).

The observed growth of embedded grain, which consumes grains in the orientation group A that are obstructed by grains in the orientation group B, is similar to the retardation of grain growth by second phase particles[5],[8]. The colonies of grains in the orientation group B correspond to particles, and the size of colonies of grains in the orientation group A corresponds to that of grains.

6. Summary

The simulation showed that when the mobility of boundary between grains in the third orientation group and matrix grains in one of their orientation groups is preferentially higher than those of other boundaries, the volume fraction of grains in the third orientation group increases more with grain coarsening in the case of matrix structure where grains make colonies of the same orientation group than in the case of matrix structure of homogeneous orientation distribution.

The observation of shapes of growing grains showed that this phenomenon corresponds to the retardation of growth of colonies surrounded by the higher number of higher mobility boundaries and the lower number of lower mobility boundaries by colonies surrounded by the higher number of lower mobility boundaries and the lower number of higher mobility boundaries.

The ratio of mixed triple lines, which is defined in this paper, represents the composition of orientations of grains surrounding an embedded grain. It is suggested that the degree of inhomogeneity in orientation distribution in a specimen will yield a stronger influence on the textural development by grain coarsening if the mobility of triple lines and quadruple points depends on the combination of related orientations. The ratio might be one of hidden factors that control this texture development.

References

[1] Kunio Ito 2012 Computational Materials Science **62** 117
[2] Kunio Ito 2015 IOP Conf. Series: Materials Science and Engineering **82** 012043 (ICOTOM 17)
[3] Kunio Ito 2017 ISIJ International **57** 1625
[4] Kunio Ito 2017 ISIJ International **57** 1631
[5] P R Rios and D. Zoellner 2018 Materials Science and Technology **34** 629
[6] Yves J M Brechet 2010 Scripta Materialia **62** 910
[7] L A. Barrales-Mora, L S Shvindlerman and G Gottstein 2013 Materials Science Forum **753** 373
[8] Takafumi OIKAWA and Masato ENOMOTO 2011 Tetsu-to-Hagane **97** 584

The Origin of the Cube ({001}<100>) Texture in Non-oriented Electrical Steel Sheets

Youliang He[1]*, M Mehdi[1, 2], E J Hilinski[3], L A I Kestens[4], A Edrisy[2]

[1]CanmetMATERIALS, Natural Resources Canada, Hamilton, Ontario, L8P 0A5, Canada
[2]Department of Mechanical, Automotive and Materials Engineering, University of Windsor, Windsor, Ontario, N9B, 3P4, Canada
[3]Tempel Steel Co., Chicago, Illinois, 60640-1020, USA
[4]EEMMeCS Department, Metals Science and Technology Group, Ghent University, Ghent B9052, Belgium

*Corresponding author: youliang.he@canada.ca

Abstract. Although cube ({001}<100>) is a preferred final texture in non-oriented electrical steel (NOES) sheets, this texture is rarely produced in commercial NOES products. The major texture of fully processed NOES is usually the unfavorable <111>//ND (normal direction) fibre, which originates from the deformed <111>//ND texture. To reduce/eliminate the <111>//ND texture and promote the cube texture, one method is to change the initial texture before cold rolling. In this research, two electrical steels containing 0.88 wt% and 2.8 wt% Si are cold rolled with the initial textures rotated by 60° around the ND before cold rolling. This rotation leads to the rotated Goss ({110}<110>) texture in the deformed microstructure. Within the shear bands of the rotated Goss grains, crystallites with cube orientation are formed. Regions of these crystallites may have lower stored energy than their neighboring areas. During annealing, these crystallites preferentially nucleate and grow, and form a strong cube texture in the final steel sheets.

1. Introduction

Producing non-oriented electrical steel sheets with desired crystallographic textures to improve the magnetic properties has been the subject of many studies [1-4]. Unlike the well-known grain-oriented electrical steel where the formation of the Goss texture ({011}<100>) in the steel sheets has been an industrial practice for more than 80 years [5], no such texture has been produced in non-oriented electrical steel that can optimize the magnetic properties in all directions in the steel sheets, as required by electric motor applications. Generally, any texture with the <100> axes in the sheet plane may contribute to good magnetic properties. Thus, the formation of the <001>//ND textures has been the aim of many investigations on non-oriented electrical steel [4]. Cube ({001}<100>) is one of these textures as it has two easy <100> axes in the sheet plane, i.e. along both the rolling direction (RD) and the transverse direction (TD). However, the cube texture has rarely been produced in non-oriented electrical steels during mass production. This is because, under conventional rolling and annealing conditions, the cube texture rarely appears in the final sheets, either in grain-oriented or non-oriented electrical steel. The formation mechanism of the cube texture in electrical steel is still not completely understood.

A few papers have discussed the formation mechanisms of the cube texture in non-oriented electrical steel [6-9]. Sha et al. [6] claimed that the initial casting texture tended to produce the cube deformation bands and shear bands that promote the cube texture in the recrystallized microstructure, while Takajo et al. [7] related the formation of the cube texture to the {114}<481> texture (on the α^*-fiber) in the cold-rolled steel. Nguyen-Minh et al. [8] reported that the formation of a rotated Goss ({110}<110>) texture in the cold-rolled steel was able to provide cube crystallites within the shear bands of the deformed {110}<110> grains, which lead to a final cube texture. He et al. [9] illustrated that by using an inclined rolling technique, it was able to produce a final cube texture in a low Si electrical steel, but the formation mechanisms were not investigated. The authors of this paper have shown [10] that through inclined rolling it was able to produce a final cube texture in a 2.8 wt% Si non-oriented electrical steel, and the formation mechanism was attributed to the rotated Goss texture in the cold-rolled steel. In this paper, the microtexture and microstructure of two incline-rolled non-oriented electrical steels (0.88 wt% and 2.80 wt% Si) are characterized by electron backscatter diffraction (EBSD), and the origin of the cube texture appearing in the final annealed sheets is examined, which reveals the importance of shear bands in the determination of the recrystallization texture of the steels.

2. Experimental

The compositions of the two electrical steels investigated in this paper are listed in Table 1. The main difference of these steels is the silicon content. It is well known that depending on the amount of silicon in the steel, the material may or may not be subjected to austenite-to-ferrite phase transformation during cooling. In this study, the Low Si steel exhibits phase transformation, while the High Si steel does not. The steels were melted in a vacuum induction furnace and cast into ingots of 200 mm × 200 mm (cross section). The steels were then reheated to 1038 °C and hot rolled in a reversing rolling mill to 25 mm (87.5% reduction). After removing the oxides on the surfaces, the steels were reheated again to 1038 °C and further hot rolled to ~2.5 mm (~85% reduction). The hot-rolled plates were then HCl-acid pickled to remove hot mill scale and annealed in a 100% dry hydrogen environment at 840 °C for 60 hours [9, 11]. The purpose was to obtain large grains in the recrystallized microstructure, which was beneficial to the formation of shear bands during the subsequent cold rolling [12].

Table 1. Chemical compositions of the two non-oriented electrical steels studied (wt%).

Steel	Si	C	Mn	S	P	Al	Fe
Low Si	0.88	0.002	0.31	0.001	0.01	0.46	Balance
High Si	2.80	0.003	0.30	0.001	0.01	0.52	Balance

Cold rolling was conducted in a different way from conventional rolling, i.e., the cold rolling direction (CRD) was inclined at 60° to the hot rolling direction (HRD) [9, 11]. The purpose was to alter the initial texture before cold rolling by rotating the plate around the ND so that the conventional cold-rolling texture, which is dominated by the <111>//ND and <110>//RD fibres, can be altered. The steel plates were cold rolled to ~0.5 mm with a thickness reduction rate of ~80%. The cold-rolled sheets were then characterized under EBSD to reveal the microtexture and microstructure. Special attention was paid to the small crystallites within the shear bands of the deformed matrix. The materials were finally annealed under different temperatures, i.e., 650 °C for the Low Si steel and 750 °C for the High Si steel, since the recrystallization temperature of the electrical steel depends on the silicon content: a higher silicon concentration results in a higher recrystallization temperature [13].

3. Results and Discussion

The initial textures of the two steels before inclined cold rolling, i.e., after 60° rotation of the hot band around the ND, are shown in Figure 1. It is seen that the textures are quite different between the two steels. The Low Si steel has a much lower maximum intensity than the High Si steel and the major

IOP Conf. Series: Materials Science and Engineering 1121 (2021) 012015 doi:10.1088/1757-899X/1121/1/012015

texture of the Low Si steel is the <001>//ND fibre (including the cube {001}<100>), while the High Si steel shows a very strong texture near the {112}<111> and a minor component near the cube. Both steels show a weak <111>//ND fibre, but no <110>//RD fibre is seen.

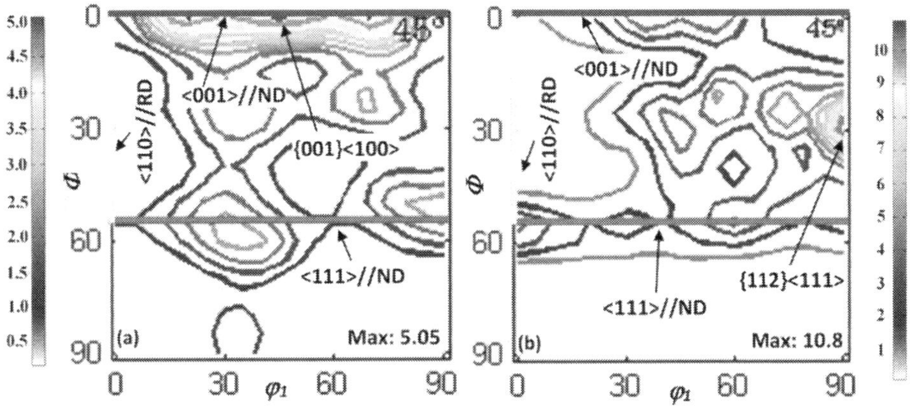

Figure 1. The initial textures of the steels before cold rolling (after 60° rotation around ND): (a) 0.88 wt% Si steel, (b) 2.8 wt% Si steel. $\varphi 2$= 45° sections of the ODFs (Bunge notation). Measured on the middle plane of the sheet by x-ray diffraction [9, 11].

After cold rolling (Figure 2), the textures are considerably strengthened and both steels show a strong rotated cube and a moderate γ-fibre (with peaks at {111}<110>), although the initial textures are quite different. The High Si steel illustrates a much higher intensity than the Low Si steel. Both steels show a weak rotated Goss texture (which is not seen in the steels before cold rolling), and the Low Si steel exhibits a higher intensity (1.8) than the High Si steel (0.92). This might be due to the rotation of other orientations to the rotated Goss or due to grain fragmentation during cold rolling. There is also a small difference in the α-fibre: the Low Si steel shows a relatively strong {112}<110>, while the High Si steel has a relatively strong {111}<110>. Thus, although the silicon contents and the initial textures of the two steels are quite different, the overall textures (measured on the middle plane of the sheet) after cold rolling are quite similar, which are typical textures of bcc metals after conventional cold rolling.

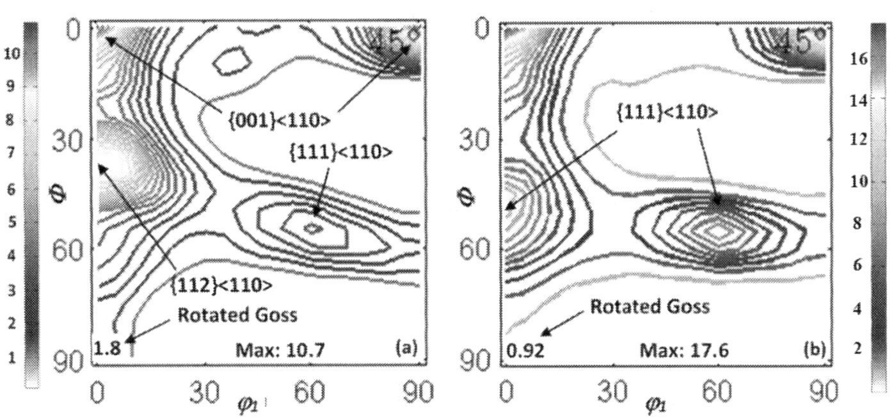

Figure 2. The textures of the steels after cold rolling: (a) 0.88 wt% Si steel, (b) 2.8 wt% Si steel. $\varphi 2$= 45° sections of the ODF (Bunge notation). Measured on the middle plane of the sheet by x-ray diffraction [9, 11].

Although the middle-plane texture did not show a strong rotated Goss texture in either steel, cross-section EBSD scans revealed that rotated Goss grains are frequently observed in both steels (Figures 3a and 3c). Finer scans on these regions (Figures 3b and 3d) indicate that, within the rotated Goss grains, there are numerous shear bands. The formation of the shear bands is due to the plastic instability caused by heterogenous deformation within the grains, which changes the local deformation geometry and results in smaller deformation resistance than under homogeneous conditions [10]. Crystal plasticity simulations [8, 10] showed that rotated Goss has the largest Taylor factor under plane-strain compression, which has a high tendency to form shear bands during rolling. The shear bands are usually inclined at 20°-30° to the rolling direction. Nevertheless, as can be seen from Figures 3b and 3d, the orientation of the rotated Goss grains (matrix) essentially remains, thus the intensity of the rotated Goss texture increases after cold rolling, despite the formation of a large amount of shear bands in these grains.

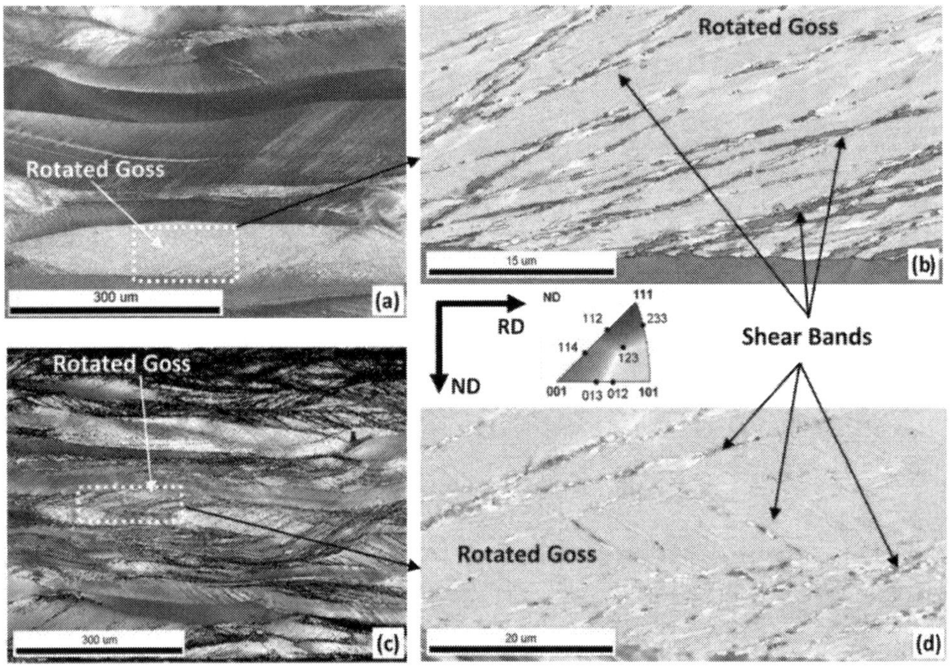

Figure 3. Cross-section (RD-ND) EBSD inverse pole figure maps of the steel sheets: (a) and (c) through thickness scans, (b) and (d) finer scans of the 0.88 wt% and 2.80 wt% Si steels showing the rotated Goss grains and the shear bands formed within them.

As shown in Figure 4, within the shear bands formed in the rotated Goss grains, numerous crystallites with cube orientation (within 15°) are noticed. Although it is not completely known how exactly the cube crystallites are formed within these shear bands during cold deformation, crystal plasticity simulations (considering simple shear on conventional crystallographic slip systems as the deformation mode) indicate that the cube orientation has the largest Taylor factor under simple shear [10] and is the most stable orientation within the shear bands of rotated Goss [8]. Thus, they tend to be retained after shear banding. Regions of these cube crystallites may have lower stored energy than their neighboring areas (e.g., due to the release of stress within the shear bands or dynamic recovery [10]) and tend to serve as the initial cube nuclei for the subsequent recrystallization process. During annealing, the cube nuclei may grow into the neighboring areas with higher stored energy and form recrystallized cube crystals (Figure 5a). The cube grains may continue to grow during the later stages of recrystallization and form a final cube texture in the annealed microstructure (Figure 5b).

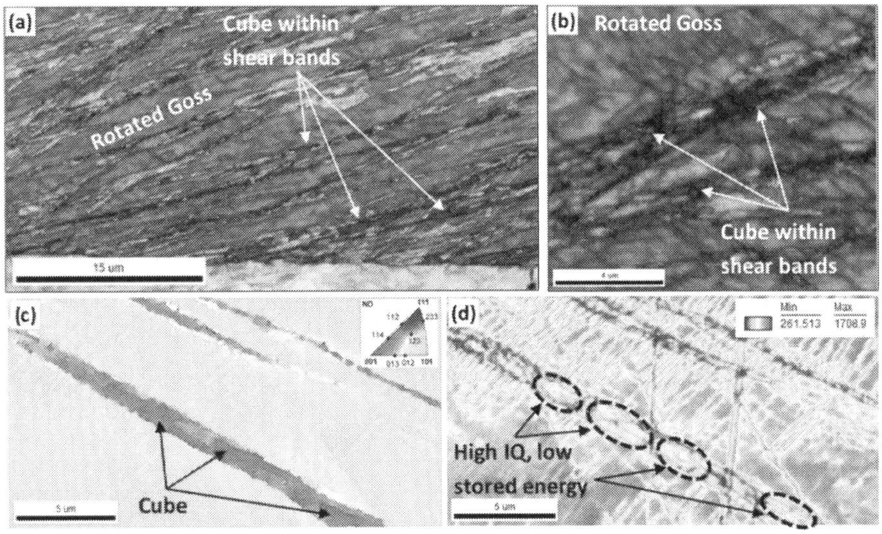

Figure 4. Cube crystallites within shear bands in rotated Goss grains: (a) 0.88 wt% Si, (b) 2.8 wt% Si steel, (c) enlarged view of a shear band in the 2.8 wt% Si steel, (d) image quality (IQ) map of (c) showing the different IQ values within the shear bands.

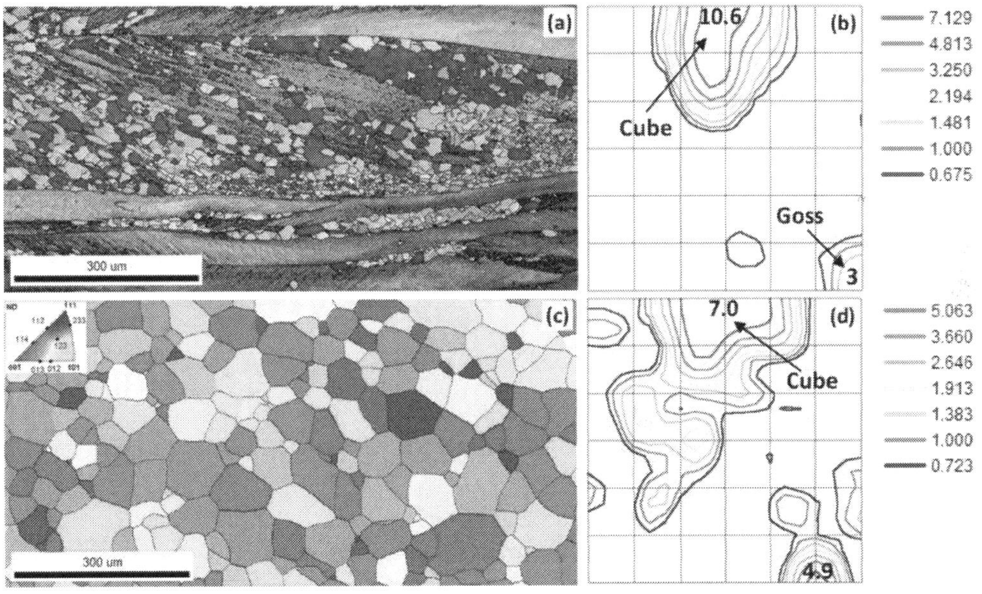

Figure 5. Recrystallization textures of the incline-rolled electrical steels: (a) image quality map of the 0.88 wt% Si steel after annealing at 650 °C for 5 min showing the cube recrystallized grains (red), (b) texture of the recrystallized grains in (a), (c) inverse pole figure map of the 2.80 wt% Si steel after annealing at 750 °C for 60 min, (d) texture of (c).

From the above analysis, it is seen that the final cube grains in the recrystallized microstructure originate from the deformed microstructure, i.e., cube crystallites formed within the shear bands of the rotated Goss grains during incline cold rolling. It has also been reported by other authors that the cube nuclei could originate from cube deformation bands and shear bands [6], or from the deformed matrix with specific orientations such as {411}<148> [7]. The growth of the cube nuclei, as reported by Takajo et al. [7], was due to the high angle boundaries around the cube colony which have high mobility during grain growth. The high mobility of these boundaries depends on the temperature, thus only under specific annealing temperatures, i.e., up to 750 °C, the cube can grow faster than other grains and form the final cube texture. This is also observed in this study, as the annealing of the 2.8 wt% Si steel at 750 °C produced the desired cube texture (Figure 5b).

4. Conclusions

Two non-oriented electrical steels with different silicon contents were cold rolled with the cold rolling direction inclined at 60° to the hot rolling direction, which produced rotated Goss grains that are rare in conventionally rolled steel. The cold rolling of the rotated Goss grains produced numerous shear bands from which the cube nuclei originated. These cube nuclei may have lower stored energy than their neighboring areas, enabling them to preferentially grow and form a final cube texture in the annealed steels.

Acknowledgements

Funding of this research was provided by the Program of Energy Research and Development (PERD), Natural Resources Canada, and by Natural Sciences and Engineering Research Council of Canada (NSERC). Michael Attard is thanked for cold rolling of the steel. Renata Zavadil and Jian Li are gratefully acknowledged for their assistance in EBSD measurements.

References

[1] Lyudkovsky G, Rastogi P K and Bala M, Nonoriented electrical steels, 1986 *JOM* **38** 18-26
[2] Moses A J, Electrical steels: past, present and future developments, 1990 *IEEE Proc A: Phys Sci, Meas Instrum Manage Educ* **137** 233-45
[3] Park J T and Szpunar J A, Evolution of recrystallization texture in nonoriented electrical steels, 2003 *Acta Mater* **51** 3037-51
[4] Kestens L and Jacobs S, Texture control during the manufacturing of non-oriented electrical steels, 2008 *Texture, Stress, Microstruct* Article ID 173083 1-9
[5] Goss N P, Electrical sheet and method and apparatus for its manufacture and test. 1934 *US Patent* #965,559
[6] Sha Y, Sun C, Zhang F, Patel D, Chen X, Kalidindi S and Zuo L, Strong cube recrystallization texture in silicon steel by twin-roll casting process, 2014 *Acta Mater* **76** 106-17
[7] Takajo S, Merriman C C, Vogel S C and Field D P, In-situ EBSD study on the cube texture evolution in 3 wt% si steel complemented by ex-situ EBSD experiment—from nucleation to grain growth, 2019 *Acta Mater* **166** 100-12
[8] Nguyen-Minh T, Sidor J J, Petrov R H and Kestens L A I, Occurrence of shear bands in rotated Goss ({110} <110>) orientations of metals with bcc crystal structure, 2012 *Scr Mater* **67** 935–38
[9] He Y, Hilinski E and Li J, Texture evolution of a non-oriented electrical steel cold rolled at directions different from the hot rolling direction, 2015 *Metall Mater Trans A* **46** 5350-65
[10] Mehdi M, He Y, Hilinski E J, Kestens L A I and Edrisy A, The evolution of cube ({001} <100>) texture in non-oriented electrical steel, 2020 *Acta Mater* **185** 540-54
[11] He Y and Hilinski E, Texture and magnetic properties of non-oriented electrical steels processed by an unconventional cold rolling scheme, 2016 *J Magn Magn Mater* **405** 337-52
[12] Ridha A A and Hutchinson W B, Recrystallization mechanisms and the origin of cube texture in copper, 1982 *Acta Metall* **30** 1929-39
[13] Shah V, Krugla M, Offerman S E, Sietsma J and Hanlon D N, Effect of silicon, manganese and heating rate on the ferrite recrystallization kinetics, 2020 *ISIJ Inter* **60** 1312-23

IOP Conf. Series: Materials Science and Engineering 1121 (2021) 012016 doi:10.1088/1757-899X/1121/1/012016

Effects of Fe, Si, and Cu on Recrystallization Behavior in High Purity Aluminum Foil

T YAMANOI

Aluminum Rolled Products Division, SHOWA DENKO K.K., Sakai, Osaka, Japan

Abstract. The correlation between the recrystallization behavior of high purity aluminum foil, which is used as the electrode material of electrolytic capacitors, and the influence of Fe, Si, and Cu contents on the formation of recrystallization texture was systematically investigated. The following results were obtained: (1) Room-temperature recrystallization, which occurs during cold rolling of the highest-purity material, was suppressed by adding approximately 10 mass ppm of Fe, Si, and Cu. The effect was strongest for Cu, followed by that for Si and Fe. (2) The main component of texture after the final heat treatment changed in the order {001}<100>→ {011}<411>→ {126}<411>→ {123}<412> as the purity of the aluminum foil decreased. In particular, {126}<411> was an characteristic orientation for extremely coarse grains and was considered to have originated from the rolling texture (β-fiber). This coarse grain growth was considered to be related to the decrease in the growth rate of the recrystallized grains depending on the purity of the matrix.

1. Introduction

In the high purity aluminum foil in electrolytic capacitors, which is one of the main applications of high purity aluminum foil, the control of grain size and texture in terms of electrostatic capacity and bending strength is one of the objectives of material design. Fe, Si, and Cu content is known to influence this phenomenon [1][2][3], but the effects on recrystallization behavior in very small amounts of other elements have not been identified. In this study, a considerable amount of coarse grains, which are obtained at temperatures slightly above room temperature, was observed. The study aimed to investigate the respective effects of Fe, Si, and Cu on recrystallization behavior and to clarify its growth process.

2. Experimental Procedures

2.1. Samples

The chemical composition of the sample used in this study is shown in Table 1. The sample preparation process is shown in Fig. 1. Samples was casting in book molds for aluminum slabs. The sample was hot-rolled at a starting temperature of 793 K and air-cooled afterwards. Samples that were heat-treated after hot rolling were dipped in the salt bath at 723 K, held for 600 s, and water-cooled immediately afterwards. The rolling reduction ratio between each pass was maintained within the range of 30±10% during the cold rolling and the temperature of the sample was kept from rising.

2.2. Observation and analysis method

The microstructure was observed using a polarizing microscope, after the sample had been polished with emery paper, buffed, and anodized through treatment with Barker's solution. The hardening and softening behaviors of the specimens that exhibited recrystallization were evaluated using Vickers hardness and tensile tests. Texture was analysed via pole figure measurement using X-ray diffraction (XRD) and via electron backscattered diffraction (EBSD) measurement using FE-SEM.

IOP Conf. Series: Materials Science and Engineering 1121 (2021) 012016 doi:10.1088/1757-899X/1121/1/012016

Table 1. Chemical compositions of the specimens (mass ppm)

	Si	Fe	Cu	Al
A1	2	1	2	Bal.
A2	2	1	11	Bal.
A3	10	1	2	Bal.
A4	2	12	2	Bal.
A5	11	12	2	Bal.
A6	1	21	2	Bal.
A7	10	10	10	Bal.
A8	9	10	15	Bal.
A9	10	11	24	Bal.
A10	12	11	49	Bal.
A11	2	52	2	Bal.

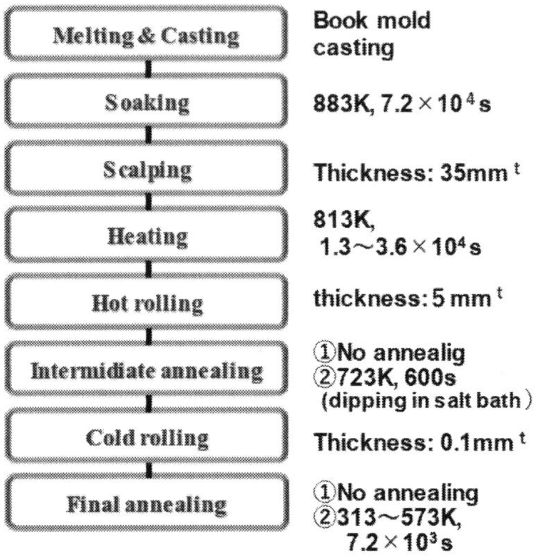

Fig. 1. Production and experimental process of samples.

3. Experimental Results

3.1. Softening behavior during cold rolling

Some of the samples in this study recrystallized during cold rolling. For example, Fig. 2 shows the microstructure and {111} pole figure after the cold rolling of the A1 composition sample in Table 1. Figure 2 shows a microstructure whose recrystallization is almost complete and the pole figure has a very sharp cube texture.

Figure 3 shows the results obtained upon evaluating the hardening after cold rolling to 0.1 mm thickness using Vickers hardness test. In the sample shown in Fig. 3, elements other than the composition concentration plotted on the abscissa are equal to or less than 2 mass ppm, indicating the influence of Fe, Si, and Cu only. Figure 3 shows that Cu content inhibits softening by only 5 atom ppm (11 mass ppm) in aluminum in the no-annealing sample after hot rolling, and that the inhibiting effect in the order of Si and Fe is attenuated. Figure 3(b) shows that Vickers hardness for cold-rolled foils annealed after hot rolled sheets increased holistically compared to that of the no-annealed foils. This is attributable to the reduction of the initial dislocation density by the annealing of the hot-rolled sheets, and the insufficiency of the total strain for recovery and recrystallization during cold rolling. However, no tendency was observed in the A4, A6, and A11 samples containing Fe only. Further, the order of Vickers hardness of foils was reversed in no-annealing and annealing samples of the hot rolled sheets containing a large amount of Fe. Researchers in a previous study on work softening in the system added only Fe to a high purity aluminum base [4]; therefore, the lattice defects may have disappeared as a result of the precipitation of Al-Fe intermetallic compounds on lattice defects such as dislocation cells, subgrain boundaries, and recrystallized grain boundaries. Based on these results, Fe is considered to slightly contribute to the increase in the recrystallization temperature for matrix aluminum, and acceleration of recrystallization by precipitation during heat treatment is thought to have an impact on this phenomenon. [5]

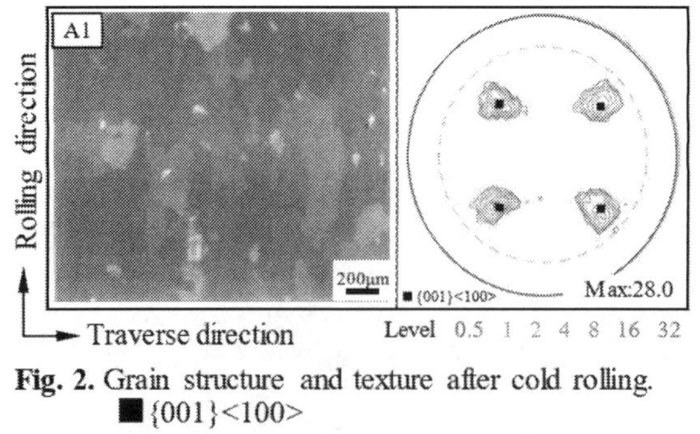

Fig. 2. Grain structure and texture after cold rolling. ■{001}<100>

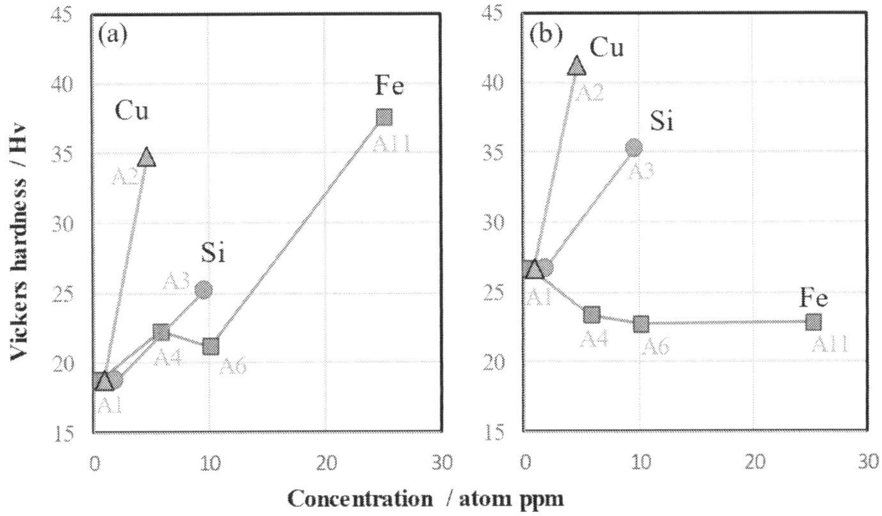

Fig. 3. Vickers hardness of foils after cold rolling, fabricated at (a) no annealing and annealing at 723 K after hot rolling, as a function of atomic content.

3.2. Effect of Fe, Si, and Cu on microstructure after final heat treatment

Figure 4 shows the microstructure and the {111}pole figure when the cold-rolled foils (0.1 mm thickness) were heated at 473 K without heating of the hot-rolled sheets.

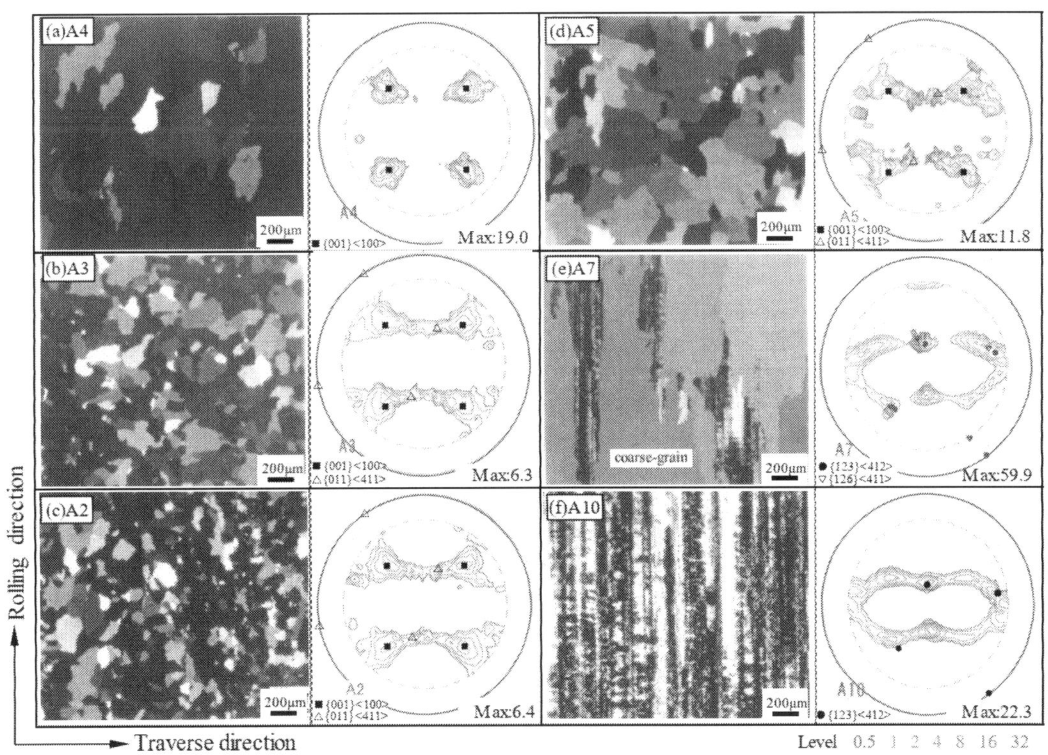

Fig. 4. Effect of Fe, Si, and Cu on grain structure and texture after final annealing. No annealing after hot rolling, final annealing conditions: 473 K × 7.2 ks

■{001}<100> ●{123}<412> △{011}<411> ▽{126}<411>

Figures 4(a), (b), and (c) show that the Fe, Si, and Cu contents had individual effects on the microstructure and texture respectively. Figure 4(a)A4 exhibited a remarkably well-developed cube texture {001}<100>. However, the main orientations of Figs. 4(b)A3 and (c)A2 were not only cube texture but also the orientation components near {011}<411>, which were intermediate between the Goss {011}<100> and brass {011}<211> orientations. Before final annealing, Fig. 4(b) represented the partial recrystallization, Fig. 4(c) represented the working structure, and the result illustrated in Fig. 3 was considered. In the case of Figs. 4(b) and (c), the growth of the cubic texture {001}<100> was suppressed; thus, the orientation developed from the rolling texture (s-orientation [6]: β-fiber [7]).
Figures 4(d), (e), and (f) show the effect of the amount of Cu at the approximately 10 mass ppm level of both Si and Fe. In sample Fig. 4(d)A5 (Cu: 2 mass ppm), relatively coarse recrystallized grains with a crystal grain size of more than 200 μm developed almost uniformly. The pole figure confirmed the existence of the cube texture {001}<100> and an almost {011}<411> texture was observed in Figs. 4 (b), (c). Next, mixed structures of extremely coarse recrystallized grains (hereafter referred to as huge grains) and un-recrystallized regions, which extended in the rolling direction of sample (e)A7 (Cu: 10 mass ppm). Based on the texture analysis, this huge grain was considered to be an orientation component near {126}<411>. This orientation was also identified in Fig. 4(d), so was considered to be not typical to Fig. 4(e). Further, the rolling texture of the un-recrystallized region was represented by the {123}<412> orientation. Finally, in Fig. 4(f)A10 (Cu: 49 mass ppm), recrystallized grains were not observed and huge grains were not also observed. In addition, rolling texture was determined based on pole figure analysis. As shown in Figs. 4(d), (e), and (f), the grain growth rate in recrystallization was considered to be related to the growth of the huge grains in Fig. 4(e) owing to a certain amount addition of Cu content. Additionally, in the samples of A8 (Cu: 15 mass ppm), huge grains were observed as Fig. 4(e), and huge grains were not observed in the sample of A9 (Cu: 24 mass ppm). Therefore, the upper threshold of Cu contents at which huge grains were expressed in this study was considered to range between 15 and 24 mass ppm.

4. Discussion

From the pole figure analysis shown in Fig. 4, the influence of Fe, Si, and Cu only on the formation of cube texture in the final annealing increased in the order of Fe <Si<Cu, and the preferred orientation of texture changed from {001}<100> to {001}<100> + {011}<411>. Moreover, in the estimated 10 mass ppm samples of Si and Fe, the preferred orientation changed from {001}<100> to {123}<412>, which is thought to have stemmed from the rolling texture (β-fiber), and grain growth was remarkably high in the process.
Figure 5 shows the tension softening curves of samples with different contents of Cu, and approximately 10 mass ppm level of Si and Fe contents. This image shows that softening began to increase in speed at 333 K in the samples of A5 and 433 K in the samples of A7. To investigate the orientation relationship between recrystallized grains and the surrounding matrix, samples of (x)A5 (annealed at 343 K for 4.2 ks) and samples of (y)A7 (annealed at 443 K for 7.2 ks) were produced, and EBSD analysis was carried out. The results are shown in Fig. 5. The IPF MAP, KAM MAP, and ODF were applied to the respective samples through EBSD analysis.
First, recrystallization was considered to be completed in the blue region where deviation of crystal orientation from adjacent regions was very small from KAM MAP, and the grains and orientations were confirmed from IPF MAP. Then, the region where the recrystallization was considered to be proceeding to the surrounding matrix was selected (inside the square frame in Fig. 6), and finally, ODF analysis in this region was carried out.

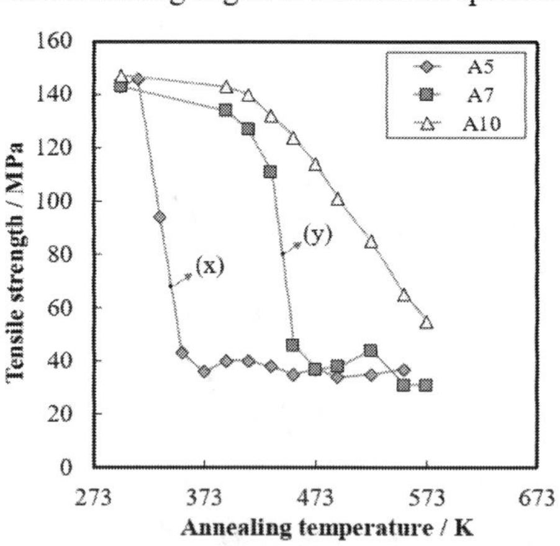

Fig. 5. Tension softening curves of high purity aluminum foil with varying Cu content.
(x)A5: after 343 K × 7.2 ks annealing
(y)A7: after 443 K × 7.2 ks annealing

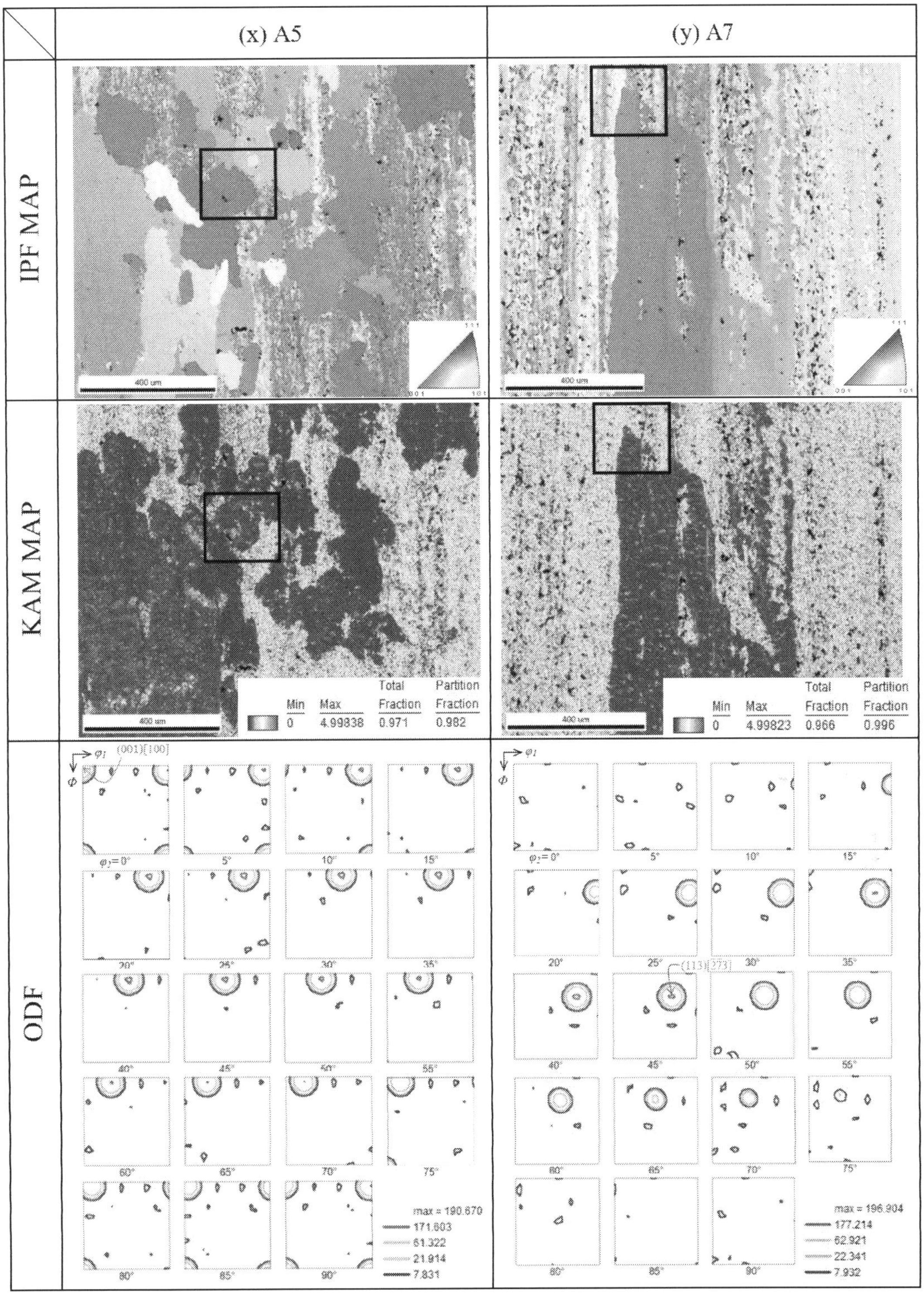

Fig. 6. Typical inverse pole figure map (IPF MAP), kernel average misorientation map (KAM MAP), and orientation distribution function (ODF) of coarse-grained specimens. (x) A5: after 343 K × 7.2 ks annealing, (y) A7: after 443 K × 7.2 ks annealing

IOP Conf. Series: Materials Science and Engineering 1121 (2021) 012016 doi:10.1088/1757-899X/1121/1/012016

Based on the ODF analysis shown in Figure 6, the preferred orientation of the recrystallized grain in sample (x) was {001}<100> and {113}<273> in sample (y). Figure 7 shows the angles between the face azimuth obtained from the region adjacent to the recrystallized grain and the face azimuth of the recrystallized grain. Figure 7 shows that the deviation angle of the crystal orientation with recrystallized grains adjacent to recrystallized grain {011}<100> of sample (x) was relatively small from approximately 4° to 27°. And the deviation angle of the crystal orientation from the adjacent un-recrystallized region was approximately 21° to 74°, which was large, albeit with some variation. Next the region adjacent to the {113}<273> grains of sample (y) was the un-recrystallized region in the observation range, and the deviation angle of the crystal orientation was mainly within the range of 35° to 45°.

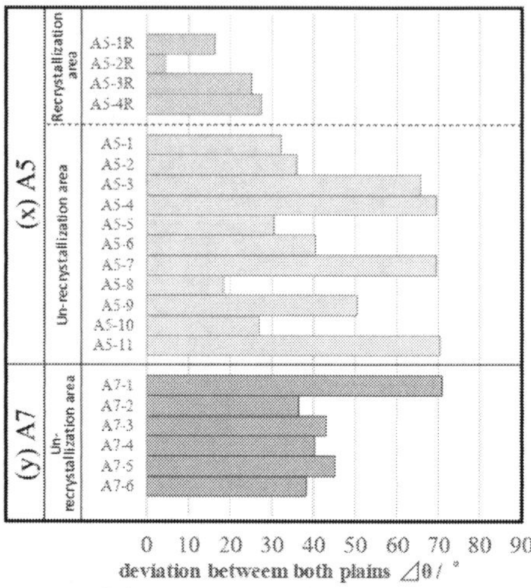

Fig. 7. Angle between crystal orientation planes between the un-recrystallized region adjacent to recrystallized grains, and the recrystallized grains.

In this analysis, the identification of common axes of rotation showing a coincidence relationship [8] in the region with the deviation angle in Fig. 7 was not accomplished. However, in sample (y), wherein remarkably grain growth had occurred, the un-recrystallized region showed a clear anisotropy of crystal orientation and development of the huge grains in the rolling direction. Therefore, it was inferred that the preferred grain growth had occurred.

5. Conclusion

In this study, high purity aluminum foils with varying Fe, Si, and Cu contents and processes were analyzed using the XRD/pole figure and the SEM/EBSP method. Based on the results, we discussed the influence of Fe, Si, and Cu content on the formation of a coarse grain texture. The results are summarized as follows:

(1) Room-temperature recrystallization, which occurs during the cold rolling of the highest-purity material, was suppressed by adding several ppm of Fe, Si, and Cu. The effect was strongest for Cu, followed by Si and Fe.

(2) The main component of texture after the final heat treatment changed in the order {001}<100>→{011}<411>→{126}<411>→{123}<412> as the purity of aluminum foil decreased.

(3) In this study, extremely coarse recrystallized grains were observed in samples wherein the Si and Fe contents were both approximately 10 mass ppm and the Cu content was within a certain range. The preferred orientations of these huge grains were {126}<412>, {113}<273>, etc., which were inferred to be the preferred growth from the rolling texture (β-fiber).

Acknowledgments

The author would like to thank Dr. M. Sakaguchi for the opportunity to begin this study, and Prof. H. Inoue for their advice on the measurement and analysis of texture. This study was supported by SHOWA DENKO K.K. and their members.

References

[1] Miki I and Warlimonto H 1968 *Z. Metallkde.* **59** 408-414
[2] Henmi Z and Nagai T 1967 *J. Japan Inst. Metals* **31** 329-333
[3] Nagahama K and Miki I 1970 *J. Japan Inst. Light Metals* **20** 137-144
[4] Ohno Y and Nakamura H 1977 *Aluminium* **53** 539-542
[5] Sakaguchi M, Yamanoi T and Hasegawa M 1987 *Z. Metallkde.* **78** 80-86
[6] Inoue H 2015 *Mater. Trans.* **56** 61-69
[7] Inoue H 2001 *Materia Japan* **40** 589-591
[8] Kronberg M L and Wilson F H 1949 *Metals trans.* **185** 501-514

Texture evolutions in aluminum and Al-3%Mg alloy subjected to shear deformation and subsequent annealing

Yoshimasa Takayama[1], Yihe Xu[2], Tsuyoshi Yoshida[2], Hiroki Tanaka[3], Yusuke Onuki[4] and Shigeo Sato[5]

[1]Department of Mechanical and Intelligent Engineering, Graduate School of Regional Development and Creativity, Utsunomiya University, 7-1-2 Yoto, Utsunomiya, Tochigi 321-8585, Japan

2Graduate Student, Utsunomiya University, Japan

[3]UACJ Corporation, 1-7-2 Otemachi, Chiyoda-ku, Tokyo, Japan

[4]Frontier Research Center for Applied Atomic Sciences, Ibaraki University, 162-1, Shirakata, Tokai, Naka, Ibaraki, 319-1106, Japan.

[5]Graduate School of Science and Engineering, Ibaraki University, 4-12-1 Nakanarusawa, Hitachi, Ibaraki 316-8511, Japan

E-mail: takayama@cc.utsunomiya-u.ac.jp

Abstract. Shear deformation is imposed on materials by several advanced techniques for microstructural and textural control. Shear texture evolved during deformation tends to remain after subsequent annealing. Texture evolutions with shear deformation and subsequent annealing in aluminum and Al-3mass%Mg alloy rolled sheets have been investigated by neutron diffraction technique. N-shaped specimen was prepared from the alloy sheet to impose shear strain in compression. The central objective part of the N-shaped specimen was sheared with slight rotation about the normal axis so as to develop preferred orientations of {111} parallel to the original shear plane and <110> parallel to the original shear direction before deformation. In-situ neutron diffraction analysis during step heating revealed that the preferred orientations formed by shear deformation remain and evolve as recrystallization texture during subsequent annealing in both materials. Evolutions of shear and recrystallization textures were compared after shear deformations with strains of 0.5 and 0.7 in two samples sheared parallel to rolling and transverse directions.

1. Introduction

Crystallographic textures often appeared in materials subjected to severe plastic deformation, because extremely large strain should be accompanied with necessary directional priority in slip deformation. The texture evolution during equal channel angular pressing (ECAP) by only the two shear systems {111}<110> and {001}<110> ({shear plane}<shear direction>) in an Al-Zn-Mg-Cu alloy having a strong initial texture was reported [1]. To an aluminum single crystal ECAP was applied with consistence of theoretical shear plane and direction to crystal slip system [2], and moreover, a crystal plasticity finite element method model showed the textural change with the lattice rotation around the transverse axis of ECAP angle [3]. These imply correspondence of microscopic shear system with macroscopic shear deformation.

Sakai *et al.*[4] pointed out that the shear texture developed by the shear rolling had a broad one spreading around the typical shear components after annealing. Shi *et al.* [5, 6] reported that the shear texture formed in the commercial purity titanium sheet subjected to a friction roll surface processing (FRSP), which was proposed as an SPD process for the surface of the sheet materials in order to control microstructure and texture, remained preferential after annealing.

A part of present authors investigated preferred orientation formation with shear deformation and annealing in Al-3mass%Mg alloy rolled by SEM/EBSD technique [7]. It was reported that grain orientation with its slip plane parallel to shear one or its slip direction parallel to shear one tends to evolved through shear deformation and subsequent annealing, and moreover, orientation E_{TD} {111}<110> grew up remarkably in annealing after shear deformation.

The aim of the present study is to examine and compare texture evolutions with shear deformation and subsequent annealing in aluminum and Al-3mass%Mg alloy rolled sheets by neutron diffraction technique.

2. Experimental procedure

Commercial purity aluminum (1050) and Al-3mass%Mg alloy sheets of 6mm thick were manufactured through casting, homoginization, hot and cold rolling, and annealing. Chemical compositions of the materials are listed in Table 1. N-shaped specimen as shown in Fig. 1 was cut from the sheet with its longitudinal direction parallel to rolling or transverse direction (RD or TD) for the compressive shear test. A central neck part was sheared by compressing the specimen in vertical or longitudinal direction during the test after annealing at 653K for 3.6ks in Ar and scanning electron microscope/ back scatter diffraction (SEM/EBSD) analysis. The neutron diffraction measurement was conducted at iMATERIA, 20th beamline at J-PARCMLF [5]. The texture was analyzed by Materials Analysis Using Diffraction (MAUD) software. Shear strain was calculated from change in relative positions of Vickers hardness indents, which had been sited on the neck part as 15mm square lattice of four fiducial markers before the test.

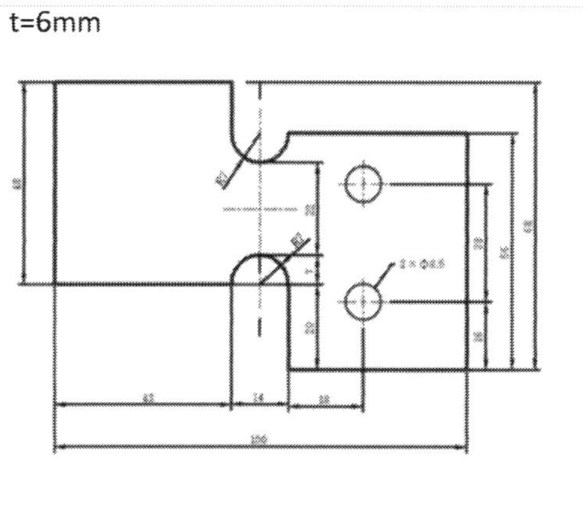

Fig. 1 N-shaped specimen.

Table 1 Chemical compositions of materials used (mass%).

Material	Si	Fe	Cu	Mn	Mg	Cr	Zn	Ti	Others	Al
CP aluminum	0.01	0.02	<0.01	<0.01	<0.01	<0.01	<0.01	0.01	<0.01	Bal
Al-3%Mg	0.01	0.02	<0.01	<0.01	2.95	<0.01	<0.01	0.01	<0.01	Bal

After indentation of the markers, the N-shaped specimen with the right side fixed by two bolts was compressed with left side in the vertical direction. By the compression, the central part of the N-shaped specimen was sheared at an ambient temperature to a given shear strain of 0.5 or 0.7. Rectangular specimens for the neutron diffraction of 7× 20× 6 mm^3 were cut out by electric discharge method from the central part.

The neutron diffraction measurement was made with the heat-treatment below after the shear. The specimen face with marker indentation was set to be perpendicular to an incident beam and its longitudinal direction was set to be parallel to vertical direction. The surface temperature of the specimen was measured by the thermocouple. Two specimens were step-heated from 260 °C to 360 °C by 20 °C Al-3%Mg alloy and from 220 °C to 320 °C by 20 °C for CP aluminium (1050Al). The holding time was 960s in each stage of temperature.

3. Experimental results and discussion

The Al-3%Mg alloy was confirmed to show a typical rolling recrystallization texture before shear deformation, that is, as received specimen. The major components were S orientation {123}<634> and Cube orientation {001}<100>. The neutron diffraction measurement was conducted as starting materials with the initial texture of rolling recrystallization.

3.1. Analysis of the Al-3%Mg alloy pole figure which sheared TD

(111), (200) and (220) pole figures before heating, 280°C, 320°C and 360°C in TD sheared specimen, are displayed in Fig. 2. The vertical direction of the figure is TD, and a horizontal direction is RD. Texture at an ambient temperature before the heat-treatment is a deformation texture formed by shear. In the texture before the heating, S orientation {123}<634> and Cube orientation {001}<100> seem to rotate about the ND axis. In addition, the texture component in which normal direction of (111) is parallel to RD direction gradually increases as temperature rises up. Because a plane (111) was slip one for fcc structure, the component in which shear plane and direction consistent with slip plane and direction, respectively developed by recrystallization. Further, the (110) pole figure revealed that a texture component of <110> parallel to a slip direction, <110>//TD somewhat grew up also.

3.2. Analysis of the Al-3%Mg alloy pole figure which sheared RD

Figure 3 illustrates (111), (200) and (220) pole figures before heating, 280°C, 320°C and 360°C in RD sheared specimen. Before heating, ND-rotated S {123}<634> and Cube {001}<100> orientations are observed. However, as shown in (111) pole figure, the highest concentration is found in the other direction than TD or RD, which is different from a result of the TD sheared specimen. In the RD shear specimen, S and Cube orientations exist in an initial state, an orientation with priority on slip deformation is formed, that is, easily deformed. In other words, preferred orientation formation naturally depends on the initial texture component before the shear deformation. In (110) pole figure the highest concentration of preferred orientation is seen near the original TD. However, the concentration is weakened as temperature rises.

3.3. Comparison with EBSD analysis of Al-3%Mg

The preferred orientation formation in Al-3%Mg was examined by SEM/EBSD [7]. Preferred orientation evolution was investigated from the EBSD data. The shear textures <111>⊥TD$_O$ and <110>//TD$_O$, which mean that slip plane and direction are consistent with shear plane and direction, respectively, evolved considerably to fractions of 19.3% and 23.0% after shear deformation in the specimen subjected to TD-compressive shear test. The fractions of the shear texture increase markedly during step heating and reach 27.4% and 44.2% at 607K. On the other hand, in RD-compressive shear specimen the shear textures on RD, <111>⊥RD$_O$ and <110>//RD$_O$, do not evolve remarkably. The fractions after shear deformation are only 10.2% and 15.7%, and moreover, less than 10% after the heating at 607K.

The difference in the preferred orientation formation between TD-shear and RD-shear tests by SEM/EBSD is similar to that by the neutron diffraction in the present study. This reveals that the

IOP Conf. Series: Materials Science and Engineering 1121 (2021) 012017 doi:10.1088/1757-899X/1121/1/012017

preferred orientation generated by shear deformation evolves more through subsequent annealing not only in the surface layer but also in whole bulk specimen.

3.4. Comparison analysis with the result of CP aluminum1050Al

The preferred orientation development in CP aluminium refers to rotation about ND of S and Cube orientations in CP aluminum specimen as well as in Al-3%Mg one. CP aluminum indicated clearer formation of the preferred orientation (Fig. 4) compared with in Al-3%Mg because of higher stacking fault energy leading to easy cross slip. On the other hand, as for the Al-3%Mg alloy, the preferred orientation developed markedly compared with in CP aluminium. This is attributed to larger strain stored and subsequent annealing.

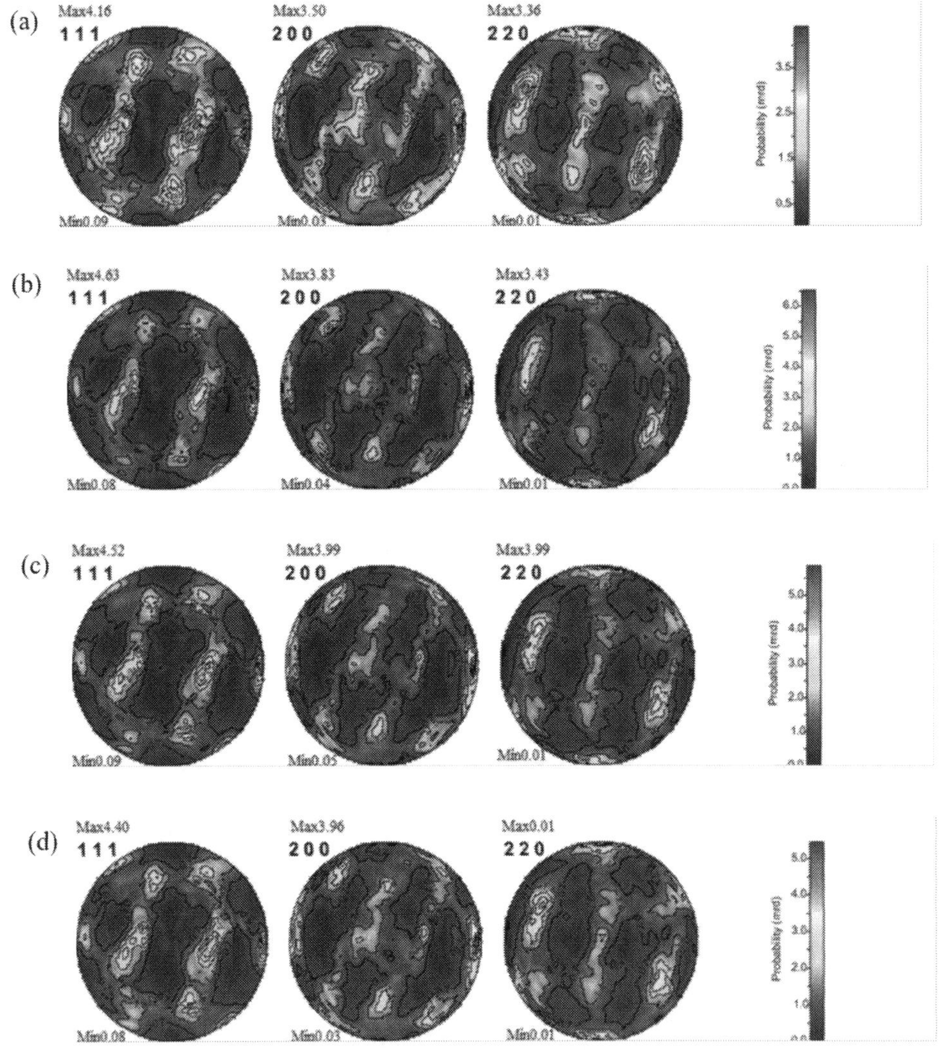

Fig. 2 Pole figures in TD specimen of Al-3%Mg alloy subjected to shear and subsequent step heating: (a) before heating, (b) heating at 280°C, (c) 320°C and (d) 360°C.

IOP Conf. Series: Materials Science and Engineering 1121 (2021) 012017 doi:10.1088/1757-899X/1121/1/012017

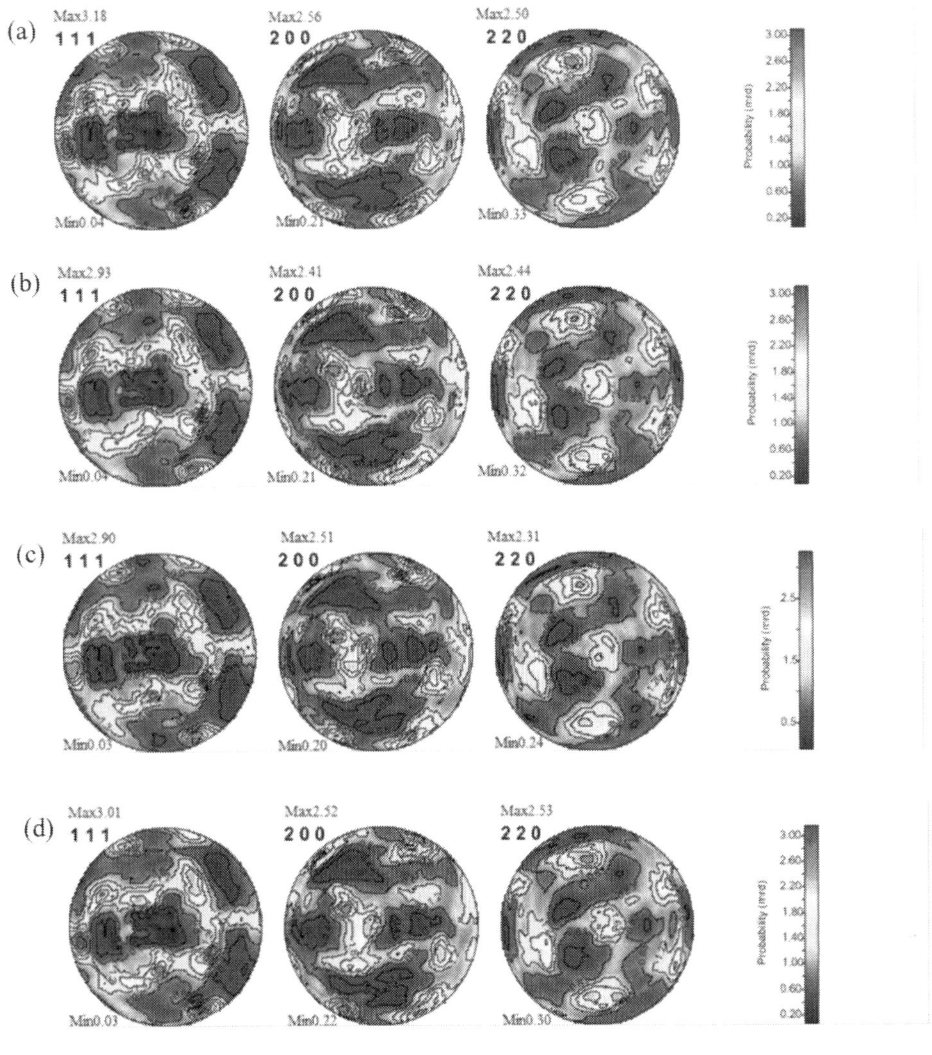

Fig. 3 Pole figures in RD specimen of Al-3%Mg alloy subjected to shear and subsequent step heating: (a) before heating, (b) heating at 240°C, (c) 280°C and (d) 320°C.

4. Conclusions

In the present study, preferred orientation formation with shear deformation and annealing in CP aluminum and Al-3mass%Mg alloy rolled sheet has been investigated by neutron diffraction. The obtained results are summarized as follows:

1. In the Al -3% Mg alloy and 1050 aluminum alloy, preferred orientations <111>⊥TDO and <110>//TDO were formed by shear in two specimens of TD shear and the RD shear, and developed by recrystallization.
2. It is revealed that TD shear led to the remarkable formation of the preferred orientations by the comparison of TD shear and the RD shear to depend on the initial rolling texture.

3. The difference in the preferred orientation formation between TD-shear and RD-shear tests by SEM/EBSD is similar to that by the neutron diffraction.

4. CP aluminum indicated clearer formation of the preferred orientation (Fig. 4) compared with in Al-3%Mg.

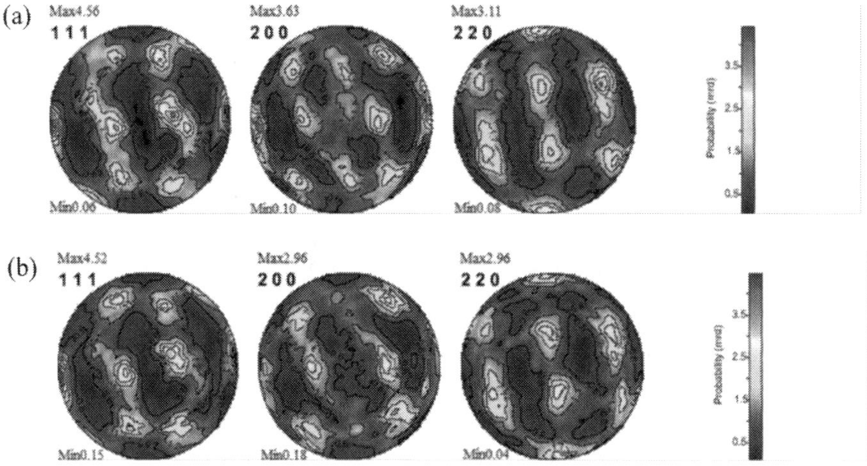

Fig. 4 Pole figures in TD specimen of CP aluminum subjected to shear and subsequent step heating: (a) before heating and (b) heating at 320°C.

References

[1] Wang S C, Starink M J, Gao N, Qiao X G, Xu C, Langdon T G 2008 *Acta Mater.* **56** 3800-3809
[2] Fukuda Y, Oh-ishi K, Furukawa M, Horita Z, Langdon T G 2004 *Acta Mater.* **52** 1387-1395
[3] Lu C, Deng G Y, Tieu A K, Su L H, Zhu H T, Liu X H 2011 *Acta Mater.* **59** 3581-3592
[4] Sakai T, Hamada S and Saito Y 2001 *Scripta Mater.* **44** 2569-2573
[5] Shi M, Takayama Y, Umetsu T, Kato H, Watanabe H, Inoue H 2009 *Mater. Trans.* **50** 210-214
[6] Shi M, Takayama Y, Ma C, Watanabe H, Inoue H 2012 *Trans. Nonferrous Met. Soc. China* **22** 2616–2627
[7] Takayama Y, Kanemaru T, Wachi K and Watanabe H 2018 IOP Conf. Series: Mater. Sci. Eng. **375** 012017 doi:10.1088/1757-899X/375/1/012017
[8] Ishigaki T, Hoshikawa A, Yonemura M, Morishima T, Kamiyama T, Oishi R, Aizawa K, Sakuma T, Tomota Y, Arai M 2009 IBARAKI materials design diffractometer (iMATERIA)—Versatile neutron diffractometer, at J-PARC. Nucl. Instrum. Methods *Phys. Res. Sect. A* **600** 189–191

IOP Conf. Series: Materials Science and Engineering 1121 (2021) 012018 doi:10.1088/1757-899X/1121/1/012018

Strong rotated cube textures in thin cold-rolled potassium-doped tungsten sheets during annealing up to 1300 °C

D Tarras Madsen[1], U M Ciucani[1], A Hoffmann[2], and W Pantleon[1]

[1] Technical University of Denmark, 2800 Kongens Lyngby, Denmark.
[2] PLANSEE SE, 6600 Reutte, Austria.

Email: pawo@dtu.dk

Abstract. Due to the high operation temperatures, microstructural changes will occur in tungsten when used as plasma-facing material in future fusion reactors. In drawn tungsten wires, potassium doping has proven to prevent such undesired changes effectively. This strategy has been adapted to thin cold-rolled tungsten sheets containing 80 ppm potassium. Their texture evolution during annealing is investigated using electron backscatter diffraction. In the as-rolled condition, a strong cube texture is present with a volume fraction of 67.0 % deviating maximal 15° from the rotated cube orientation. This texture intensifies strongly during isochronal annealing for 2 h at temperatures between 1000 °C and 1300 °C; the higher the temperature, the higher the rotated cube fraction. The volume fraction of 94.8 % obtained after 2 h at 1300 °C does not change significantly during further annealing. These are remarkably strong textures for a body-centered cubic metal compared e.g. to commonly reported high volume fractions of 30 % for Goss orientations in silicon steels. Reliable quantification of such strong texture components requires analysis of orientations individually.

1. Introduction

Tungsten is considered for plasma-facing components in future fusion reactors as armor material for the first wall and the divertor. Pure annealed tungsten has a high brittle-to-ductile transition temperature and behaves brittle at room temperature [1] restricting its use as plasma-facing material. On the contrary, plastically deformed tungsten behaves in general more ductile at ambient temperatures and large plastic deformation has been utilized for fabrication of ductile tungsten wires by wire drawing [2]. During operation as plasma-facing component at high temperatures, the deformation structure induced by plastic deformation becomes unstable. Restoration processes as recovery, recrystallization and grain growth will unavoidably alter the microstructure and impair the desired mechanical properties [3]. In particular, recrystallization will reinstate the intrinsic brittleness of tungsten. Several concepts have been pursued to increase the thermal stability of the microstructure or at least to control the microstructural changes by restricting the motion of grain boundaries. Such an impedance of grain boundary motion can be achieved by alloying tungsten with dispersed oxides or carbides pinning the grain boundaries (e.g. [4]). Alternatively, tungsten can be doped with small amounts of potassium; potassium is insoluble in tungsten and forms bubbles in the microstructure hindering grain boundary motion. Doping tungsten with potassium has been successfully applied in manufacturing of heavily drawn tungsten wires [2]. The same strategy has been adapted to commercially rolled tungsten plates. The texture evolution during annealing of cold-rolled tungsten sheets with a comparably high potassium content of 80 ppm is investigated in detail.

2. Materials and techniques

2.1. *Material*
Thin tungsten sheets are provided by PLANSEE SE. The material is doped with 80 ppm potassium – a higher content of potassium than commonly used in WVM (tungsten vacuum metallizing) material. The cold-rolled sheets with bright finish extend 180 x 30 x 0.1 mm^3 along transversal, rolling and normal direction (TD, RD, and ND), respectively. The sheets are cut by electro discharge machining into smaller pieces of 5.5 x 4.5 x 0.1 mm^3. For protection against oxidation and formation of volatile WO_3 during annealing, cut specimens are encapsulated individually in quartz glass ampoules. The ampoules are evacuated, flushed with Argon (with purity higher than 99.999%), evacuated again and sealed with a blowtorch. Specimens in their ampoules are put in a pre-heated ceramic tube furnace NaberTherm RHTC 80/230/15, removed after the desired annealing time and cooled to room temperature by air-cooling. Encapsulated specimens are annealed in an isochronal series for 2 h at different temperatures (800 °C, 1000 °C, 1100 °C and 1300 °C). An additional isothermal series is performed at 1300 °C for longer times (2 h, 24 h, 48 h, 96 h, 168 h, 336 h and 504 h).

2.2. *Microstructural investigation*
Individual specimens are embedded conductively sandwiched between two protective steel plates to avoid delamination. Cross sections containing transversal and normal direction are prepared for electron backscatter diffraction by mechanical grinding (subsequently on SiC-paper of grit sizes 500, 1000, 2000, and 4000) and mechanical polishing (with diamond suspension with grain size 3 μm). Due to delamination issues and severe edge effects caused by electro-polishing, chemo-mechanical polishing by an alkaline colloidal silica suspension (OP-S by Struers ApS) is applied as final step leading to suitable specimen surfaces. Orientation data are gathered by electron backscatter diffraction on freshly prepared cross sections using a Bruker NOVA NanoSEM 600 equipped with a Bruker e-Flash HD EBSD detector applying a voltage of 15 kV. Large, statistically representative maps through the entire thickness are recorded on the cross sections with a step size of 0.1 μm. Without any filtering or removal of non-indexed points, the gathered EBSD data are analyzed using the MTEX toolbox Version 5.5.0 (cf. [5]) and evaluated further by own purposely developed routines.

3. Results

3.1. *Microstructure of the as-rolled condition*
Figure 1 presents orientation maps obtained on the TD/ND section of specimens in the as-rolled condition. The maps are colored according to the crystallographic direction along the rolling direction (figure 1a) and the normal direction (figure 1b). The respective dominating green and red colors, reveal the preference of aligning <110> directions with RD (α-fiber) and <100> directions with ND or, equivalently, {100} planes with the rolling plane (θ-fiber) – both typical fiber texture components after rolling of body-centered cubic (bcc) metals [6]. Only a small number of high angle boundaries are discerned in the orientation maps indicating that only minor orientation differences less than 15° exist between neighboring orientations.

To quantify the texture, the orientation distribution function (ODF) [7] is calculated from all individual orientations in the map using a de la Valle Poussin kernel [5] with a half width of 5°. Figure 2 shows the orientation density with respect to a random distribution of orientations in a section where the Euler angle φ_2 is kept constant to be 45°. The ODF section reveals a strong preference of orientations with Euler angles $(\varphi_1,\Phi,\varphi_2) = (0°,0°,45°)$. This ND rotated cube orientation {100}<011> can be obtained by rotating an ideal cube orientation, (0°,0°,0°) or {100}<001>, around the normal direction by 45°. In figure 2a, one of the typical texture components after rolling of bcc metals [6], the γ-fiber with one of the {111} planes in the rolling plane, seems to be missing entirely. When choosing a different scaling for the orientation density as in figure 2b, the presence of γ-fiber components is confirmed, but only to a very small extend.

IOP Conf. Series: Materials Science and Engineering 1121 (2021) 012018 doi:10.1088/1757-899X/1121/1/012018

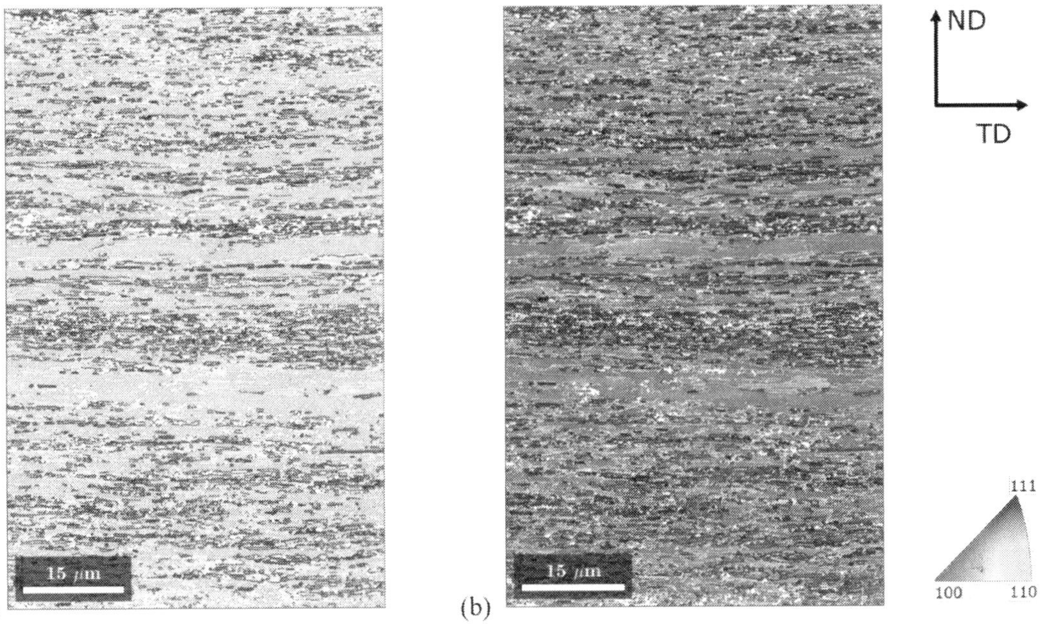

(a) (b)

Figure 1. Orientation maps of the TD/ND cross section of a thin cold-rolled potassium-doped tungsten sheet. The colors reflect the crystallographic directions along (a) the rolling direction and (b) the normal direction according to the inset. High angle boundaries with disorientation angles above 15° are marked in black, low angle boundaries with angles between 2° and 15° in white.

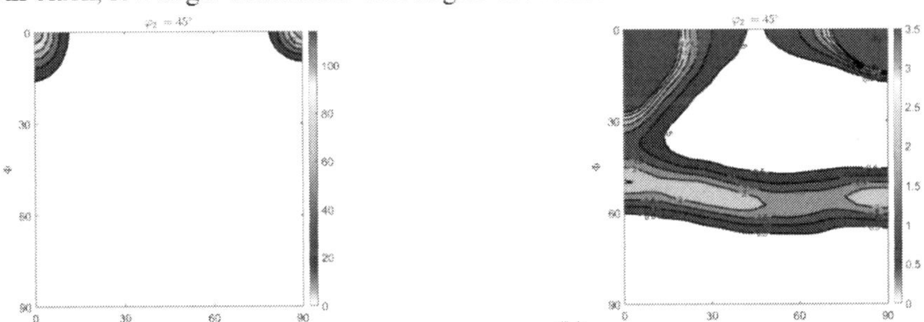

(a) (b)

Figure 2. Orientation distribution function in the section $\varphi_2 = 45°$ of a thin cold-rolled potassium-doped tungsten sheet with different scaling: (a) to the maximum orientation density of 114 and (b) to an orientation density of 3.5. All orientation densities are given in multiples of random distribution.

The texture strength can be quantified by the maximal orientation density, the texture index [7], or the texture entropy [8]. All three measures are listed in table 1. Additionally, the volume fractions for different fiber components typical for cold-rolled metals are determined. The values in table 1 and figure 3 depend on the half width of 5° used for calculating the ODF. Choosing a lower half width will result in even higher orientation density, texture index and fiber volume fractions for sharp textures.

Table 1. Quantitative texture analysis of thin cold-rolled potassium-doped tungsten sheets.

Condition	Max. orient. density	Texture index	Texture entropy	Volume fraction of fibers from ODF / %			Vol. fraction rotated cube / %			
							ODF	from all orientations		
		(for resolution 1°)		α	γ	θ	15°	5°	10°	15°
As-rolled	114	28.6	-2.28	82.4	9.6	72.7	59.8	19.2	51.4	67.0
1300 °C, 2 h	201	68.2	-3.53	95.6	0.3	96.0	87.4	35.6	85.6	94.8
1300 °C, 96 h	194	65.4	-3.44	95.4	2.3	93.1	85.2	34.5	82.0	93.2

Further analysis of the texture is not based on the ODF to avoid artefacts of smoothing by the de la Valle Poussin kernel and its chosen half width. Instead all orientations in the map are tested individually. The deviation of an orientation from the ideal rotated cube orientation is evaluated by its disorientation angle. The volume fraction of the rotated cube component defined as the fraction of indexed points having disorientation angles not exceeding a chosen threshold value is illustrated in figure 4. Allowing larger deviations from the rotated cube orientation, a larger volume fraction is revealed. For threshold angles of 5°, 10° and 15°, volume fractions for the rotated cube of 19.2 %, 51.4 % and 67.0 % are obtained, respectively. This confirms that a strong rotated cube texture is present. For comparison, the corresponding numbers for the rotated cube orientation in a random distribution of orientations are 0.08 %, 0.67 % and 2.27 % [9].

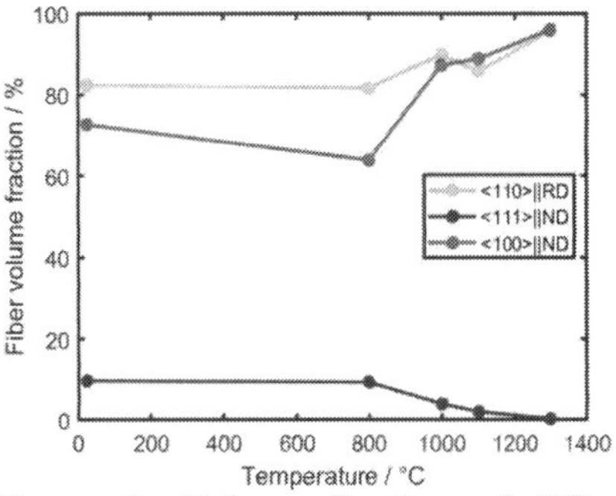

Figure 3. Volume fraction of different fiber texture components in a thin cold-rolled potassium-doped tungsten sheet during isochronal annealing for 2 h at different temperatures.

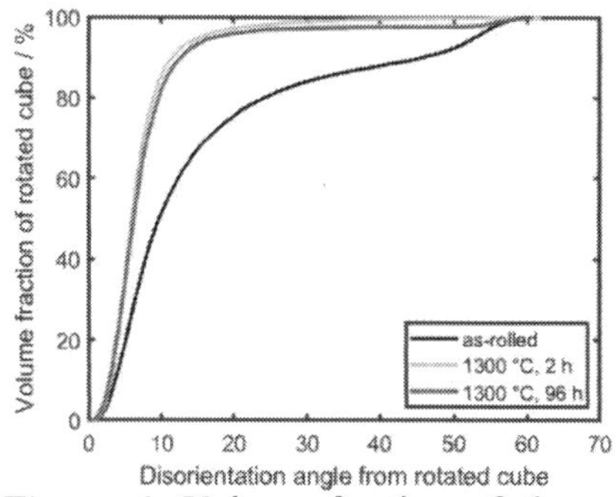

Figure 4. Volume fraction of the rotated cube texture component in dependence on the tolerated disorientation angle from the ideal {100}<011> orientation.

3.2. *Annealed conditions*

Orientation maps after annealing for 2 h and 96 h are shown in figure 5 as an example. The dominance of the red color is even stronger than in the as-rolled condition indicating an even stronger preference for texture components of the θ-fiber. High angle boundaries are even less frequent than in the as-rolled condition. A preliminary texture analysis of the annealed conditions is based on texture index and the volume fraction of the characteristic fibers (as determined from the orientation distribution function). Table 1 reveals that the texture index (obtained with a resolution of 1°), which has a rather large value already in the as-rolled condition, becomes even higher during annealing and the texture sharpens. As seen from figure 3, the low volume fraction of γ-fiber components of about 10 % in the as-rolled condition is reduced by annealing to less than 1 %. This is confirmed by the observation of less blue color in the orientation maps of figure 5 compared to figure 1b – mainly in a single surviving band. The volume fraction of the θ-fiber texture component rises above 80 % at 1000 °C and even 90 % at 1300 °C (cf. figure 3); the strong α-fiber strengthens further. Due to the simultaneous strength of α- and θ-fiber, the most dominating orientation must be the rotated cube orientation {100}<011>.

The strength of the rotated cube component is further evaluated by an analysis of all individual orientations in the maps and their orientation difference from the ideal rotated cube orientation {100}<011>. Taking into account cubic crystalline symmetry, the disorientation angle between each orientation and the ideal rotated cube orientation is calculated. The accumulated probabilities (corresponding to volume fractions) for annealing at 1300 °C for 2 h and 96 h are illustrated in figure 4. For both annealed conditions much sharper distributions are obtained and large deviations from the rotated cube orientation are less likely than in the as-rolled condition. For instance, half of the orientations deviate less than 5.9° or 6.1° from the ideal rotated cube orientation after annealing at 1300 °C for 2 h or 96 h, respectively, compared to 9.7° in the as-rolled state.

The different volume fractions of the rotated cube component obtained on all annealed conditions are illustrated in figure 6 accepting a maximum disorientation angle of 15° from the {100}<011>

orientation. The rotated cube component, which already occupied a high volume fraction of 67.0 % in the as-rolled state, remains almost unaltered upon annealing for 2 h at 800 °C. For annealing for 2 h at higher temperatures, the volume fraction increases with annealing temperature as seen from figure 6a. For the highest investigated temperature of 1300 °C, a volume fraction of 94.8 % is reached after 2 h. During longer annealing at 1300 °C, the volume fraction does not increase further and remains almost constant (cf. figure 6b). Table 1 illustrates the effect of the chosen threshold angle for the allowed deviation from the ideal {100}<011> orientation. Clearly smaller volume fractions are determined, if only smaller disorientation angles are tolerated. Nevertheless quite significant volume fractions are resolved even for low angles as 5° and 10°. The apparent discrepancy of a larger volume fraction for 15° deviation from rotated cube than the θ-fiber volume fractions is explained by the difference in deriving volume fractions directly from individual orientations instead by means of the ODF – the latter leads to too low fractions for the rotated cube component allowing 15° deviation (cf. table 1).

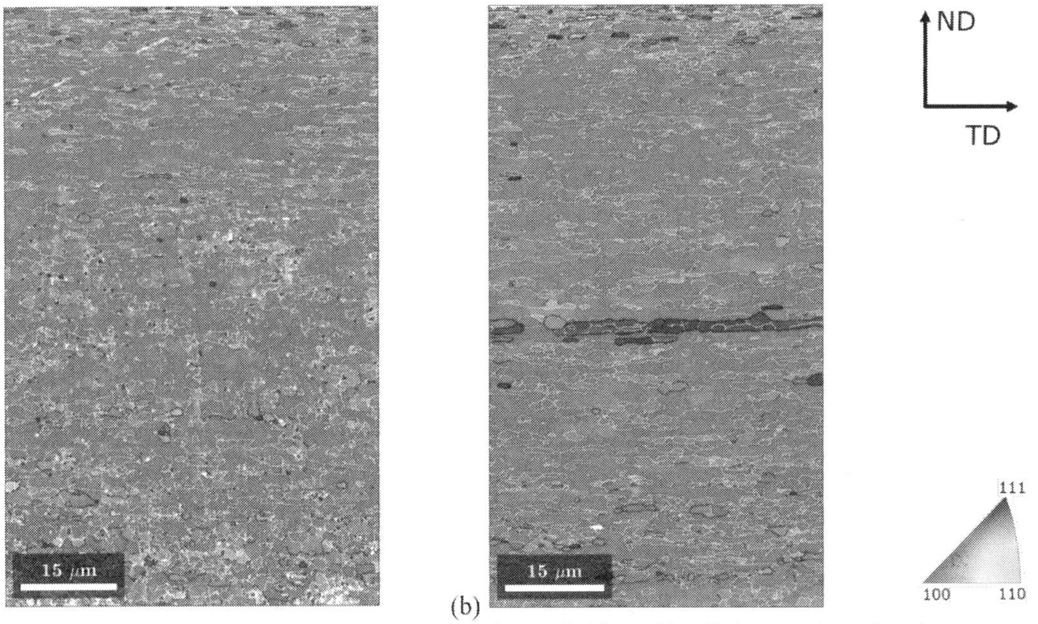

(a) (b)

Figure 5. Orientation maps of TD/ND cross sections of thin cold-rolled potassium-doped tungsten sheets after annealing at 1300 °C for (a) 2 h and (b) 96 h. The colors reflect the crystallographic directions along the normal direction according to the inset. High angle boundaries with disorientation angles above 15° are marked in black, low angle boundaries with angles between 2° and 15° in white.

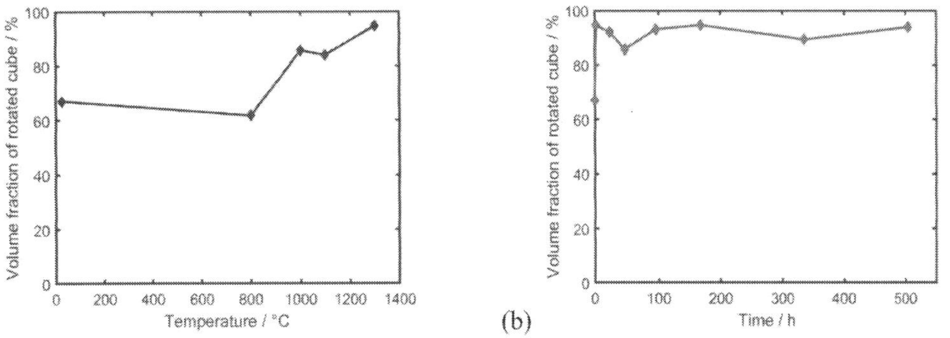

(a) (b)

Figure 6. Volume fraction of the rotated cube texture component (accepting a maximum disorientation angle of 15°) in thin cold-rolled potassium-doped tungsten sheets after annealing: (a) isochronally for 2 h at different temperatures and (b) isothermally for different times at 1300 °C.

4. Discussion

A rather strong rotated cube texture is present in cold-rolled potassium-doped tungsten sheets which increases even further during annealing. During the first 2 h of annealing at a temperature of 1300 °C, grains become slightly larger and less elongated (as seen comparing the boundaries in figures 1b and 5a), nevertheless the appearance of a deformed, yet coarsened microstructure is kept, ruling out primary recrystallization as restauration process. The observed coarsening is driven by elimination of high angle boundaries leaving a network of immobile low angle boundaries behind. The process must be addressed as extended recovery (in accordance with observations [10] that nucleation in bcc metals in the rotated cube component is indolent) and texture strengthening is achieved solely by minor local motion of high angle boundaries. No long-range motion of high angle boundaries is required; hence, the process cannot qualify as primary recrystallization [11].

The texture strength achieved by annealing is remarkable. Usually textures with much lower orientation densities and texture indices are considered strong (e.g. in rolled pure tungsten plates [12]). For face-centered cubic metal, a cube volume fraction of 96 % has been achieved for Ni-W substrates [13], whereas in the classical case for bcc materials, a volume fraction of Goss orientations {110}<001> of 30 % is considered high in hot-rolled silicon steels [14]. These volume fractions are obtained after optimizing the process for the desired texture. This is not attempted here yet and one may expect that even higher volume fractions of rotated cube orientation are achievable.

5. Conclusion

The texture of cold-rolled tungsten sheets with a high potassium content of 80 ppm and its evolution during annealing between 800 °C and 1300 °C is investigated. Electron backscatter diffraction reveals a strong rotated cube texture component (with volume fraction 67.0 %) in the as-rolled state, which strengthens during annealing for 2 h at 1000 °C and above. Annealing at 1300 °C causes a remarkably high volume fraction of 94.8 % not changing significantly with further annealing up to 504 h. All orientations must be considered individually to quantify such strong texture components.

Acknowledgments

This work has been carried out partially within the framework of the EUROfusion Consortium and has received funding from the Euratom research and training programme 2014-2018 and 2019-2020 under grant agreement No 633053. The views and opinions expressed herein do not necessarily reflect those of the European Commission.

References

[1] Lassner E and Schubert W-D 1999 *Tungsten: Properties, Chemistry, Technology of the Element, Alloys, and Chemical Compounds* (New York: Kluwer Academic) p 24
[2] Schade P 2010 *Int. J. Refract. Met. Hard Mater.* **28** 648
[3] Alfonso A, Juul Jensen D, Luo G N, and Pantleon W (2014) *J. Nucl. Mater.* **455** 591
[4] Battabyal M, Schäublin R, Spätig P, and Baluc N 2012 *Mater. Sci. Eng. A.* **538** 53
[5] Bachmann F, Hielscher R, and Schaeben H 2010 *Solid State Phenom.* **160** 63
[6] Kestens L A I and Pirgazi H 2016 *Mater. Sci. Techn.* **32** 1303
[7] Bunge H-J 1982 *Texture Analysis in Materials Science* (Butterworth & Co) p 88
[8] Schaeben H 1988 *J. Appl. Phys.* **64** 2236
[9] Mackenzie J K 1958 *Biometrika* **45** 229
[10] Raabe D, Lücke K 1992 *Scripta Metall. Mater.* **27** 1533
[11] Doherty R D, Hughes D A, Humphreys F J, Jonas J J, Juul Jensen D, Kassner M E, King W E, McNelley T R, McQueen H J, and Rollett A D 1997 *Mater. Sci. Engng. A* **238** 219
[12] Bonnekoh C, Jäntsch U, Hoffmann J, Leiste H, Hartmaier A, Weygand D, Hoffmann A, and Reiser J 2019 *Int. J. Refract. Met. Hard Mater.* **78** 146.
[13] Wulff A C, Mishin O V, and Grivel J-C 2012 *J. Alloy Comp.* **539** 161
[14] Mehdi M, He Y, Hilinski E J, Kestens L A I, and Edrisy A 2019 *steel research intern.* **90** 1800582

IOP Conf. Series: Materials Science and Engineering 1121 (2021) 012019 doi:10.1088/1757-899X/1121/1/012019

Secondary recrystallization in grain-oriented silicon steel

Y Ushigami

Steel Research Laboratories, Nippon Steel Corporation, Futtsu, Japan

E-mail: ushigami.b2y.yoshiyuki@jp.nipponsteel.com

Abstract. Grain-oriented silicon steel is a soft magnetic material widely used for transformer cores. Magnetic properties are closely related to the sharpness of Goss texture, which is evolved by secondary recrystallization. An overview of our results will be presented; secondary recrystallization behaviour has been investigated by in situ observation utilizing synchrotron x-ray topography. The results support the selective growth mechanism. Migration of Goss grains is controlled by inhibitor and sharper Goss grains, which have higher frequency of CSL-boundaries to the matrix, start to grow preferentially while the other grains are stagnated by inhibitor. Secondary recrystallization behaviour can be explained based on this CSL-model. At the initial stage, inhibitor gradient through the thickness promotes Goss selective growth from the subsurface layer and at the later stage, inhibitor drop rate dominates the Goss selective growth. Inhibitor and CSL-boundaries synergistically affect Goss selective growth and Goss grain evolves to a coarse grain.

1. Introduction

Iron-silicon crystal has anisotropy and <001>-axes are easy magnetization directions [1]. Then, magnetic properties of grain-oriented silicon steel basically depend on the sharpness of {110}<001> texture, i.e. Goss texture, which evolves by secondary recrystallization [2].

When grain-oriented silicon steel sheet is annealed at high temperature after the completion of primary recrystallization, Goss grains grow into coarse grains more than 10^3 times larger than matrix grains. This phenomenon is secondary recrystallization. To stabilize secondary recrystallization, fine precipitates called "inhibitor" play an important role to stagnate the grain boundary migration (Figure 1). In the presence of inhibitor, the growth of grains is restrained by the pinning effect in the lower temperature region and at some temperature only Goss grains start to grow into coarse grains, as shown in Figure 2.

Many studies have been performed to clarify the mechanism of secondary recrystallization; why only Goss grains evolve to coarse grains more than 10^3 times larger than matrix grains [3-8]. Models proposed, so far, are classified into two categories; one is based on oriented-nucleation due to size-advantage of Goss colonies [9, 10] and the other based on selective growth due to some special boundaries. Selective growth model is recently evaluated as plausible, because computer simulation [11] and the theoretical analysis [12, 13] suggest that size-advantage is not sufficient to explain secondary recrystallization. And selective growth of Goss grains has been demonstrated [14].

We have investigated the mechanism by in situ observation of secondary recrystallization utilizing synchrotron x-ray topography and have established the secondary recrystallization model.

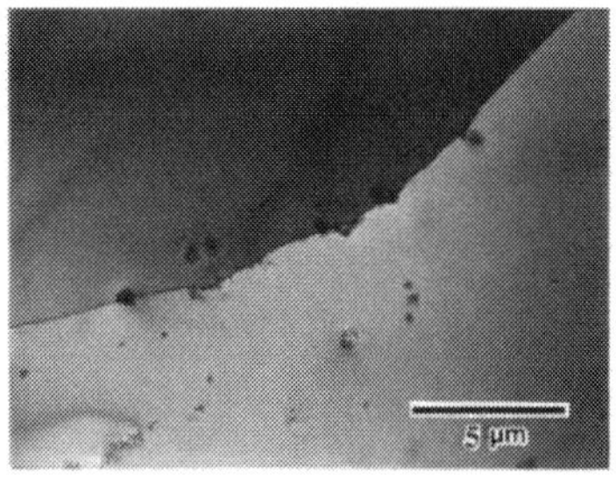

Figure 1. Transmission electron micrograph which shows the pinning effect of precipitates [14].

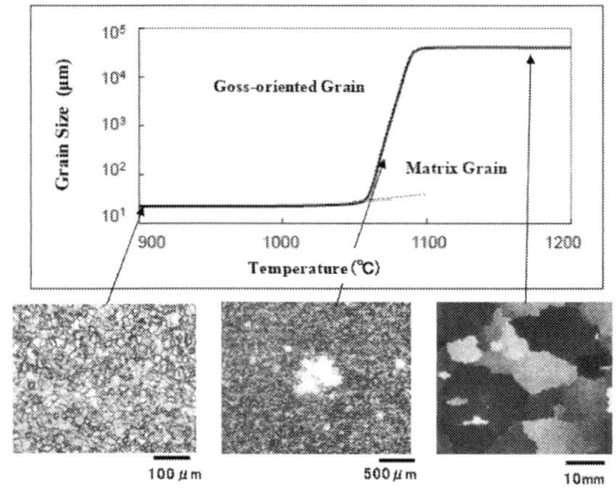

Figure 2. Secondary recrystallization behaviour [15].

2. In-situ observation of secondary recrystallization

2.1. Macroscopic grain growth behaviour of Goss grains [16- 18]

The grain growth behaviour of the two secondary grains, sharp {110}<001> grain and deviated {110}<115> grain, was precisely investigated by in situ observation utilizing synchrotron X-ray topography. As shown in Figure 3, grain growth is classified into three regions, (1) stagnated region: below 980°C (2) transition region: 980~1020°C and (3) steady state region: above 1020°C. Sharp {110}<001> grain starts to grow at 980°C and deviated {110}<115> grain at 1000°C and both grains grow steadily above 1020°C . It can be deduced that sharper {110}<001> grain evolves preferentially in the temperature range from 980°C to 1020°C (transition region).

Figure 4 shows the topographic images of {110}<001> secondary grain annealed in the two temperature regions. Goss secondary grain is divided into several subgrains and their grain growth is basically inhomogeneous. In the steady state region (1040°C), the shape of growing front is smooth and grain grows uniformly. In contrast, the shape of the growing front is jagged and its migration is localized (see arrows in Figure 4(b)) in the transition region (1000°C). This localized grain growth is deduced to be the elementary process of the selective growth of Goss secondary grain based on the grain boundary character. Therefore, orientation relationship between the Goss secondary grain and the localized consumed matrix grains in the transition region was investigated.

2.2. Relationship between Goss grain and consumed matrix grains [17, 18]

Figure 5 shows OIM map of the consumed matrix grains by the localized grain growth. It was found that among the seven consumed grains, two grains, A and C, have a special orientation relationship (near-Σ9 orientation relationship) to the Goss secondary grain.

To confirm this orientation relationship statistically, the frequency of the orientation relationship between the Goss secondary grain and the neighbouring grains was measured and compared with that between the Goss secondary grain and the non-neighbouring grains. If some grains are preferentially consumed by Goss secondary grain, they are depleted in the interface and the ratio, frequency of Goss and neighbouring grains to that of Goss and non-neighbouring grains, should be less than one.

As shown in Figure 6, near-Σ9 boundaries are deficit in the Goss-matrix interface and thus preferential migration of near-Σ9 boundaries is verified. The critical misorientation angle is evaluated to be 10°, which is twice as large as that of Brandon's criterion [19]. The frequency of near-Σ9 boundaries is estimated to be about 15%. The similar phenomenon of the extension of critical misorientation angle of CSL boundaries has been reported in the case of aluminium grain boundary sliding [20].

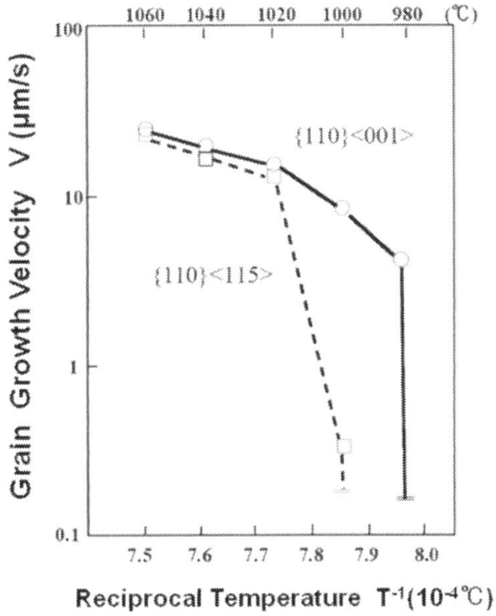

Figure 3. Effect of temperature on grain growth velocity of the two secondary grains; {110}<001> and {110><115> [16, 17].

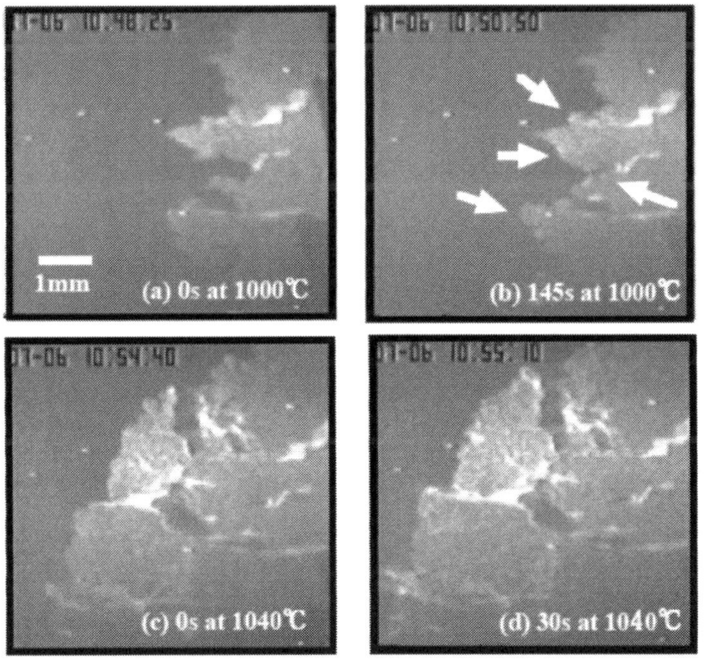

Figure 4. X-ray topographs of {110}<001> secondary grain annealed at two temperature regions [17]. (a), (b): transition region (annealed 145s at1000°C) . Arrows indicate the localized grain growth areas. (c), (d): steady state region (annealed 30s at 1040°C).

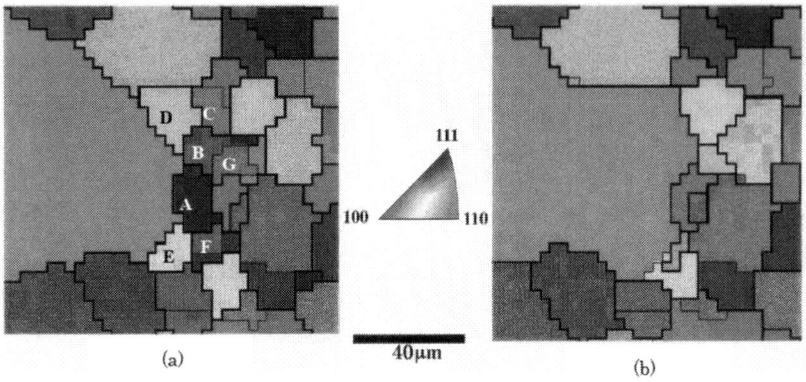

Figure 5. OIM-map of the localized consumed matrix grains in the transition region [17]. (a) before annealing. (b) after annealing.

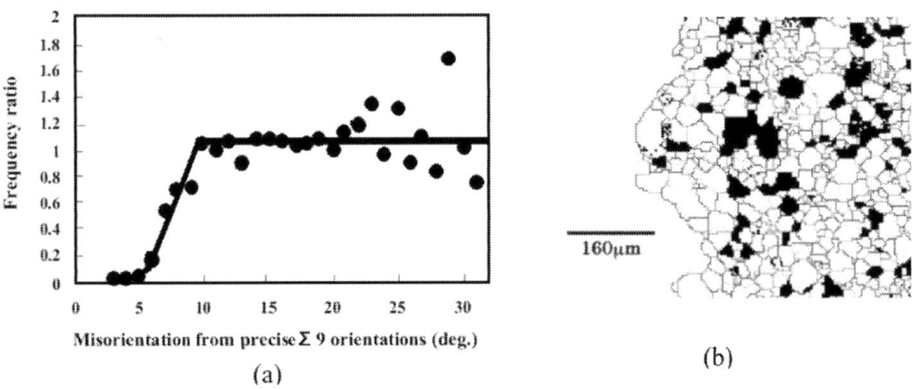

Figure 6. (a) Distribution of frequency ratio of Goss and neighbouring grains to that of Goss and non-neighbouring grains with respect to deviation angle from precise Σ9 orientations [17]. (b) Distribution of near-Σ9 grains in the vicinity of interface (black grains). [18]

2.3. Mechanism of Goss secondary recrystallization : CSL model [17,23]

From these observations, the kinetics of Goss secondary recrystallization is describes as follows; in the lower temperature region, the pinning force derived from the precipitates exceeds the driving force and grain boundary migration is prohibited (stagnated region). As temperature rises, the inhibitor intensity deteriorates by dissolution, ripening and chemical reaction at the surface. In the transition region, the pinning force decreases to the same level of the driving force. CSL boundaries have a periodic structure and have lower grain boundary energy [15] and higher mobility than general boundary. Thus, CSL boundaries are supposed to suffer weaker pinning force from the inhibitor and start to migrate at higher inhibitor level or lower temperature. As shown in Figure 7, CSL boundaries which adjoining Goss grain are unpinned from the inhibitor at first and this triggers the migration of triple junctions of the neighbouring matrix grains. This localized grain growth is the elementally process of the selective growth of Goss secondary grains. In the steady state region, the inhibitor intensity further decreases and general boundaries gradually start to migrate in addition to CSL boundaries, which leads to uniform and stationary grain growth. The frequency of CSL boundaries for {110}<001> grain is higher than that of {110}<115> grain, and then {110}<001> grain starts to grow at lower temperature.

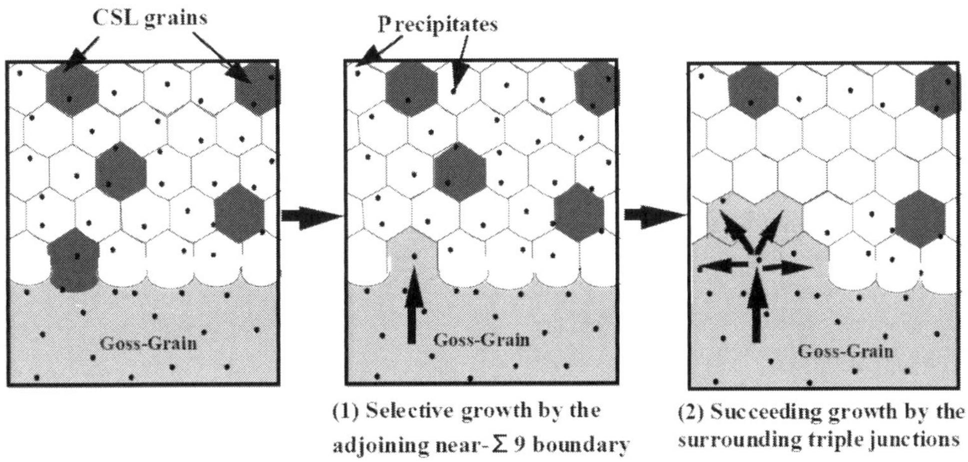

Figure 7. Elementary process of selective growth of Goss secondary grain due to CSL boundaries [17, 23].

3. Theoretical analysis by statistical grain growth model

3.1. Maximum grain size of Goss secondary grains [23, 15]

Kinetics of Goss secondary recrystallization has been theoretically analyzed using a statistical model of grain growth [22]. This model is schematically presented in Figure 8 and assumes the driving force from the matrix grains as the average field (E/R_c) and takes into account the influence of inhibitor and texture (grain boundary energy). Using this model, we have investigated the possibility of Goss grains growing into coarse grains by comparing the growth rate of Goss grain expressed by Equation (1) with that of matrix grains in the steady state expressed by Equation (2).

$$\frac{dR}{dt} = AM\left(\frac{E}{R_C} - \frac{E_G}{R} - \frac{E_G I_Z}{A}\right) \quad (1)$$

$$\frac{dRc}{dt} = \frac{AME}{4Rc}\left(1 - \frac{RcIz}{A}\right)^2 \quad (2)$$

where R is the radius of the individual Goss grain, R_c is the critical radius of the matrix grains, t is time, A is the geometrical factor, M is the mobility, E is the mean grain boundary energy of the matrix grains, E_G is the statistical grain boundary energy between Goss and matrix interface and I_z is the Zener pinning factor.

Secondary recrystallization can be judged by criterion parameter of C, which is the ratio of the relative growth rate of the Goss grain to that of matrix grain, expressed by Equation (3).

$$C = \frac{dR}{R} \bigg/ \frac{dRc}{Rc} \quad (3)$$

Secondary recrystallization occurs when $C > 1$, that is, when the relative growth rate of the Goss grain is greater than that of the matrix grain.

Figure 9 shows an example. It can be seen that secondary recrystallization does not occur ($C < 1$) when only the inhibitor is introduced ($z = 0.5$, $\Delta ke = 1 - ke = 0$). Secondary recrystallization occurs ($C > 1$) when not only the inhibitor but also the peculiarity of the grain boundary energy is introduced ($z = 0.5$, $\Delta ke = 0.2$) and the maximum grain size of Goss secondary grains (u_{max}) can be evaluated, where $u(=R/R_c)$, $z(=I_zR_c)$, $ke(=E_G/E)$ are the normalized grain size, inhibitor, and grain boundary energy, respectively.

Figure 10 shows the effect of inhibitor (z) and grain boundary energy (ke) on maximum grain size (u_{max}). It can be seen that these two parameters synergistically affect secondary recrystallization and it is verified that maximum grain size (u_{max}) can become 10^3 or more when these two parameter increases, which corresponds to (u_{max}) strong inhibitor and high frequency of CSL boundaries.

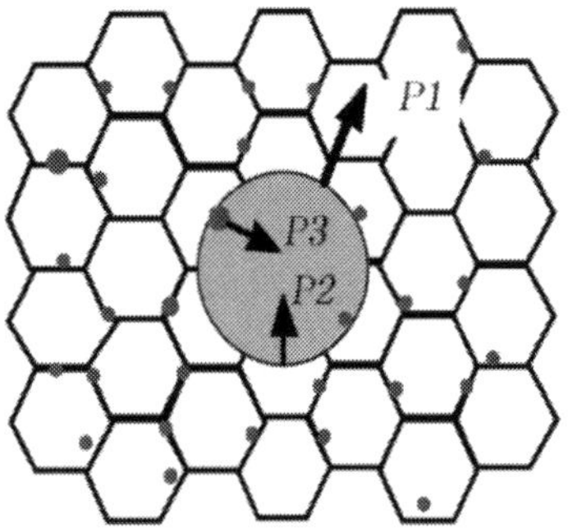

Figure 8. Schematic illustration of microstructure and three forces that affect Goss grain [23, 15].

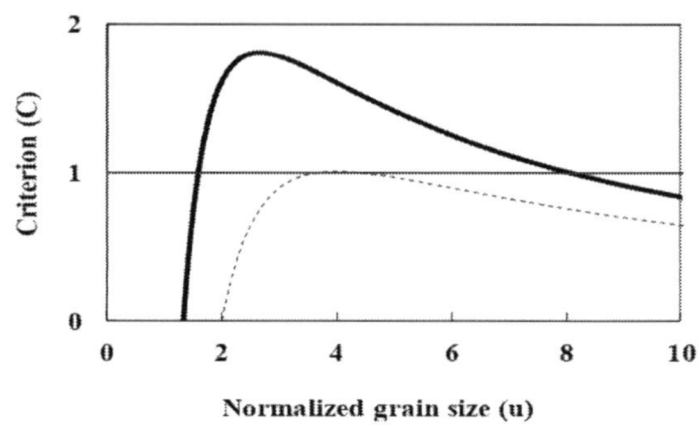

Figure 9. Effect of inhibitor (z) and grain boundary energy (Δke) on criterion parameter of C [23, 15]. dotted line: z=0.5, Δke=0, solid line: z=0.5, Δke =0.2)

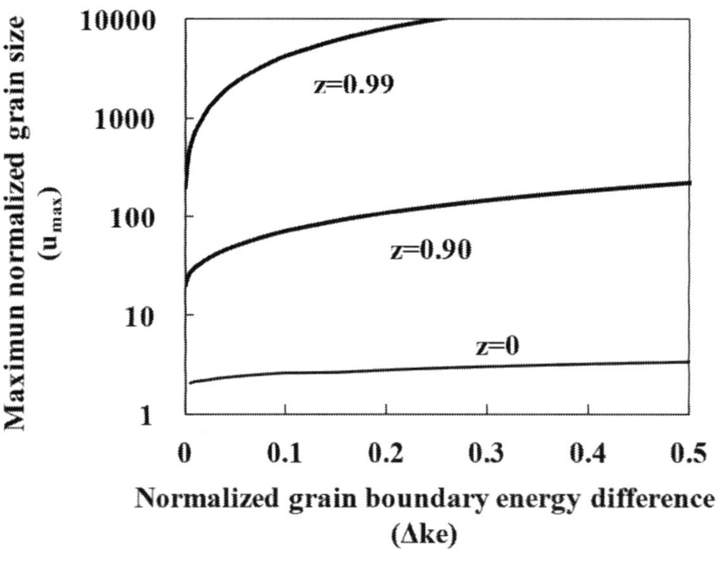

Figure 10. Effect of inhibitor intensity (z) and grain boundary energy (Δke) on maximum normalized grain size (u_{max}) [23, 15].

3.2. Initial stage of Goss secondary recrystallization [24]

In the initial stage of secondary recrystallization, it was reported that Goss grains nucleate at the subsurface layer due to the grain structure [9, 10]. As the matrix grain of the subsurface layer start to grow, Goss grains also grow at subsurface layer and then penetrate thorough the thickness direction due to size-advantage from the view of "oriented nucleation".

In general, Goss secondary grains evolve during the deterioration process of inhibitor and in the initial stage of secondary recrystallization inhibitor intensity decreases from the surface layer [25]. Then, kinetics of the Goss secondary recrystallization in the initial stage is theoretically analyzed by CSL model assuming the inhibitor gradient through the thickness.

Figure 11 schematically illustrates the evolution of Goss grain in the thickness direction. This model assumes that Goss grain, initial grain radius of R_i, grows isotropically from the surface layer into the central layer and then the grain radius is expressed as $R_i+\Delta x$, where x is the distance from the surface. The critical inhibitor intensities that balances the driving force of grain growth was evaluated for the for cases; Goss grain and the matrix grain with the initial grain radius of R_c and $5R_c$ and the effects of texture (grain boundary energy) and initial grain size are investigated.

Figure 12 shows the critical inhibitor levels of the above four cases. When the inhibitor intensity becomes lower than these critical inhibitor levels, the grain can grow. It can be seen that in the subsurface region up to 0.2 of sheet thickness, initial grain size (R_i) dominate the grain growth behavior and larger grains preferentially grow, irrespective of Goss grain and matrix grain. However, in the center region, the effect of texture (Δke) exceeds the size effect and Goss grain can preferentially penetrate the sheet, irrespective of initial grain size.

Assuming the inhibitor gradient through the thickness, CSL model can explain the two-stage grain growth behavior in the thickness direction. Both Goss grain and matrix grain can grow at subsurface layer, but only Goss grains can penetrate into the center layer. In the initial stage of secondary recrystallization, inhibitor gradient through the thickness promotes Goss selective growth.

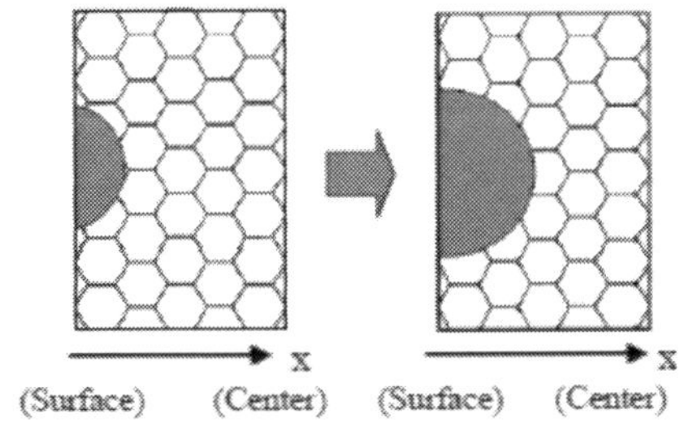

Figure 11. Schematic illustration of the initial stage of Goss secondary recrystallization.
Goss grain evolves from the surface layer due to inhibitor gradient through the thickness [24].

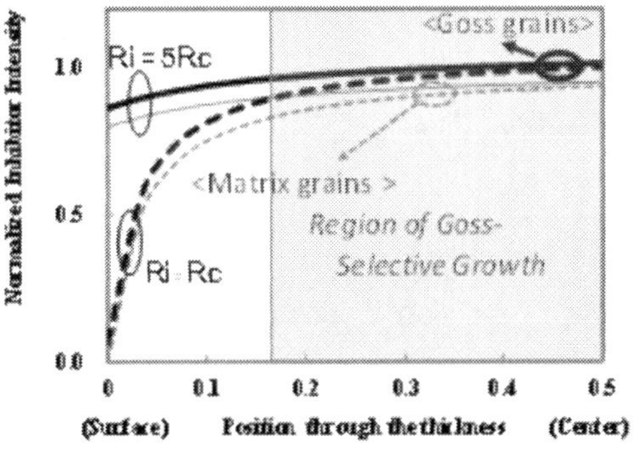

Figure 12. Distributions of critical inhibitor level through the thickness of four cases [24].
(Δke=0.04 for Goss grain, Δke=0 for matrix grain R_i= R_c and 5 R_c, sheet thickness: T=30R_c)

4. Conclusions

Secondary recrystallization behaviour has been investigated by in situ observation utilizing synchrotron x-ray topography and kinetics of Goss secondary recrystallization has been theoretically analyzed using a statistical model of grain growth.

(1) Grain growth of Goss secondary grain is classified into three regions, stagnated region, transition region and steady state region, and sharper Goss grains grow in the transition region. In the transition region, Goss grain preferentially consumes matrix grains which have coincidence site lattice (CSL) relationship.

(2) CSL boundaries are supposed to have lower grain boundary energy than general boundary, thus suffer lower pinning force from the precipitates and unpinned migrate preferentially at higher inhibition level. Sharper Goss grain which has higher frequency of CSL boundaries and grows preferentially at lower temperature.

(4) Characteristics of Goss secondary recrystallization, evolution to coarse grain size and initial grain growth behavior in the thickness direction, have been successfully explained by the statistical model of grain growth.

References

[1] Honda K, Kaya S 1926 *Sci. Rep. Tohoku Univ.* **15** 721
[2] Goss N P 1934 *U.S. Patent No1965559*
[3] May J E, Turnbull D 1958 *Trans. Met. Soc. AIME.* **212** 769
[4] Nakayama T, Ushigami Y 1992 *Mater. Sci. Forum* **94-96** 413
[5] Abbruzzese G, Fortinati S and Campopiano A 1992 *Mater. Sci. Forum* **94-96** 405
[6] Hayakawa Y, Szpunar J A 1997 *Acta Mater.* **45** 1285
[7] Hutchinson B, Homma H 1998 *Proc. 3rd Int. Conf. on Grain Growth* 387
[8] Park H, Kim D, Hwang N, Joo Y, Han C H and Kim J 2004 *J. Appl. Phys.* **95** 5515
[9] Matsuo M, Sakai T, Tanino M, Shindo T and Hayami S 1982 *Proc. 6th Int. Conf. on Textures of Materials* 918
[10] Inokuti Y, Maeda C, Ito Y and Shimanaka H 1982 *Proc. 6th Int. Conf. on Textures of Materials* 948
[11] Srolovitz D J , Anderson M P, Sahni P S and Grest G S 1985 *Acta Metall.* **33** 2233
[12] Nakayama T, Ushigami Y 1986 *Proc. 7th RISO Int. Symp. Met. Mat. Sci.* 463
[13] Thompson C V, Frost H J and Spaepen F 1987 *Acta Metall.* **35** 887
[14] Ushigami Y , Kubota T and Takahashi N 1998 *ISIJ International* **38** 553
[15] Ushigami Y 2013 *Nippon Steel Technical Report* **102** 25
[16] Ushigami Y, Kawasaki K, Nakayama T, Suga Y, Harase J and Takahashi N 1994 *Mater. Sci. Forum* **157-162** 1081
[17] Ushigami Y, Kumano T, Haratani T, Nakamura S, Takebayashi S and Kubota T 2004 *Mater. Sci. Forum* **467-470** 853
[18] Ushigami Y, Nakamura S and Takebayashi S 2010 *Netushori* **50** 179
[19] Brandon D G 1966 *Acta Metal.* **14** 1479
[20] Kohara H, Watanabe T and Karashima S 1981 *Phil. Mag.* **A44** 1239
[21] Haason G C and Goux C 1971 *Scripta Metall.* **38** 889
[22] Hillert M 1965 *Acta Metall.* **13** 227
[23] Ushigami Y, Nakamura S 2012 *Mater. Sci. Forum* **715-716** 122
[24] Ushigami Y, Morishige N and Yamamoto S 2018 *CAMP-ISIJ* **31** 370
[25] Harase J, Shimizu R, Takashima K and Watanabe T 1987 *Trans. ISIJ* 965

IOP Conf. Series: Materials Science and Engineering 1121 (2021) 012020 doi:10.1088/1757-899X/1121/1/012020

Grain growth in soft magnetic ferritic stainless steels under compressive stresses at high temperatures

S. Suzuki[1], Y. Onuki[2], M. Uchida[2], S. Sato[2], T. Naruse[3], M. Watanabe[3], T. Sato[3] and T. Ebata[3]

[1] Micro Integration System Center, Tohoku University, Sendai 980-8577, Japan
[2] Ibaraki University, Hitachi 316-8511, Japan.
[3] Tohoku Steel Co. Ltd., Miyagi 989-1393, Japan

Email: shigeru.suzuki.e6@tohoku.ac.jp

Abstract. Precipitation-hardened ferritic stainless steels are used for soft magnetic actuators of engines, as these steels exhibit high strength and soft magnetic properties. These ferritic stainless steels are hardened by nanoscale precipitates formed during an aging process after solution treatment. Furthermore, texture control of these steels is required in order to improve the soft magnetic properties. Therefore, texture control of ferritic stainless steels with <100> fiber texture by deformation at high temperatures is attempted in this study, as it has been demonstrated that the texture of ferritic Fe-Si alloys is significantly changed by deformation conditions, including temperature and strain rate. The results demonstrate that grains with the <100> fiber texture in the present stainless steels are preferentially evolved by compressive deformation under specific strain rates at high temperatures.

1. Introduction

Soft magnetic stainless steels are widely used as magnetic core materials of solenoid valves in fuel injectors of automobiles because of their excellent soft magnetic and mechanical properties [1–8]. As their hardness (typical Vickers hardness of 85–200 HV) is lower than that required in automobile components (more than 300–350 HV), these materials are subjected to surface hardening treatments, such as hard chromium plating and/or nitriding, for the practical solenoid valves. Therefore, in order to improve the mechanical properties without the surface modification process, precipitation-hardened stainless steels have been developed with alloying elements, such as copper, nickel, titanium, aluminum, and molybdenum [1]. For example, the hardness of Fe–17Cr–4Ni–4Cu stainless steels is increased by nanometer-sized Cu precipitates [2]. In Fe–20Ni–23Co–0.07Al–0.17Ti austenitic steels, the hardening is primarily increased by precipitation of a nanometer-sized Ni_3Ti intermetallic phase in the austenite matrix [3]. A martensitic precipitation-hardened stainless steel containing nickel and aluminum is known to be hardened by fine β-NiAl precipitates [4–8]. However, studies on the application of precipitation-hardened stainless steels as a soft magnetic material have been reported, as exemplified by a precipitation-hardened soft magnetic stainless steel containing alloying elements Ni, Al, and Mo [9]. These steels exhibit high hardness (typical Vickers hardness of 370 HV) with excellent soft magnetic properties coupled with corrosion resistance. The properties are achieved by uniformly-dispersed nanoscale precipitates during adequate aging. Detailed microstructural characterization of the size and number density of the precipitates were performed using small-angle X-ray scattering (SAXS), to determine the factors controlling the mechanical properties of these steels [10].

However, control of the microscopic texture of the steels is also required, in order to improve the soft magnetic properties of these ferritic steels. It is interesting to note that the preferential texture evolution has been controlled in ferritic steel by deformation at high temperatures [11, 12]. In this process, the low density of small angle grain boundaries and a high fraction of <100> oriented grains are achieved by deformation at low strain rates. Therefore, it is interesting to investigate the texture evolution of the <001> and <111> components in the present ferritic stainless steels under different conditions.

2. Experimental

The samples used in this study were a ferritic steel of Fe-14.5Cr-3Ni-2Mo-1Al-1Si (in mass%). The samples for the uniaxial compression deformation test were comprised of a cylinder of φ10 × H15 mm, which is prepared from bars produced by Tohoku Steel Co. Ltd. These samples were compressed under different strain rates at high temperatures between 973 and 1073 K. The microstructure and texture of the samples deformed up to 0.75 in true strain were characterized by analyzing the cross section of the cylindrical samples using electron backscatter diffraction (EBSD). The inverse pole figure (IPF) maps and the volume fractions of <100> and <111> texture components in the sample were primarily investigated in this work. The results of the texture components obtained by EBSD were compared with the process conditions at high temperatures.

3. Results and discussion

3.1. Mechanical properties of soft magnetic stainless steels at high temperatures

Figure 1 shows the true-stress-true-strain curves of the samples deformed under different strain rates at 1073 and 1173 K. These results demonstrate that flow stress is lower at higher deformation temperatures under a constant strain rate; flow stress is lower under lower strain rates at a constant temperature. Furthermore, the dislocation density in the sample appears to be unchanged during deformation, since the curves reveal little work hardening.

In order to discuss the deformation mechanism of the samples at high temperatures, the relationship between the strain rate and true stress of the samples deformed under different conditions are plotted, as shown in Figure 2. The flow stress, σ, is related to the strain rates at high temperatures as follows:

$$\sigma = A\left[\varepsilon \exp\left(\frac{Q}{kT}\right)\right]^{1/n}, \qquad (1)$$

where ε is the strain rate, Q is the activation energy for deformation, k is Boltzmann constant, T is temperature, and n is the stress index. The value of n (stress index) is often utilized in the discussion on the deformation mechanism and dislocation motion at high temperatures [13]. The present value of n is determined from the slope of the plot shown in Figure 2 to be about 3.9 at 1173 K and about 4.9 at 1073 K. It is expected that the deformation process is controlled by phenomena including diffusion of solute atoms or grain boundary sliding in materials, when the value of n approaches 1. However, the high n values in the present cases suggest that the dislocation motion in the matrix is dominant at high temperatures, where accumulating energy by dislocations increases and some deformation texture is formed in the present ferritic steels.

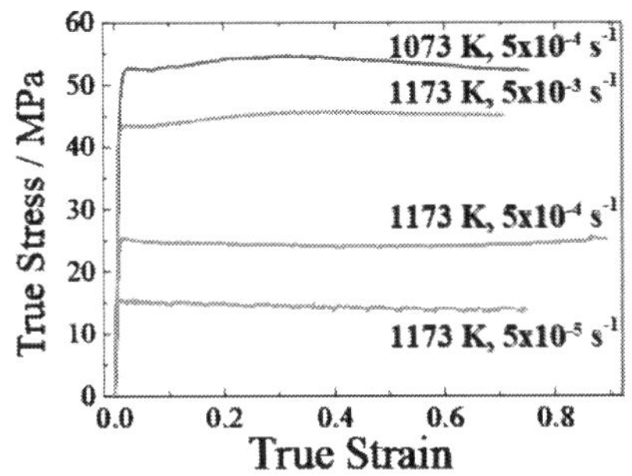

Figure 1. True stress-true strain curves of samples deformed up to 0.75 in true strain under different strain rates at 1073 and 1173 K.

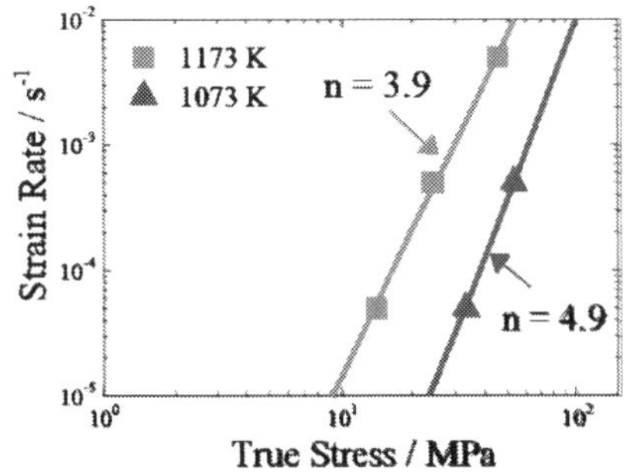

Figure 2. Strain rate versus true stress of samples deformed under different strain rates at 1073 and 1173 K.

3.2. *Texture evolution under different strain rates at high temperatures*

Figures 3 (a), (b), and (c) show IPF maps of the samples compressively deformed up to 0.75 in true strain under 5×10^{-4} s^{-1}, which were deformed at 973 K, 1073 K, and 1173 K, respectively. The results demonstrate that the red region showing the <100> texture component increases and the blue region showing the <111> texture component decreases in the sample deformed at higher temperatures.

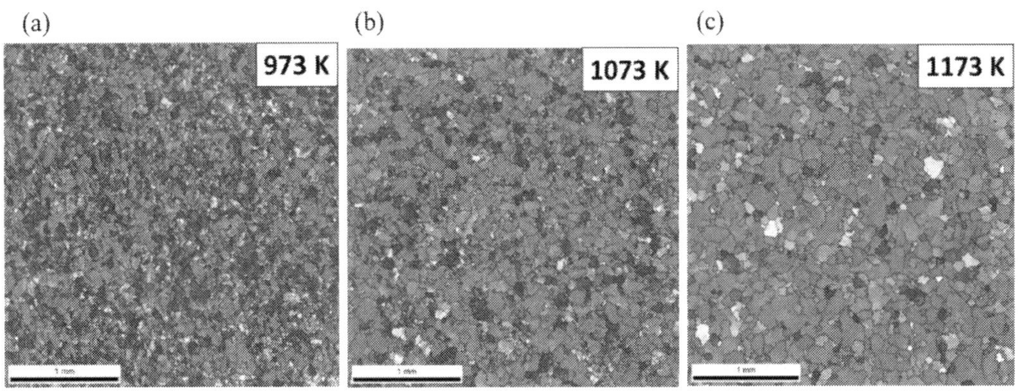

Figure 3. IPF maps of samples deformed by compression under 5×10^{-4} s^{-1}, which were deformed at 973 K (a), 1073 K (b), and 1173 K (c).

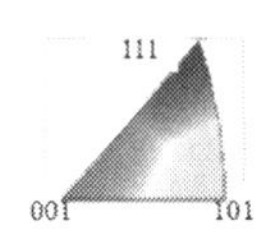

Pole figures of {001} and {111} in the samples compressively deformed under 5×10^{-4} s^{-1} at 973, 1073, and 1173 K are shown in figures 4 (a), (b), and (c), respectively. These results indicate that <100> and <111> texture components in the samples deformed at different temperatures are changed under a constant strain rate. In particular, the volume fraction of the <100> texture component increases and a texture component is formed in the direction perpendicular to compression with increasing deformation temperature. It is noted that the orientation distribution in the circular direction in the pole figures is inhomogeneous, which is thought to result from evolution of an initial texture component due to anisotropic elasticity of ferritic steels at high temperatures.

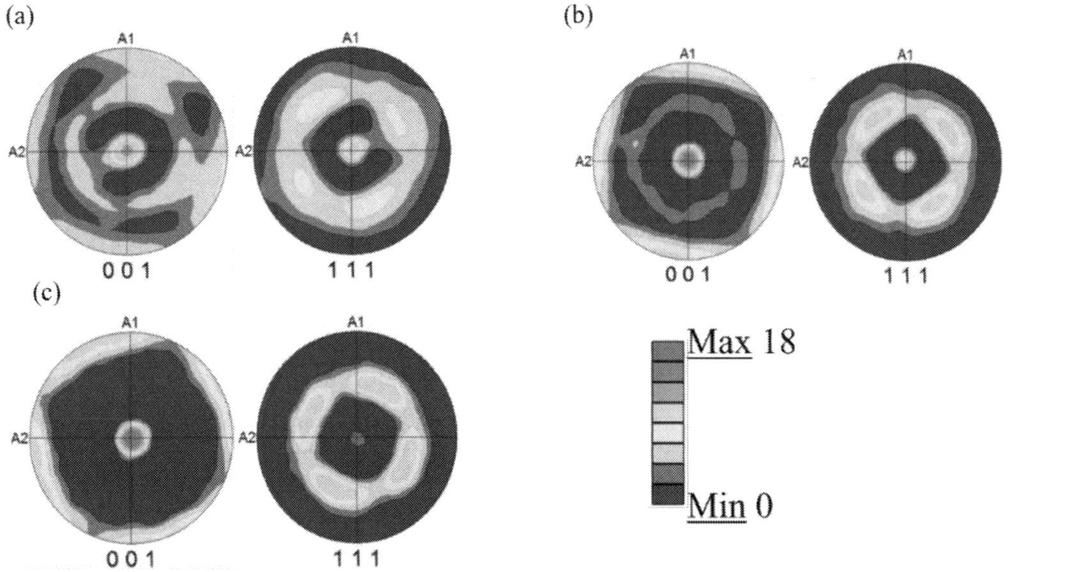

Figure 4. Pole figures of {001} and {111} in the samples compressively deformed under 5×10^{-4} s^{-1} at (a) 973, (b) 1073, and (c) 1173 K.

Figure 5 summarizes the area fraction of the <100> and <111> texture components in the samples deformed under 5×10^{-4} s^{-1} at 973, 1073, and 1173 K. This also indicates that dynamic grain growth occurs at high temperatures, and the texture evolution depends on the deformation conditions at high temperatures.

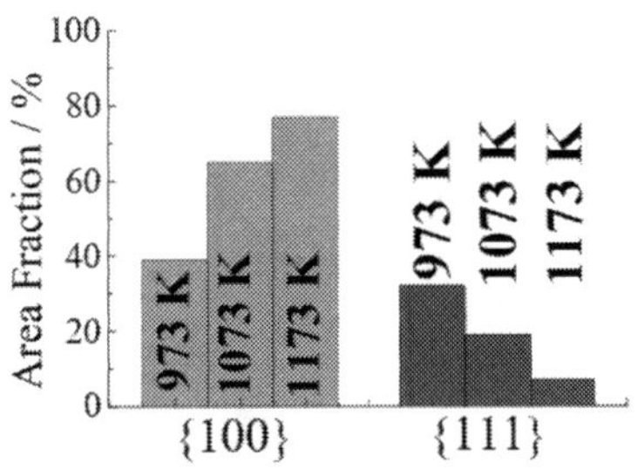

Figure 5. Area fraction of the <100> and <111> texture components in samples deformed under 5×10^{-4} s^{-1} at 973, 1073, and 1173 K.

3.3. Optimum conditions to control the {100} texture

Figures 6 (a), (b), and (c) show IPF maps of the samples compressively deformed under 5×10^{-3} s^{-1}, 5×10^{-4} s^{-1}, and 5×10^{-5} s^{-1} at 1173 K, respectively. Taylor factor maps of the sample area corresponding to these IPF maps of the samples compressively deformed under 5×10^{-3} s^{-1}, 5×10^{-4} s^{-1}, and 5×10^{-5} s^{-1} at and 1173 K are shown in figures 7 (a), (b), and (c), respectively. These results reveal that grains with the <100> texture in IPF maps exhibit lower Taylor factors, and grains with the <111> texture exhibit higher ones. Therefore, it is considered that the dislocation density is higher in <111> grains than in <100> grains, indicating that the accumulating energy is high in grains with the <111> texture. As the flow stress is lower under low strain rates, as shown in the true-stress-true-strain curves, the dislocation density is considered to be low under such conditions, where the accumulating energy for grain growth is relatively low. Thus, the dislocation density is lowered by lowering the flow stress, and the accumulating energy for grain growth decreases, resulting in a decrease in the <100> component.

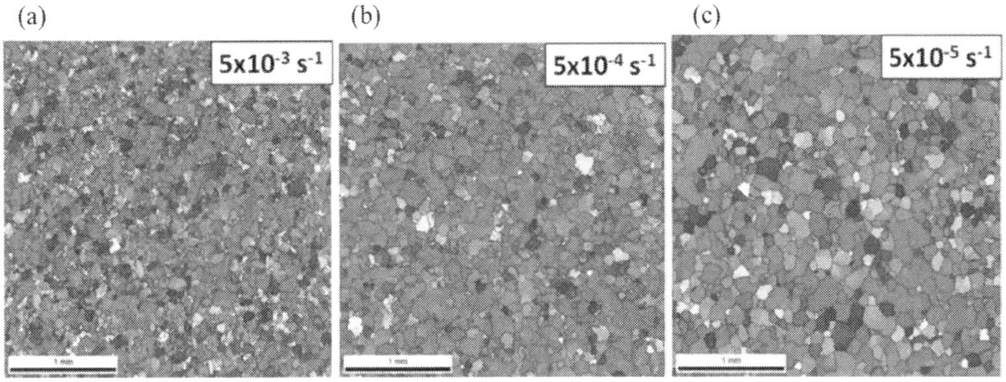

Figure 6. IPF maps of samples compressively deformed under 5×10^{-3} s^{-1} (a), 5×10^{-4} s^{-1} (b), and 5×10^{-5} s^{-1} (c) at 1173 K.

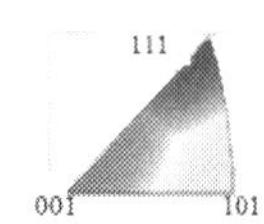

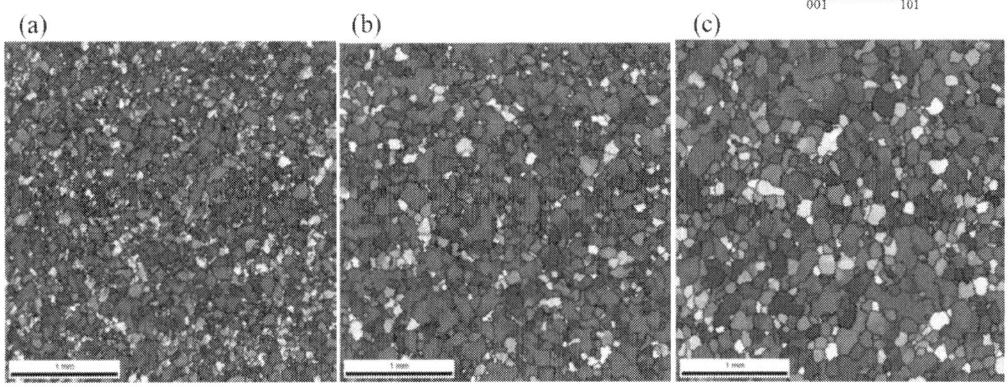

Figure 7. Taylor factor maps of the samples compressively deformed under 5×10^{-3} s^{-1} (a), 5×10^{-4} s^{-1} (b), and 5×10^{-5} s^{-1} (c) at 1173 K. The red region reveals a high Taylor factor, while the blue region reveals a low one.

Figure 8 summarizes the area fraction of the <100> and <111> texture components in the samples compressively deformed under 5×10^{-3} s^{-1}, 5×10^{-4} s^{-1}, and 5×10^{-5} s^{-1} at 1173 K. The optimum strain rate to obtain the large <100> texture is not 5×10^{-3} s^{-1} but 5×10^{-4} s^{-1}. One of the reasons for this is that the strain rate is related to the adequate deformation time, since the dynamic grain growth or preferential evolution of grains with the <100> texture occurs by creating a balance between adequate deformation temperature and time.

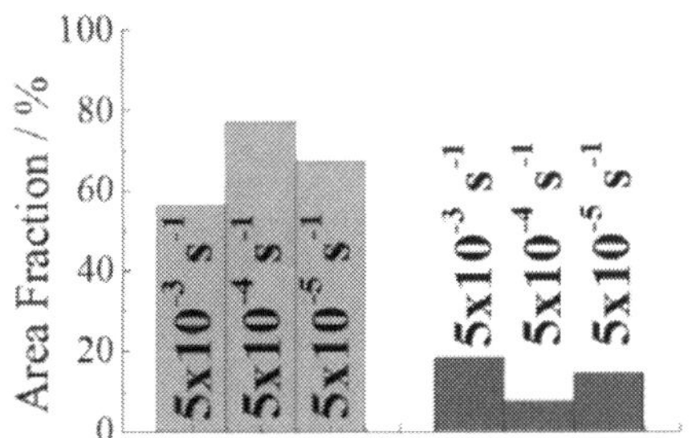

Figure 8. Area fraction of the <100> and <111> texture components in samples compressively deformed under 5×10^{-3} s^{-1}, 5×10^{-4} s^{-1}, and 5×10^{-5} s^{-1} at 1173 K.

In addition, the sample after compressive deformation under 5×10^{-4} s^{-1} at 1173 K was annealed at 1173 K for 30 minutes without any static applied stress, to investigate the influence of static applied stress on the microstructure. However, the volume fractions of the <100> and <111> texture components are not significantly changed by annealing without applied stress. This suggests that the <100> texture component is almost unchanged irrespective of static applied stress, and applied flow stress is an important part of the formation of the <100> component. Thus, preferential dynamic grain growth (PDGG) fundamentally occurs in ferritic alloys at adequate strain rates and temperatures [11]. This phenomenon is achieved by the strain-induced grain boundary migration due to the difference in stored energy between grains with different crystal orientations. Since grains with the <100> orientation have a lower Taylor factor than those with <111>, other deformation texture components during uniaxial deformation are expected to occur as a result of a lower dislocation density in <001> grains than in <111> grains. Therefore, it is considered that <100> oriented grains expand by consuming <111> oriented grains, causing the total stored energy in the bulk to be reduced. The present results also indicate that the PDGG occurs in practical ferritic stainless steels.

4. Concluding remarks

The present results indicate that grains with the <100> texture component preferentially evolve during compressive deformation under low strain rates at higher temperatures. The optimum conditions for the <100> texture evolution are a strain rate of 5×10^{-4} s^{-1} at 1173 K, although the soft magnetic properties should be further investigated. The dislocation density is considered to be lowered during deformation under low flow stress, where the evolution of the <100> texture component is suppressed. When the samples are annealed without applied stress at high temperatures after loading, the <100> and <111> texture components were almost unchanged, indicating that dynamic flow stress is important in the texture formation. By decreasing flow stress, the dislocation density decreases and the <100> texture component evolves, which implies that the <100> texture formation during deformation is affected by the deformation conditions and the dislocation density variation due to flow stress.

Acknowledgments
This work was partially supported by the Grant-in-Aid for Scientific research by the Japan Society for the Promotion of Sciences and Devices and the Adaptable and Seamless Technology transfer Program by the Japan Science and Technology Agency.

References

[1] Lo KH, Shek CH and Lai JKL 2009 *Mater. Sci. Eng. R* **65** 39
[2] Viswanathan UK, Banerjee S and Krishnan R 1988 *Mater. Sci. Eng. A* **104** 181
[3] Cheng LL and Thomas T 1968 *Trans. ASM* **61** 14
[4] Seetharaman V, Sundararaman M and Krishnan R 1981 *Mater. Sci. Eng.* **47** 1
[5] Hochanadel PW, Robino CV, Edwards GR and Cieslak MJ 1994 *Metall. Mater. Trans. A* **25** 789
[6] Marcus HL, Peistrup JN and Fine ME 1965 *Trans. ASM* **58** 176
[7] Taillard R, Pineau A and Thomas BJ 1982 *Mater. Sci. Eng.* **54** 209
[8] Taillard R and Pineau A 1982 *Mater. Sci. Eng.* **56** 219
[9] Ebata T and Takiguchi T 2004 *Electr. Furn. Steel* **75** 289
[10] Satoh K, Sato S, Ohnuma M, Naruse T, Kim Y, Enata T, Suzuki S and Wagatsuma K 2017 *ISIJ Int.* **57** 2028
[11] Onuki Y, Hongo R, Okayasu K and Fukutomi H 2013 *Acta Mater.* **61** 1294
[12] Onuki Y, Okayasu K and Fukutomi H 2011 *ISIJ Int.* **51** 1564
[13] Blum W 1993 *High Temperature Deformation and Creep of Crystalline Solids* (VCH Weinheim)

IOP Conf. Series: Materials Science and Engineering 1121 (2021) 012021 doi:10.1088/1757-899X/1121/1/012021

Variant Selection in Phase Transformation and its Influence on Texture and Martensite Starting Temperature in Steel

T Tomida and S Sato

Frontier Research Center for Applied Atomic Sciences, Ibaraki University, 162-1, Shirakata, Tokai, Ibaraki 319-1106, Japan.

toshiro.tomida.tomida_tsr@vc.ibaraki.ac.jp

Abstract. A mechanism is proposed that can predict the textures as well as the influence of austenite grain size on martensite starting temperature in steels. The anisotropic elastic energy by shape change of martensite changes depending upon variants in neighbour austenite grains, whereas it does not in immediate parent grains in which martensite grows. A mechanism based on this behaviour of elastic energy can explain not only the texture formation of martensite but also the well-known austenite grain size dependence of Ms, particularly the abrupt drop of about 30K in the grain size range below 20 μm.

1. Introduction

Variant selection during phase transformation, in which some of the permitted child orientations by the orientation relationship between parent and child phases are preferred than others, affects microstructures and crystallographic textures of materials, thus influencing various properties. In the martensite (austenite (γ) to bcc or bct) in steels, it has been reported that anisotropic elastic energy stored in "neighbouring" γ is the most influential factor to determine the preferred variants [1, 2], while for diffusive transformation holding the orientation relation to two or more neighbouring γ grains at the same time is the most influential [2, 3]. The purpose of this article is to show that the mechanism due to the anisotropic elastic energy affects not only the microstructure and texture of martensite but also the starting temperature of martensite transformation (Ms) in steels.

Ms is well known to shift when changing austenization temperature [4] or the grain size of γ before quenching [5, 6, 7], whereas the former is now known as caused through the latter. Ms gradually decreases as the γ grain size decreases from over a few hundred μm to about 10 μm. Then, Ms abruptly drops by about 30 K in the range below 20 μm [6, 7]. This grain size dependency of Ms is still left unclarified in its mechanism.

One of the most researched mechanisms for this phenomenon is perhaps a Hall-Petch-type mechanism related to the grain refinement strengthening of γ, in which the martensite transformation is retarded due to the hardening of γ, since the nucleation and growth of martensite would cost more energy in such a hardened matrix [5, 7]. However, there is a controversy that the Hall-Petch mechanism that requires migration of dislocations over grains cannot influence Ms [6]. Although there are several other mechanisms proposed for the grain size dependence of Ms, no commonly agreed mechanism for this phenomenon exists. In this contribution, a mechanism is proposed that is related to the anisotropic elastic energy in neighbour γ grains and explains the dependence of Ms on the γ grain size well, particularly the abrupt drop below 20 μm.

2. Theory by elastic anisotropy

In the martensite transformation in steels, the orientation relationship between γ and martensite is only a few degrees away from the Kurdjumov-Sachs (K-S) relation [8], $\{111\}_\gamma // \{110\}_\alpha$ and $<110>_\gamma // <111>_\alpha$, and there are 24 variants due to the cubic symmetry of crystals. Preferential selection of the variants during the martensite transformation is obvious, since for instance packets and subblocks are formed, in which the variants having similar habit planes gather side by side and each variant is paired with a specific variant respectively [9]. The texture of the martensite is also known to be stronger than expected with no variant selection [1].

Proposed mechanisms for the variant selection span from several versions of habit-plane-orientation-related models to stress- or strain-related models [1]. In most of them variants are determined due to phenomena in the inside or the boundary of immediate parent grains where the variants grow in, such as stresses and dislocations within the grains and grain shape. Instead, the authors have proposed that variants may be chosen being related to "neighbour" grains, that is, the elastic energy stored in "neighbour γ grains" by displacive transformation is responsible for the variant selection [1]. Although the elastic energy is one of the major sources that require a large excess energy for the martensite transformation to occur, it does not depend on variants in the immediate parent grains, since all the variants are crystallographically equivalent. Nevertheless, outside of the parent grains, the elastic energy is dependent on the variants as well as orientations of neighbours, since the variants are not equivalent in the neighbour γ crystals anymore and γ is elastically anisotropic, thus strongly influencing the variant selection as shown in Figure 1 [1].

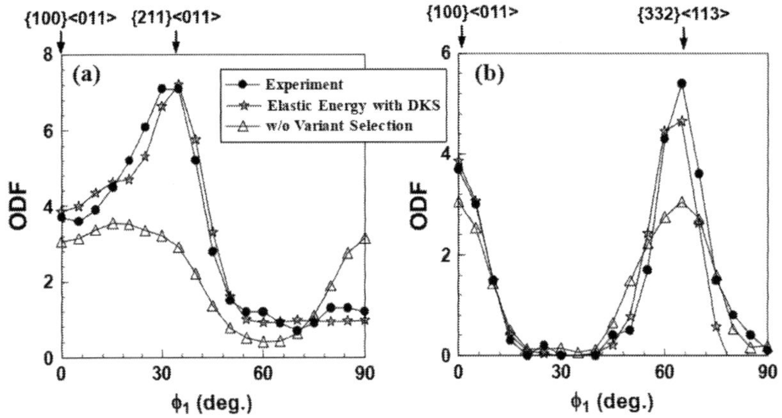

Figure 1 Comparison between textures of martensite by an experiment and prediction based on elastic energy in neighbour γ. (a) the RD fiber at 0° in Φ and 45° in ϕ_2 and (b) TD fiber at 90° in Φ and 45° in ϕ_2.

Given the elastic stiffness of the averaged matrix c_{ijkl} and the shape change of martensite ε_{ij}, the stored elastic energy E due to the shape change of martensite is given by

$$E = \frac{E_c}{2} \sum c_{ijkl} \varepsilon_{ij} \varepsilon_{kl}. \quad (1)$$

E_c is a coefficient introduced to roughly express the effect for which a lath-shaped martensite is embedded in a matrix; better approximation can be given by a micromechanics theory [10], however it is out of the scope of this contribution. This energy is distributed in a range including not only the parent γ grain but also neighbour grains, especially since martensite mostly nucleates on γ grain boundaries. Thus, this energy in the neighbour γ has been thought to be a cause of variant selection and influence the texture in martensite [1, 2]. In the following it will be explored and discussed that this elastic energy in neighbour γ should be also the main mechanism of the grain size dependency of Ms.

Here we assume that the energy E spreads homogeneously in a spherical region of a radius R_c. In a neighbour γ grain in this region, having the orientation of g_γ and the grain volume of V_γ, the stored energy E_γ may be expressed as follows,

$$E_\gamma = \frac{3V_\gamma \cdot E_c}{8\pi R_c^{\,3}} \sum C^\gamma{}_{ijkl} \cdot ({g_\gamma}^{-1} \cdot \varepsilon \cdot g_\gamma)_{ij} ({g_\gamma}^{-1} \cdot \varepsilon \cdot g_\gamma)_{kl}. \quad (2)$$

The coordinates used are fixed to the γ grain in which martensite grows except for the stiffness tensor of the neighbour γ grain $C^\gamma{}_{ijkl}$ that uses the coordinates fixed to this particular neighbour grain for simpler expression. The shape strain ε changes as variants change as

$$\varepsilon_n = {g_n^c}^{-1} \cdot \varepsilon_1 \cdot g_n^c, \quad (3)$$

where ε_n and $g^c{}_n$ are the shape strain of the n-th variant and the corresponding rotation matrix of the cubic symmetry group. Then the energy E is the sum of E_γ for the γ grains in the region of the radius R_c.

Thus, the energy E depends on variants as well as the circumstance in which martensite nucleates and grows, such as the orientations of neighbour grains, i.e. textures, and the number of γ grains within R_c, i.e. "the grain size of γ". It also fluctuates from a site to a site to nucleate in a material. It is obvious that the larger the fluctuation around the average of E, the lower the smallest limit of the energy E. Therefore, Ms that should be determined by the lower limit of E should be increased as the fluctuation increases, which depends on the texture and the grain size of γ.

3. Influence on Ms and discussion

When the γ grain size is very large as compared to the radius R_c, the number of neighbour γ grains are only one at plain grain boundaries of γ or two at triple junctions as shown in Figure 2a. The calculated distributions of the energy E/E_c in those cases are shown in Figures 3a and b. The energy was assumed to be equally distributed to the parent grain and one (or two) neighbour grain(s) in the former (or latter) case. The elastic moduli used is that for Fe-15%Ni-15%Cr [11], and the shape strain is the one calculated by the phenomenological theory of martensite by Kelly using lattice invariant shears of $(\bar{1}00)[0\bar{1}1]_\gamma$ and $(\bar{1}3\bar{1})[10\bar{1}]_\gamma$ [1, 12]. E_c was assumed to be constant for simplicity. Ten thousand of neighbour austenite orientations (or orientation pairs) were chosen randomly without considering textures; variants are not necessary to be considered in the texture-less case. It is observed that the elastic energy scatters in a wide range from about 65% to 135% of the averaged value in both cases. The calculated lowest and highest E/E_c in these cases are 0.74×10^{10} and 1.52×10^{10} $J{\cdot}m^{-3}$ respectively. Note that these energies should be one to three orders of magnitude larger than the reality, because of a small value of E_c as will be discussed later.

As the number of γ grains in the strained region increases as shown in Figure 2b, the energy distribution changes as shown in Figures 3c and d. Due to averaging effect by many grains, the distribution sharpens and the fluctuation decreases markedly. If the start of martensite transformation is detected by experiment when nucleation and growth occur for the lower, say, 1% of the energy distribution, the elastic energy at Ms increases with increasing the number of γ grains within R_c as

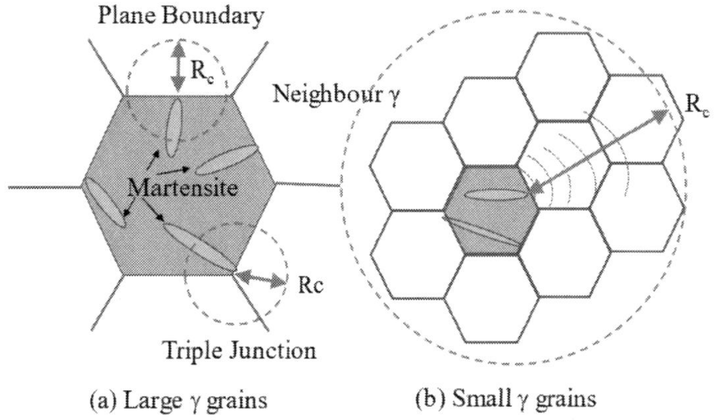

Figure 2 Schematic representation of stressed regions in γ by martensite (a) near plane boundaries and triple junctions in large γ grains and (b) in the case of small γ grains.

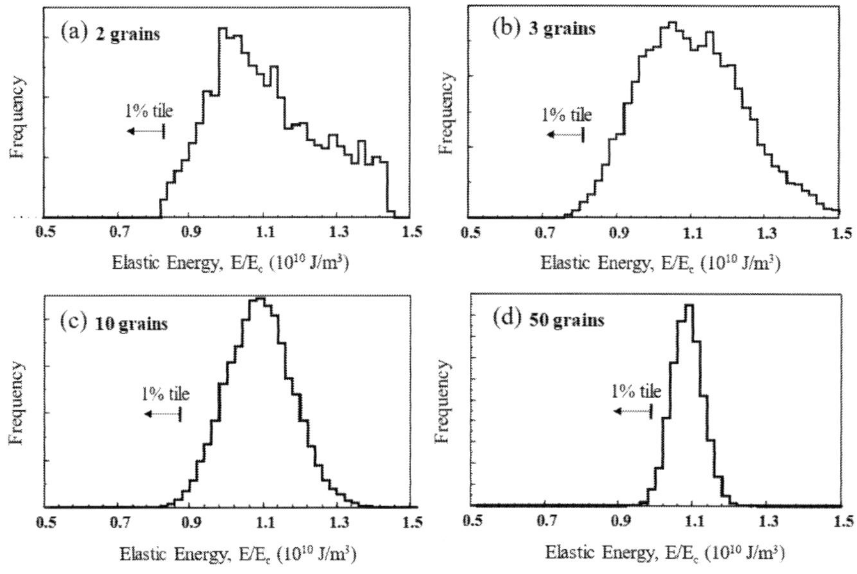

Figure 3 Distribution of elastic energy in γ where there are (a) 2, (b) 3, (c) 10, (d) 50 grains in the stressed region.

seen in Figure 4. The elastic energy just above the lower 1% tile increases by about 30% as the number of γ grains increases.

The number of austenite grains N_g in the radius R_c is a function of the average γ grain dimeter D as R_c is constant. Since the first two cases with two and three grains shown in Figure 2a and Figures 3a and b correspond to an infinite grain size, the following function may be appropriate,

$$N_g = 8\left(\frac{R_c}{D}\right)^3 + 3. \quad (4)$$

The elastic energy E is a part of the excess energy required for martensite transformation, and for this Ms is much lower than T_0 temperature where Gibbs energy for γ and ferrite are equal. The excess energy ΔG that is dissipated as elastic, plastic and interfacial energies is known to be a function approximately linear to transformation temperature [7] and becomes zero at T_0. It is also known that ΔG and Ms for a large grain size (ΔG_∞ and Ms_∞) are about 1200 $J \cdot mol^{-1}$ (or 1.7×10^8 $J \cdot m^{-3}$) and about 300 K lower than T_0, respectively [7]. Therefore, assuming E is $\Delta G/3$, E in $J \cdot m^{-3}$ can be expressed as a function of Ms in K as

$$E = \frac{1}{3}\left[\frac{1{,}7x10^8}{300}(M_\infty - Ms) + 1.7x10^8\right]\ (J \cdot m^{-3}).\ (5)$$

Then it follows that

$$M_\infty - Ms = (5.3x10^{-6} \cdot E - 300)\ (K).\ (6)$$

From this equation, E is about 5.7×10^7 $J \cdot m^{-3}$ at the temperature of Ms_∞. On the other hand, E/E_c at Ms_∞, where Ng is two to three in our model, is about 8.2×10^9 $J \cdot m^{-3}$ as observed in Figure 4. Therefore, E_c is derived as around 7×10^{-3}. This small value of the coefficient tells us something about the aspect ratio of a martensite lath, which is estimated to be of the order of 10^{-2} by micromechanics [10].

From equations 4 and 6, the above value of E_c and the data in Figure 4, the influence of γ grain size on Ms is predicted as shown in Figure 5a, where three cases of R_c=5, 8 and 15 μm are presented. An abrupt drop of Ms is observed below the average γ grain size of about $2R_c$, and the total decrease is about 30 K in all the cases.

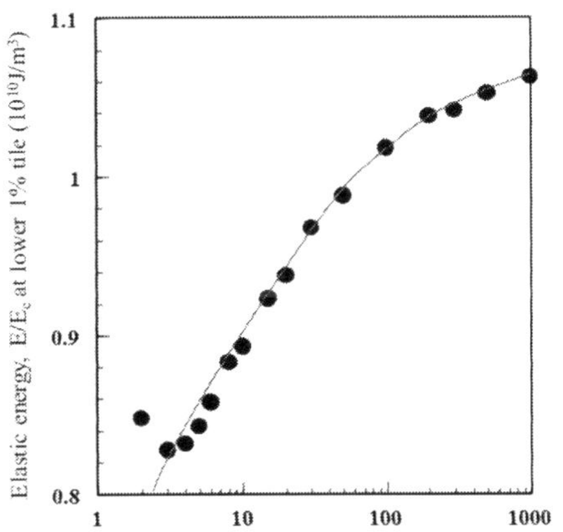

Figure 4 Elastic energy at lower 1% tiles of elastic energy distributions vs the number of γ grains in the stressed region.

The above theoretical results particularly for R_c being 8 μm agree well with the experimental results for Fe-5%Ni-2.3%Mn-C shown in Figure 5b [6] where Ms rapidly decreases by about 30K as the γ grain diameter decreases from 20 to a few μm. However, the gradual decrease of about 10 K observed in the range over 20 μm cannot be well explained by the present theory. Nevertheless, it is important that this elastic-energy-based prediction of Ms has only one parameter of R_c that has a clear physical meaning, "the radius of the elastically strained region". The model is capable of predicting how Ms decreases as γ grain refines by knowing the internal energy variation between austenite and ferrite, elastic moduli of γ, the shape strain and Ec for martensite and R_c, all of which can be evaluated theoretically.

Justification of R_c of around 8 μm is a matter for discussion. Elastic displacement by inclusions is known to change being inverse proportional to the square of distance in a remote distance, and its behaviour in a close distance is complicated [10]. A relevant question is how large the size of martensite lath that determines R_c at Ms is. If it is the size of an embryo of martensite, R_c would not be as large as 8 μm. The texture of γ is an influential factor as well. When a strong texture is present in austenite, the distribution and fluctuation in the elastic energy as shown in Figure 3 would change largely. However, further work is required to answer those questions.

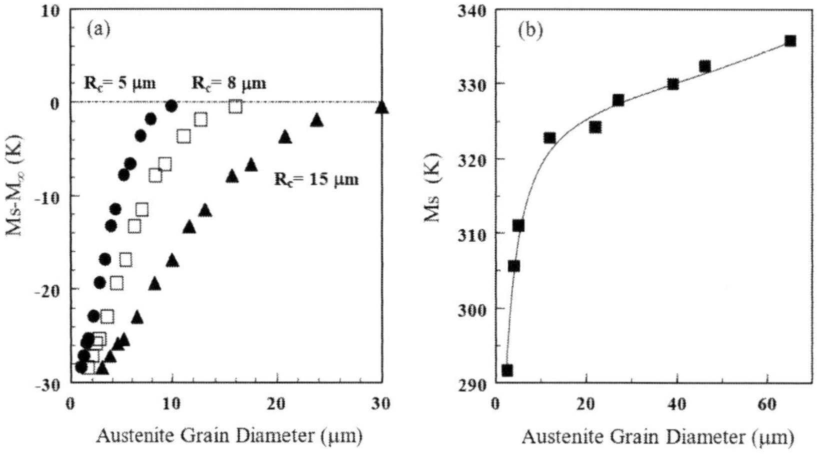

Figure 5 (a) Predicted and (b) observed changes of Ms by grain refinement of γ. Figure b was a replot of the data in ref. 6.

4. Conclusion

The influence of elastic energy in neighbour γ grains on variant selection as well as Ms of martensite transformation in steels has been studied. A mechanism has been introduced that can predict the textures as well as the grain size dependence of martensite starting temperature in steels. Whereas the elastic energy by shape strain of martensite in immediate parent grains does not depend on variants, the elastic energy in neighbour austenite grains does depend on the variants and largely affects the textures of martensite and Ms. It is predicted by the proposed mechanism that Ms rapidly decreases when the average grain size of γ decreases to below 20 μm as observed experimentally, if the elastic energy is distributed in a surrounding region of 5 to 10 μm in radius.

References

[1] Tomida T. 2018 *Acta Mater.* **146** 25-41.
[2] Humbert M., Gardiola B., Esling C., Flemming G. and Hensger K.E. 2001 *Acta mater.* **50** 1741-7.
[3] Tomida T., Wakita M., Yasuyama M., Sugaya S., Tomota Y. and Vogel S. C. 2013 *Acta Mater.* **61** 2828.
[4] Ankara O.A., Sastri A.S., West D.R.F. 1966 *JISI* **204** 509–11.
[5] Brofman P. J., Ansell G. S. 1983 *Metal. Trans. A* **14A** 1929–31.
[6] Yang H.–S. and Bhadeshia H. K. D. H. 2009 *Scripta Materialia* **60** 493–5.
[7] van Bohemen S.M.C. and Morsdorf L. 2017 *Acta Mater.* **125** 401-15
[8] Kurdjumov G., Sachs G. 1930 *Z Physik* **64** 325.
[9] Morito S., Tanaka H., Konishi R., Furuhara T., Maki T. 2003 *Acta Mater.* **51** 1789-99.
[10] Eshelby J. D. 19657 *Proc. Royal Soc. London Series A* **241** 376-96.
[11] Teklu A., Ledbetter H., Kim S., Boatner L. A., McGuire M. and Keppens V. 2004 *Metal. Mater. Trans. A* **35A** 3149-54.
[12] Kelly P. M. 1992 *Mat. Trans. JIM.* **33** 235-42.

Orientation dependence of transformation induced plasticity in high carbon bainitic steel

R Ueji, Y Kimura, K Ushioda, T Ohmura, T Inoue and A Shibata

National Institute for Materials Science, 1-2-1 Sengen, Tsukuba, Ibaraki 305-0047, Japan.

E-mail: UEJI.Rintaro@nims.go.jp

Abstract. The crystallographic orientation dependence of the transformation induced plasticity (TRIP) in the high carbon bainitic steel was studied. 0.6%C-2.0%Si-1%Cr steels were austenitized at two conditions to obtain different size of prior-austenite grains. Subsequently, they were austempered to evolve the bainitic structure composed mainly of bainitic ferrite and retained austenite. The characteristic of this sample is that it has much larger amount of carbon content compared with that of the conventional low alloyed TRIP steels. The bainitic steels with different sizes of mean prior-austenite grain show high strength with large ductility. The measurement of electron back scattering diffraction (EBSD) of the samples both before and after the tensile test clarified that much of the retained austenite transformed to ferrite while the austenite grains having the tensile orientation nearly parallel to <111> kept remaining after the fracture. This change indicates that the retained austenite with its tensile axis parallel near to <001> is preferential for the deformation-induced martensitic transformation. This behavior was found in the samples with different prior-austenite grain sizes.

1. Introduction

Transformation induced plasticity (TRIP) steel [1] is one of the advanced high strength steels. It is well known that the strengthening of TRIP steel is achieved by the increasing of carbon content [2], although the research works on the TRIP steel with relatively higher carbon content is limited to a few papers [3]. In addition, for the optimization of mechanical properties, the relationship between the microstructural morphology, such as prior-austenite grain size, and the deformation-induced martensitic transformation should be studied adequately. Consequently, this paper is aimed to clarify the behaviors of deformation-induced martensitic transformation in high carbon TRIP steels with different prior-austenite grain sizes.

2. Experimental procedures

A high-carbon Si-bearing steel (0.62%C-2.02%Si-0.23%Mn-1.01%Cr-bal.Fe) was examined. The samples with a dimension of 14 mm x 14 mm x 150 mm were austenitized at 850 °C or 1050 °C for 600 sec. Subsequently, the samples were soaked in a salt bath at 400 °C and kept for 1800 sec. The heat treated samples were cut to the tensile test pieces with a gage length of 42 mm and a diameter of 6 mm. Tensile test was conducted at ambient temperature at a constant cross head speed of 0.85 mm/min. Microstructures were examined by a scanning electron microscope (SEM) with an EBSD measurement system.

3. Results and discussion

Figure 1(a,b) shows the phase color maps of the austempered samples austenitized at T_γ = 850 °C (a) or T_γ = 1050 °C. The white lines indicate the prior-austenite grain boundaries. The higher temperature for the austenitization brought the larger mean diameter of prior austenite grains, d_γ. Both of the samples were fulfilled with bainitic ferrite with retained austenite. The retained austenite in the smaller prior- austenite grains (a) shows relatively equiaxed morphology, while the coarse prior-austenite grains have the elongated grains of retained austenite. The 001 pole figures (c,d) show the BCC phase orientations in one prior-austenite grain indicated by the dotted line in (a) and (b). These distributions were reasonable for the Kuldumov-Sachs (KS) orientation relationship [4,5].

The true stress, σ, - true strain, ε, curves of these two austempered samples were shown in Fig.2. The ends of the stress - strain curves indicate the breaking of the test pieces. Both of the austempered samples show high strength with adequate ductility. The difference between the samples with different prior-austenite grain sizes was not significant. The work hardening, dσ/dε, curves corresponding to these stress - strain curves were also presented in Fig.2. The work hardening in both samples kept higher than true stress, indicating that the fracture occurs without necking.

The samples were tensile deformed not only to the fracture but also to some tensile strains, and the samples deformed to different strains were examined by EBSD. These results were shown in Fig.3 or Fig.4 for the samples austenitized at 950°C or 1050°C, respectively. These figures indicate the BCC and FCC orientations parallel to the tensile orientations according to the color key at the top-right of these figures. Both samples with different prior-austenite grain sizes show similar changes: with increasing of the tensile strain, the retained austenite transformed to martensite and the volume fraction of austenite ($V\gamma$) decreased. Although the deformation-induced transformation created new grains, the block (the aggregation of martensitic crystals with similar orientations [4,5]) kept its original size

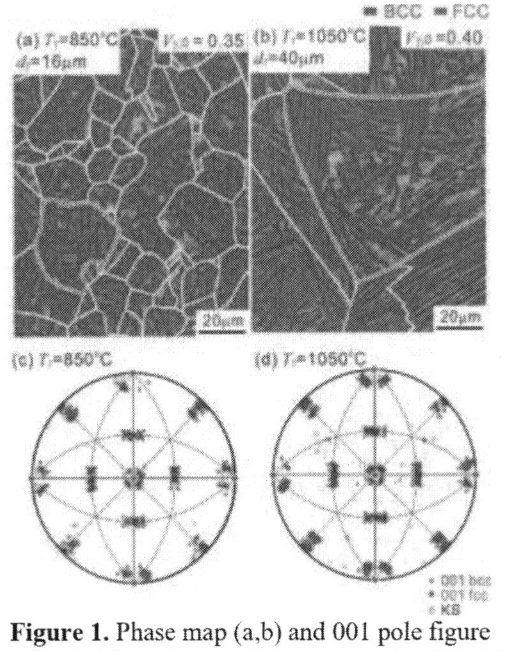

Figure 1. Phase map (a,b) and 001 pole figure (c,d) of high carbon steels austenitized at 850 °C (a,c) or 1050 °C (b,d) followed by isothermal holding at 400 °C. The pole figure shows the distribution of $<001>_{bcc}$ with both the horizontal and vertical axes parallel to $<001>_{fcc}$. Open circles indicate $<001>_{bcc}$ orientations having the Kurdjumov-Sachs orientation relationship.

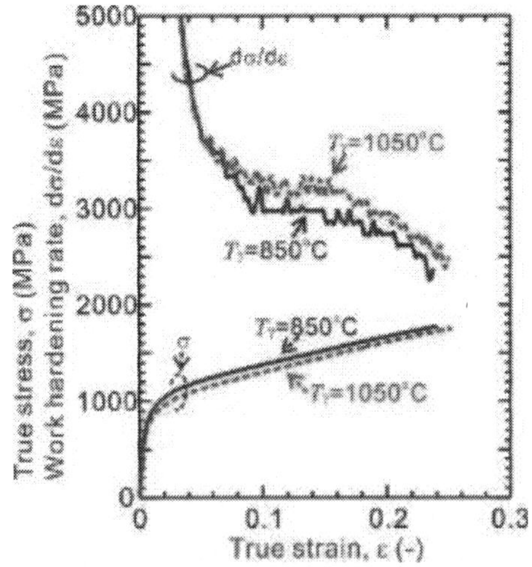

Figure 2. True stress (σ) - true strain (ε) curves and work hardening rate.

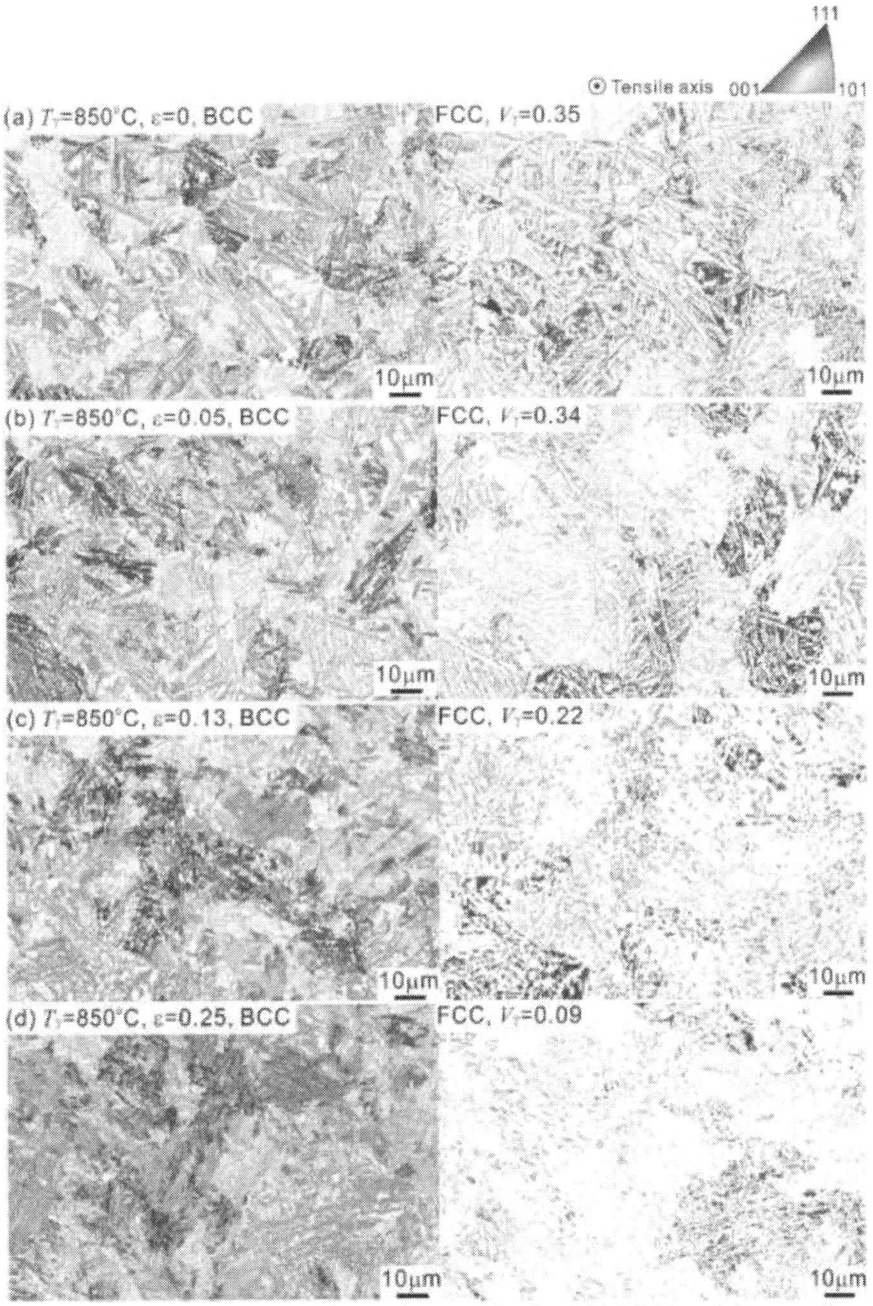

Figure 3. Orientation color maps of the steel austenitized at 850 °C (a) and then tensile strained to a true strain of 0.05 (b), 0.13 (c) or 0.25 (d). The orientations of the BCC and FCC phases are shown at the left and right sides, respectively. The observation plane is parallel to the tensile axis

similar to that of the as-austempered samples, indicating that the orientation of deformation-induced martensite was similar to that of pre-existing adjacent bainitic ferrite.

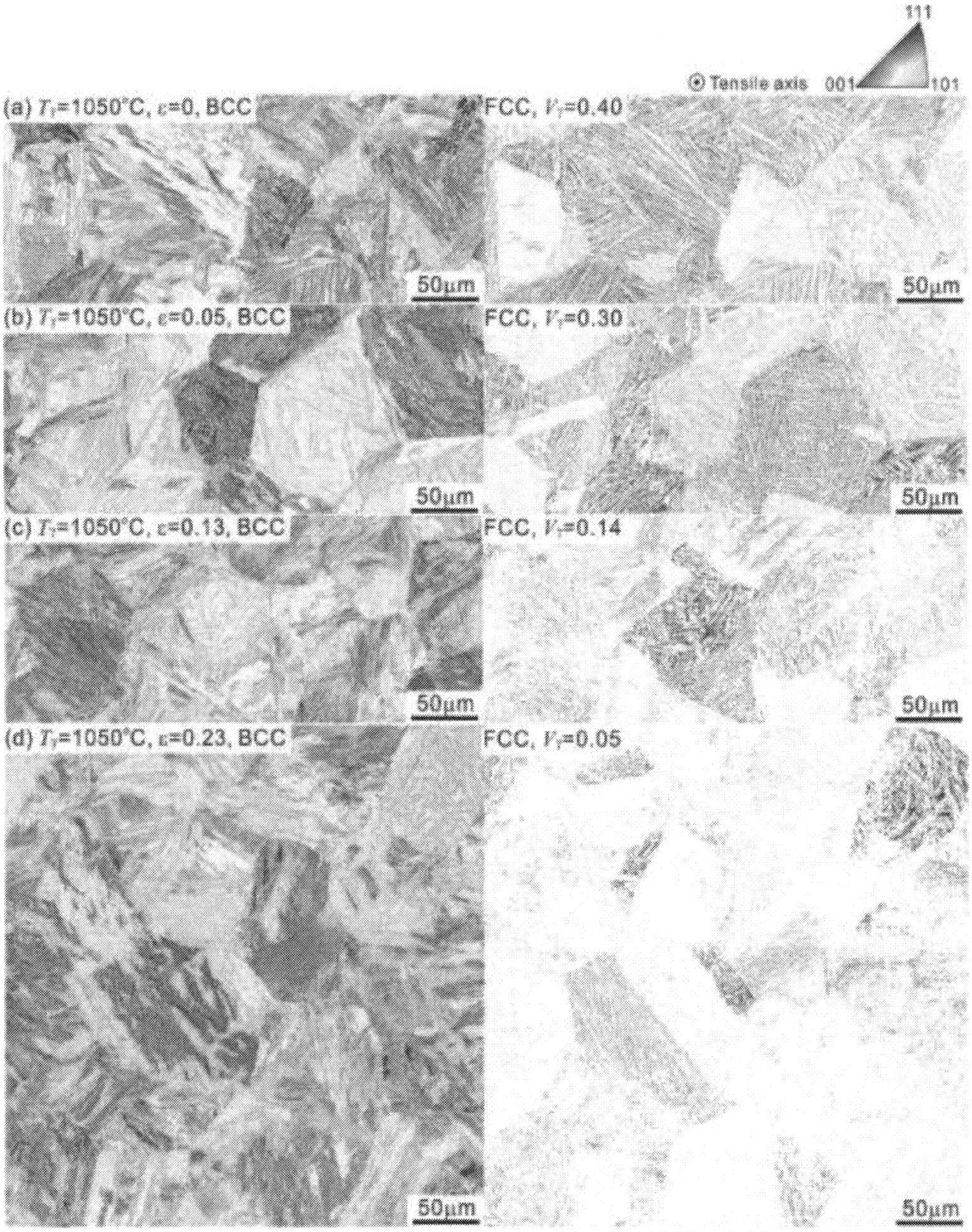

Figure 4. Orientation color maps of the steel austenitized at 1050 °C (a) and then tensile strained to a true strain of 0.05 (b), 0.13 (c) or 0.23 (d). The normal direction on the observation plane is parallel to the tensile axis

Figure 5 shows the fraction of retained austenite in the samples deformed to ε. The reference data of several steels which perform the deformation-induced martensitic transformation are shown in addition [6-14]. The conventional low-alloyed low-carbon TRIP steels have relatively small amount of retained austenite before the deformation, while the metastable austenitic stainless steels such as 304 consist of only austenite when these keep solution-treated state. The high carbon TRIP steel in this work shows

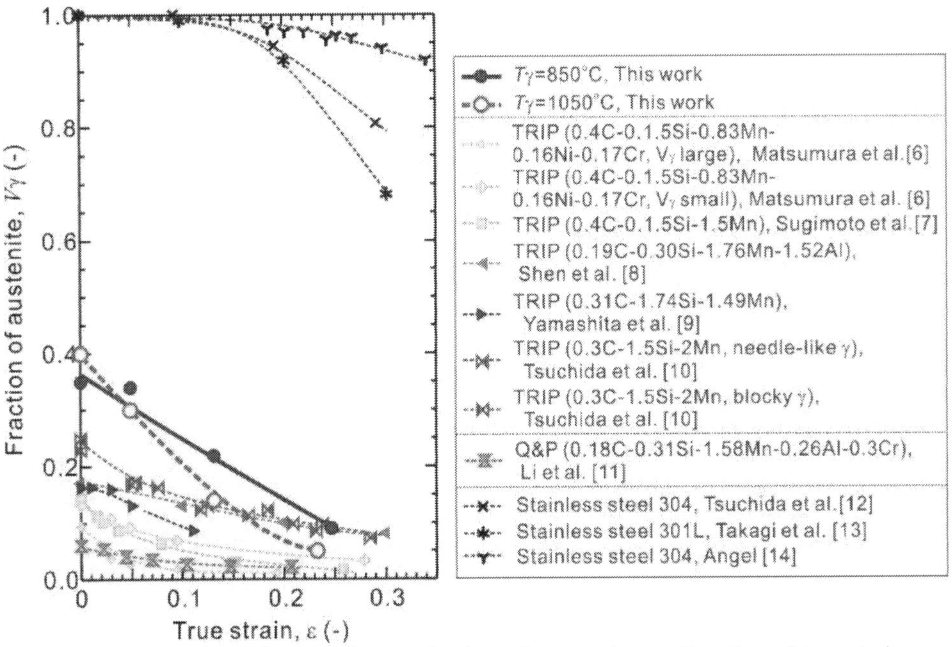

Figure 5. Fraction of retained austenite in various steels as a function of true strain.

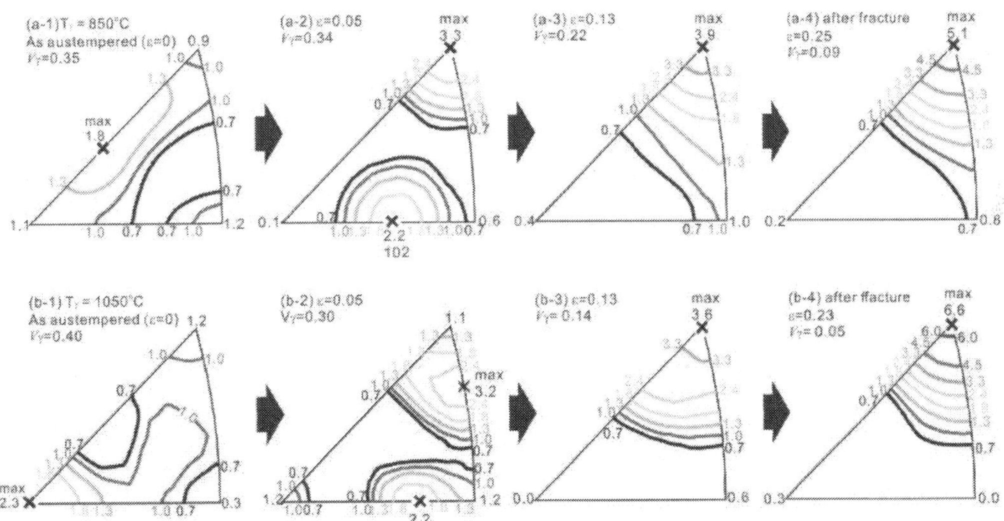

Figure 6. Inverse pole figures showing intensity of crystallographic orientation parallel to the tensile axis in the FCC phase of the steels austenitized at 850 °C (a1-4) or 1050 °C (b1-4) followed by austempering (a1,b1) and tensile deformation (a2-4, b2-4).

the behavior between the conventional low-alloyed TRIP steels and metastable austenitic stainless steels. The volume fraction of austenite is larger at the initial state and reduces more rapidly by the tensile deformation than those in the conventional low-alloyed TRIP steels.

Figure 6 shows the inverse pole figures of the tensile orientations of austenite. With increasing tensile strain, the distribution of the tensile orientation favored <111>. This means that the deformation-induced martensitic transformation occurs more preferentially in the grains in which the tensile orientation is around <001> than in those around <111>. This tendency is found in both samples with different prior-austenite grains sizes. The authors lately found that the orientation dependence on the deformation-induced martensitic transformation can be explained by the first primitive shear for the transformation when the elastic isotropy is taken in account [15]. This implies that the tensile orientation dependence on the transformation is controlled by the stress condition which is influenced by the tensile orientation rather than the grain/phase boundaries. Consequently, the finding of this study seems consistent to the controlling mechanism of the deformation-induced martensitic transformation.

4. Summary

The crystallographic orientation dependence of the transformation induced plasticity in the high carbon bainitic steel (0.6%C-2.0%Si-1%Cr-Fe) with two different mean sizes of prior-austenite grains (16μm, 40μm) was studied. The bainitic steels with different sizes of mean prior-austenite grain diameters show high strength with large ductility. In both samples, the austenite grains having the tensile orientation nearly parallel to <111> kept remaining as FCC even after the fracture. This tendency implies that the process determining the tensile orientation dependence on the martensitic transformation is mainly affected by the tensile orientation rather than the grain/phase boundaries.

Acknowledgments

This study is based on work supported by Grant-in-Aid for Scientific Research (ID: 20H02488, 19H02459) through the Japan Society for the Promotion of Science (JSPS).

References

[1] Zackay V F , Parker E R, Fahr D and Busch R 1967, *Trans. ASM* **60** 252
[2] Sakuma Y, Matsumura O and Akisue O 1991, *ISIJ Int.* **31** 1348
[3] Shinoda K and Yamada T 1980, *Netsu-Shori* **20** 326
[4] Morito S, Tanaka H, Konishi R, Furuhara T and Maki T 2003 *Acta Mater.* **51** 1789
[5] Kitahara H, Ueji R, Tsuji N and Minamino Y 2006 *Acta Mater.* **54** 1279
[6] Matsumura O, Sakuma Y and Takechi H 1987 *Scr. Metall.* **21** 1301
[7] Sugimoto K, Kobayashi M and Hashimoto S 1992 *Metall. Trans. A*, **23A** 3085
[8] Shen Y F, Qiu L N, Sun X, Zuo L, Liaw P K and Raabe D 2015 Mater. Sci. Eng. A. **636** 551
[9] Yamashita T, Koga N and Umezawa O 2018 *ISIJ Int.* **58** 1155
[10] Tsuchida N, Okura S, Tanaka T and Toji Y 2018 *ISIJ Int.* **58** 978
[11] Li W S, Gao H Y, Nakashima H, Hata S and Tian W H 2016, *Mater. Sci. Eng. A* **649** 417
[12] Tsuchida N, Morimoto Y, Tonan T, Shibata Y, Fukaura K and Ueji R 2011 *ISIJ Int.* **51** 124
[13] Takagi Y, Ueji R, Mizuguchi T and Tsuchida N 2011 *Tetsu-to-Hagane* **97** 450
[14] Angel T 1954 *J. Iron Steel Inst.* **177** 165
[15] Ueji R, Shibata A, Ushioda K, Kimura Y, Ohmura T and Inoue T 2021 *Scripta Mater.* in-press, 113666

IOP Conf. Series: Materials Science and Engineering 1121 (2021) 012023 doi:10.1088/1757-899X/1121/1/012023

Variant selection during β to α transformation for Ti-6Al-4V alloy produced by Selective Laser Melting printing

H. Xiang[1*], **L.A.I. Kestens**[1], **W. Van Paepegem**[2]

[1]Department of Electromechanical, Systems and Metals Engineering, Faculty of Engineering and Architecture, Ghent University, Technologiepark Zwijnaarde 46, B-9052,

[2]Department of Materials, Textiles and Chemical Engineering (MaTCh), Faculty of Engineering and Architecture, Ghent University, Technologiepark Zwijnaarde 46, B-9052

Email addresses: Hao.Xiang@UGent.be (H. Xiang); Leo.Kestens@UGent.be (L. Kestens)

Abstract: During 3D printing by Selective Laser Melting (SLM) of the alloy Ti-6Al-4V, the phase transformation of BCC to HCP is associated with selection of particular crystallographic variants. In the present paper, the distribution of misorientation angle along grain boundaries was investigated by EBSD. It is revealed that the main misorientation pairs were located in the interval between 56° and 66°, which contains three theoretical misorientation angles, i.e. 60.00°, 60.83° and 63.26°. The observed misorientation axis/angle pairs were represented in the Rodrigues–Frank space with a certain tolerance angle, which illustrated clearly the distribution of the observed misorientations around the 5 theoretical values. The main peak of the misorientation pairs was observed for [$\overline{10}$ 5 5 $\bar{3}$]/ 63.26° with 43.8% frequency, followed by [1 1 $\bar{2}$ 0]/ 60° with 21.8% population, whereas a distribution in the absence of variant selection would have produced values of 18.2% and 36.4%, respectively.

1. Introduction

Since in 1934 Burgers [1] identified the specific orientation relationship (OR) between the parent body-centered cubic crystal structure and the hexagonal closed packed crystal structure during phase transformation, many researchers have performed detailed studies on the mechanism of variant selection in phase transformation, which is important for controlling the microstructure and the related mechanical properties.

Because of the symmetry of cubic and hexagonal structures in Ti-6Al-4V alloy, a single β-BCC crystal would transform 12 different α-HCP variants. Theoretically, it is equally statistically possible for all 12 product orientations to nucleate and grow during phase transformation, which would imply that the phase transformation occurs without variant selection, giving rise to a weak or nearly random α texture. However, in reality, due to different factors, the phenomenon of variant selection is often observed. The possible causes of variant selection include: the difference of lattice parameters between parent and product phase [2], externally applied loads and/or strain [3, 4], the specific nature of the pre-existing α grains [5], the reduced transformed strain energy with variant clusters and special grain boundary in β grains [6-9]. Consequently, for the SLM printed Ti-6Al-4V alloy under consideration, the phenomenon of variant selection is intricately linked to phase transformation, which results in a specific crystallographic texture determining the final mechanical properties of the alloy.

In the present work, the texture of SLM Ti-6Al-4V alloy is studied by EBSD, the misorientation profile is examined along grain boundaries and compared with the theoretical distribution to assess the occurrence of variant selection. The Rodrigues – Frank Space (R – F Space) is employed to demonstrate clearly the misorientation pairs in 3D space.

2. Experiment

2.1. Materials
Ti-6Al-4V rod shaped samples were produced by selective laser melting without any post-processing. With the EDS element analysis, the normalized weight percentage of elements were: Al: 4.4%, V: 3.1% and Ti: 92.5%.

2.2. Microstructural characterization
With the defined sample coordinate system (x_1//scanning direction, x_3//building direction), the EBSD scans were acquired with a SEM of type Quanta 450F with field emission gun equipped with a fully automated EBSD device, operated under the following conditions: 20 kV accelerating voltage, 16.0 mm working distance with hexagonal scanning grid with step size of 4 μm. The standard preparation procedures were used for EBSD observation. Necessary cleanup procedures were conducted before post-processing with TSL ® Analysis software, version 7.8.

2.3. Misorientation in Rodrigues – Frank (R–F) Space
In R – F space, misorientation between two grains with rotation matrix $\Delta\mathbf{g}$ can be illustrated by rotation axis/angle pair, which is represented by a single point [10]. Based on the Burgers OR, the theoretical misorientation between product α can be depicted as reference points in the fundamental zone. In the present work, the observed misorientations will be presented as number density within a tolerance angle ω. This number density is obtained by dividing the experimentally observed number fraction *dr* by the hypothetical number fraction *dn*, which assumes that there is no variant selection and all variants would obey the precise Burgers correspondence. The ratio of *dr*/*dn* representing the number density $D(\Delta\mathbf{g}_r)$ can be evaluated for the considered sample and interpreted as the degree of variant selection to the extent it deviated from unity. Matlab and MTEX toolbox [11] were employed for the calculation and plot.

3. Results and discussion

3.1. Microstructure and texture
Fig. 1 displays the microstructure and pole figures of the scanned product α phase and reconstructed parent β phase by ARPGE [12]. Because of the limited statistics of the scanned dataset, there are ~15% non-identified points in the reconstructed database. On the pole figures, the strongest peak is observed in the center position of the $(1\ 1\ \bar{2}\ 0)$ PF, which implies that the building direction is predominantly parallel to the $(1\ 1\ \bar{2}\ 0)$ pole, the corresponding β phase demonstrates a peak in the center of (0 0 1) and (1 1 1) pole. The maximum intensity of the (0 0 0 1) α PF is 1.868 mrd and 3.118 mrd for the (0 0 1) β PF.

For the SLM printing procedure, the β grains are formed during solidification and the β to α phase transformation occurs during cooling at fast rate. Based on the theory of solidification [13], the preferred growth direction is (0 0 1) for BCC crystallographic structure. In the meanwhile, the maximum thermal gradient is along the building direction. Hence, the β grains grow in the (0 0 1) direction along the building direction, forming the strong (0 0 1) texture, as observed in Fig. 1(b).

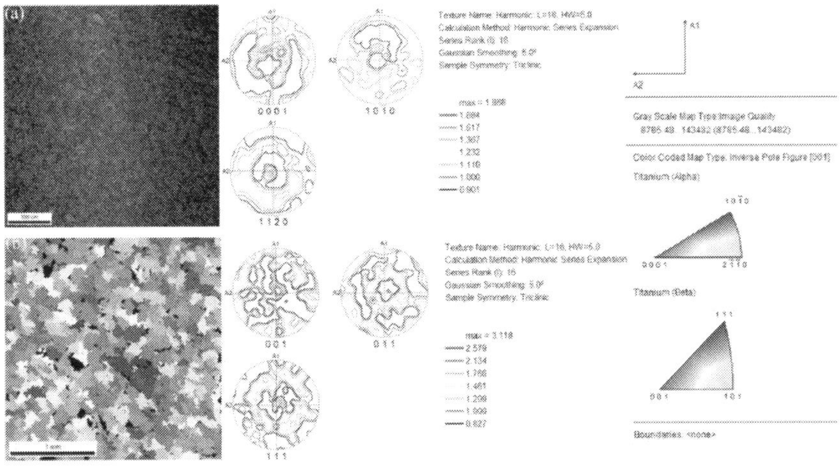

Fig. 1 (a): The microstructure and pole figure of measured α phase; (b) the reconstructed β phase by ARPGE

3.2. Misorientation distribution between product grains

Theoretically, the phase transformation from β phase to α phase follows the Burgers correspondence, i.e. : $\{1\ 1\ 0\}_{\beta} \parallel \{0\ 0\ 0\ 1\}_{\alpha}$; $<1\ 1\ 1>_{\beta} \parallel <1\ 1\ \bar{2}\ 0>_{\alpha}$. With the operation of the cubic and hexagonal crystal structural symmetry, there are 12 product variants from a single β parent grain, as listed in Table 1. Assuming absence of variant selection, Wang [14] figured out that only 5 different types of misorientation pairs between product were induced, cf. Table 2. It is seen from Fig. 2 (a) that there are 3 obvious peaks in the misorientation angle distribution in the following ranges: 8° – 12°; 56° – 66° and 88° – 94°, which corresponds to the 5 theoretical misorientation angles according to the Burgers orientation relation, cf Table 1. Fig. 2 (b) depicts the difference between experimental results and theoretical values for 5 different misorientation peaks, and the data are also shown in Table 2. It is clear that the misorientation pair $[\overline{10}\ 5\ 5\ \bar{3}]$/ 63.26° is the dominant type with percentage of 43.8%, followed by $[1\ 1\ \bar{2}\ 0]$/ 60° with 21.8%. From Fig. 2 and Table 2, it is concluded that the phenomenon of variant selection occurs during phase transformation from β phase to α phase. However, because of the experimental uncertainty, it is virtually impossible to distinguish the angular distances of the misorientations $[1\ 1\ \bar{2}\ 0]$/ 60°, $[\overline{1.377}\ \bar{1}\ 2.377\ 0.359]$/ 60.83° and $[\overline{10}\ 5\ 5\ \bar{3}]$/ 63.26°. Therefore, it is necessary to also consider the misorientation axis, which implies a representation in 3D Rodrigues-Frank space.

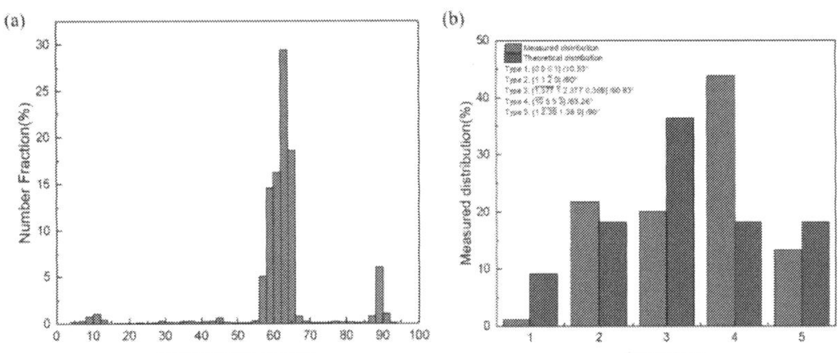

Fig.2 (a) The distribution of misorientation angle along α/α grain boundaries; (b) the misorientation angle fractions compared to the 5 Burgers reference misorientations

Table 1 12 possible α variants following the Burgers OR during phase transformation applying, the cubic symmetry operation and ensuing misorientation pairs between product variants

Variants	Orientation relationship	Symmetry operation	Misorientation pairs from Variant A
A	$(1\,\bar{1}\,0)_\beta \parallel (0\,0\,0\,1)_\alpha$ $[1\,1\,1]_\beta \parallel [1\,1\,\bar{2}\,0]_\alpha$	$\begin{bmatrix} & 1 & \\ & & -1 \\ -1 & & \end{bmatrix}$	-
B	$(1\,0\,\bar{1})_\beta \parallel (0\,0\,0\,1)_\alpha$ $[1\,1\,1]_\beta \parallel [1\,1\,\bar{2}\,0]_\alpha$	$\begin{bmatrix} 1 & & \\ & -1 & \\ & & -1 \end{bmatrix}$	$[1\,1\,\bar{2}\,0]$ / 60°
C	$(0\,1\,\bar{1})_\beta \parallel (0\,0\,0\,1)_\alpha$ $[1\,1\,1]_\beta \parallel [1\,1\,\bar{2}\,0]_\alpha$	$\begin{bmatrix} & & 1 \\ -1 & & \\ & -1 & \end{bmatrix}$	$[1\,1\,\bar{2}\,0]$ / 60°
D	$(1\,1\,0)_\beta \parallel (0\,0\,0\,1)_\alpha$ $[\bar{1}\,1\,1]_\beta \parallel [1\,1\,\bar{2}\,0]_\alpha$	$\begin{bmatrix} & -1 & \\ & & 1 \\ -1 & & \end{bmatrix}$	$[1\,\overline{2.38}\,1.38\,0]$/ 90°
E	$(1\,0\,1)_\beta \parallel (0\,0\,0\,1)_\alpha$ $[\bar{1}\,1\,1]_\beta \parallel [1\,1\,\bar{2}\,0]_\alpha$	$\begin{bmatrix} 1 & & \\ & 1 & \\ & & 1 \end{bmatrix}$	$[\overline{10}\,5\,5\,\bar{3}]$/ 63.26°
F	$(0\,1\,\bar{1})_\beta \parallel (0\,0\,0\,1)_\alpha$ $[\bar{1}\,1\,1]_\beta \parallel [1\,1\,\bar{2}\,0]_\alpha$	$\begin{bmatrix} & & -1 \\ -1 & & \\ & 1 & \end{bmatrix}$	$[\overline{1.377}\,\bar{1}\,2.377\,0.359]$/ 60.83°
G	$(1\,1\,0)_\beta \parallel (0\,0\,0\,1)_\alpha$ $[1\,\bar{1}\,1]_\beta \parallel [1\,1\,\bar{2}\,0]_\alpha$	$\begin{bmatrix} & 1 & \\ & & 1 \\ 1 & & \end{bmatrix}$	$[1\,\overline{2.38}\,1.38\,0]$/ 90°
H	$(1\,0\,\bar{1})_\beta \parallel (0\,0\,0\,1)_\alpha$ $[1\,\bar{1}\,1]_\beta \parallel [1\,1\,\bar{2}\,0]_\alpha$	$\begin{bmatrix} -1 & & \\ & -1 & \\ & & 1 \end{bmatrix}$	$[\overline{1.377}\,\bar{1}\,2.377\,0.359]$/ 60.83°
I	$(0\,1\,1)_\beta \parallel (0\,0\,0\,1)_\alpha$ $[1\,\bar{1}\,1]_\beta \parallel [1\,1\,\bar{2}\,0]_\alpha$	$\begin{bmatrix} & & -1 \\ 1 & & \\ & -1 & \end{bmatrix}$	$[\overline{10}\,5\,5\,\bar{3}]$/ 63.26°
J	$(1\,\bar{1}\,0)_\beta \parallel (0\,0\,0\,1)_\alpha$ $[1\,1\,\bar{1}]_\beta \parallel [1\,1\,\bar{2}\,0]_\alpha$	$\begin{bmatrix} & -1 & \\ & & -1 \\ 1 & & \end{bmatrix}$	$[0\,0\,0\,1]$/ 10.53°
K	$(1\,0\,1)_\beta \parallel (0\,0\,0\,1)_\alpha$ $[1\,1\,\bar{1}]_\beta \parallel [1\,1\,\bar{2}\,0]_\alpha$	$\begin{bmatrix} -1 & & \\ & 1 & \\ & & -1 \end{bmatrix}$	$[\overline{1.377}\,\bar{1}\,2.377\,0.359]$/ 60.83°
L	$(0\,1\,1)_\beta \parallel (0\,0\,0\,1)_\alpha$ $[1\,1\,\bar{1}]_\beta \parallel [1\,1\,\bar{2}\,0]_\alpha$	$\begin{bmatrix} & & 1 \\ 1 & & \\ & 1 & \end{bmatrix}$	$[\overline{1.377}\,\bar{1}\,2.377\,0.359]$/ 60.83°

Table 2 Comparison of the number fractions of misorientation pairs according to the Burgers OR and for the current experiment

Type Reduced axis/angle pairs	Burgers Correspondence	Experiment
I		
$[0\,0\,0\,1]$/ 10.53°	9.1%	1.2%
$[1\,1\,\bar{2}\,0]$/ 60°	18.2%	21.8%
$[\overline{1.377}\,\bar{1}\,2.377\,0.359]$/ 60.83°	36.4%	20.0%
$[\overline{10}\,5\,5\,\bar{3}]$/ 63.26°	18.2%	43.8%
$[1\,\overline{2.38}\,1.38\,0]$/ 90°	18.2%	13.2%

3.3. Rodrigues - Frank Space

The misorientation $\Delta\mathbf{g}$ of two orientations $\mathbf{g}_A$ and $\mathbf{g}_B$ is given by $\Delta\mathbf{g} = \mathbf{g}_B\,\mathbf{g}_A^{-1}$. The Rodrigues vector $\boldsymbol{R}$ corresponds to the misorientation axis/angle pair ($\boldsymbol{r}$, ω), as the vector is defined by: $\boldsymbol{R} = \tan(\omega/2)\boldsymbol{v}$, whereby $\boldsymbol{v}$ is a unit vector parallel to the axis $\boldsymbol{r}$. Fig. 3 (a) and (e) show the distribution of all misorientation pairs in correlated condition as observed in the scanned dataset, and non-correlated condition as calculated from the scanned dataset while assuming that in the non-correlated condition, all possible variants would appear near the checked variants. It is clear that all measured misorientation pairs are located around the theoretical values, and the three important misorientation pairs with rotation angle between 56° ~ 66° can be identified readily.

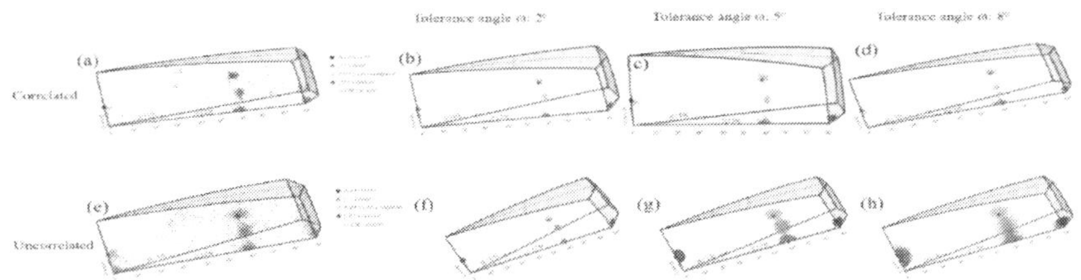

Fig. 3 (a) and (e): The experimental correlated and non-correlated misorientation pairs distribution in R - F space; (b)~(d): the distribution of misorientation pairs between variants with different tolerance angle in correlated condition, respectively; (f)~(h): the distribution of misorientation pairs between variants with different tolerance angle in non-correlated condition, respectively

With the number fraction of misorientation pairs *dr* and *dn* in correlated and non-correlated conditions, respectively, the number density of different theoretical types can be expressed as $D(\Delta\mathbf{g}_r) = dr/dn$. If there is no variant selection during β to α transformation, the value of $D(\Delta\mathbf{g}_r)$ is equal to unit. By allowing different tolerance angle, the actual values of $D(\Delta\mathbf{g}_r)$ may change, cf Table 3. Consistent with the misorientation profile along grain boundaries, the number density results conclude that the phenomenon of variant selection occurs during phase transformation following SLM printing.

During β to α phase transformation, the lattice cells of BCC crystal structure with lattice parameters of 3.196 *Å* have to transform to the lattice cells of HCP crystal structure with parameters of a = 2.943 *Å*, c = 4.680*Å* [15]. the difference of lattice parameters between β and α phase induces transformation strain. In order to minimize the transformed strain, different variants may cluster together during growth, this phenomenon of variants clustering is known as *self-accommodation* and leads to the triangular morphology in microstructure [16]. Another reason for variant selection is the occurrence of residual stresses and defects during printing, such as lack of fusion and micro-voids. Such defects and residual stresses would change the stresses field within samples, resulting in the preferred nucleation and growth of some variants.

Table 3 Relative number density $D(\Delta\mathbf{g}_r)$ for different misorientation pairs and tolerance angle ω

Type Reduced axis/angle pairs	$\omega = 2$	$\omega = 5$	$\omega = 8$
I			
[0 0 0 1]/ 10.53°	1.4	0.5	0.4
[1 1 $\overline{2}$ 0]/ 60°	3.8	1.9	1.6
[$\overline{1.377}$ $\overline{1}$ 2.377 0.359]/ 60.83°	2.0	0.9	0.7
[$\overline{10}$ 5 5 $\overline{3}$]/ 63.26°	4.7	2.2	1.8
[1 $\overline{2.38}$ 1.38 0]/ 90°	3.1	1.4	1.3

4. Conclusion

Through the study of microstructure and misorientation distribution of a Ti-6Al-4V alloy produced by Selective Laser Melting printing, the phenomenon of variant selection has been verified during β to α phase transformation. The misorientation angle profile demonstrates that the main peak in the interval is located between 56° and 66°, which contains 3 major misorientation pairs. The Rodrigues – Frank space is used to clarify the difference among the misorientation pairs of [1 1 $\overline{2}$ 0]/ 60°, [$\overline{1.377}$ $\overline{1}$ 2.377 0.359]/ 60.83° and [$\overline{10}$ 5 5 $\overline{3}$]/ 63.26°. The main misorientation pair is [$\overline{10}$ 5 5 $\overline{3}$]/ 63.26° with a number density of 4.7 (with a tolerance angle of 2°), followed by [1 1$\overline{2}$ 0]/ 60° with 3.8 number density. It can be concluded that variant selection has occurred during phase transformation following SLM printing.

References

[1] W.G Burgers, On the process of transition of the cubic-body-centered modification into the

hexagonal-close-packed modification of zirconium, Physical, 1(7-12) (1934) 561-586.

[2] J.S. Bowles, C.M. Wayman, The bain strain, lattice correspondences, and deformations related to martensitic transformations, Metallurgical Transaction, 3(5) (1972) 1113-1121.

[3] G.B. Olson, M. Cohen, Stress-assisted isothermal martensitic transformation: application to TRIP steels, Metallurgical Transaction A, 13(11) (1982) 1907-1914.

[4] S. Kundu, A.K. Verma, V. Sharma, Quantitative analysis of variant selection for displacive transformations under stress, Metallurgical and Materials Transaction A 43(7) (2012) 2552-2565.

[5] J. Romero, M. Preuss, J.Q. Da Fonseca, Texture memory and variant selection during phase transformation of a zirconium alloy, Acta Materialia, 57(18) (2009) 5501-5511.

[6] G. Obasi, S. Birosca, J.Q. Da Fonseca, M.J.A.m. Preuss, Effect of β grain growth on variant selection and texture memory effect during α→ β → α phase transformation in Ti - 6 Al - 4 V, Acta Materialia, 60(3) (2012) 1048-1058.

[7] N. Stanford, P. Bate, Crystallographic variant selection in Ti–6Al–4V, Acta Materialia, 52(17) (2004) 5215-5224.

[8] D. Bhattacharyya, G. Viswanathan, R. Denkenberger, D. Furrer, H.L. Fraser, The role of crystallographic and geometrical relationships between α and β phases in an α/β titanium alloy, Acta Materialia, 51(16) (2003) 4679-4691.

[9] M. Humbert, L. Germain, N. Gey, P. Bocher, M. Jahazi, E. A, Study of the variant selection in sharp textured regions of bimodal IMI 834 billet, Materials Science and Engineering A, 430(1-2) (2006) 157-164.

[10] V. Randle, A. Day, Use of rodrigues–frank space for representation of microtexture and grain boundary parameters, Materials science and technology, 9(12) (1993) 1069-1078.

[11] F. Bachmann, R. Hielscher, H. Schaeben, Texture analysis with MTEX–free and open source software toolbox, Solid State Phenomena, Trans Tech Publ, 2010, pp. 63-68.

[12] C. Cayron, ARPGE: a computer program to automatically reconstruct the parent grains from electron backscatter diffraction data, Journal of applied crystallography 40(6) (2007) 1183-1188.

[13] J.A. Dantzig, M. Rappaz, Solidification: 2nd Edition - Revised & Expanded, EPFL Press2016.

[14] S.C. Wang, M. Aindow, M.J. Starink, Effect of self-accommodation on α/α boundary populations in pure titanium, Acta Materialia, 51(9) (2003) 2485-2503.

[15] R. Shi. N. Ma. Y. Wang, Predicting equilibrium shape of precipitates as function of coherency state, Acta Materialia, 60(10) (2012) 4172-4184.

[16] D. Srivastava, K. Madangopal, S. Banerjee, S. Ranganathan, Self accommodation morphology of martensite variants in Zr-2.5wt%Nb alloy, Acta Metallurgica et Materialia 41(12) (1993) 3445-3454.

IOP Conf. Series: Materials Science and Engineering 1121 (2021) 012024 doi:10.1088/1757-899X/1121/1/012024

Cyclic ring fiber textures in single tungsten fiber-reinforced tungsten composites

U M Ciucani[1], L Haus[1,2], H Gietl[3], J Riesch[3], and W Pantleon[1]

[1] Technical University of Denmark, 2800 Kongens Lyngby, Denmark.
[2] Technical University Freiberg, 09599 Freiberg, Germany.
[3] Max-Planck-Institute for Plasma Physics, 85748 Garching, Germany.

Email: pawo@dtu.dk

Abstract. Tungsten fiber-reinforced tungsten composites are considered as plasma-facing material in future fusion reactors. Such composites are obtained by chemical vapor deposition of tungsten on potassium-doped, drawn tungsten wires. In model composites containing single fibers, particular texture types develop due to the cylindrical geometry of the deposition process. The vapor-deposited tungsten layers form a cyclic <100> ring fiber texture with one of the <100> directions pointing radially along the growth direction. The procedure for revealing this non-standard texture type from orientation data obtained by electron backscatter diffraction is presented. Identification of cyclic textures requires carefully chosen acquisition regions as well as a suitable coordinate system for their analysis. It is demonstrated that quite erroneous conclusions about the texture of the layer would be drawn if this is not accounted for properly.

1. Introduction

Tungsten is considered for plasma-facing components in future fusion reactors as armor material for the first wall and the divertor. In particular, tungsten fiber-reinforced tungsten composites have achieved certain interest due to their pseudo-ductile behavior [1]. Such composites can be obtained by chemical vapor deposition of tungsten on drawn tungsten wires [2]. The microstructure of a model composite containing a single potassium-doped tungsten fiber is investigated by means of electron backscatter diffraction [3]. Focus is on revealing the particular texture caused by deposition geometry.

2. Materials and techniques

2.1. Material

A tungsten fiber-reinforced tungsten composite is produced by chemical vapor deposition of tungsten on a single tungsten fiber: A drawn tungsten wire doped with 60 ppm potassium and having a diameter of 150 μm provided by OSRAM GmbH is coated in a two-step process by reactive magnetron sputtering with a 1 μm thin interlayer of erbia. A thick layer of pure tungsten (referred to as matrix) is chemically vapor-deposited on this interlayer to a total diameter of 1.5±0.1 mm (for details see [3]). Figure 1 sketches the geometry of the cylindrical specimen. A cross section is cut perpendicular to the cylinder axis, i.e. the wire axis, and prepared for electron backscatter diffraction by mechanical grinding (on SiC-paper of grit size 2000 and 4000) and polishing (with diamond suspension with grain size 3 μm). In a final step, electro-polishing is applied using an aqueous solution containing 3 wt.% NaOH at room temperature with an applied voltage of 12 V and a current of approximately 2 A.

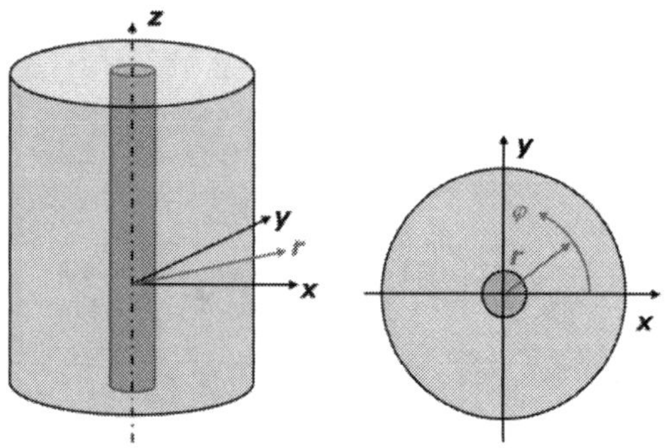

Figure 1. Sketch of the geometry of a cylindrical single tungsten fiber-reinforced tungsten composite (left) and its cross section (right). Upon a drawn, potassium-doped tungsten wire (shown in dark orange) coated with a thin erbia layer (not shown), tungsten is chemically vapor-deposited (light orange). Additional to the Cartesian coordinate system (black), a cylindrical coordinate system is introduced (blue). The radial direction r points in a transversal xy-plane outwards from the wire center, the azimuthal direction φ along the perimeter.

2.2. Microstructural investigation

Orientation data were gathered by electron backscatter diffraction on freshly prepared cross sections using a Bruker NOVA NanoSEM 600 equipped with a Bruker e-Flash HD EBSD detector applying a voltage of 20 kV. A large overview map 2000x1725 µm^2 of the entire cross section is recorded at low magnification with a step size of 5 µm. Without any filtering or removal of non-indexed points, the gathered electron backscatter diffraction data are analyzed using the MTEX toolbox Version 5.5.0 [4] and evaluated further by own purposely developed routines.

3. Results

3.1. Conventional analysis

Figure 2 presents the obtained orientation maps colored according to the crystallographic direction along the three different directions of a Cartesian coordinate system: the z-direction is normal to the mapped surface, the x- and y-direction correspond to the horizontal and vertical direction in the map, respectively. The cylindrical specimen can be recognized by the indexed points surrounded by a white, non-indexed region in the rectangular map. A clearly discernible central region of non-indexed points with diameter of 150 µm marks the locations of the drawn wire and the erbia interlayer. Due to defects formed by the large plastic deformation during wire drawing, orientations within the wire cannot be resolved with the chosen acquisition conditions for obtaining a large overview map. The successfully acquired orientations belong overwhelmingly to the chemically vapor-deposited tungsten matrix.

The orientation maps in figure 2 also highlight high angle boundaries which together with the orientation coloring reveal that in the vicinity of the wire a large number of small grains prevail which are not even resolved properly. In slightly larger distances from the wire, large grains are observed which stretch radially from the vicinity of the wire to the outer surface. These matrix grains grow radially and their wedge-like shape is a signature of the deposition process. The orientation map in figure 2c highlighting the crystallographic directions along the z-direction show dominantly colors from red over yellow to green, i.e. along the line [100]-[110], whereas bluish colors (blue, cyan or magenta) are rarely observed. This indicates the presence of preferred orientations. Further details about the texture are revealed from the corresponding pole figures in figure 3, displaying the crystallographic poles as a function of the spatial directions. The pole figures are derived based on the orientation distribution function calculated from all individual orientations in the map using a de la Valle Poussin kernel [4] with a half width of 10°.

Figure 3a presents the pole figures for the 100, 110 and 111 poles in stereographic projection onto the xy-plane. A maximum pole density of 2.6 compared to a random distribution of orientations is observed in the 100 pole figure where also an increased pole density along the outer perimeter is noticed. Judging solely from this 100 pole figure, the existence of a weak <100> fiber texture along the cylinder axis would be concluded. Further support for an ideal <100> fiber texture is gained from the very weak ring at 45° in the 110 pole figure, but the apparent ring in the 111 pole figure at about 36° contradicts the idea entirely, as such a ring is expected at 54° for an ideal <100> fiber texture.

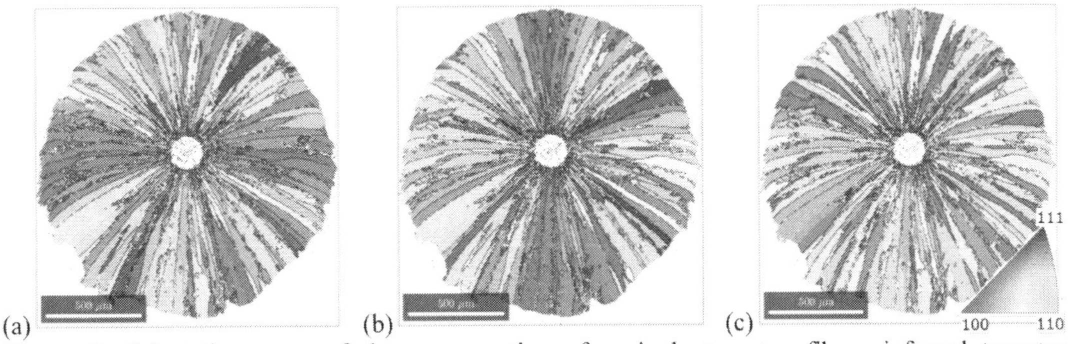

Figure 2. Orientation maps of the cross section of a single tungsten fiber-reinforced tungsten composite with erbia interlayer. The colors reflect the crystallographic directions along different sample directions according to the inset: (a) along x-, (b) along y- and (c) along z-direction, i.e. along the wire axis. High angle boundaries with disorientation angles above 15° are indicated in black.

These observations are confirmed by the inverse pole figure in figure 3b along the z-axis which indeed shows a slight preference of [100] directions, but all directions along the symmetry line [100]-[110] are much more frequent than expected for an ideal <100> fiber texture along the z-direction.

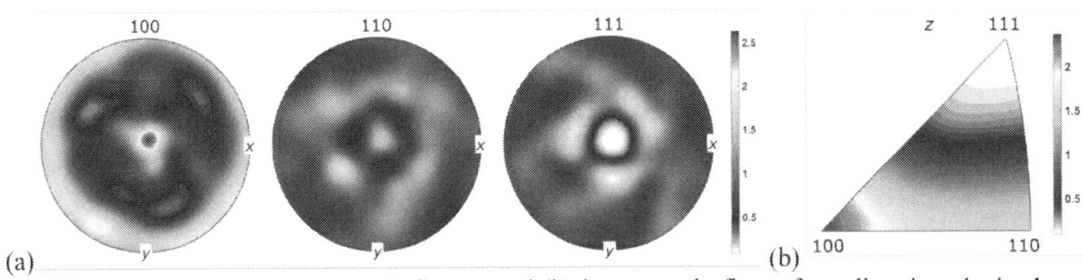

Figure 3. (a) 100, 110, and 111 pole figures and (b) inverse pole figure for z-direction obtained on a single tungsten fiber-reinforced tungsten composite with erbia interlayer. The data include all acquired orientations from the cross section shown in figure 2 and correspond overwhelmingly to locations in the matrix. All densities are given in multiples of random distribution according to the scale bar.

3.2. Improved analysis

In view of this evidence, the texture of the matrix cannot be a <100> fiber texture with a fiber axis along the wire and a more appropriate description of the texture is required. Revisiting the orientation maps in figure 2 exposes a hint: in figure 2a showing the crystallographic direction along the x-direction, the color red is dominating along a horizontal stripe in the center of the cross section revealing that horizontally aligned grains extend along one of their <100> directions. A similar observation can be made from figure 2b showing the crystallographic direction along the y-direction; here the red color of vertically aligned grains indicates that these also extend along one of their <100> directions, which in their case points along the y-direction, i.e. vertically instead of horizontally. Considering the cylindrical symmetry of the specimen, it seems plausible to conclude that all grains actually extend along one of their <100> directions radially outwards.

In order to exploit the observation that the grains exhibit a particular direction of extension along which one of their <100> directions is aligned, but that this direction is different from grain to grain, a special procedure for analyzing the texture is adapted. In view of the geometry of the specimen and the deposition process, a cylindrical coordinate system is introduced as shown in figure 1 where the radial r-direction points radially outwards from the wire center and the azimuthal φ-direction along the corresponding perimeter (the z-axis still coincides with the wire axis). In such a cylindrical coordinate system, the coordinate axes r and φ point in different directions at each position in a transversal plane.

IOP Conf. Series: Materials Science and Engineering 1121 (2021) 012024 doi:10.1088/1757-899X/1121/1/012024

For calculating pole figures and inverse pole figures with respect to these new coordinate axes, their local dependence must be taken into account. Such an evaluation is presently not implemented in any standard tool for evaluating orientation data. An appropriate procedure has been developed and implemented in MATLAB. The idea is basically to use standard evaluation tools for creating orientation maps, pole figures and inverse pole figures – not on the original orientations, but after a straightforward modification of the orientations in the map: Realizing that the cylindrical coordinate system is rotated by the azimuthal angle φ with respect to the Cartesian system at any position in the map, the Euler angle φ_2 of each orientation is adjusted accordingly. The resulting orientation maps, pole figures and inverse pole figures are on display on figures 4 and 5.

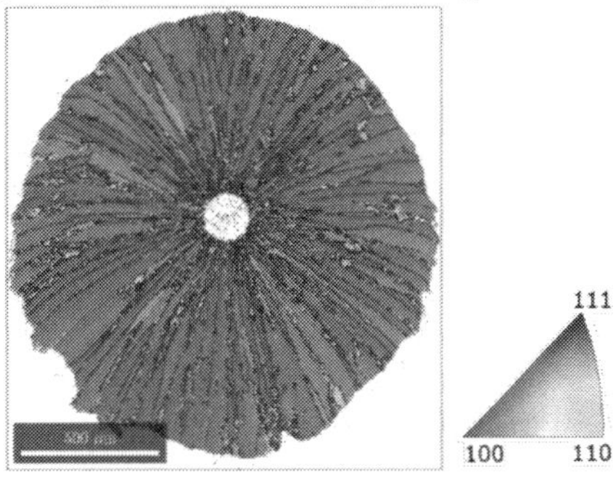

Figure 4. Orientation map of the cross section of a single tungsten fiber-reinforced tungsten composite with erbia interlayer (same data as in figure 2). The colors reflect the crystallographic directions along the radial direction of a cylindrical coordinate system according to the inset. High angle boundaries with disorientation angles above 15° are indicated in black.

In the orientation map in figure 4 colored according to the crystallographic direction along the radial direction, a dominating red color appears exposing an overwhelming dominance of <100> directions pointing radially outwards. The character of the texture is further confirmed by the pole figures in figure 5a. In the 100 pole figure, a strong alignment of crystallographic <100> directions with the radial direction is seen (with a maximum 100 pole density of 10.5), the ring in the plane comprising the azimuthal and axial direction is a direct consequence of this strong alignment and the angle of 90° between <100> directions. In a similar way, <110> directions form either an angle of 45° or 90° degrees with <100> explaining neatly the observed rings in the 110 pole figure. Finally, the angle of 54° between <111> and <100> directions rationalizes the position of the rings in the 111 pole figure. All rings in the pole figures are rather smoothly populated and no systematic variation is observed along them indicating the presence of an ideal <100> fiber texture along the radial direction.

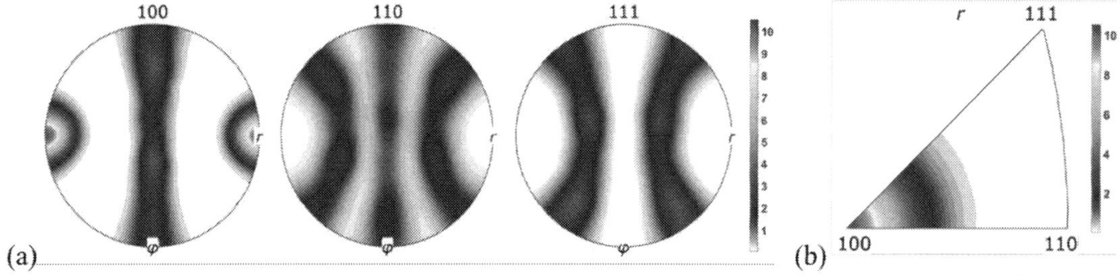

Figure 5. (a) 100, 110, and 111 pole figures with respect to cylindrical coordinates and (b) inverse pole figure along the radial r-direction obtained on a single tungsten fiber-reinforced tungsten composite with erbia interlayer. The data include all acquired orientations from the cross section shown in figure 2 and correspond overwhelmingly to locations in the matrix. The densities are given in multiples of random distribution according to the scale bar.

In consequence, the texture is a strong, ideal <100> fiber texture along the radial direction in the cylindrical coordinate system and not a weak <100> fiber texture along the axial direction as may have been concluded from investigating the texture in a Cartesian coordinate system. In view of these findings, the texture in the sample system must be described differently: At first, there is a preferred alignment of <100> directions in the transversal plane with free rotation around that aligned direction.

Such textures are classified as ring fiber textures [5] (alternatively, the term planar texture is used [6]). Additionally to one of the <100> directions occurring in the transversal plane (and free rotations around it), this specific direction aligns with the radial direction causing a different preferred orientation at any spatial position. Textures featuring a certain crystallographic direction aligned with the radial direction are termed cyclic textures [5,7] (or cylindrical textures [8] or circular textures [9]) and usually discussed in connection with cylindrical objects (wires or tubes). In consequence, the texture of the deposited layer must be classified as cyclic <100> ring fiber texture.

4. Discussion

A cyclic <100> ring fiber texture is concluded for the deposited layer with <100> directions aligned in the transversal plane perpendicular to the wire axis and the particular feature from cylindrical symmetry, that these <100> directions point radially. The possibility of cyclic ring fiber textures has been discussed theoretically [5], but to the knowledge of the authors never been reported before.

Cyclic fiber textures and cyclic ring fiber textures might be more widespread than commonly reported, because it might be difficult to resolve spatial correlations between preferred orientations as in the present case. To illustrate the danger of underestimating the impact of spatial correlations for obtaining a proper texture description, different regions of the original map are analyzed separately. Four different subsets of orientations are obtained from four smaller quadratic or rectangular regions (each comprising about half the number of indexed points) as illustrated in the top row of figure 6.

The corresponding 100 pole figures in the bottom row of figure 6 show rather different pole distributions: From the 100 pole figure of the entire map (figure 6a), a <100> fiber texture along the z-axis would be concluded naively. For the square region in figure 6b, 100 poles are observed under 45° with respect to x- and y-direction implying preferred orientations belonging to a {100}<011> texture component (a cube orientation rotated by 45° around z); for the rotated square region (figure 6c), 100 poles along both x- and y-direction are dominating implying the presence of an ideal {100}<001> cube component; for the horizontal rectangle, 100 poles appear along the x-direction and an additional ring in the yz-plane (in figure 6d) implying a <100> fiber texture along the x-axis. Just the opposite is true for the vertical rectangle; the 100 pole figure in figure 6e indicates a <100> fiber texture along the y-direction. Hence, depending on the choice of the region from which orientations are acquired, rather different texture types are concluded based on the 100 pole figures as summarized in table 1: in some cases, fiber textures with different fiber axes (<100> fiber texture along x-, y-, or z-direction), in other cases, textures with orthorhombic symmetry (cube or rotated cube).

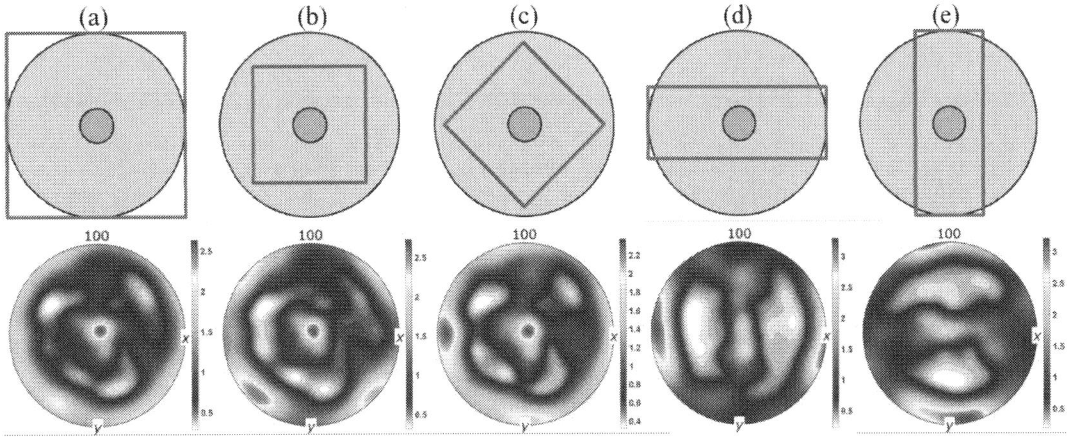

Figure 6. Schematic drawing of different acquisition regions on the cross section of a single tungsten fiber-reinforced tungsten composite with erbia interlayer (top row) and corresponding 100 pole figures (bottom row) for (a) data acquired for the entire cross section corresponding to figure 2, (b) to (e) different square and rectangular regions with about half of the number of indexed points.

Table 1. Quantitative texture analysis for different regions on the cross section (cf. figure 6)

Region	Max. 100 pole density	Texture index	Texture entropy	Texture type (as concluded from 100 pole figure)
Full map (Cartesian coord.)	2.6	1.55	-0.28	<100> fiber texture along *z*
Full map (cylindrical coord.)	*10.5*	*5.09*	*-1.16*	*Cyclic <100> ring fiber texture*
Central square	2.7	1.62	-0.29	{100}<011> *z*-rotated cube texture
Rotated square	2.4	1.51	-0.26	{100}<001> cube texture)
Horizontal rectangle	3.3	1.92	-0.39	<100> fiber texture along *x*
Vertical rectangle	3.2	1.84	-0.38	<100> fiber texture along *y*

The cyclic nature of the texture can be substantiated further by the measures of texture strength in table 1: When using a Cartesian coordinate system, independent of the chosen region rather weak textures are indicated by 100 pole densities of maximal 3.3, texture indices [10] less than 2 and texture entropies [11] above -0.4. Using an appropriate cylindrical coordinate system with spatially different coordinate axes for the description of the orientations confirms the strong preference of certain directions and orientations seen in the pole figures and inverse pole figure in figure 4. The maximal 100 pole density of 10.5 verifies that a much better texture description is achieved by realizing the presence of a cyclic texture. The existence of a strong cyclic ring fiber texture is further substantiated by the high texture index above 5 and the large negative value -1.16 of the texture entropy.

5. Conclusion

A tungsten fiber-reinforced tungsten composite has been investigated by electron backscatter diffraction. The chemically vapor-deposited tungsten matrix shows a peculiar texture identified as cyclic <100> ring fiber texture. The required thorough texture analysis is detailed and the effect of inappropriate choices for the acquisition regions outlined. This clearly demonstrates how important an adequate characterization becomes and how strongly results can be affected by spatial correlations, if sample symmetry is not respected. When using an inappropriate coordinate system, completely erroneous textures might be concluded. On the other hand, when utilizing an appropriate coordinate system even more complicated texture types can be identified as the cyclic <100> ring fiber texture.

Acknowledgments

This work has been carried out partially within the framework of the EUROfusion Consortium and has received funding from the Euratom research and training programme 2014-2018 and 2019-2020 under grant agreement No 633053. The views and opinions expressed herein do not necessarily reflect those of the European Commission.

References

[1] Riesch J, Höschen T, Linsmeier C, Wurster S, and You J H 2014 *Phys. Scr.* **2014** 014031
[2] Du J, You J H, and Höschen T 2012 *J. Mater. Sci.* **47** 4706
[3] Ciucani U M, Haus L, Gietl, H, Riesch J, and Pantleon W 2021 *J. Nucl. Mater.* **543** 152579
[4] Bachmann F, Hielscher R, and Schaeben H 2010 *Solid State Phenom.* **160** 63
[5] Wassermann G and Grewen J 1962 *Texturen metallischer Werkstoffe* 2nd edition (Berlin: Springer Verlag) pp 7-11
[6] Saraf R F 1994 *Polymer* **35** 1359
[7] Stüwe P 1961 *Z. Metallkde.* **52** 34
[8] Leber S 1961 *Trans. Amer. Soc. Metals* **52** 697
[9] Kocks U F, Tomé C N, and Wenk H.-R. 1998 *Texture and Anisotropy* (Cambridge: Cambridge University Press) p 151
[10] Bunge H.-J. 1982 *Texture Analysis in Materials Science* (Butterworth & Co) p 88
[11] Schaeben H 1988 *J. Appl. Phys.* **64** 2236

Improving Ductility in Dual-Phase Steel by Cold Rolling and Intercritical Annealing

Alok Kumar Singh[1*], Basudev Bhattacharya[2], Somjeet Biswas[1]
[1]Department of Metallurgical and Materials Engineering, IIT Kharagpur, 721302, India
[2]R & D Division, Tata Steel, Jamshedpur, Jharkhand, 831001, India
alok.ks009@gmail.com, drbasudevb@gmail.com, somjeetbiswas@metal.iitkgp.ac.in
corresponding author*

Abstract. Dual-phase steels offer huge potential to provide a cost-effective solution in the automobile industry to fulfill the demand for high strength with formability. The desirable strength is achieved by increasing geometrically necessary boundaries and ferrite grain refinement but not by increasing martensite fraction. The major challenge is to improve the ductility and formability, without compromising its strength. In this work, cold rolling reductions to ~84% was given to hot rolled annealed steel, followed by intercritical annealing and water quenching. Tensile tests, Optical microscopy, Electron Back Scattered Diffraction and X-Ray characterizations were carried out. The improvement in strength and ductility were correlated with microstructure and texture.
Keywords: Dual-phase steel; Cold rolling; Intercritical annealing; Microstructure; Texture; Ductility

1. Introduction

Dual-phase (DP) steels are one of the most important members of the advanced high strength steel (AHSS) family, widely used as automobile structural components [1,2]. These steels are low carbon alloyed steels with Mn, Si, Cr, Nb, Ti, Mo, and B additions up to 4% [2,3]. The low alloying in DP steels leads to lower the production cost, ease of casting due to less segregation effect, better weldability and simple thermomechanical treatments in comparisons to other steels in the AHSS family [2,3]. These steels are industrially produced using a combination of hot/cold rolling and intercritical heat treatments [2,4–6]. The microstructure of DP steels mainly consists of ferrite and martensite phases, with some bainite and retained austenite [1,7]. This composite microstructure provides continuous yielding, high tensile strength with limited ductility and formability [7–10]. The reason for limited ductility and formability is the low damage tolerance in DP steels due to martensite cracking and martensite-ferrite interface decohesion [7,9]. Damage tolerant DP steels could be produced by engineering the microstructure and texture. Ultrafine ferrite grains with finely dispersed martensitic islands ~30% volume fraction are the most desirable microstructural features in DP steels for better endurance limit and formability [2,11].

It is important to carry out a fundamental study to develop a deeper understanding of microstructure, texture and deformation mechanisms to guide novel strategies to develop ductile, formable, and damage-tolerant DP steels. In this work, cold rolling (CR) studies of an annealed DP steel has been carried out in conjunction with intercritical heat treatment (IHT). The evolution of the microstructure and texture in correlation with ductility and formability is investigated.

2. Experiments and Methodologies

A DP steel (chemical composition: C < 0.10%, Mn < 2.0%, Si < 0.5%, and Cr < 1.0%) was used in this study. Hot rolled steel sheets were annealed at 1163K (890°C) for 60 $mins$ to obtain a full ferrite microstructure as the initial material for this study (figure 1a,d). The initial steel sheets were subjected to CR up to ~84% ($e_{VM} = 2.1$) rolling reductions, followed by intercritical annealing at 1113K (840°C) for 60 min and water quenching. These intercritically annealed samples were further annealed at 873K (600°C) for 15 min and water quenched. Tensile tests were performed as per ASTM E-8 on a miniature sample geometry. Optical and EBSD analysis were carried out on the ND-RD plane.

IOP Conf. Series: Materials Science and Engineering 1121 (2021) 012025 doi:10.1088/1757-899X/1121/1/012025

EBSD data were analyzed using TSL-OIM software. Crystallite size and dislocation density were determined by X-ray line profile analysis [12,13].

3. Results

3.1 Microstructural Features

The optical micrographs, inverse pole figure (IPF) maps and grain size distributions for the initial, CR and CR+IHT steels are shown in figure 1. The IPF maps (figure 1d-f) represent the orientation of the grains by different colors as per the crystallographic triangle code. The initial steel had a unimodal grain size distribution that ranges from $\sim 1-25\mu m$ (figure 1g) with an average grain size of $8.2 \pm 3.2\mu m$. After CR (figure 1b) thin elongated grains could be observed (figure 1b,e). A bimodal grain size distribution ranging from $\sim 0.20-20\mu m$ (figure 1h), with an average grain size of $8.2 \pm 8\mu m$ was observed. The first peak lies at the start of distribution around $\sim 0.2\mu m$ in small grains range, and these small grains have formed due to the phenomena of dynamic recrystallization (DRX) during deformation. The other peak lies at the end of distribution around $\sim 21\mu m$ which indicate elongated deformed grains, where DRX did not take place. The CR +IHT processed steel sheet possesses island type ferrite - ~34% martensite morphology (figure 1c,f) with equiaxed grains, size ranging from $\sim 0.40-16\mu m$ and average grain size, $5.5 \pm 3.5\mu m$.

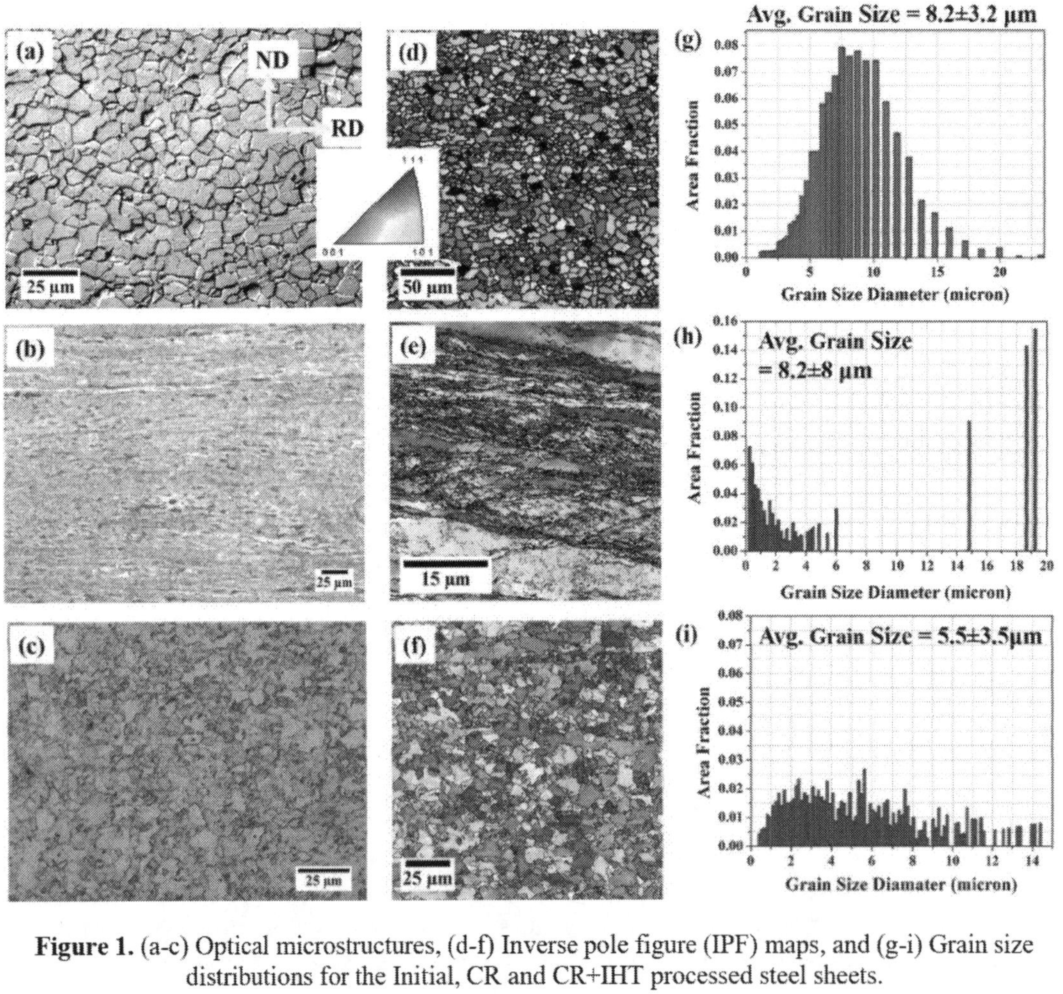

Figure 1. (a-c) Optical microstructures, (d-f) Inverse pole figure (IPF) maps, and (g-i) Grain size distributions for the Initial, CR and CR+IHT processed steel sheets.

Further, the density of geometrically necessary boundaries (GNB) with $2° - 15°$ misorientation angles, random high angle boundaries (RHAGB) with $15° - 65°$ misorientation angles and coincidence site lattice (CSL) boundaries (a subset of $15° - 65°$ boundaries) were determined from the EBSD data (figure 2a). The GNB are defined as curvature type dislocations arising during deformation due to dislocation activity inside the grains [14]. They are subgrain feature with $2° - 15°$ misorientation angle and usually captured during EBSD analysis using a fine step size. The GNB and RHAGB density increases from the initial state (~$0.05 \times 10^{12}m^{-2}$ and ~$0.04 \times 10^{12}m^{-2}$) to after CR (~$0.6 \times 10^{12}m^{-2}$ and ~$1.39 \times 10^{12}m^{-2}$), respectively. It reduces after the IHT to (~0.5 $\times 10^{12}m^{-2}$ and ~0.42 $\times 10^{12}m^{-2}$). The CSL density remains the same and negligible ~0.05 $\times 10^{12}m^{-2}$ for all the samples.
The (110) X-ray diffraction peak was used to obtain the crystallite size and statistically stored dislocation (SSD) density [12,13]. The SSD density showed a similar trend, as the GNB density obtained from EBSD (figure 2b). Corroborating the observation the crystallite size decreases from 56nm to 48 nm after CR followed by an increase to 63nm after IHT (figure 2b).

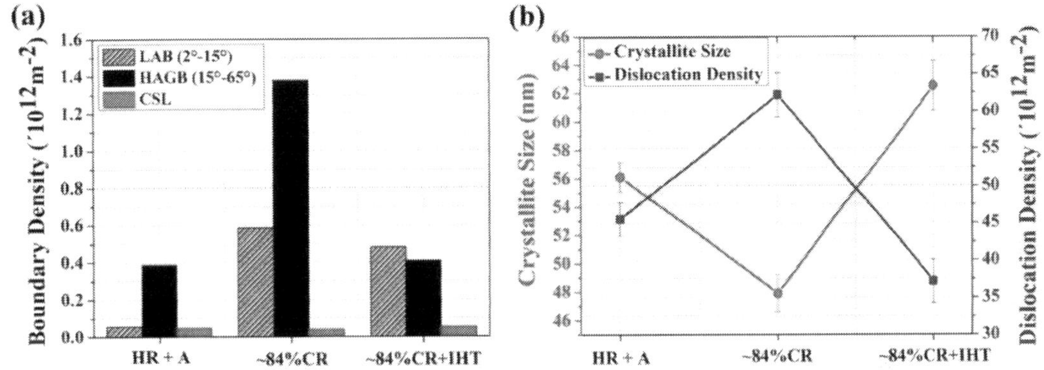

Figure 2. (a) GNB, RHAGB, CSL boundary density; and (b) Crystallite size, dislocation density; for the the initial, CR and CR+IHT steel sheets.

3.2. Crystallographic Texture
The $\varphi_2 = 0°$ and $\varphi_2 = 45°$, sections of the orientation distribution functions (ODF) sections were utilized to represent the texture in figure 3a-c for the initial, CR and CR+IHT steel sheets. The ideal orientations for rolling of BCC materials are shown in figure 3d. The initial material possesses a weak α-fiber, β-fiber as well as partial γ-fiber with ~2.6 multiples of random distribution (MRD). After CR γ-fiber with the intensity of ~5 MRD, and a partial but strong θ-fiber, with intensity of ~10 MRD at the rotated cube positions could be observed. The texture spreaded as well as diffused after IHT with the presence of faint θ, β and γ- fibers.

3.3 Mechanical Properties
Table 1 compares the yield strength (YS), ultimate tensile strength (UTS), ductility (ε_f), and uniform elongation (n) of the initial, CR, and CR+IHT steel sheets. The YS and UTS increase substantially after CR, but ductility decreases from ~0.58 to ~0.15. The ductility is restored to 0.51 after IHT with a reasonable compromise in YS and UTS to ~396MPa and ~544MPa, respectively. The uniform elongation, which is equivalent to strain hardening exponent and is an index to show formability, reduces after CR. However, it regains and become quite high, ~0.35 after IHT. After CR+IHT, DP steel with desirable ferrite-martensite morphology, strength and formability was obtained.

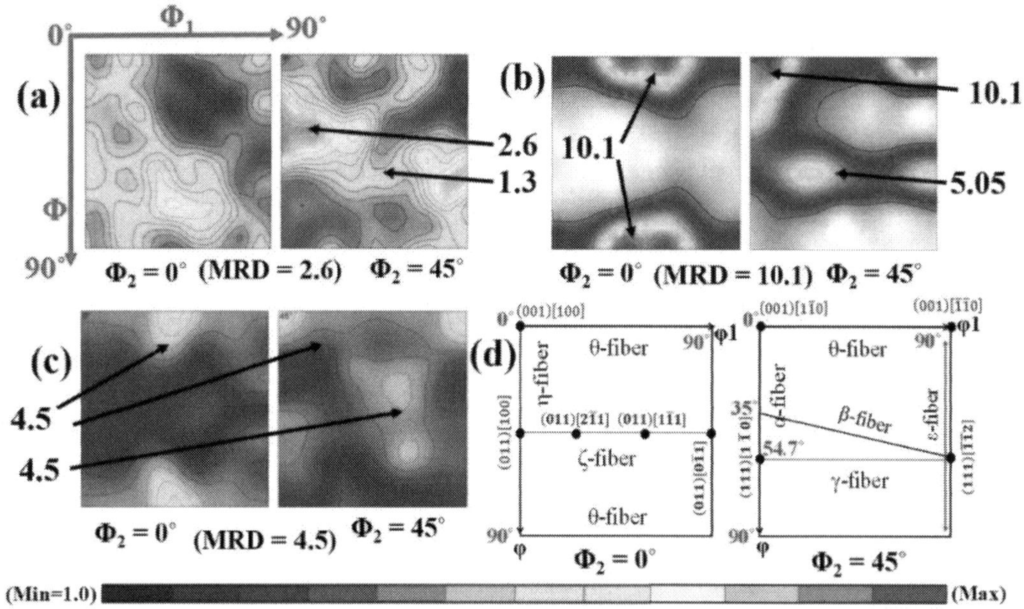

Figure 3. $\phi_2 = 0^{\circ}$ and 45° ODF sections for steel samples (a) Initial, (b) CR and (c) CR+IHT and (d) Ideal end orientations of BCC texture fibers.

Table 1. Mechanical properties of the initial, CR, and CR+IHT steel sheets.

Sample Name	YS (MPa)	UTS (MPa)	ε_f	n
Initial	220	438	0.58	0.40
CR	650	790	0.15	0.07
CR+IHT	396	544	0.51	0.35

4. Discussions

CR of the initial hot rolled and annealed ferritic steel sheet led to the breakdown of the microstructure into elongated laminar type grains with heterogenous bimodal grain size distribution (figure 1). After CR a large strain hardening took place in the material which leads to the increase in YS and UTS to ~650 MPa and ~790 MPa with reduced ductility (table 1). This strengthening is reflected in terms of the increase in SSD, GNB, RHAGB density with the decrease in crystallite size in figure 2. The Hall-Petch as well as dislocation hardening both took place during the CR process [2,8]. Dislocation hardening consists of both GNB (ρ_{GNB}) and SSD (ρ_{SSD}) present in the microstructure and their contribution in strength is given by the relation: $\sigma = \sigma_o M\alpha Gb(\rho_{SSD} + \rho_{GNB})^{-0.5}$, where σ_o is the frictional stress, α is a constant coefficient (between 0 to 1), M is the Taylor factor, G is the shear modulus and b is the Burgers vector [14,15].

Further, the IHT treatment of CR steel by intercritical annealing at 1113K(840°C) and quenching, with secondary annealing at 873K(600°C) and quenching led to the formation of desirable microstructure with ferrite-martensite island type structure. The martensite fraction was ~34%, which is desirable for the higher formability and endurance limit [2,11]. High strength of $\sim 544MPa$, ductility of 0.51, and $n = 0.35$ could be obtained in this inexpensive grade steel. The improvement in strength and ductility could also be associated with (i) equiaxed grains with a lower average grain size of $5.5 \pm 3.5\mu m$, (ii) low SSD, GNB, RHAGB density, large crystallite size; and (iii) diffused crystallographic texture with the low intensity that improves the isotropy.

5. Conclusions

Hot-rolled and annealed ferritic steel sheets were cold rolled up to ~84% reduction. Thereafter, intercritical annealing at $1113K(840°C)$ for $60min$ and water quenching, followed by secondary annealing at $873K$-$(600°C)$ for $15min$ and water quenching was carried out. DP steel with ~34% volume fraction martensitic structure in island type ferrite morphology was obtained, which is desirable. The DP steel possesses a high strength of ~544MPa, ductility of 0.51, and n=0.35, and is attributed to equiaxed grains, recovered microstructure and weak texture.

Acknowledgement

The authors would like to acknowledge the facilities availed in 'Light Metals and Alloys Research Lab' at the Department of Metallurgical and Materials Engineering and Central Research Facility in Indian Institute of Technology, Kharagpur, India.

References

[1] Keeler S, Kimchi M and Mooney P J 2017 Advanced high-strength steels spplication guidelines version **6.0** 1-314

[2] Zhao J and Jiang Z 2018 Thermomechanical processing of advanced high strength steels, *Prog. Mater. Sci.* **94** 174–242

[3] Tamarelli C M 2011 AHSS 101: the evolving use of advanced high-strength steel for automotive applications *Steel Mark. Dev. Inst.* 1-45

[4] Mazaheri Y, Kermanpur A and Najafizadeh A 2014 A novel route for development of ultrahigh strength dual phase steels *Mater. Sci. Eng. A.* **619** 1–11

[5] Mazaheri Y, Jahanara A H, Sheikhi M and Kalashami A G 2019 High strength-elongation balance in ultrafine grained ferrite-martensite dual phase steels developed by thermomechanical processing, *Mater. Sci. Eng. A* **761** 138021

[6] Karmakar A, Sivaprasad S, Nath S K, Misra R D K and Chakrabarti D 2014 Comparison between different processing schedules for the development of ultrafine-grained dual-phase steel *Metall. Mater. Trans. A* **45** 2466–79

[7] Mazinani M and Poole W J 2007 Effect of martensite plasticity on the deformation behavior of a low-carbon dual-phase steel *Metall. Mater. Trans. A* **38** 328–39

[8] Song R, Ponge D and Raabe D 2005 Improvement of the work hardening rate of ultrafine grained steels through second phase particles *Scr. Mater.* **52** 1075–80

[9] Calcagnotto M, Adachi Y, Ponge D and Raabe D 2011 Deformation and fracture mechanisms in fine- and ultrafine-grained ferrite/martensite dual-phase steels and the effect of aging *Acta Mater.* **59** 658–70

[10] Calcagnotto M, Ponge D and Raabe D 2010 Effect of grain refinement to 1 μm on strength and toughness of dual-phase steels *Mater. Sci. Eng. A* **527** 7832–40

[11] Sherman M and Davies R G 1981 The effect of martensite content on the fatigue of a dual-phase steel *Int. J. Fatigue* **3** 36–40

[12] Singh R B, Mukhopadhyay N K, Sastry G V S and Manna R 2017 Development of High Strength Bulk Ultrafine-Grained Low Carbon Steel Produced by Equal-Channel Angular Pressing, *Metall. Mater. Trans. A* **48** 5449–66

[13] Chouhan D K, Biswas S, Singh A K, Shukla A J 2020 High tensile strength-ductility combination in cold multiaxial plane-strain forged and rolled nanostructured Titanium *Materialia* **11** 100698

[14] Kundu A and Field D P 2018 Geometrically necessary dislocation density evolution in

interstitial free steel at small plastic strains *Metall. Mater. Trans. A* **49** 3274–82
[15] D A Hughes and N Hansen 2000 Microstructure and strength of nickel at large strains Acta Mater. **48** 2985-3004

Twin induced Strain Hardening, Grain Fragmentation, and Texture Evolution during Cold Compression of CP-Ti

Devesh Kumar Chouhan*, Somjeet Biswas
Light Metals and Alloys Research Lab, Department of Metallurgical and Materials Engg, Indian Institute of Technology Kharagpur-721302, India
chouhan.devesh@gmail.com*, somjeetbiswas@metal.iitkgp.ac.in

Abstract. This work is a systematic investigation of the twin induced strain hardening behavior, grain fragmentation, and texture evolution during titanium's cold compression. The compression tests were stopped at intermediate strains for quantitative microscopy by electron backscattered diffraction. The microstructural examination indicates the evolution of $\{10\bar{1}2\}$ extension twins (ET), $\{11\bar{2}2\}$ contraction twins (CT) and the interaction between them. The strain hardening rate and its derivative plot could be corroborated with the microstructural features and distinguishes regions of slip and twin dominating zones. The texture evolution indicates that dislocation slips were active apart from deformation twins during deformation. Texturally hard ET evolves, broadens, and interacts in texturally soft grains at low and intermediate strains. The ET regions are suitable for the nucleation of texturally soft CT with further strain. During deformation, ET-ET ~56.8°$\langle 10\bar{1}0\rangle$, CT-CT ~77°$\langle 10\bar{1}0\rangle$, ET-CT ~87°$\langle 4\bar{2}\bar{2}1\rangle$ interactions boundaries and CT-ET ~44.5°$\langle 5\bar{1}\bar{4}0\rangle$ double twins develop.

Keywords: Titanium; Strain hardening; Grain fragmentation; Extension twinning; Contraction twinning;

1.Introduction

Commercially pure titanium (CP-Ti) is widely used in various aviation, chemical, sports, and biomedical applications due to its high specific strength, corrosion resistance, and biocompatibility [1]. Many researchers have improved strength and ductility in low-density hexagonal close-packed (HCP) materials via microstructure and texture engineering through thermo-mechanical processing [2-4]. An in-depth understanding of deformation behavior is required for all-around improvement in ambient mechanical properties. Owing to the HCP crystal structure with a low c/a ratio, Ti possesses complex deformation behavior compared to cubic crystals [5,6]. To accommodate the imposed stress at ambient temperature, deformation twins get activated subsequently after micro-yielding via two independent prismatic slip to satisfy the Von-Mises criteria [7]. The activation of each slip and twin system requires a critical resolved shear stress [8]. Mainly, two types of twin systems $\{10\bar{1}2\}$ extension (ET) and $\{11\bar{2}2\}$ contraction twins (CT) occur in Ti at ambient temperature [5]. The evolution of twins occurs in sequences such as ET-CT-ET or CT-ET-CT, depending on the initial texture and direction/type of external loading [9]. The activation of ET and CT reorients the parent matrix by ~ 85° about $\langle 11\bar{2}0\rangle$ and ~ 63.5° about $\langle 10\bar{1}0\rangle$, respectively. Each twin system has six twin variants, and their activation is governed by the angular relation between crystallographic orientation and loading direction. In the separate investigation by Chouhan and Shina et al. [8,10] showed the three different stages of twinning, namely nucleation, propagation, and lateral thickening during plastic deformation. It is reported that activation of multi twin variants and the intersection of propagating twin fronts enhance the grain boundary strengthening [10]. Hence, the grain fragmentation, crystallographic orientation changes, and textural hardening/softening are accelerated mainly by deformation twinning instead of dislocation slip

in Ti. There are few investigations on the grain refinement via twin-twin intersection, splitting of twins during consecutive deformation, and twin growth in CP-Ti.
In this work, uniaxial compression tests on CP-Ti were carried out at ambient temperature to observe ET and CT sequential evolution and their effect on strain hardening behavior, texture evolution, and microstructure refinement. Multiple samples were collected at the intermediate strains for quantitative microstructure and texture analysis. The various grains were cropped from deformed samples. Here, we present the grain by grain analysis to link the twin and its morphology, such as lamella, intersecting, and lateral broadening with strain hardening behavior and flow curve feature followed by texture evolution.

2.Materials and Method

Compression tests of hot extruded grade-2 Ti bar with length to width ratio of ~1.5 as per ASTM E09 were performed at a strain rate of $0.005s^{-1}$ on the Instron 1344 Universal Testing Machine. Samples were collected at various intermediate true strains from ~0.05 to 0.69 to carry out quantitative microscopy by electron backscattered diffraction (EBSD) in the AURIGA field emission gun scanning electron microscope. In this regard, the samples were prepared by mechanically polished out up to 1μm SiC abrasive paper, followed by electropolishing in LectroPol-5 (STRUTS) at a voltage of 18V for 15s at 25°C via electrolytic solution containing 700ml Ethanol, 120ml distilled water, 100ml 2-butoxyethanol, 80ml $HClO_4$. The EBSD data were analyzed using ATEX software [11].

3.Results and Discussion

3.1.Flow Curve and strain hardening Behavior

The microstructure of the as-received material in figure 1(a) shows twin free equiaxed grains with an average grain size of ~ 20 μm. During uniaxial compression, a significant grain size reduction takes place. Figure 1(b) shows the variation in grain size with increasing true strain. The grain size reduces to ~ 5 μm after ~ 0.69 true strain. The experimental flow curve is shown in figure 1(c). A typical 'S' type flow curve depicts that the imposed plastic strain is accommodated by a profuse amount of deformation twins along with dislocation slip [7, 12]. The markers show the intermediate strains at which the samples were collected for microstructure and texture analyses.

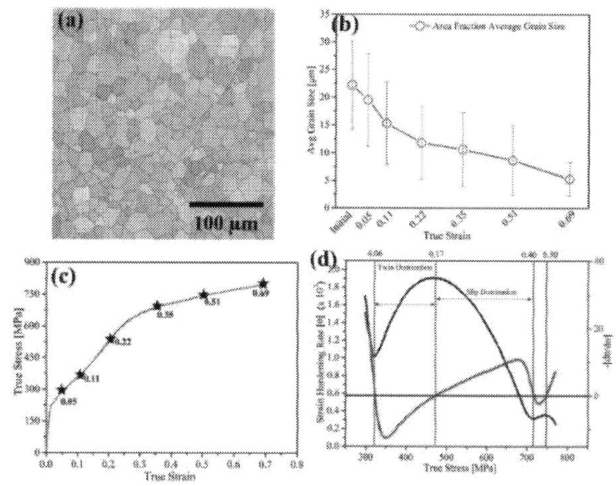

Figure 1. (a) Image quality map of the as-received material, (b) Average grain size for CP-Ti concerning true compressive strain, (c) Flow curve with markers representing the intermediate strains at which samples were collected for analysis, and (d) Strain hardening rate and it is derivative vs true stress curves for uniaxial compression along extrusion direction of CP-Ti

The activation of $\{10\bar{1}2\}\langle 10\bar{1}\bar{1}\rangle$ type ET [5,13] orient the part of parent grain by ~ 85° about $\langle 11\bar{2}0\rangle$ towards compression direction (CD). The formation of ET increases the hard orientations in the microstructure. It could be further corroborated with the strain hardening rate (SHR) and derivative of the SHR plot with respect to true stress, as shown in figure 1(d). After the micro yielding (at $\varepsilon \approx 0.06$), the decrease in the SHR denotes the material is deformed by slip along with deformation twinning. Whereas, at $\varepsilon \approx 0.06$ derivative of SHR became zero and reached its minima at $\varepsilon \approx 0.10$. From the $\varepsilon \approx 0.06$ to 0.10, the twins are nucleated, and its activity increases. After that, an increase in strain (at $\varepsilon \approx 0.22$) the rise in strain hardening (figure 1c) and SHR (figure 1d) in a material due to the change in crystallographic orientation via ET. Therefore, in the strain range $\varepsilon \approx 0.06$ to 0.17, the material is mainly deformed by deformation twinning. A horizontal line corresponds to zero value of derivative of SHR, divides the slip and twin dominating strain range, i.e., the strain ranges ≈ 0.06 to 0.17 and ≈ 0.40 to 0.50 are denoted the twin domination. The detailed description, along with the microstructure evidence, is reported by Chouhan et al. [8] in 2019

3.2. Texture Evolution

Figure. 2(a-d) shows the evolution of deformation texture using inverse pole figure along compression direction (CD). The as-received CP-Ti had axially symmetric $\{10\bar{1}0\}-\{11\bar{2}0\}$ prismatic fiber texture with a maximum multiple of a random distribution (MRD) of ~3.15 along the compression direction (CD) shown in figure 2(a). After, uniaxial compression of ≈0.05 (figure 2b), basal texture fiber was initiated and intensified after the strain of ≈ 0.22 to MRD ~ 4.9 MRD (figure 2c). With the further increase in the strain ≈ 0.69, the basal fiber shifts with an increase in its angular spread form $\{10\bar{1}7\}-\{11\bar{2}7\}$ axially symmetric fiber texture (figure 2d) along CD. The dotted line shows the position of the axially symmetric fiber in figure 2d.

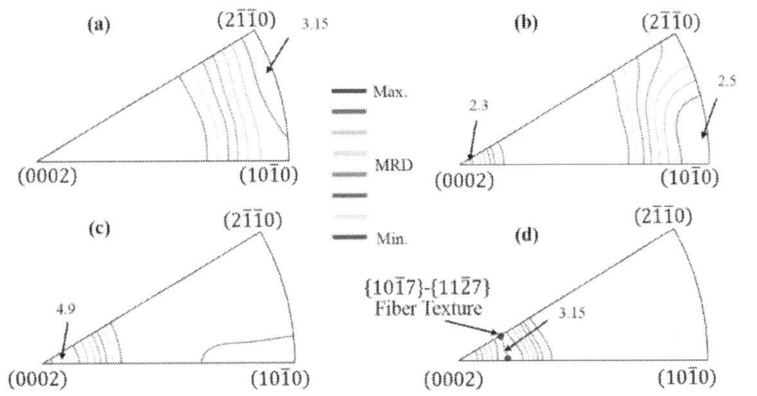

Figure 2. Texture representation via Inverse Pole Figure along compression direction for the (a) initial and after the effective strains of (b) ~0.05, (c) ~0.22, and (d) ~0.69

3.3. Effect of Extension Twin

The effect of deformation-induced ET, four different individual grains containing prominent ET were cropped and shown in figure 3(a-d). The point to point misorientation across twin domain and angular inverse pole figure 85 °$\langle 11\bar{2}0\rangle$ are shown in figure 3(e-f). The unit cell of these grains and the ET domains are also superimposed in these figures. ET regions have orientated the basal poles towards compression direction. These ET domains have a higher Taylor factor and, therefore, texturally harder than the parent matrix [8,12]. The compression along $\{10\bar{1}0\}$ and $\{11\bar{2}0\}$ axes are deformed by the activation of two and four ET variants [12]. The evolution of one and two ET variants are shown in figure 3(a,b). Figure 3(c,d) shows the parent lattice's ideal crystal orientation for the evolution of two parallel ET variants. These grains are cropped from ≈ 0.11 and ≈ 0.22 deformed samples. ET lamellae are broadened and consumed the parent matrix with further deformation. The newly formed ET domains have lower dislocation density concerning the matrix region. After the effective strain of ≈ 0.10, twin domain growth occurred by strain-induced twin boundary migration toward the higher strain energy region of the parent matrix. Basinski-type hardening may take place due to the sessile nature of dislocation inside twin domains [8].

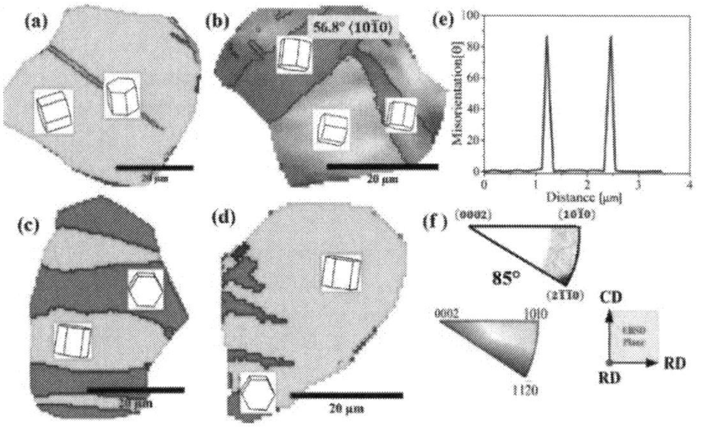

Figure 3. Gran by grain analysis in the strain range of ~0.05-0.22 (a) Nucleation of primary extension twin, (b) ET-ET interaction, (c) ET lamellae formation, (d) Broadening of ET and remnant of the parent matrix, (e) point to point misorientation of ET, and (f) ~85° angular inverse pole figure along with IPF color key code triangle.

3.4. Effect of Contraction Twin

The microstructure features formed due to CT are shown in figure 4. Compressive deformation along the (0002) axis is accommodated by activation of CT. Figure 4(a) shows that the matrix's basal axis (in green color) is oriented towards CD with a small angular deviation.

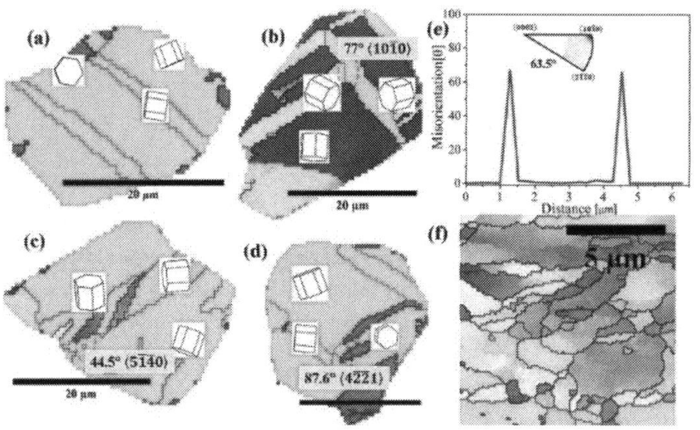

Figure 4. Grain by grain analysis from ~0.11-0.69 (a) formation of secondary contraction twins at strain range ~0.15 – 0.22, (b) CT-CT interaction, (c) nucleation of tertiary ET lamellae inside CT domain, (d) ET-CT interaction, (e) point to point misorientation of CT, and (f) microstructure after ~0.69 effective strain.

CT are nucleated in the primary ET domains and confirmed from remnant (in red color). The (0002) axis is orientated normal to the CD. Thus (red color) initial parent matrix deformed via activation of primary ET and oriented the (0002) toward the CD. Therefore activation of the CT in primary ET is designated as secondary CT. These are $\{11\bar{2}2\}\langle11\bar{2}\bar{3}\rangle$ type CT [5,13], reorients the matrix by $\sim 63.5°$ about $\langle10\bar{1}0\rangle$ axis confirmed via point to point misorientation and angular IPF shown in figure4(e). CT's evolution could increase the texturally soft orientation in microstructure, confirms from the superimposed crystal lattices. It reorients the basal pole away from the CD. Further, an increase in the strain the interaction of CT-CT, ET-CT, and tertiary ET formed fixed angle axis pairs: CT-CT ~77°$\langle10\bar{1}0\rangle$, ET-CT ~87°$\langle4\bar{2}\bar{2}1\rangle$ interactions boundaries and CT-ET ~44.5°$\langle5\bar{1}\bar{4}0\rangle$ are shown in figure 4(b-d). The CT has evolved after the ~0.15 along with basal and pyramidal $\langle c + a\rangle$ type slip systems [8].

4.Conclusions

Quasi-static uniaxial compression of Ti at ambient temperature is performed to investigate the role of deformation twinning on the strain hardening rate, texture, and microstructure evolution. Grain by grain analysis was carried out, and the strain hardening response is correlated at different strain stages. The major findings of this study are listed below:

1. As per Initial texture and loading direction, ET-CT-ET type sequential twinning was formed along with dislocation slip.
2. Slip and twin domination zones could be identified by the strain hardening rate curve and its derivative.
3. $\{10\bar{1}2\}$ $\langle10\bar{1}\bar{1}\rangle$ type ET increases the texturally hard domains; whereas, $\{11\bar{2}2\}\langle11\bar{2}\bar{3}\rangle$ CT evolved inside primary ET domains and produced texturally softer orientations.
4. With the increase in strain, the various twin reactions such as ET-ET ~56.8°$\langle10\bar{1}0\rangle$, CT-CT ~77°$\langle10\bar{1}0\rangle$, ET-CT ~87°$\langle4\bar{2}\bar{2}1\rangle$ interactions boundaries and CT-ET ~44.5°$\langle5\bar{1}\bar{4}0\rangle$ double twins develop

Acknowledgments
The authors would like to acknowledge the financial grants provided by the 'ISIRD, SRIC, IIT Kharagpur India' and 'SERB' (Ref. No. ECR/2016/000125), DST, Govt. of India to carry out the experiments. The work also used the 'Light Metals and Alloys Research Lab' setup at the Department of Metallurgical and Materials Engineering and 'Central Research Facility' in the IIT Kharagpur, India.

References

[1]. J.C.W. G. Lutjering, Titanium, Springer Berlin Heidelberg, Berlin, Heidelberg, 2007. doi:10.1007/978-3-540-73036-1.
[2]. Zhao X, Yang X, Liu X, Wang X and Langdon T G 2010 The processing of pure titanium through multiple passes of ECAP at room temperature *Mater. Sci. Eng. A* **527** 6335–6339
[3]. Biswas S and Suwas S 2012 Evolution of sub-micron grain size and weak texture in magnesium alloy Mg-3Al-0.4Mn by a modified multi-axial forging process *Scr. Mater.* **66** 89–92
[4]. Chouhan D K, Biswas S, Singh A K, Shukla A J 2020 High strength-ductility combination in cold multiaxial plane –strain forged and rolled nanostructured Titanium *Materialia* **11** 100698
[5]. Yoo M H 1981 Slip, twinning, and fracture in hexagonal close-packed metals *Metall. Trans. A* **12** 409–418
[6]. Rout M, Biswas S, Ranjan R, Pal S K and Singh S B 2018 Deformation behavior and evolution of microstructure and texture during hot compression of AISI 304LN stainless steel *Metall. Mater. Trans. A* **49** 864-880
[7]. Biswas S, Dhinwal S S and Suwas S 2010 Room-temperature equal channel angular extrusion of pure magnesium *Acta Mater.* **58** 3247-3261

[8]. Chouhan D K, Singh A K, Biswas S and Mondal C 2019 On strain hardening behavior and Twin – induced grain refinement of CP-Ti under ambient temperature compression *Metall. Mater. Trans. A* **50** 2169-2188
[9]. Xu S, Gong M, Schuman C, Lecomte J S, Xie X and Wang J 2017 Sequential $\{10\bar{1}2\}$ twinning stimulated by other twins in titanium, *Acta Mater.* **132** 57–68
[10]. Sinha S and Gurao N P 2016 In situ electron backscatter diffraction study of twinning in commercially pure titanium during tension-compression deformation and annealing *Mater. Des.* **116** 686-693
[11]. Beausir B and Fundenberger J J, Analysis Tools for Electron and X-Ray Diffraction, ATEX - Software, Www.atex-Software.eu, Université de Lorraine - Metz, 2017.
[12]. Sahoo S K, Biswas S, Toth L S, Gautam P C and Beausir B 2020 Strain hardening, twinning and texture evolution in magnesium alloy using the all twin variant polycrystal modeling approach *In. J. Plast.* **125** 102660
[13]. Partidge P G 1967 The crystallography and deformation modes of hexagonal close-packed metals *Metall. Rev.* **12** 169-194

IOP Conf. Series: Materials Science and Engineering 1121 (2021) 012027 doi:10.1088/1757-899X/1121/1/012027

The role of deformation twins in recrystallization texture formation of the FeGa alloy

V A Milyutin[1], I V Gervasyeva[2],

[1] Institute of Materials Research, Slovak Academy of Sciences, Watsonova 47, 040 01 Kosice, Slovak Republic

[2] M.N. Miheev Institute of Metal Physics of Ural Branch of Russian Academy of Sciences, Ekaterinburg, Russia

vmilyutin@saske.sk

Abstract. It has been found that at cold axial deformation of the $(Fe_{83.4}Ga_{16.6})_{99.9}(NbC)_{0.1}$ alloy by hydrostatic extrusion, along with the slip processes, deformation twins are formed. The orientations of these formations in the plane perpendicular to the deformation direction coincide with the crystallographic planes {100} or {110}. It is believed that in bcc alloys, the axial deformation texture <110> is stable and undergoes only a small scattering upon recrystallization. Using the EBSD technique in this work, we have shown that the desired <100> // DD grains can grow into a deformed <110> // DD matrix upon primary recrystallization. At the same time, recrystallization of as-deformed samples leads to almost complete destruction of the original texture. The <100> orientation probably develops in connection with the presence of nuclei in the form of the least deformed twins, which are not observed in ordinary iron alloys. This feature of Fe-Ga alloys gives principal possibility of creating necessary cube texture and achieve a high magnetostriction value.

1. Introduction

The need to create a cubic texture in bcc (body-centered cubic) iron-based alloys is dictated by their field of application. The most widely known representatives of this class of materials are FeSi alloys, which are widely used as materials for magnetic cores of transformers and for electric motors. To achieve the best magnetic properties, it is necessary that the magnetic flux flows in one of the directions of easy magnetization <100>. Fortunately, in the case of magnetic cores, this may not necessarily be the cube texture {100}<100>, but also the Goss texture {110}<100>, which also contains the directions <100> // rolling direction (RD). This texture component (<100> // RD) is also called η-fiber. FeGa alloys near the first magnetostriction peak (~20% at. Ga) with anomalously high magnetostriction [1] are another representative of the group of Fe-based materials in which the η-texture is desirable. This is due to the anisotropy of magnetostriction, which in the <100> single crystal can reach 400 ppm, and in the <111> single crystal, at equal conditions, its value approaches zero [2]. Technology of Goss texture creation during secondary recrystallization was successfully applied to FeGa by various authors [3,4]. However, large grains after secondary recrystallization with diameter up to centimeters led to significant deterioration of the alloy strength, which is an important property for many contact applications of FeGa. For this reason, it is necessary to find a technology of η-texture creation using primary recrystallization process. To develop the technology, it is necessary to detailed investigate texture formation processes in FeGa alloys. Last few years such studies are actively carried out [2,5]. In [6], we studied deformation behavior and texture in FeGa after cold axial deformation by hydrostatic extrusion and recrystallization annealing. Strong axial <110> texture that is characteristic for bcc alloys was observed after deformation. It is well known that such kind of deformation texture in bcc is stable, and undergoes only a small scattering upon recrystallization. It was shown for FeGa also [7]. The aim of this work is twofold: first, to study the texture of the FeGa alloy after axial deformation in detail; second to study the recrystalization behavior of the <110> axial texture of deformation and find the possibility of increasing of the <100> // deformation direction (DD) orientations during primary recrystallization. It has both fundamental and practical importance because it can improve our knowledge about texture formations in bcc materials and it may help us to develop technology of desirable texture creation in FeGa.

2. Material and methods

A non-oriented polycrystalline ingot $(Fe_{83.4}Ga_{16.6})_{99.9}NbC_{0.1}$, obtained by arc melting and conventional casting into a copper mold, was used as a starting material. A cylindrical ingot with a diameter of 12.2 mm was placed in a brass shell and subjected to hydrostatic extrusion at room temperature. This deformation was carried out in two passes: the first from 12.2 to ~ 10.5 (the exact diameter is unknown, since after the first pass the sample was not removed from the shell) and the second to a final diameter of 8.4 mm. The degree of deformation was 53%. Samples were cut from the deformed rod to study the structure and texture after deformation, as well as to carry out annealing in different modes. To remove residual stresses without structural transformations, we used annealing at 550°C 60 min. The purpose of this annealing was to improve quality of EBSD analysis of the texture of deformation. Recrystallization annealings of deformed samples were carried out at 800 or 950°C with a holding time of 40 minutes to get samples with different recrystallization stages. In addition, some of the deformed samples were annealed with a slow heating of 8°C/min from 400 to 1000°C without holding at the final temperature. To study the microstructure and texture of samples SEM FEI Quanta 200 and Tescan Vega 3 with EBSD attachments were used. Post processing of the data obtained, was realized using commercial EBSD software and MTEX toolbox [8]. Color-coding in the orientation maps always corresponds the directions along deformation direction (DD). In more detail this means that structure elements with <100> // DD orientations are painted red, <110> // DD are painted green and so on.

3. Results and discussion

The initial texture of the ingot is multicomponent without any prevailing orientations. The average grain size is about 600 μm. NbC particles are evenly distributed throughout the ingot body [6]. The structure after the deformation is shown in figure 1. Structure after 550°C 60 min annealing is also presented here (fig.1.b) In the course of such annealing, the processes of recovery and polygonization begin, and the quality of structure image, obtained by EBSD method, improves. It can be seen that the <110> orientation prevails in the cross section of the deformed sample; axial deformation during hydrostatic extrusion, as for other bcc alloys, leads to the axial texture <110>. Besides the stable orientation <110>, there are scattered orientations near the direction <113> (fig.1e and f). In bcc metals slip systems are {hkl}<111>. The most-density packed planes are the {110}, although the packing density is only slightly different from the planes {112} and {123} [9]. Plane (110) has four equivalent directions <111>; two of them should be located symmetrically about the axis of deformation. This is possible for two crystallographic directions of the axis <100> and <110> [10]. Practically, <110> direction is realized because angles between <110> and <111> are less than between <100> and <111>. This is the case for all initial orientations except ones, which lie on the line of symmetry <001> - <111> of standard orientational triangle. Such orientations have a trend to align along <113> [10]. In figures 1a and b we can see structural elements with parallel boundaries and with a sharp change in orientation relative to the matrix. Despite these elements differ from "canonical" twins – narrow straight areas, everything points to the fact that they are result of twining. Their irregular shape can be explained by the fact that if they were formed at the initial stage of deformation, then in the course of subsequent deformation, they undergo changes. Orientation of such elements depends on the surrounding matrix, one example presented in figure 2.
For a more detailed study of the texture features, we carried out selective scanning with a higher magnification and a smaller scan step. One of these structure fragments is presented in figure 2.

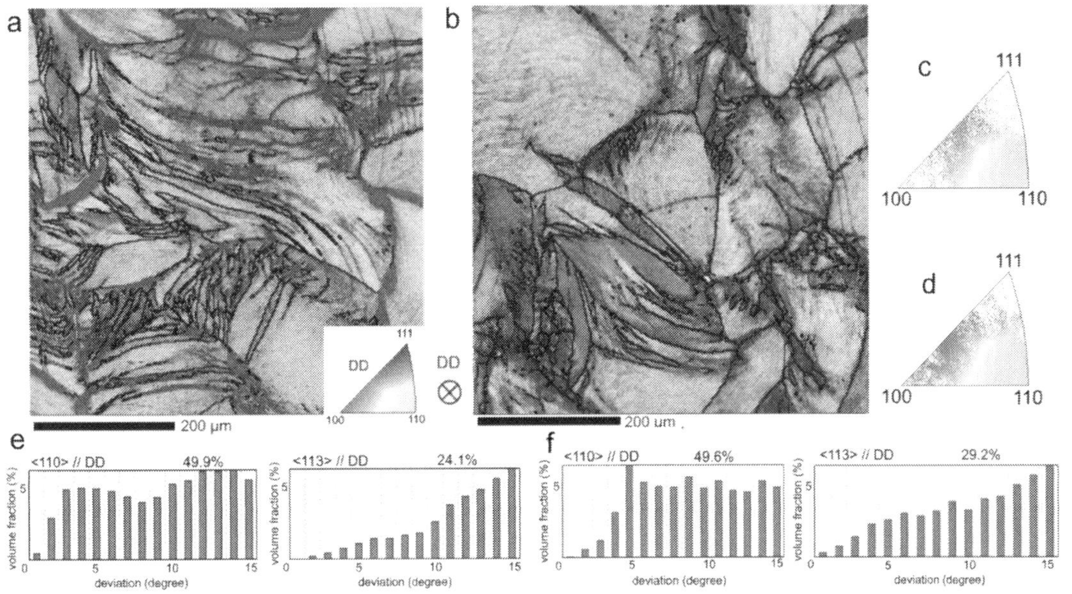

Fig. 1. Orientation maps of the sample after 53% cold deformation by hydrostatic extrusion (a) and after 550°C 60 min annealing (b) with corresponding Inverse pole figures (IPF) (c,d) and distribution of the main components of the deformation texture by the angle of deviation from the ideal position (e,f).

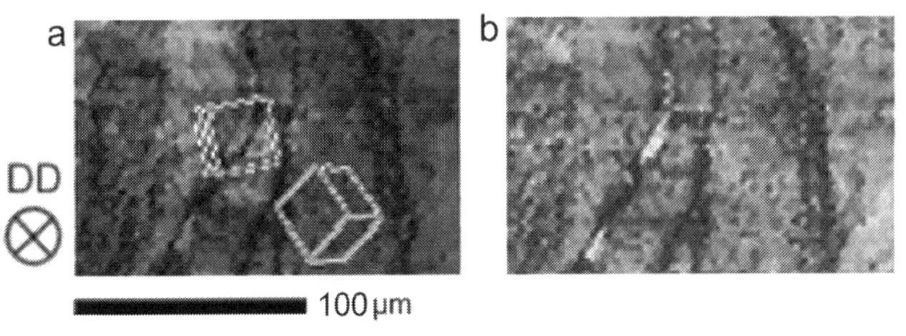

Fig. 2. Orientation map (x500) of the sample after 53% deformation and 550°C 60 min annealing (a) with the corresponding image quality map (b).

Here we can see narrow, parallel-sided twins, between other structural elements of the deformed material. This areas have higher image quality compared with the surrounding matrix, it is may be result of lower level of internal stresses here. To realize partial recrystallization we carried out annealing at 800°C 40 min. The main axial texture components are shown in figure 3a. After such annealing, ratio of recrystallized and unrecrystalized (deformed) areas is about 50:50 (fig.3b). Unrecrystalized areas are presented by large grains with "cube of the edge" orientation {110}<100>. This orientation is known to be stable, hence it is still retained after annealing at 800°C. Not all green grains have the orientation {110}<100>, there are new recrystallized grains with different <110>//DD orientations also (fig.3a). It is seen, how recrystallized grains with different orientations grow into large <110> grains (black dotted circle in fig.3a). This feature of grain growth during recrystallization may be caused by presence of thin long twins inside grains after deformation. This twins can serve as recrystallization nuclei, a similar phenomenon was observer in FeSi [11]. The volume fraction of η-grains after such partial recrystallization is 14.4%.

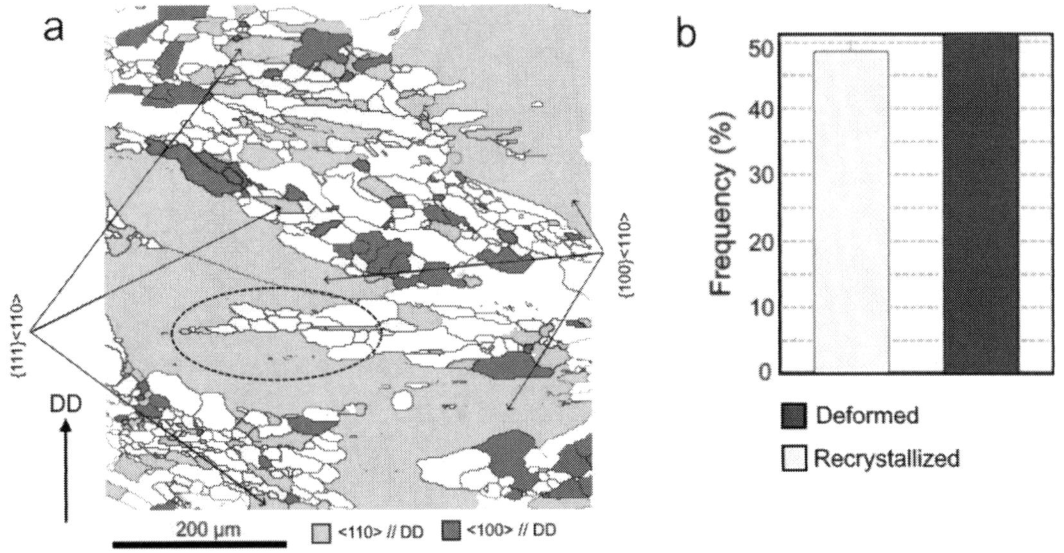

Fig. 3. The main texture components <110>//DD and <100>//DD with grain boundaries after partial recrystallization at 800°C 40 min (a); volume fraction of recrystallized and deformed structure areas (b).

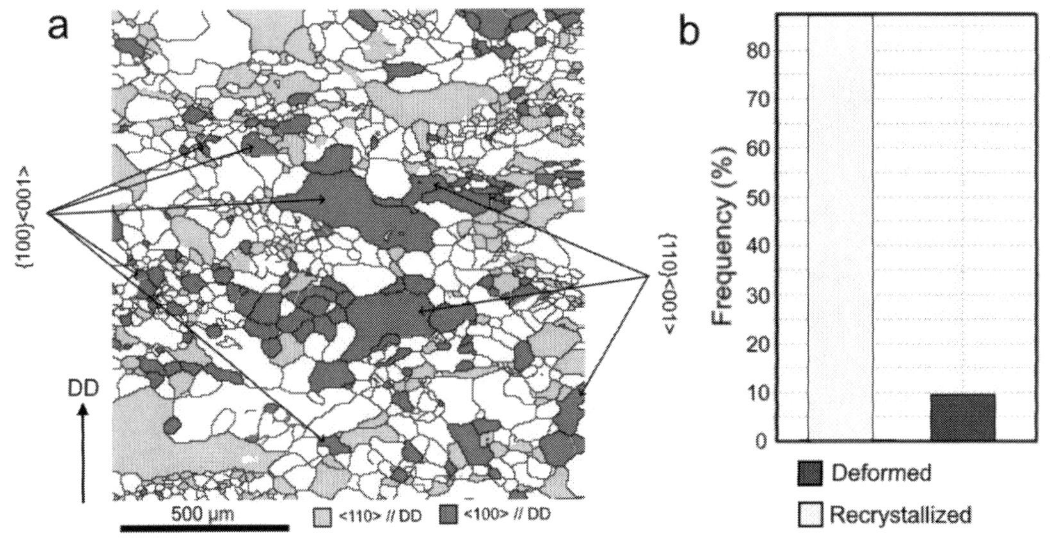

Fig. 4. The main texture components <110>//DD and <100>//DD after recrystallization at 950°C 40 min (a); volume fraction of recrystallized and deformed structure areas (b).

After high temperature annealing at 950°C 40 min, primary recrystallization almost completed (fig.4b); however, structure is still quite uneven-grained (fig.4a). Components of texture of deformation almost disappeared, whereas volume fraction of <100>//DD was increased to 18.6%. Both {100}<001> and {110}<001> orientations are present. Annealing at higher temperature led to increase in η-texture volume fraction. To study the effect of annealing conditions on the formation of the grains with the <100> // DD, we carried out additional annealing with gradual heating from 400 to

1000°C at 8°C/min. The starting point of 400°C instead of room temperature was chosen in order to reduce the annealing time, as we found that below 400°C structure transformation processes (recovery) have extremely low intensity.

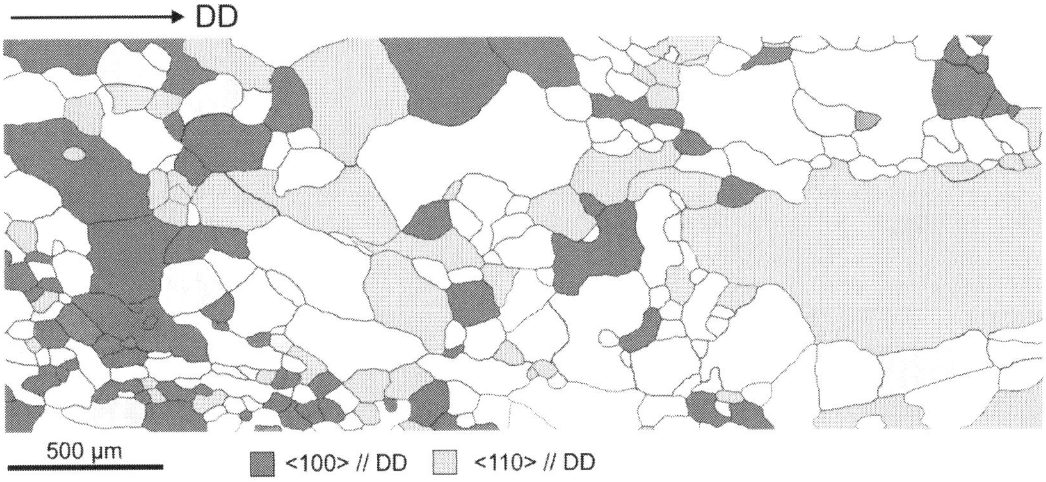

Fig. 5. Orientation map of the sample after heating from 400 to 1000 at 8°C/min.

We can see that structure still contains large deformed grains with initial orientation. At the same time, η-grains are significantly bigger than after different annealing regimes, its volume fraction is 20%. We consider that annealing with slow heating can promote low stored energy nucleation process due to recovery prior recrystallization onset during gradual heating [12]. Accordingly well-known orientation dependency of stored energy in bcc metals [13]; η-orientations have low level of stored energy after deformation and, therefore, low ability to grow in frame of high stored nucleation conception. Obviously, cold axial deformation and slow heating of FeGa sample create conditions for the nucleation and growth of these orientations.

In summary, we can say that during deformation of the FeGa alloy by cold hydrostatic extrusion, not only slipping, but also twinning is observed. We consider that reason of twinning is low plasticity of this alloy and the limited ability to slip during cold axial deformation with high intensity. It is known that hot and warm drawing of FeGa led to axial texture <110> [7], which remains stable during recrystallization; only its slight scattering occurs. The similar phenomena observed also in other bcc materials, for example Fe-5%Ni [8]. Probably, this happens because as a result of slipping processes during such deformations there are no structural elements that are sufficiently misoriented with the matrix to be able to grow into surrounding matrix. The appearance of deformation twins upon cold deformation of an alloy with low plasticity makes it possible for them to be nuclei of recrystallization and leads to a sufficiently large volume of η-texture in the recrystallized material. This occurs even despite the fact that the twin boundaries have low-mobility.

4. Conclusions

Deformation by the hydrostatic extrusion of the alloy $(Fe_{83.4}Ga_{16.6})_{99.9}NbC_{0.1}$ led to a pronounced axial texture <110>. In contrast to other cases of axial deformation of bcc iron-based alloys after hydrostatic extrusion of FeGa, deformation twins with different orientations including <100> // DD were observed in the texture of deformation. Recrystallization annealing of the deformed alloy led to significant volume of <100> // DD orientations in the texture. We consider that the reason is that twins with this orientations can play the role of recrystallization nuclei in the axial <110> deformation texture. At the same time, annealing with the slow heating enhances this tendency.

Acknowledgment
The research was carried out within the MoRePro program (project No. 19MRP0061) supported by state assignment of Ministry of Education and Science, Russia (theme "Magnet" No. AAAA-A18-118020290129-5).

References
[1] Golovin I S, Palacheva V V, Mohamed A K and Balagurov A M 2020 Structure and Properties of Fe–Ga Alloys as Promising Materials for Electronics *Phys. Met. Metallogr.* **121** pp 851–93
[2] Fu Q, Sha Y H, Zhang F, Esling C and Zuo L 2019 Correlative effect of critical parameters for η recrystallization texture development in rolled Fe 81 Ga 19 sheet: Modeling and experiment *Acta Mater.* **167** pp 167–80
[3] He Z, Sha Y, Fu Q, Lei F, Jin B, Zhang F and Zuo L 2016 Sharp Goss texture and magnetostriction in binary Fe81Ga19sheets *J. Magn. Magn. Mater.* **417** pp 321–6
[4] Yuan C, Li J, Zhang W, Bao X and Gao X 2015 Secondary recrystallization behavior in the rolled columnar-grained Fe-Ga alloys *J. Magn. Magn. Mater.* **391** pp 145–50
[5] Na S M, Smith M and Flatau A B 2018 Deformation Mechanism and Recrystallization Relationships in Galfenol Single Crystals: On the Origin of Goss and Cube Orientations *Metall. Mater. Trans. A Phys. Metall. Mater. Sci.* **49** pp 2499–512
[6] Milyutin V A, Gervasyeva I V, Volkova E G, Alexandrov A V, Cheverikin V V, Mansouri Y, Palacheva V V and Golovin I S 2020 Texture formation in FeGa alloy at cold hydrostatic extrusion and primary recrystallization *J. Alloys Compd.* **816** p 153283
[7] Boesenberg A J, Restorff J B, Wun-Fogle M, Sailsbury H and Summers E 2013 Texture development in Galfenol wire *J. Appl. Phys.* **113** pp 10–3
[8] Bachmann F, Hielscher R and Schaeben H 2011 Grain detection from 2d and 3d EBSD data-Specification of the MTEX algorithm *Ultramicroscopy* **111** pp 1720–33
[9] Gottstein G 2004 *Physical Foundations of Materials Science*, Berlin: Springer, 1st edition p 502
[10] Babareko A A 1967 *Texture development in metals and alloys under deformation and recrystallization* in: "Metallurgy and Heat Treatment", Moscow p 83 *(in Russian)*
[11] Redikul'tsev A A, Lobanov M L, Rusakov G M and Gervas'ev A M 2008 Deformational twinning in Fe-3% Si engineering alloy *Steel Transl.* **38** pp 719–23
[12] Kestens L A I and Pirgazi H 2016 Texture formation in metal alloys with cubic crystal structures *Mater. Sci. Technol. (United Kingdom)* **32** pp 1303–15
[13] Every R L and Hatherly M 1974 Oriented Nucleation in Low-Carbon Steels. *Texture* **1** pp 183–94

Fracture toughness of hot rolled pure magnesium: Correlation with microstructure and texture

Prakash C. Gautam[1*], H.N. Bar[2], S. Sivaprasad[2], S. Tarafder[2], Somjeet Biswas[1*]

[1]*Light Metal* and alloy research Lab, Department of Metallurgical & Materials engineering, *Indian Institute of Technology - Kharagpur, Kharagpur, India.*
[2]*National Metallurgical Laboratory - Jamshedpur, Jamshedpur, India.*

Email: pcgautam@iitkgp.ac.in,
somjeetbiswas@metal.iitkgp.ac.in

Abstract. Pure magnesium possesses high specific strength, and hence it has excellent potential for biodegradable structural bioimplants. Such a load-bearing application requires the material to have sufficient fracture toughness to sustain the presence of undesirable microcracks. In this work, biomedical grade pure magnesium was hot-rolled to obtain equiaxed microstructure with basal texture. Single edge notch bending specimens with a notch along the rolling direction, transverse direction, and 45° to both were prepared. Fatigue pre-cracking was performed, followed by the fracture toughness tests. All the samples show sufficient plasticity during the fracture toughness test to evaluate J_{1C}. The characterization was done by electron backscatter diffraction. The influence of initial texture and the strain state on the evolution of twins in the vicinity of the crack path and fracture toughness was comprehended.

Keywords: Magnesium; Bioimplant; Microstructure; Texture; Fracture toughness; Twins;

1. Introduction

The demand for temporary load-bearing bio-implant has increased in recent years. From several decades, the traditional metallic bio-implants such as titanium alloys, stainless steels, cobalt-chromium, and others have been used for load-bearing applications. These are usually biocompatible but not biodegradable [1,2]. Apart from that their mechanical properties are mismatched with the natural bones. Thus, the stress shielding effects due to their high modulus, second surgical procedure and risk of toxic metal ion release may lead to several health care issues [3]. In recent year pure magnesium (Mg) and Mg alloys are being viewed as a structural load-bearing component for the bio-implant applications owing to its biocompatibility and biodegradability [4]. Moreover, Mg is a vital element for the human body, and the generated biodegradation product can be easily absorbed and metabolized by the human body. Thus, the major advantages are that there is no requirement for another surgery to remove it after the healing process [5]. Moreover, its mechanical properties are well-matched with the natural bones. It possesses elastic moduli of about 40-45 GPa which is much closer to that of the natural bone. Thus, it has the potential for avoiding the stress shield [2-5]. Apart from that, it has several striking properties such as low density and higher specific strength [3-6]. Despite owing such remarkable properties, its application is still limited for bio-implant due to its poor strength and fracture toughness [6]. Thus, the primary focus on improving the fracture toughness is needed. Additionally, Mg is highly anisotropy in nature due to the activation of only two independent basal slips at ambient temperature, as its critical resolved shear stress (CRSS) is much lower than that of non-basal slips. Hence the governing basal slips produce sharp basal texture during processing that produces high plastic anisotropy at ambient temperature. Consequently, its application potentials are further impeded [7-9]. Thus, the analysis of fracture toughness in various directions need to be elaborated before using it as bio-implant, considering the possibilities of various loading configuration inside the material.

2. Experimental procedure

Biomedical grade pure Mg (99.94 % purity) was received in the form of the hot-rolled plate to determine its fracture toughness. Prior to fracture toughness testing, the microstructure and texture observation were carried out on the rolling plane by using electron backscattered diffraction technique. Further, yield strength (YS) and tensile strength (TS) was obtained by ambient temperature tensile testing of the miniature sample obtained from the hot-rolled plate. Single edge notch bend (SENB) specimen were prepared as per ASTM E-1820 [10] for the fracture toughness test. Three different samples were prepared from the so obtained rolled plate; notch length parallels to RD, perpendicular to RD, and 45° to RD to measure the variation in fracture toughness in different directions. A fatigue pre-crack length of 0.5 W was introduced prior to the fracture toughness test. This was done at a frequency of 5 Hz and a constant stress intensity factor range (ΔK) of 3 MPa$\sqrt{m}$ so that the maximum load corresponding to this ΔK value could be kept below $P_f = \frac{0.5\,B\,b^2\sigma_Y}{S}$ as per ASTM E-1820 [10]. Where B is the thickness, b is the uncracked ligament, $(w - a_0)$. $\sigma_Y = (\sigma_{YS} + \sigma_{TS})/2$, and S is the span length. After the introduction of fatigue pre-crack, the specimens were loaded to determine the fracture toughness. The microstructure of the fracture sample was examined in the plane containing crack propagation by using an optical microscope. The fracture surface was observed using SEM.

3. Result and discussion

3.1. *Initial material*

The inverse pole Figure (IPF) map of the as-received material and their grain size distribution is shown in Fig. 1. The as-received hot-rolled Mg mostly contains large equiaxed grains with an average AF (NF) grain size of ~51.4 (~12) µm. The microstructure portrays the presence of mostly basal orientation in the rolling plane. The texture of the as-received material is plotted in terms of (0002), $(10\bar{1}0)$ and $(11\bar{2}0)$ pole figures and are shown in Fig. 2. The texture shows the (0002) poles parallel to the plane perpendicular to the ND with $\{10\bar{1}0\}$ and $\{11\bar{2}0\}$ fibre axis parallels to the rolling direction (RD). This indicates the formation of sharp basal fiber texture as a result of a hot rolling operation [6,11].

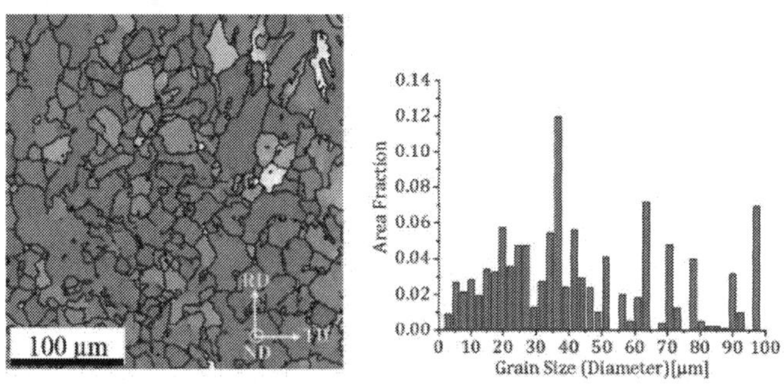

Fig. 1. IPF map of hot rolled Mg and their grain size distribution.

The deformation texture after the hot rolling of Mg is (0002) $<11\bar{2}0>$ as reported in the literature [6]. However, during the dynamic recrystallization, the crystal rotates from $<11\bar{2}0>$ to $<10\bar{1}0>$ i.e., 30° around the c-axis [8,11-14]. Therefore, the recrystallization texture in the Mg is represented by (0002) $<10\bar{1}0>$. Hence, from the pole figure analysis, deformation, as well as recrystallization texture, could be observed representing that the as-received sample was dynamically recrystallized.

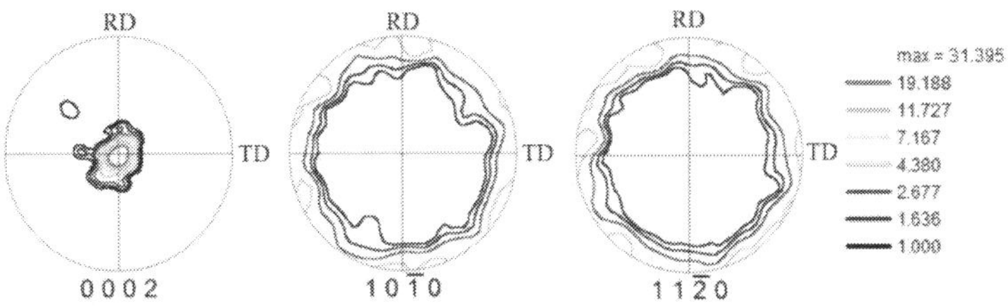

Fig. 2. (0002) (10$\bar{1}$0) and (11$\bar{2}$0) pole Figures of the hot-rolled Mg with their reference direction and the intensities.

3.2. *Fracture toughness*

The load-displacement curve during the fracture toughness test for all the samples showed non-linear behavior before it reaches the maximum load. The maximum load (P_{max}) was obtained during the test for all the samples. Further, a load value (P_Q) was obtained from an intersection of a 95% secant line (from the origin) with the load-displacement curve. The ratio between P_{max} and P_Q was evaluated, which was found greater than 1.11. Thus, it suggested that the samples had undergone enough plastic deformation during the loading. Moreover, the dimensions required for the test to have a plane strain fracture toughness was below its minimum value according to the following equation.

$$a, B, W - a \geq 2.5(K_Q/\sigma_{ys})^2 \quad (1)$$

Therefore, the test was not valid to determine the K_{IC} [10]. However, the elastic-plastic fracture toughness (J_C) values were obtained for all the samples. In this regard, the provisional fracture toughness (K_Q) value was obtained by using the formula given below for the SENB specimen as per ASTM-1820 [10].

$$K_Q = \left[\frac{P_Q S}{BW^{1.5}}\right] f\left(\frac{a}{W}\right) \quad (2)$$

$$\text{where } f\left(\frac{a}{W}\right) = \frac{\left[3\left(\frac{a}{W}\right)^{0.5}[1.99-\left(\frac{a}{W}\right)\left(1-\frac{a}{W}\right)\times\left(2.15-3.93\left(\frac{a}{W}\right)+2.7\left(\frac{a}{W}\right)^2\right)\right]}{2\left(1+2\frac{a}{W}\right)\left(1-\frac{a}{W}\right)^{1.5}} \quad (3)$$

Now the J_C was calculated as follow;

$$J_C = J_{el} + J_{pl} \quad (4)$$

$$\text{i.e. } J_C = K_Q{}^2(1-v^2)/E + J_{pl} \quad (5)$$

$$J_{pl} = \frac{2\,A_{pl}}{B_N b_0} \quad (6)$$

A_{pl} is the area enclosed by the load-displacement curve and the line drawn parallel to the initial linear part of load-displacement curve. All the calculations were done to get K_Q and J_C values for all the samples. The values are shown in Table 1 below. Now the minimum thickness required to have a size-independent elastic-plastic fracture toughness (J_{IC}) was achieved for all the samples as per the expression below [10].

$$B, W\text{-}a = 25\, J_C / \sigma_{ys} \quad (7)$$

From the calculated data, the provisional fracture toughness (K_Q) value is found maximum for the a_n-45° to RD configuration, followed by $a_n \perp$ RD and $a_n \parallel$ RD. However, the elastic-plastic fracture toughness (J_{IC}) is in the order; $a_n \parallel$ RD > $a_n \perp$ RD > a_n-45° to RD. From the pole figure analysis, it could be noticed that along the RD; the maximum intensities are contributed by <10$\bar{1}$0> directions. Whereas, along TD, and 45° to RD, maximum intensities are contributed by <11$\bar{2}$0> directions.

Table 1

Notch length to RD	P_{max} (N)	P_Q (N)	P_{max}/P_Q	K_Q $(MPa\sqrt{m})$	A_{pl} (Nmm)	J_{pl} (N/mm)	J_{IC} (N/mm)
Parallel	374	255	1.46	5.42	58	3.86	4.15
Perpendicular	368	279	1.31	5.98	49.4	3.29	3.61
45 degree	370	325	1.13	6.92	32	2.13	2.61

Thus, it could be concluded here that the energy required to propagate the crack along the <10$\bar{1}$0> is more than along the <11$\bar{2}$0> direction. The close-packed directions are actively distributed perpendicular to and 45° to the RD as a result of dynamic recrystallization [15]. In general, dislocations easily glide on the close-packed plane and directions as deformation proceed. Therefore, it is reasonable to postulate that the pre-crack having notch length 45° to the RD and perpendicular to the RD are easy to propagate [16].

3.3. Fractography

The typical SEM images of the fracture samples for all the samples (a) Notch parallel to RD, (b) Notch perpendicular to RD, and (c) Notch 45° to RD was obtained after the fracture toughness test. Fig. 3 shows the fracture surface in the rapid fracture, i.e., beyond the fatigue pre-crack region. All the samples show a combination of ductile and brittle fracture behavior. Overview of the fracture surface reveals that significant fracture area is dominated by shear lip along with cleavage fracture surface associated with river pattern.

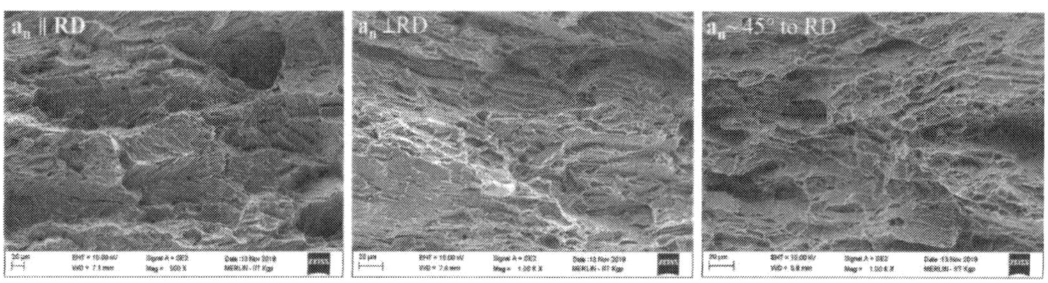

Fig. 3. SEM image of the fracture surface for the samples with their notch parallel, perpendicular, and 45° to the rolling direction.

The fracture surface of a_n || RD contains shallow dimples, representing enough plasticity during the fracture. The level of plastic deformation at the crack-tip produces the hindrance to the fracture because typical dimples decide the amount of plastic deformation at the crack-tip [16-18]. The fracture surface of $a_n \perp$ RD is dominated by cleavage fracture with some shear lip. However, the fracture surface of a_n - 45° to RD comprises of shallow dimples with few shear lips and cleavage fracture.

3.4. Optical microstructure

Fig. 4 shows the optical microstructure of the fracture samples in the plane perpendicular to ND. All the samples show the formation of twins of thin lamellar structure in the vicinity of the crack path. This could be possible because of the establishment of the stress triaxiality in the plastic zone at the crack tip. In this regard, various types of twins could form in the region of plastic zone size, depending upon the triaxial state of the strain component corresponding to the various stress configuration on the crack tip [18,19]. The amount of twin formation can be seen maximum for the sample $a_n \parallel$ RD followed by a_n $\perp$ RD and a_n 45° to RD. Thus, in this context, the amount of twin formation can be well correlated with the fracture toughness of the samples. In this work, the fracture toughness is found to be increased with the increase in twin formation.

The present result is supported by previous works [17,18], where they have shown that the energy required for the separation of two surfaces increases with the formation of twins. From Fig. 4, various twin structure such as parallel and crossing type of morphology is observed. Twinning leads to a change in the crystallographic orientation, which may lead to the textural hardening [20,21]. Besides, the dislocations produced within the parent grains can get pinned at the twin and the twin-twin intersection boundaries. Further, within the twin domain, slips can get activated. Therefore, the dislocation-dislocation interaction and pile-up of dislocations at the twin boundaries lead to the strain hardening. Thus, it increases the work of separation [17,18,20,21].

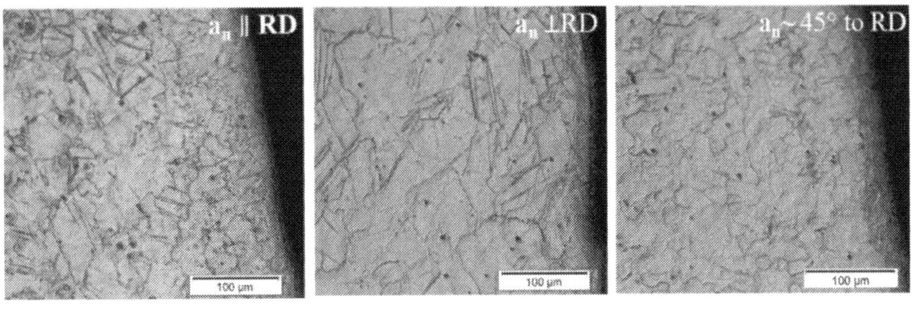

Fig. 4. The optical image in the vicinity of a crack path for the samples with their notch parallel, perpendicular, and 45° to the rolling direction.

4. Conclusions

1. The elastic-plastic fracture toughness (J_{IC}) was found maximum in the orientation having notch length parallel to rolling direction followed by notch length perpendicular to the RD and notch length 45° to the RD
2. From the texture analysis, it could be perceived that the energy required to propagate the crack along the $<10\bar{1}0>$ directions are more; as a result, the higher fracture toughness is found along the notch length parallel to RD.
3. The fracture surface comprises of mixed fracture behavior, revealing that the significant fracture area is dominated by shear lip along with cleavage fracture surface associated with river pattern.
4. Fracture toughness was found to be increased with the increase in the number of twins.

Acknowledgement

The authors are very grateful to the Science and Engineering Research Board (Ref. no.: ECR/2016/000125), Department of Science and Technology, Government of India for the financial grant. The work used the facility of Material Engineering Division in National Metallurgical Lab, Jamshedpur, India to carry out the fracture toughness test. Sample preparation and material characterization was performed at 'Light Metals and Alloys Research Lab' setup at the Department of Metallurgical and Materials Engineering, and Central Research Facility, both in Indian Institute of Technology, Kharagpur, India.

References

[1] Ren L and Yang K (2013) Bio-functional design for metal implants, a new concept for development of metallic biomaterials *J Mater. Sci. Technol.* **29** 1005–10

[2] Cifuentes S C, Gavilán R, Lieblich, Benavente R and González-Carrasco J L (2016) In vitro degradation of biodegradable polylactic acid/magnesium composites: Relevance of Mg particle shape *Acta Biomater.* **32** 348–57

[3] Cai C, Song R, Wen E, Wang Y and Li J (2019) Effect of microstructure evolution on tensile fracture behavior of Mg-2Zn-1Nd-0.6Zr alloy for biomedical applications *Mater. Des.* 108038

[4] Zhang E, Xu L and Yang K (2005) Formation by ion plating of Ti-coating on pure Mg for biomedical applications. *Scripta Mater* **53** 523–27

[5] Li Z, Gu X, Lou S and Zheng Y (2008) The development of binary Mg-Ca alloys for use as biodegradable materials within bone *Biomater.* **29** 1329–44

[6] Estrin Y, Nene S S, Kashyap B P, Prabhu N and Al-Samman T (2016) New hot rolled Mg-4Li-1Ca alloy: A potential candidate for automotive and biodegradable implant applications *Mater. Lett.* **173** 252–56

[7] Agnew S R and Duygulu Ö (2005) Plastic anisotropy and the role of non-basal slip in magnesium alloy AZ31B *Int. J. Plast.* **21** 1161–93

[8] Biswas S, Singh Dhinwal S and Suwas S (2010) Room-temperature equal channel angular extrusion of pure magnesium *Acta Mater.* **58** 3247–61

[9] Miller V M, Berman T D, Beyerlein I J, Jones J W and Pollock T M (2016) Prediction of the plastic anisotropy of magnesium alloys with synthetic textures and implications for the effect of texture on formability *Mater. Sci. Eng. A* **675** 345–60

[10] ASTM E1820 Standard Test Method for Measurement of Fracture Toughness E1820 2017 1–53

[11] Biswas S, Singh D S, Beausir B, Toth L S and Suwas S (2015) Thermal Response on the Microstructure and Texture of ECAP and Cold-Rolled Pure Magnesium *Metall. Mater. Trans. A* **46** 2598–13

[12] Biswas S, Dhinwal S S, Bhowmik A and Suwas S (2008) Study of Texture Evolution of Pure Magnesium during ECAE Using EBSD *Mater. Sci. Forum* **584-586** 343–48

[13] Biswas S, Gautam P C, Shukla A J and Chouhan D K (2020) Dynamic recrystallization and its effect on microstructure and texture evolution in magnesium alloys *Refer. Module Mater. Sci. Mater. Eng.* B 978-0-12-815732-9.00016-4

[14] Biswas S, Beausir B, Toth L S and Suwas S (2013) Evolution of texture and microstructure during hot torsion of a magnesium alloy *Acta Mater.* **61** 5263–77

[15] Wu W X, Jin L, Wang F H, Sun J, Zhang Z Y, Ding W J and Dong J (2013) Microstructure and texture evolution during hot rolling and subsequent annealing of Mg–1Gd alloy *Mater. Sci. Eng. A* **582** 194–02

[16] Somekawa H and Mukai T (2006) Fracture toughness in a rolled AZ31 magnesium alloy. *J. Alloys Comp.* **417** 209–13

[17] Verma R, Srinivasan A, Nath S K and Jayaganthan R (2018) Tensile and fracture toughness behaviour of ultrafine grained Mg-4Zn-4Gd alloy processed through hot rolling followed by hot pressing *Mater. Sci. Eng. A* **742** 318–33

[18] Prasad N S, Naveen Kumar N, Narasimhan R and Suwas S (2015) Fracture behavior of magnesium alloys - Role of tensile twinning *Acta Mater.* **94** 281–93

[19] Kondori B and Benzerga A A (2014) Effect of stress triaxiality on the flow and fracture of Mg alloy AZ31 *Metall. Mater. Trans. A* **45** 3292–07

[20] Sahoo S K, Toth L S and Biswas S (2019) An analytical model to predict strain-hardening behaviour and twin volume fraction in a profoundly twinning magnesium alloy *Int. J. Plast.* **119** 273–90

[21] Sahoo S K, Biswas S, Toth L S, Gautam P C and Beausir B (2020) Strain hardening, twinning and texture evolution in magnesium alloy using the all twin variant polycrystal modelling approach. *Int. J. Plast* 102660

IOP Conf. Series: Materials Science and Engineering 1121 (2021) 012029 doi:10.1088/1757-899X/1121/1/012029

Change in intragranular misorientation during stress relaxation in Al-Cu-Mg-Mn alloy subjected to continuous cyclic bending

Takumi Hoshino [1], Kouki Miura[1], Yoshimasa Takayama[2] and Hideo Watanabe[2]

[1]Graduate student, Utsunomiya University

[2]Graduate Program in Mechanical and Intelligent Engineering, Graduate School of Regional Development and Creativity, Utsunomiya University, Utsunomiya 321-8585, Japan

Abstract. Change in intragranular misorientation during stress relaxation in Al-Cu-Mg-Mn (2024) alloy sheet subjected to continuous cyclic bending (CCB) has been investigated by electron back scatter diffraction (EBSD) technique. EBSD analysis revealed that kernel average misorientation (KAM) value was heitened not only in the sheet worked by CCB but also during stress relaxation test. Grain orientation spread (GOS) value, another misorientation parameter, was also calculated and compared with KAM value of each sample. Both of KAM and GOS values varied with four stages about stress and stored strain: (a) unloaded before stress relaxation test (SRT), (b) loaded before SRT, (c) loaded after SRT and (d) unloaded after SRT. Change in KAM value was likely corresponding to sum of applied and residual stresses. Quantitative relationship between increase and decrease in KAM value between the stages was divided into two types according to dynamic restoration mechanisms.

1. Introduction

Copper wires with high electrical conductivity are generally used for wiring harnesses in automobiles. In recent years, for the purpose of reducing the weight of vehicles, aluminum alloys which are close to copper in terms of electrical conductivity but with half of the weight are being used. When the aluminum alloys are used as current-carrying members, their stress relaxation characteristics are required to be known for assuring contact reliability.

Takayama and Szpunar [1] investigated crystallographic orientation distribution in the surface layer of an Al-Mg alloy sheet subjected to continuous cyclic bending to clarify the relationship between the KAM value corresponding to the local accumulated strain or stored strain energy and the Taylor factor (TF) assuming a plane strain state. As a result, the KAM value generally increased with increasing TF and increased somewhat in the region where TF was close to the minimum value of 2. On the other hand, Norhafiza *et. al.* [2] and Takayama *et. al.* [3] reported that the intragranular orientation difference also increased during a softening process, that is, stress relaxation. In addition, the increase of intragranular orientation difference with high temperature deformation has been reported by several studies [4-6].

In the present study, change in intragranular misorientation during stress relaxation in an aged-hardened Al-Cu-Mg-Mn alloy sheet subjected to continuous cyclic bending (CCB) was investigated by electron back scatter diffraction (EBSD) technique. The stress relaxation process was analyzed by using the intragranular misorientation in microstructure of the alloy at each stage of (a) unloaded before stress relaxation test (SRT), (b) loaded before SRT, (c) loaded after SRT and (d) unloaded after SRT. Further, the relationship between the changes in the KAM (kernel average misorientation) and GOS (grain orientation spread) values and the stress relaxation was investigated [5].

2. Experimental Methods

2.1. Materials and specimens

An Al-Cu-Mg-Mn alloy (2024 Al-T3) sheet was received as a starting material. The chemical composition of the 2024 Al alloy is listed in Table 1. The received sheet was solution-treated at 768 K for 30 min, and then machined into the stress-relaxation specimen of 24mm long in rolling direction (RD), 7mm wide in transverse direction (TD) and 1.5mm thick in normal direction (ND).

Table 1. Chemical composition of material (mass%)

Si	Fe	Cu	Mn	Mg	Cr	Zn	Zr+Ti	Ti	Al
0.07	0.18	4.55	0.48	1.58	0.02	0.09	0.03	0.02	Bal.

2.2. Continuous cyclic bending

The CCB processing equipment was used to work 40pass and 160pass specimens at a roll drive speed of 40 rpm, indentation of 0.5 mm, and an ambient temperature. These specimens are hereafter referred to 40pass and 160pass materials. The front side and the back side of the specimen was not changed during CCB process.

2.3. Aging process

The starting material was aged at 463K after solution treatment (ST). The optimal aging time was determined for each sample by using the Vickers hardness-aging time relationship. The specimen without CCB was aged for 8 hours, which was hereinafter referred to "aged specimens." Some of specimens were subjected to CCB passes before aging. 40pass and 160pass CCBent specimens were aged for 7 and 10 hours, referred to 40p/Aged and 160p/Aged, respectively.

2.4. Stress relaxation testing

Stress relaxation test was performed using a special specimen holder with which the specimen was allowed SEM/EBSD analysis in four stages: Stage I, unloaded before SRT, Stage II, stress loading (elastic strain), Stage III, stress relaxation (elastic strain + plastic strain) and Stage IV, unloaded after SRT (plastic strain). The analysis area was sited in the center and on the front and back sides of CCB on the TD plane and sized as the RD180μm × ND240μm, respectively. Top and Bottom mean top and bottom sides of the specimen, and besides, correspond to tensile and compressive strain for bending in the stress relaxation test. During the stress relaxation process the permanent strain occurs when the loaded deflection is released. The stress relaxation ratio is expressed as the ratio of the permanent deflection displacement produced to the initial deflection displacement loaded. The stress relaxation rate is calculated by the following equation.

$$\text{stress relaxation ratio (\%)} = \frac{\delta_t}{\delta_0} \times 100$$

δ_t: Permanent deflection displacement of the specimen caused by stress unloading after the test (mm)

δ_0: Initial deflection displacement of the test specimen at a given stress load (mm)

IOP Conf. Series: Materials Science and Engineering 1121 (2021) 012029 doi:10.1088/1757-899X/1121/1/012029

3. Experimental results and discussion

Figure 1 shows change in stress relaxation ratio for five kinds of specimens. As the stress relaxation ratio is lower, the stress relaxation characteristics is superior. 160p/Aged has the best stress relaxation resistance among them.

The grains were extracted one by one from the inverse pole figure (IPF) map obtained by EBSD analysis, and their KAM values were analyzed one by one (figure 2). There is a strong correlation in KAM difference between Stage II to Stage III and Stage I to Stage II CCB and aged specimens, and the data of aged specimens are more scattered than those of CCB (figure 3). In the case of CCB and aged specimens, the dislocations shifted from Stage I to Stage II are restored by the same amount before and after the relaxation from Stage II to Stage III, which may be related to the slip deformation of dislocations. The correlation of 160p/Aged was not observed in the aged specimens. In both specimens, the dynamic restoration process proceeded because they were held at high temperature under the external force in Stage II during the stress relaxation test. Therefore, the stress relaxation phenomena of 2024Al alloy can be divided into two types: one is the change in the KAM value due to dynamic restoration, as in the case of aging, and the other is the change in the KAM value, which is strongly related to the slip deformation of dislocations, as in the case of 160p/Aged, when CCB and aging are combined.

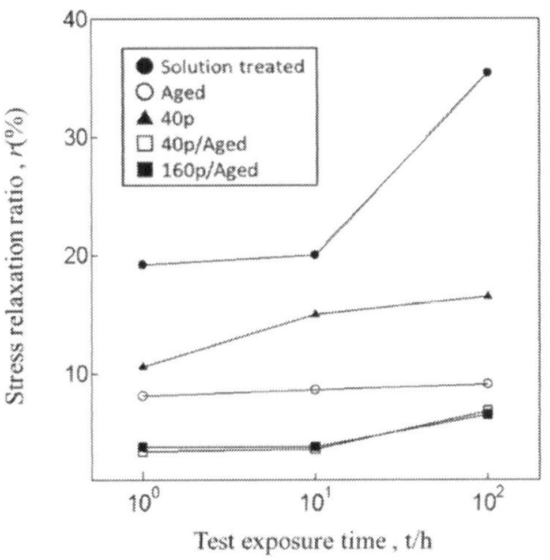

Fig. 1 Stress relaxation ratio of five kinds of specimens.

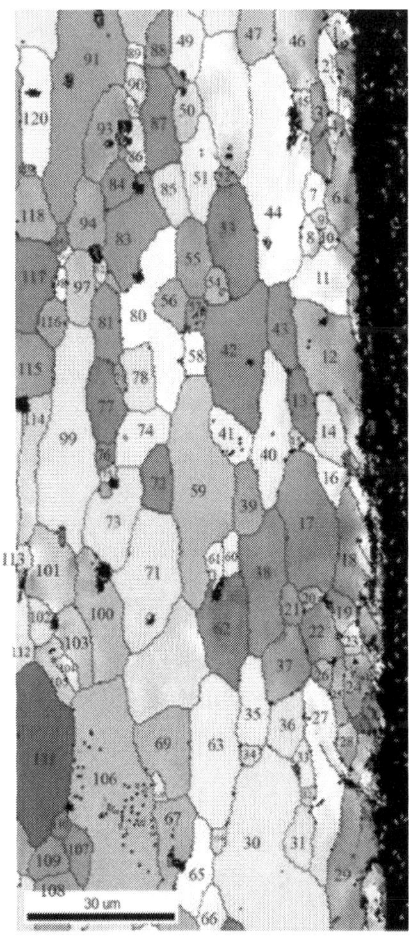

Fig. 2 160p/Aged Stage I Top IPF map

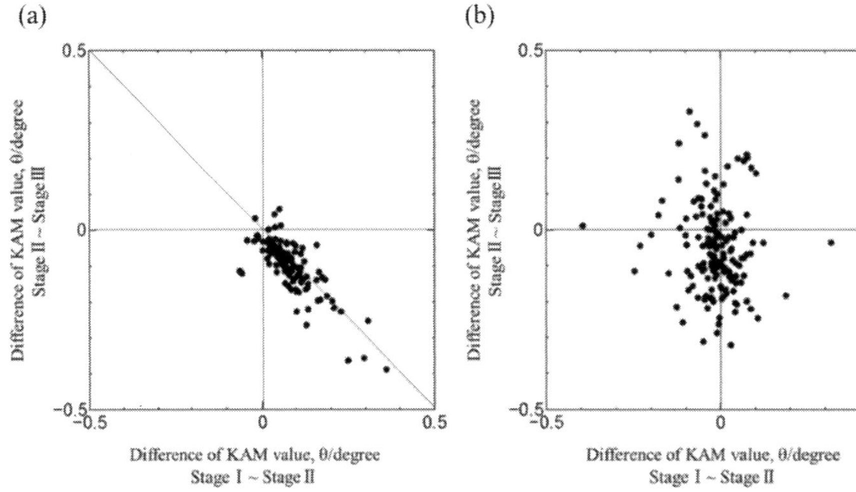

Fig. 3 Correlation of difference of KAM value between prior and posterior stages; (a) 160p/Aged and (b) Aged specimens.

Therefore, the line profiles of misorientations taken for arbitrary grains of 160p/Aged with the superior stress relaxation ratio and the aged specimen with the inferior stress relaxation ratio are shown in figure 4. Point to point (red graph) shows the misorientation from the neighboring measurement point, and point to origin (blue graph) shows the misorientation from the first measurement point. Focusing on the point to origin, it can be seen that the misorientation increases as the distance from the origin point increases for the 160p/Aged, whereas for the aged material the change in misorientation does not change much with distance. This indicates that 160p/Aged is an extensive change in orientation, whereas the change in orientation is localized for the aged specimen.

Next, the grains were extracted one by one from the IPF map and their KAM and GOS values were analyzed one by one, and the mean values of KAM and GOS for each stage are shown in figure 5. The black and red lines represent the GOS and KAM values, respectively. The KAM value, which is the local misorientation value, refers to the adjacent measurement points, while the GOS value, which is the intragranular misorientation average, refers to all the measurement points within the grain, so that the KAM value corresponds to the local misorientation change and the GOS value corresponds to the change in misorientation due to a wide area. These results suggest that the two phenomena of dislocation slip deformation and dynamic restoration lead to the intragranular misorientation.

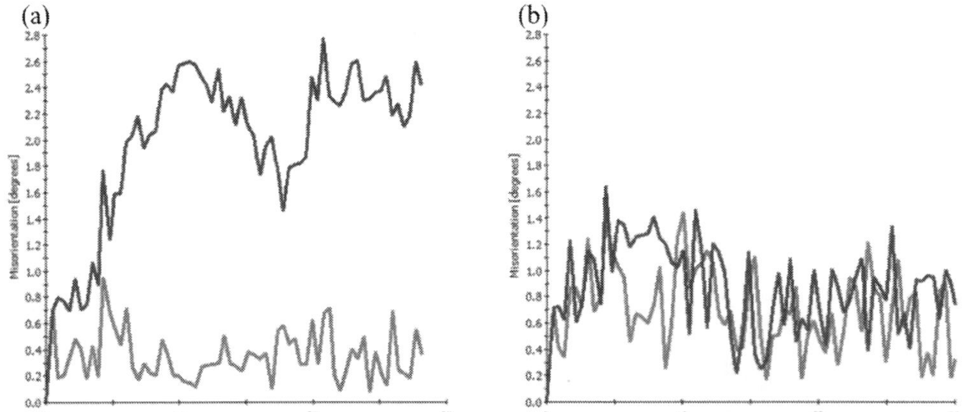

Fig. 4 Line profile of misorientations; (a) 160p/Aged and (b) Aged specimens.

IOP Conf. Series: Materials Science and Engineering 1121 (2021) 012029 doi:10.1088/1757-899X/1121/1/012029

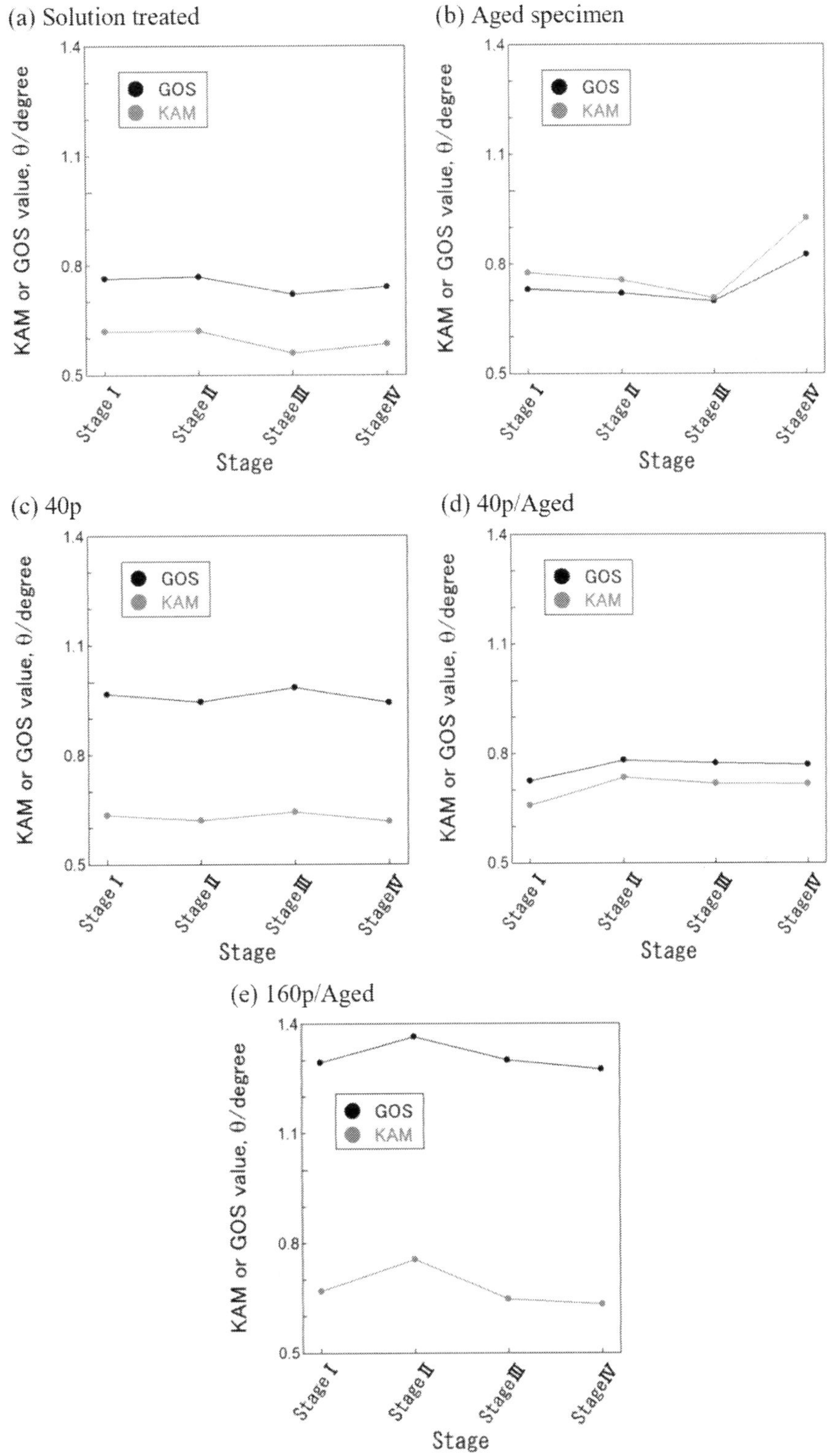

Fig. 5 Changes in average KAM and GOS values in each stage of SRT.

4. Conclusions

In the present study, change in intragranular misorientation during stress relaxation in an aged-hardened Al-Cu-Mg-Mn alloy sheet subjected to CCB has been investigated by EBSD technique. The stress relaxation process was analyzed by using the intragranular misorientation in microstructure of the alloy at each stage of (a) unloaded before SRT, (b) loaded before SRT, (c) loaded after SRT and (d) unloaded after SRT. Further, the relationship between the changes in the KAM and GOS values and the stress relaxation was investigated. The obtained results are summarized as follows.

1. 160p/Aged specimen has the best stress relaxation resistance among five materials.

2. Stress relaxation phenomena can be divided into two types: those that show a change in the KAM value due to dynamic recovery, as in the case of aged materials, and those that show a change in the KAM value, which is strongly related to the slip deformation of dislocations, by combining CCB and aging, as in the case of 160p/Aged.

5. References

[1] Takayama Y and Szpunar J: Mater. Trans. 45(2004), 2316-2325.
[2] Norhafiza S, Takayama Y and Watanabe H: *Copper and copper alloy(J. Jap. Inst. Copper)*, 52(2013), 103-108.
[3] TakayamaY, Sasaki T and Watanabe H: *Copper and copper alloy*, 55(2016), 6-10
[4] Yoda R, Yokomaku T and Tsuji N: Mater. Character., 61(2010) 913-922.
[5] Kubushiro K, Sakakibara Y and Ohtani T: *Journal of the Society of Materials Science*, 64(2015), 106-112
[6] Harte A, Atkinson M, Preuss M and Quinta da Fonseca J 2020 Acta Mater. **195** PP 555-570

IOP Conf. Series: Materials Science and Engineering 1121 (2021) 012030 doi:10.1088/1757-899X/1121/1/012030

Change in intragranular misorientation during stress relaxation behavior in Cu-Ni-Si alloy subjected to continuous cyclic bending

Tatsuya Fukutomi[1], **Narumi Komei**[1], **Yoshimasa Takayama**[2] **and Hideo Watanabe**[2]

[1]Graduate student, Utsunomiya University

[2]Graduate Program in Mechanical and Intelligent Engineering, Graduate School of Regional Development and Creativity, Utsunomiya University, Utsunomiya 321-8585, Japan

Abstract. Stress relaxation resistance is often required in application of electrical parts for copper and its alloys. The stress relaxation behavior should be influenced by stored strain through manufacturing process. In the present study, a Cu-Ni-Si alloy solution-treated sheet was subjected to continuous cyclic bending (CCB), which was proposed as a useful straining technique to impose higher strain on the surface and lower strain in the center layer of metal sheets. Samples were analyzed by scanning electron microscope/ electron back scatter diffraction (SEM/EBSD) technique to investigate stored strain and stress relaxation process. CCB raised up the strength of Cu-Ni-Si alloy sheets at room temperature. The stress relaxation ratios of the CCBent sheets increased with an increment of test exposure time at 423K. The stress relaxation process was accompanied with change in intragranular misorientation of the samples. Change in intragranular misorientation through the stress relaxation test was understood as a result of release of residual and applied stresses with consumption of stored strain.

1. Introduction

Smaller size, higher performance and multi-functions are required for electrical components of transportation vehicles, made of copper alloys, whose properties should be improved. In particular, for current-carrying members, stress relaxation characteristics are most important from assurance of reliability at the contacts. As lots of commercial copper alloys are precipitation-strengthened ones, the effect of precipitation on their stress relaxation resistance should be paid attention. Effect of continuous cyclic bending (sometimes abbreviated as CCB, below), which can affect particle size of precipitation on the stress relaxation resistance of the commercial alloys, should be extremely interesting. The author's group reported previously that the stress relaxation process of a Cu-Ni-Si alloy bent repeatedly can be monitored by a change in intragranular misorientation, kernel average misorientation (KAM). [4]

In the present study, the stress relaxation process is divided into four stages: (I) unloaded before stress relaxation test (SRT), (II) loaded before SRT, (III) loaded after SRT and (IV) unloaded after SRT. The relationship between the stress relaxation and change in KAM of a Cu-Ni-Si alloy subjected to continuous cyclic bending was examined. Grain orientation spread (GOS) [6] was investigated by electron back scattering diffraction (EBSD) [5,6,7].

IOP Conf. Series: Materials Science and Engineering 1121 (2021) 012030 doi:10.1088/1757-899X/1121/1/012030

2. Experimental procedure

2.1. Material and specimen

A Corson alloy (Cu-Ni-Si alloy) sheet solution-treated was received as a starting material. Chemical composition of the sample is listed in Table 1. Dimensions of workpiece for CCB were 200mm long in rolling direction (RD), 25mm wide in transverse direction (TD) and 1.2mm thick in normal direction (ND). From CCBent workpiece, stress relaxation specimen is machined as 24mm long in RD, 7mm wide in TD and 1.2mm thick in ND.

Table 1. Chemical composition of Corson alloy used

	Ni	Si	Mn	Zn	Cu
Cu-Ni-Si	2.44	0.49	0.03	0.03	Bal.

2.2. Continuous cyclic bending (CCB)

CCB is one of severe straining process and can impose strain to a specimen by continuously bending it by passing the specimen between five rolls. Table 2 shows the conditions for continuous and repeated bending. Three kinds of specimens, As-received, aged and 40pass-CCBbent/aged specimens were prepared in this experiment,

Table 2. Continuous bending conditions

Roll drive speed (rpm)	Roll radius (mm)	Number of processes (pass)	Offset amount (mm)	Processing temperature
40	16	0, 40	0.5	room temperature

2.3. Aging process

Using a muffle furnace, heat at 723K (heating time 10 min) and then remove from the muffle furnace to cool naturally.

2.4. Polishing procedure

In order to perform SEM/EBSD analysis, mechanical polishing with emery papers (#800/ #1200/ #2000) and buffing (alumina oxide abrasive, 3μm/ 1μm/ 0.3μm/ 0.05μm, 20 minutes each degree) were applied, and followed by electropolishing. The conditions for electropolishing are listed in table 3.

Table 3. Electrolytic grinding conditions

Electrolytic solution	HNO_3 : CH3OH = 3 : 7
Temperature	238K
Electric current	0.2A
Time	90s
Electrode plate	Stainless steel electrode

2.5. Stress relaxation testing
Using a muffle furnace, stress relaxation test was performed at 423K. The heating time was 10 min, the test exposure time was ranged from 1 to100 h, and the test was carried out in an Ar atmosphere. A laser displacement meter was used to measure the deflection displacement. During the stress relaxation process the permanent strain occurs when the loaded deflection is released. The stress relaxation ratio is expressed as the ratio of the permanent deflection displacement produced to the initial deflection displacement loaded. The stress relaxation ratio is calculated by the following equation.

$$\text{stress relaxation ratio}(\%) = \frac{\delta_t}{\delta_0} \times 100$$

$$\delta_t: \textit{Permanent deflection displacement of the specimen caused by stress unloading after the test } (mm)$$

$$\delta_0: \textit{Initial deflection displacement of the test specimen at a given stress load}(mm)$$

The stress relaxation process is divided into four stages: (I) unloaded before stress relaxation test (SRT), (II) loaded before SRT, (III) loaded after SRT and (IV) unloaded after SRT, as illustrated in figure 1.

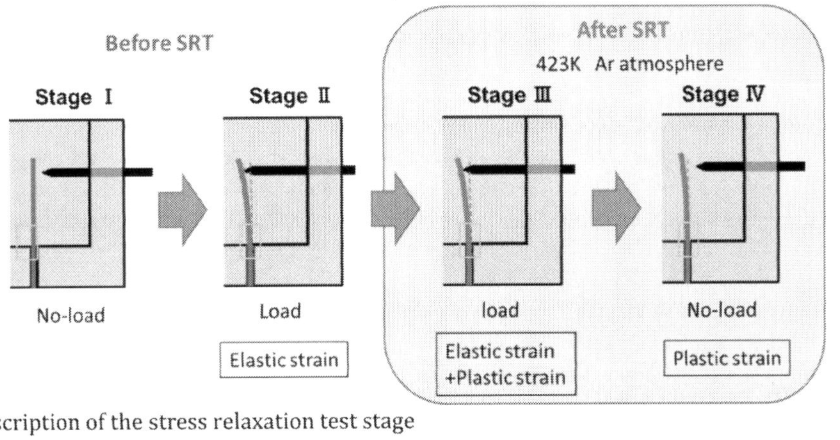

Figure 1. Description of the stress relaxation test stage

2.6 EBSD Analysis
The analysis was performed on solution-treated, aged and 40 Pass/aged samples before and after stress relaxation. The analysis area was 180 µm x ND 1200 µm from the center and front and back of the RD plane, respectively. The step size of the electron beam was set to 1 µm and minimum misorientation angle to recognize grain boundaries was set to 5°

3. Experimental results and discussion

3.1. Stress relaxation test
The relationship between the stress relaxation ratio and test exposure time at 423 K in the stress relaxation tests (SRT) for as-received, aged and CCBent/aged materials is shown in figure2. SRT of CCBent/aged materials were performed with the high-hardness back side as the top surface and subjected to initial deflection displacement. As a result, aging and CCB on the as-received material reduce the stress relaxation ratio. In addition, at a test exposure time of 100h showed that the aged specimen had better stress relaxation characteristics than the aging and CCBent specimen. This is attribute to the effect of CCB did not work effectively precipitation site formation in the aging process. It is also likely that the effect of CCB was not observed in the 40P/aged specimen because a sufficient amount of strain was not added.

IOP Conf. Series: Materials Science and Engineering 1121 (2021) 012030 doi:10.1088/1757-899X/1121/1/012030

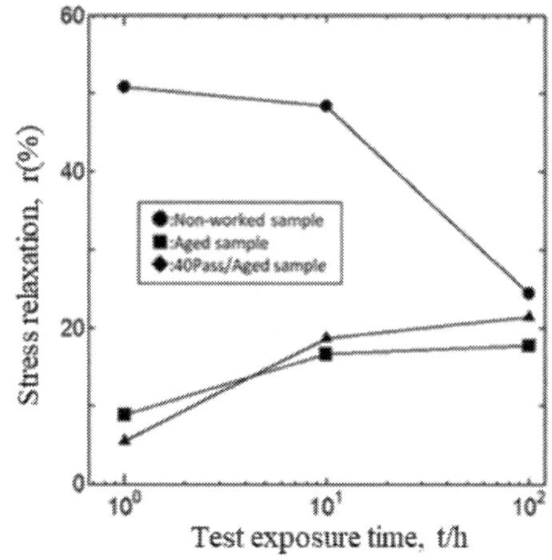

Figure 2. Stress relaxation behavior for non-worked, 723K aged and CCBent/aged specimens, tested at 423K as a function of test exposure time.

3.2. EBSD Analysis

3.2.1 Variation of KAM value near the surface in the process of stress relaxation. Figure3 shows the changes in KAM values near both surfaces (distance from bottom surface,40-80 μm and 1120-1160 μm) for (A) As-received, (B) 40p/aged specimens. the Top side, KAM value decreased by about 0.1 from stage II and decreased to stageIV-1h. After that, it can be seen that KAM value increased by about 0.8 in stage III-1h and decreased by about 0.3 in stage IV-1h. On the top side of 40Pass/aged material, KAM value decreased by about 0.1 from stage I to stage II, and increased by about 0.5 in stage III-1h and stage IV-1h. Thereafter, KAM values decreased by about 0.5 in Stage III and Stage IV, and increased by about 0.2 in Stage III and Stage IV. On the bottom side, there was no significant difference, but KAM value increased about 0.3 from stage II to stage III-1h, and KAM value decreased about 0.1 in stage IV-1h and stage III-10h. Thereafter, KAM values increased by about 0.1 at stage3-100h and stage IV-100h.The difference between the Top and Bottom of 40P/aged specimen could be the effect of external stresses due to residual stresses and stress loading and the effect of releasing stored strains due to SRT.

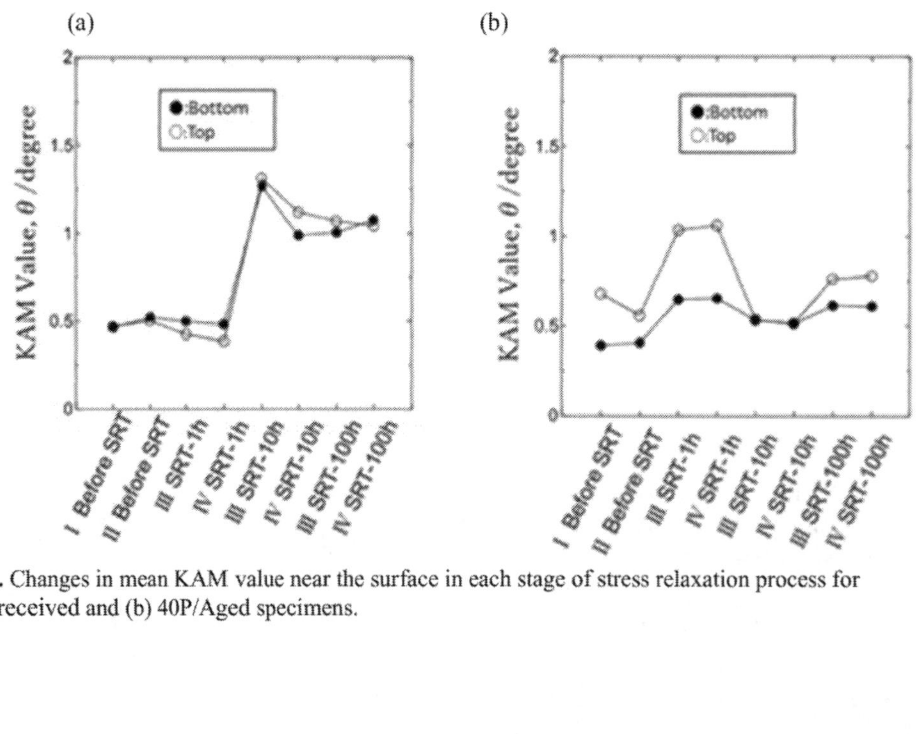

Figure 3. Changes in mean KAM value near the surface in each stage of stress relaxation process for (a) As-received and (b) 40P/Aged specimens.

3.2.2. Comparison of KAM value distribution near the surface. Two figures comparing KAM change distributions between the bottom of as-received (or solution treated) and aged specimens are shown in figure 4. The vertical axis is the change in stage II to stage III-1h and the horizontal axis is the change in stage III-1h to stage III-10h. For the as-received specimen (figure 4(a)), there was almost no change between no load and 1h of stress relaxation, and the KAM value increased by about one between stage III stress relaxation 1h and stage III stress relaxation 10h, indicating that there are many points in the positive direction of the Y-axis. This means that the KAM value does not increase with stress loading, but the KAM value increases with stress relaxation, suggesting that a dynamic recovery process may have taken place. For the aged specimen (figure 4(b)), the KAM value increased by about 0.5 between stage II and stage III stress relaxation 1h, The KAM value decreased by about 0.5 between stage III stress relaxation 1h~stage III stress relaxation 10h. Therefore, there is a negative correlation for this sample. This means that the KAM value increases with stress loading and decreases with stress relaxation, which may be due to sliding dislocation deformation.

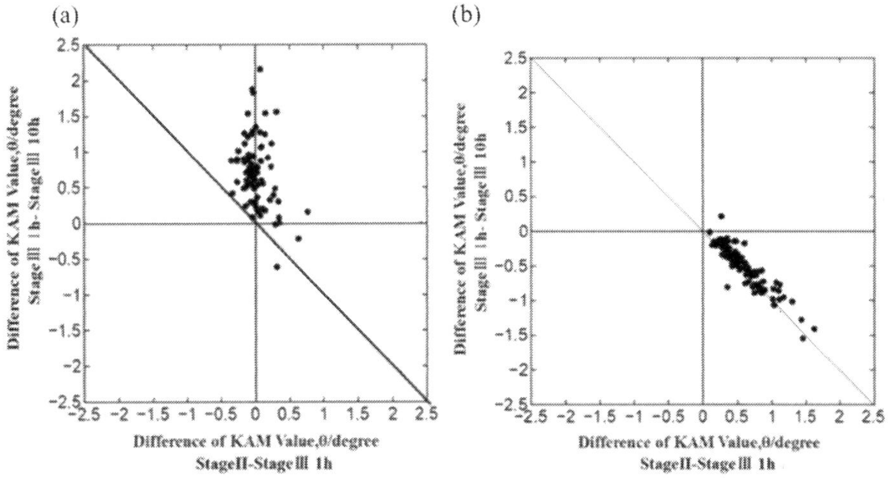

Figure 4. Variation of average KAM values of grains near the surface at each stage of the stress relaxation process (a) As-received specimen and (b) Aged specimen.

3.2.3. Comparison of GOS and KAM values. Figure 5 shows the results of investigating the average KAM and GOS values of the grains of each specimens. The KAM value was higher than the GOS value for each specimen. The difference between the two values for the aged specimens compared to the other specimens may be due in part to the recovery after the aging process. The 40p/aged specimens were subjected to CCB treatment, which introduced strain, but the aging treatment recovered the strain and the amount of strain was considered to have decreased. It is expected that further CCB will lead to accumulation of strain and the GOS value will exceed the KAM value. It is expected that further CCB processing will result in strain accumulation and the GOS value will exceed the KAM value.Next, since some crystal grains show higher GOS values than KAM values, the orientation difference within the grains was investigated using line profiles. Grains with an orientation difference of up to 3.5° showed a KAM value of 0.538 and a GOS value of 1.71. For grains with an orientation difference of up to 0.5°, the KAM value was 0.257 and the GOS value was 0.185. Thus, depending on the conditions, the change in GOS value was observed when the change in KAM value was small.

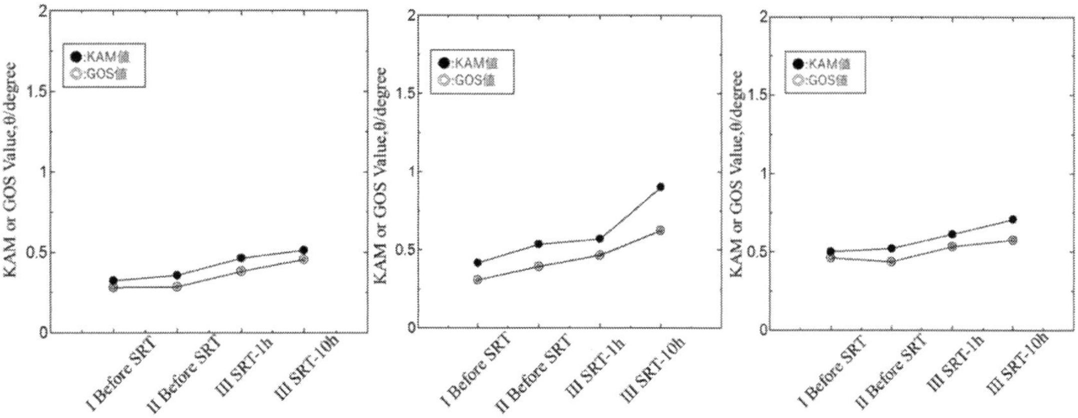

Figure 5. Comparison of the average KAM and GOS values for each specimen

4. Conclusions

In the present study, the stress relaxation process was divided into four stages: (I) no loading, (II) stress loading, (III) stress relaxation, and (IV) unloading. The relationship between the stress relaxation and the intragranular misorientation difference of Cu-Ni-Si alloys subjected to continuous cyclic bending was investigated. The obtained results are summarized as follows.

(1) The stress relaxation properties of Cu-Ni-Si alloys are improved by CCB and aging.

(2) The kernel average misorientation (KAM) of as-received, aged and 40P/aged specimens changed due to the effects of external stresses, residual stresses and stress loads and the release of accumulated strains by stress relaxation tests.

(3) The mechanisms of stress relaxation were different for as-received (or solution-treated) and aged and CCBent/aged specimens.

(4) A change in the GOS value was observed when the change in the KAM value was obviously small in some conditions of the stress relaxation process.

5. References

[1] Takayama Y, Yamaguchi M, Tozawa T, Kato H, Watanabe H and Izawa T 1999 Proc. *ReX'99* (JIMIS10) JIM pp 321-326

[2] Takayama Y, 2004 .*Plasticity and processing* 45 pp 507- 512

[3] Takayama Y, Sasaki Y and Watanabe H 2016 *Copper and copper alloy* 55 pp 6-10

[4] Narumi K, Takayama Y,Miyata Y and Takada Y 2019 *Copper and copper alloy* 58 pp 35-39

[5] Wright S I and Nowell M M, 2006 *EBSD image quality mapping* Microsc. Microanal 12 pp 72–84

[6] Bouquerela J, Diawaraa,b,c, Duboisb A, Dubarb M, Vogta J B and Najjarc D 2015 *Investigations of the microstructural response to a cold forging process of the 6082-T6 alloy* Materials and Design 68 pp 245–258

[7] Stuart I. Wright , Matthew M. Nowell and David P. Field 2011 *A Review of Strain Analysis Using Electron Backscatter Diffraction* Volume 17 Issue 3 June pp 316-329

IOP Conf. Series: Materials Science and Engineering 1121 (2021) 012031 doi:10.1088/1757-899X/1121/1/012031

Heterogeneity of microstructure, texture and mechanical properties along the building direction of Ti-6Al-4V alloy developed by SLM

C Widomski[1], D Solas[1], T Baudin[1], F Brisset[1], S Lebel[2], A-L Helbert[1]

[1]Université Paris-Saclay, CNRS, Institut de chimie moléculaire et des matériaux d'Orsay, 91405 Orsay, France.
[2]AddUp, 5 Rue Bleue, 63118, Cébazat, France.

caroline.widomski@universite-paris-saclay.fr, denis.solas@universite-paris-saclay.fr, thierry.baudin@universite-paris-saclay.fr, francois.brisset@universite-paris-saclay.fr, anne-laure.helbert@universite-paris-saclay.fr

Abstract: Selective Laser Melting (SLM) is of great interest to the aerospace industry due to its ability for producing components with complex geometries. The laser melting process induces a high cooling rate (105-107 K/s) and a germination by epitaxy which leads to a columnar microstructure. In the case of Ti-6Al-4V the rate of cooling from the β domain generates a martensitic α' structure made up of fine needles. The present work describes the microstructural, textural and mechanical heterogeneities along the building direction of Ti-6Al-4V samples produced by SLM with two strategies that have different melt pool size. Characterizations show that both strategies lead to a martensitic microstructure but only the SLM with the greater melting area allows to get homogeneous hardness, texture and β grain size (reconstructed by ARPGE) along building direction.

1. Introduction

The Selective Laser Melting (SLM) powder bed process is the most attractive technique for building parts with a high degree of complexity as indicated in the work by Kruth et al. [1]. The Ti-6Al-4V titanium alloy elaborated by the SLM process and the mechanical properties obtained have been intensively studied in the literature [2] [3]. One of the challenges facing additive manufacturing process is the ability to achieve identical microstructure and mechanical properties throughout the elaborate piece. The high cooling rate of the SLM process generates Ti-6Al-4V parts with predominant martensitic α′ microstructure where prior β grains grow epitaxially throughout the deposition layers. The β grain solidification is influenced by the laser scan strategy and the β phase has a strong ⟨001⟩ texture along its grain growth direction parallel to the Z-axis [4] [5]. This rapid solidification behavior is due to large thermal gradients along the building direction that generates the parts with high strength and low ductility, residual stresses and solidification texture that induce anisotropy in the final product [6]. Some studies reported that despite the fact that each layer is thermally affected by the deposition of a new one, the morphology and size of the α′ grains change along the building direction [7] [8]. The aim of this work is to compare the microstructures obtained with two different strategies and to check their

IOP Conf. Series: Materials Science and Engineering 1121 (2021) 012031 doi:10.1088/1757-899X/1121/1/012031

homogeneity along the building direction. The Classical Linear (CL) strategy is compared to a new strategy called Laser Boost (LB) that allows a wider melting area in order to improve melt flow rate and mechanical properties. Scanning Electron Microscope (SEM) and Electron BackScatter Diffraction (EBSD) were used to characterize the microstructure and the texture. EBSD data were used to reconstruct the prior β grains, in order to study the grain solidification microstructure. The β-phase was quantify using X-ray diffraction to follow the microstructure evolution along building direction and mechanical properties were characterized by micro hardness.

2. Experimental conditions

2.1 Material and process

The powder of Ti-6Al-4V alloy (titanium base, 6% aluminum and 4% of vanadium wt.%) was manufactured by gas atomization method and the spherical particle size ranged from 5μm to 25μm. With the layer-by-layer process deposits, metal epitaxially regrows from the previously fused layer. Moreover, the high temperature gradient with a cooling rate of 10^5-10^7 K/s [9] [10] generates a columnar structure of β grains with a solidification direction parallel to the $<001>_\beta$ crystallographic direction. The Ti-6Al-4V fabricated by SLM process generates α′ martensitic laths that originate from the parent β grains precipitate according to the Burgers orientation relationship. The LB strategy uses a larger melting area with a higher power and a lower scan speed in comparison to the CL strategy. Cylindrical bar-shaped samples of each strategy were built vertically, parallel to Z-axis (figure 1(a)), with a laser scanning path using unidirectional scanning with a 90° rotation between each layer. After fabrication, the samples underwent a stress-relieve treatment at 540°C during 2h under argon followed by furnace cooling. To study the heterogeneity of mechanical properties in the parts along the building direction, one pellet is taken at the TOP and one at the BOTTOM of each bar elaborated with CL and LB strategies. The characterization is conducted on the pellet surface perpendicular to Z-axis (figure 1(b)).

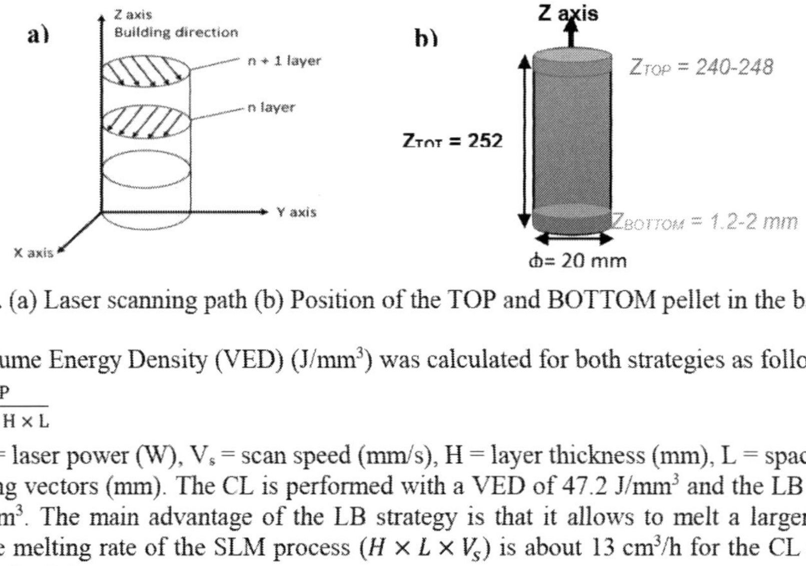

Figure 1. (a) Laser scanning path (b) Position of the TOP and BOTTOM pellet in the bar sample

The Volume Energy Density (VED) (J/mm³) was calculated for both strategies as follows (Eq.1):

$$\mathrm{VED} = \frac{\mathrm{P}}{\mathrm{V_s \times H \times L}} \tag{1}$$

With P = laser power (W), V_s = scan speed (mm/s), H = layer thickness (mm), L = spacing between laser hatching vectors (mm). The CL is performed with a VED of 47.2 J/mm³ and the LB with a VED of 53.6 J/mm³. The main advantage of the LB strategy is that it allows to melt a larger quantity of powder. The melting rate of the SLM process ($H \times L \times V_S$) is about 13 cm³/h for the CL strategy and 49 cm³/h for the LB strategy.

2.2 Microstructure and mechanical characterization

Examination of the microstructure in the (XY) plane occurred after grinding with SiC paper up to a fine 2400 grid size and then an electro-chemical polishing is carried out with the Struers A3 solution. Microstructure and crystallographic orientations were examined by EBSD. Due to the stress-relieved and the Z-position of the pellets, a fraction of martensitic microstructure may have returned to equilibrium phases ($\alpha+\beta$). To quantify this phase transformation, the proportion of β-phase was measured from XRD diffraction diagrams using $(110)_\beta$ and $(0002)_\alpha$ peak intensities [11]. According to the Burgers orientation relationship, these two planes are parallel. The fabrication by SLM induces a grain orientation such that the <001> direction of the β-phase is parallel to Z-axis. As a consequence, the $\{110\}_\beta$ planes are inclined at 45° relative to Z-direction. A texture goniometer is used because it allows to tilt the sample with an χ-angle between 40 and 50° in order to place itself in the Bragg conditions to measure the $(110)_\beta$ and $(0002)_\alpha$ peak intensities. This phase identification was performed on (XY) plane, using XRD with an Inel CPS 120 curved detector. The XRD patterns were obtained with in a χ range from 40° to 50° with an increment of 2.5° and a ϕ between 0°-355° with an increment of 5°. The mechanical properties were evaluated by Vickers micro hardness. The average and the standard deviation correspond to 7 measures with a load of 0.3kg during 15s realized on the (XY) plane.

3. Results

3.1 Martensitic microstructure along the building direction

The figure 2 shows EBSD Z-IPF of the (XY) plane obtained with both strategies. The microstructure is only composed of martensitic α' needles. The applied strategy does not change the α' microstructure and there is no difference in needle size. With the CL strategy, α' needles have 2.5µm of width and 3µm of width with LB strategy. According to the Burgers relation for the Ti-6Al-4V alloy, one β orientation gives twelve α' orientations that's why the α' overall texture is random [12]. Nevertheless, the microstructure exhibits some domains which correspond to the prior β gain structure and they are larger for the LB process (Fig. 2(d)) compared to those obtained with the CL strategy (Fig.2 (b)).

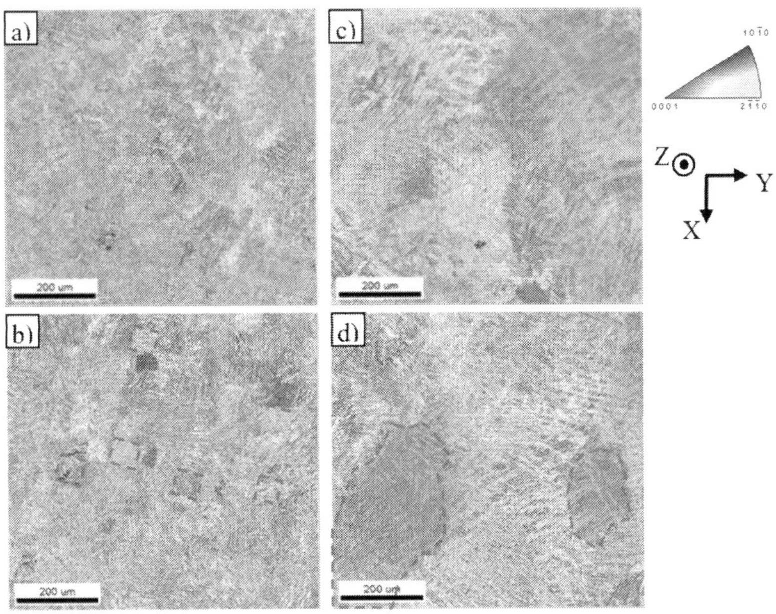

Figure 2. EBSD [001] Inverse Pole Figure (IPF) orientation map of TA6V sample obtained after stress relief. The IPF map showing the α' microstructure and texture on the (a) TOP and (b) BOTTOM with CL strategy and on the (c) TOP and (d) BOTTOM with LB strategy.

3.2 β-phase morphology along building direction

Because the β phase is difficult to observe directly by EBSD, the corresponding maps were reconstructed from figure 2 (IPF α' maps) using the ARPGE software [13]. The reconstruction of the β grains is based on the Burgers crystallographic relationship that governs the α → β phase transformation and especially the directions relations $(0001)_\alpha$ // $(110)_\beta$ and $<111>_\beta$ // $<11\bar{2}0>_\alpha$. The figure 3 shows β-phase microstructures after reconstruction. On the β-phase map corresponding to the CL laser strategy, small square areas are present due to the laser scanning direction (figure 1). It generated periodic patterns in each layer that lead to a grid microstructure of β-phase with different crystallographic orientations. The β grains have a size in the order of 60 µm (± 9µm) at the BOTTOM and around 105 µm (± 9µm) at the TOP. This grain size increase from BOTTOM to TOP can be explained by grain growth selection and the temperature rise induced by thermal cycling with the CL strategy. The LB strategy induces larger melting area and therefore larger and irregular β grains are observed. The average size of β grains is 110µm (± 43 µm) at the BOTTOM and 102 µm (± 80 µm) at the TOP because of the homogeneous thermal cycling due to the LB strategy. In figure 3, the β-reconstructed orientation map and the IPF of the LB strategy highlight a preferential growth direction $<001>_\beta$ // Z. The texture of the LB sample is similar along the building direction. For the CL strategy the β-reconstructed orientation map, reveal that a majority of β grains are oriented in the direction $<001>_\beta$ // Z. The figure 3 also highlights that the texture is more pronounced at the TOP regarding the IPF.

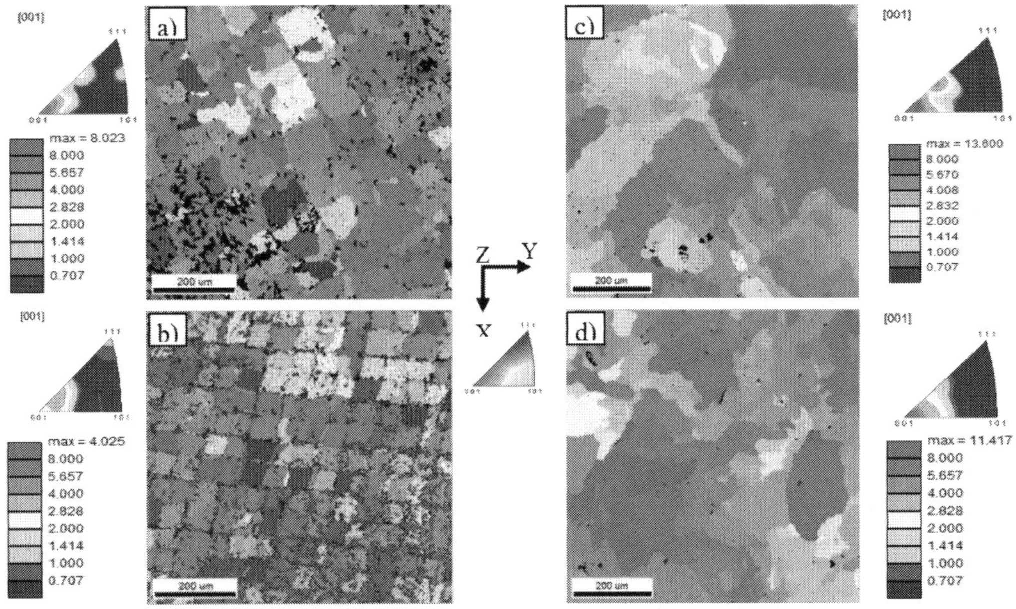

Figure 3. EBSD [001] Inverse Pole Figure (IPF) orientation map of the reconstructed β texture of TA6V is observed on the (a) TOP and (b) BOTTOM with CL strategy and on the (c) TOP and (d) BOTTOM with LB strategy.

The β-phase proportion is correlated to the hardness; hardness globally decreases with the β-phase proportion [14]. To calculate the β proportion evolution along the building direction, a XRD measure is realized. The XRD spectra after pic separation are obtained from the TOP and the BOTTOM pellet with CL and LB strategies are shown in figures. 4 (a), (b) (c) and (d) respectively. The spectra are represented in χ range of 40-50°, because the $(110)_\beta$ and $(0002)_\alpha$ peaks are respectively reflected at 46.4° and 47.4°. The calculated proportions of β phase in the samples are reported in figure 4 (e). At equilibrium state the β phase proportion is around 10% at room temperature for the Ti-6Al-4V alloy [15]. In this study the maximum β proportion is equal to 3.59% at the BOTTOM and 4.8 % at the TOP sample for CL strategy and about 3.34% at the BOTTOM and 2.6 % for the TOP with the LB strategy. The small proportion of β phase signals that the decomposition of α' into (α + β) is limited and not uniform. Careful multiple micro indentation measurements on the (XY) planes on each pellet were conducted in order to measure the hardness. Figure 4 (f) shows the average hardness values and reveals that hardness decreases with the number of layer deposit for the CL strategy with 395 HV on the BOTTOM and 365 HV on the

TOP. For the LB strategy with 399 HV on the BOTTOM and 406 HV on the TOP the hardness is similar considering the incertitude. The figure 4 (g) shows that the hardness globally decreases with the β-phase proportion. The LB strategy allows a better homogeneity of the hardness properties along the building direction and this despite a greater β-phase proportion difference between the top and the bottom of the bar. It means that other parameters such as grain size or thermal history must play a role on hardness.

(a)

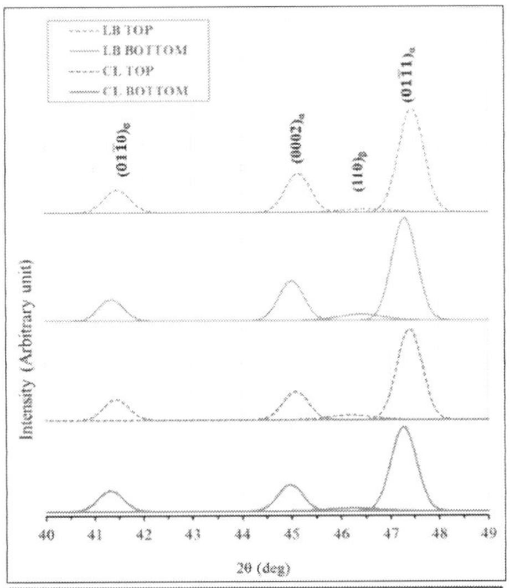

(b)

Sample	CL(BOTTOM)	CL(TOP)	LB(BOTTOM)	LB(TOP)
% β	3.59	4.80	4.34	2.61

(c)

(d)

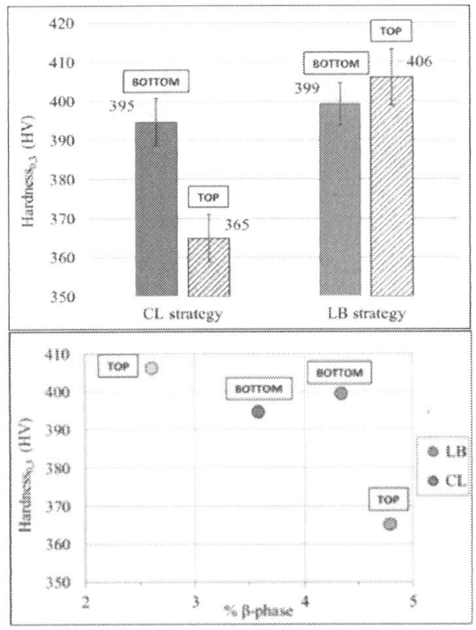

Figure 4. (a) XRD patterns of SLM-fabricated Ti–6Al–4V (XY) plane showing distinctive phase constituents (b) Summary of β phase proportion measured by XRD of each sample. (c) Hardness measurements on (XY) plane of each sample. (d) Hardness evolution as a function of β -phase.

4. Discussion

The melt flow rate is 49 cm^3/h for the LB strategy and 13 cm^3/h for the CL strategy, therefore the LB strategy is interesting due to a faster melting process. The EBSD studies have shown that for both strategies, the resulting microstructure is composed of needles of α' martensitic that is consistent along the building direction. It is clear that the prior β-phase has a dominant <100>//Z solidification texture. However, the applied strategy changes the size and the organization of β grains. With the CL strategy, the β grain size (about 60µm) is related to the process parameters that lead to a paving structure and with the LB strategy, the β grains have an irregular shape and are bigger (110µm) due to the bigger melting area. For the CL strategy there is therefore a heterogeneity of microstructure along the manufacturing direction with β grains that grow up to 2 times the initial size as the number of layers increases. For the CL strategy, this evolution can be explained by grain growth selection. The LB strategy generates less microstructural and textural heterogeneities along the building direction. For the Ti-6Al-4V alloy, the β phase is more ductile than α' martensitic which means the increase of β-phase should imply a decrease of hardness of the sample [16]. Moreover the hardness usually increases with the decrease of grain size. In our study the grain size obtained with LB strategy is higher than the CL strategy however the hardness of the LB strategy is higher than the CL strategy. It is difficult to determine the cause of the change in hardness as it can be influenced by the grain size, the texture and the thermal history of the sample. However, these results have shown that by using the LB strategy, the influence of Z-position on microstructural and mechanical properties is reduced and the texture is uniform along the Z-axis.

5. Conclusion

The influence of Z-position on microstructure and the mechanical properties of samples elaborated by the LB strategy and the CL strategy is compared. The following conclusions are drawn from this work:

- The microstructure obtained by CL and LB strategies is a martensitic needle microstructure.
- Parent β grains are larger with the LB strategy and the CL strategy induces a paved grain structure. For both strategies, a heterogeneity of β microstructure is observed along the building direction thereby inducing β-grain magnification for the highest layers.
- LB strategy induces a better homogeneity of texture and mechanical properties along the building direction.
- The CL strategy induces a heterogeneity of hardness along the building direction that is influenced by the β proportion.

To sum up, the LB strategy, remains better in terms of texture and hardness homogeneity along the building direction. Moreover, it guaranties a higher melting rate.

6. References

[1] Kruth J, Froyen L, Vaerenbergh J, Mercelis P, Rombouts M and Lauwers B 2004 Selective laser melting of iron-based powder *J. Mater. Process. Technol.* **149** 616-22

[2] Liu S and Shin Y 2013 Additive manufacturing of Ti-6Al-4V alloy: A review *Mater. Des.* **164** 107552

[3] Banerjee D and Williams J 2013 Perspectives on Titanium Science and Technology *Acta Mat.* **61** 844-79

[4] Simonelli M, Tse Y and Tuck C 2014 On the Texture Formation of Selective Laser Melted Ti-6Al-4V *Metall Mater Trans A* **45** 2863-72

[5] Thijs L, Verhaeghe F, Craeghs T, Van Humbeeck J and Kruth J 2010 A study of the microstructural evolution during selective laser melting of Ti-6Al-4V *Acta Materialia* **58** 3303-12

[6] Neikter N, Huang A and Wu X 2019 Microstructural characterization of binary microstructure pattern in selective laser-melted Ti-6Al-4V *Int. J. Adv. Manuf. Technol.* **104** 1381-91

[7] Xu W, Brandt M, Sun S, Elambasseril J, Liu Q, Latham K, Xia K and Qian M 2015 Additive manufacturing of strong and ductile Ti-6Al-4V by selective laser melting via in situ martensite decomposition *Act. Mat* **85** 74-84

[8] Simonelli M, Tse Y and Tuck C 2014 The formation of α + β microstructure in as-fabricated selective laser melting of Ti–6Al–4V *Focus Issue: The Mat. Sc.of Additive Manufacturing* **29** 2028-35

[9] Yang J, Yu H, Yin J, Gao M, Wang Z and Zeng X 2016 Formation and control of martensite in Ti-6Al-4V alloy produced by selective laser melting *Mater. Des.* **108** 308-18

[10] DebRoy T, Wei H, Zuback J, Muckherjee T, Milewski J, Beese A, Wilson-Heid A, De A and Zhang W 2018 Additive manufacturing *Prog. Mater. Sci.* **92** 112-224

[11] Bach M, Broll N, Cornet A and Gaide L 1996 Diffraction X en traitement thermiques : dosage de l'austénite résiduelle par diffraction des rayons X *J. Phys IV* **6** C4-887 - C4-895

[12] Simonelli M, Tse Y and Tuck C 2012 Further understanding of Ti-6Al-4V selective laser melting using texture analysis *Annual International Solid Freeform Fabrication Symposium - An Additive Manufacturing Conference* 480-91

[13] Cayron C 2007 ARPGE: a computer program to automatically reconstruct the parent grains from electron backscatter diffraction data *J. Appl. Crystallogr* **40** 1183-88

[14] Magalini E, Facchini L, Robotti P, Molinari A, Höges S and Wissenbach K 2010 Ductility of a Ti-6Al-4V alloy produced by selective laser melting of prealloyed powders *Rap. Prot. J.* **16** (6) 450-59

[15] Gey N 1997 THESE : Etude des changements de textures par transformation de phase β → α dans les produits TA6V laminés à chaud

[16] Vrancken B, Thujs L, Kruth J and Humbeeck J 2012 Heat treatment of Ti6Al4V produced by Selective Laser Melting: Microstructure and mechanical properties *J. Alloys Compd.* **541** 177-85

[17] DebRoy T, Wei H, Zuback J, Muckherjee T, Elmer J, Milewski J, Beese A, Wilson-Heid A, De A and Zhang W 2018 Additive manufacturing *Prog. Mater. Sci.* **92** 112-224

The influence of the crystallographic texture and phase composition of Ti-Nb-Zr alloys with shape memory and superelasticity on their functional properties

M M Zaripova, M G Isaenkova, V A Fesenko and A V Osintsev

Institute of Nuclear Physics and Engineering, National Research Nuclear University MEPhI (Moscow Engineering Physics Institute), Moscow, 115409, Russian Federation

MMZaripova@mephi.ru

Abstract. Currently, Ti-Zr-Nb-based biocompatible alloys are considered as prospective for medical applications. In this work, the mechanisms of the formation of the crystallographic texture of five alloys Ti-(17-19)Zr-(14-16)Nb (at.%) have been compared. The presence of martensitic transformations during the rolling process determines the features of the formed texture. At the initial stage of deformation (ε = 50%), the texture {112}<011> is formed in all five alloys. With an increase of the degree of deformation to 92%, the texture dissipates somewhat, which is due to an increase in the fraction of the martensitic phase in the foils. Recrystallization of rolled foils (ε = 92%) at 650°C leads to an exacerbation of the texture component close to {100}<011>, the blurring of which varies in different alloys. Cyclic tensile tests along three directions: the rolling direction (RD), the transverse direction, at an angle of 45° to the RD showed the presence of anisotropy in the samples. It was shown, that the effect of superelasticity is orientation- and structure-depending, and the anisotropy of mechanical properties.

1. Introduction

At present, Ti-Zr-Nb-based alloys (TNZ), having biomechanical and biochemical compatibility with bone tissue, are considered as prospective for medical purposes. These alloys contain only safe chemical elements permitted for medical application, have high corrosion resistance in environments of the body, characterized by a low modulus of elasticity 40-60 GPa, comparable to that of bone tissue, and the effect of superelasticity guaranteed above 0.5%. The effects of superelasticity in such alloys are realized due to the reversible martensite transformation β (body-centered cubic lattice) $\leftrightarrow$ α'' (orthorhombic lattice). It becomes relevant to create in a superelastic alloys such a crystallographic texture that would ensure an increase in their functional and operational characteristics.

Hypoallergenic alloys based on Ti-Nb, alloyed with additional elements biocompatible with human organisms [1]: Zr, O, N, Ta, Al, Pt, etc. are promising alloys for biomedical purposes.

It is becoming urgent to create in an alloy with shape memory effect (SME) and superelasticity (SE) such a crystallographic texture that provides an increase in the functional and operational characteristics necessary for them.

The aim of this work is to determine the effect of the crystallographic texture on the properties of shape memory alloys and superelasticity based on Ti-Zr-Nb and the possibility of controlling the properties by changing it during deformation and subsequent annealing. It is also necessary to choose an alloy with the most stable functional properties.

2. Materials and methods of their research

The work was carried out on foils made of Ti-(17-19)Zr-(14-16)Nb alloys (at.%) (Table 1). The ingots of the indicated alloys were melted in an arc furnace MEPhI-9 in an argon atmosphere, homogenized in a vacuum furnace at a temperature of 1000°C for 2 h, and quenched in water to fix the β structure of the alloy. Then the samples were forged at a temperature (at 900°C, $\varepsilon \approx 40\%$) in order to refine the grain size of the original workpiece. Further, on a laboratory rolling mill, cold rolling of the plates was carried out to degrees of deformation of 92-97%, calculated from the change in the thickness of the plate. Subsequent heat treatment in a temperature range of 650-900°C for 0.5 h in a vacuum oven.

Table 1. Composition of studied alloys, at.%.

№	Ti	Zr	Nb
1 (18-14)	67.6	17.9	14.5
2 (18-15)	66.4	18.4	15.2
3 (18-16)	65.4	18.4	16.2
4 (17-15)	67.4	17.1	15.5
5 (19-15)	65.1	19.3	15.2

According to the data of [2, 3], this regime of thermomechanical processing corresponds to the formation in the alloy of a nanosubstructure with a subgrain size of less than 100 nm. Holding at 600°C for half an hour leads to the manifestation of the best functional fatigue life of the alloy.

X-ray analysis of the structural state of foils, including determination of phase composition, an evaluation of the structure perfection by means of the X-ray line profile analysis, and texture estimation, was performed on X-ray diffractometers DRON-3, DRON-3M and D8 Discover with the Cu k_α-radiation. The texture was analyzed in terms of the direct pole figures {110}, {100}, {112} and {111} recorded by reflections (110), (200), (112) and (222), respectively, using the standard tilt method [4, 5]. For X-ray studies, samples of 17x17 mm^2 were cut from rolled and annealed foils, which were etched in a mixture of acids (HNO_3:H_2O:HF = 9: 9: 2) at 30-50 μm to lighten their surface.

Mechanical tests were carried out on the versatile electromechanical machine Instron 5966 (P_{max} = 10 kN). Tensile tests of the investigated foils were performed at 3 directions: in the rolling direction (RD), transvers direction (TD) and at an angle of 45° to the RD. In addition, cyclic tests (stretching to a few percent deformations followed by complete unloading of the sample) were performed in the same directions.

Uniaxial tension tests were also carried out. Tensile test specimen dimensions: thickness 0.5 ± 0.1 mm, width 1.5 ± 0.5 mm, and working area length 14 mm. To determine Young's modulus from the tensile test results, the digital image correlation technique [6] was used by means of an optical extensometer. The elastic modulus was calculated using the VIC-3D software [7].

3. Results and discussion

3.1 Phase composition

Typical fragments of the diffraction spectra of the foils of the alloy Ti-18Zr-15Nb (at.%) are shown in Figure 1, in which the reflection indices for the β-phase and the additional α''-phase are indicated in different colors. It should be mentioned, that the phase composition for samples of other alloys changes in a similar way.

From the spectra, it can be seen that foils deformed to 92–93% consist mainly of the β-phase and are characterized by broad X-ray reflections, which is due to the presence of a large number of defects in the deformed material. The lines of the additional (martensitic) α"-phase are also visible, which indicates the occurrence of martensitic transformations during deformation (rolling).

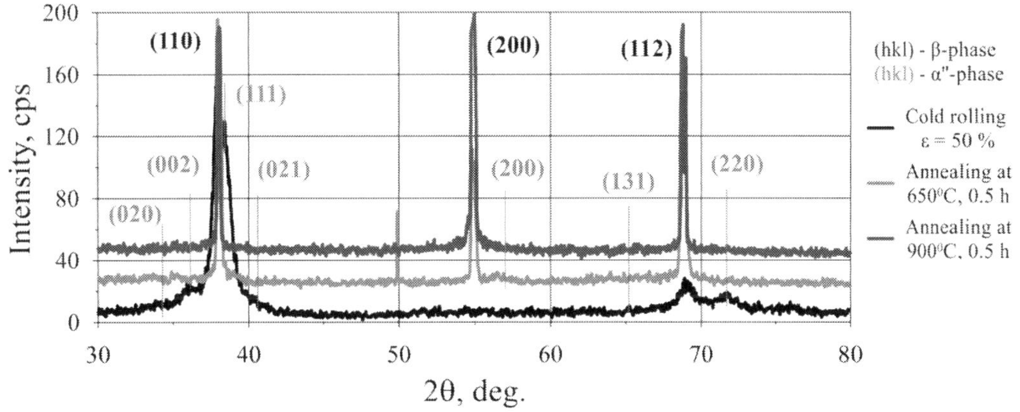

Figure 1. Diffraction spectra of Ti-18Zr-15Nb (at.%) alloy samples.

Because of annealing at temperatures of 650 and 900°C in all five alloys, the crystal structure of the annealed foils is improved, as evidenced by the decrease in the half-width (FWHM) of the X-ray lines. In the case of annealing TNZ alloys at a temperature of 650°C with subsequent quenching in water, the foils also remain in the β-phase state, however, reflections of the additional α″-phase are also visible, while annealing at 900°C after quenching does not allow the precipitation of α″-phase.

3.2 Texture analysis

Considering that during rolling of materials with SME and SE, a significant fraction of plastic deformation can occur in the additional phase, which is formed in the alloy due to martensitic transformation, it is necessary to analyze the patterns of texture formation in such alloys.

At the initial stage of deformation (ε = 50%) in all five alloys, the {112}<011> texture is formed. As the degree of deformation increases to 92–93%, the texture is somewhat scattered, which is due to an increase in the proportion of the martensitic phase in the deformed foil. Moreover, in two alloys (Ti-18Zr-16Nb and Ti-19Zr-15Nb (at.%)), in comparison with the others, the process of reorientation of grains is inhibited and, as a consequence, the formation of a crystallographic texture due to the high value of the critical shear stresses. However, in the Ti-17Zr-15Nb (at.%) alloy, the texture becomes sharper.

The regularities of changes in the rolling texture as a result of annealing at different temperatures are revealed. The recrystallization of rolled (up to 92–97%) foils at a temperature of 650°C for 0.5 h leads to a sharpening of the texture component close to {100}<011>, the blurring of which varies in different alloys. For example, in alloy 18-15, the texture {100}<011> is blurred in the {112}<110> and {110}<100> directions (Figure 2). After annealing at 900°C for 0.5 h, a one-component sharp texture {100}<011> is formed in the samples of all five alloys.

3.3 Results of tensile tests

Mechanical properties and deformation behaviour are also strongly dependent on the formed crystallographic texture. Cyclic tensile tests showed the presence of anisotropy in the samples of all five alloys (Figure 2). Moreover, the greatest anisotropy is observed at an angle of 45° to the RD due to the formed crystallographic texture.

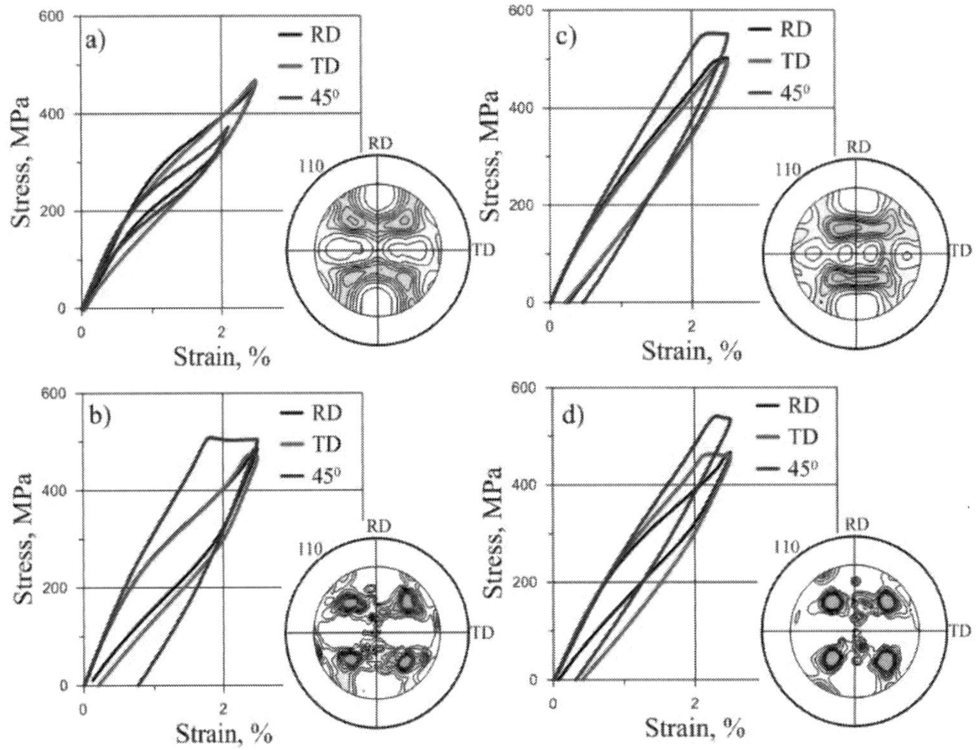

Figure 2. Results of cyclic tensile tests and texture analysis of foils (ε = 92%) obtained at room temperature: a) Ti-18Zr-15Nb (at.%), annealed at 650°C for 0.5h; b) Ti-18Zr-15Nb (at.%), annealed at 900°C for 0.5h; c) Ti-17Zr-15Nb (at.%), annealed at 650°C for 0.5h; d) Ti-17Zr-15Nb (at.%), annealed at 900°C for 0.5h.

As mentioned above, a sharper texture is formed in samples of alloy 17-15 than in alloy 18-15. For this reason, for these two alloys, which are close in composition, the shape of the stress-strain curves is different (Figure 2a, c). Moreover, specimens cut at an angle of 45° to RD from alloy 18-15 exhibit superelasticity, while specimens from alloy 17-15 exhibit a shape memory effect.

Mechanical tensile also show the presence of anisotropy of mechanical properties in all five alloys, both in the deformed and in the annealed states. After annealing at 900°C, a sharper texture is formed in the samples of all five alloys compared to annealing at 650°C. Therefore, there is a strong dependence of the yield stress and elongation of the sample on the direction in which stretching is performed.

From the diagrams shown in Figure 3, it can be concluded that in the samples annealed at 900°C for 0.5 h we observe a large elongation to break. To reveal the nature of this phenomenon in the materials under study using the digital correlation method, it was revealed that, along with the occurrence of martensitic transformation, the effect of a running (blurred) neck appeared, since it moves along the length of the sample without causing localized compression. With such a quasi-uniform deformation, a large elongation is achieved when the sample is stretched. However, large elongation in the alloys is also supposed to be due to transformation-induced plasticity (TRIP) and twinning-induced plasticity (TWIP) effects [8–10].

More than that, most often, specimens cut at an angle of 45° to the rolling direction are stretched to lower percent of deformation. This is also due to the crystallographic texture formed during the previous thermo-mechanical treatment. Texture {100}<011> is formed (Figure 2,b), where crystals with different orientations are oriented along different directions (RD || <011>, TD || <011>, at an angle 45° to RD || <100>).

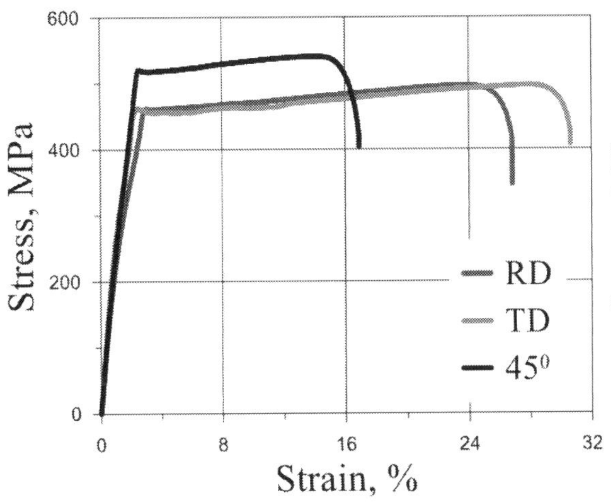

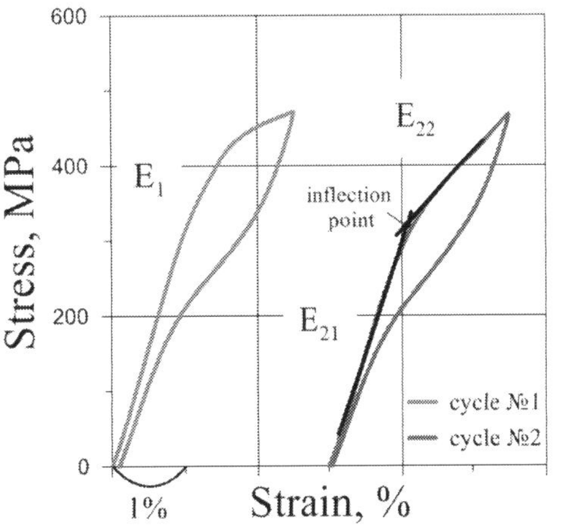

Figure 3. Tensile test results obtained at room temperature on Ti-18Zr-15Nb (at.%) alloy specimens annealed at 900°C for 0.5 h.

Figure 4. Scheme for measuring Young's modulus using the example of a Ti-18Zr-15Nb (at.%), sample cut along the RD annealed at 650°C, 0.5 h.

During tensile tests, it was found that the stress-strain diagrams of specimens made of alloys with SE and SME for the first and second test cycles differ significantly. In most alloys, in the first cycle, there is no inflection point indicating the occurrence of an martensitic transformations, but already in the second and subsequent cycles, the zone in which the phase transformation occurs is clearly visible. Based on this, it was decided to measure Young's modulus not only at the first deformation cycle, but also at the second, in order to compare the values obtained before and after the phase transformation. The scheme used to measure Young's modulus is shown in Figure 4.

Based on the results obtained, the values of Young's modulus for samples of all five alloys in the unloaded state are 45–93 GPa, which corresponds to the value of Young's modulus for bone tissue. Young's modulus for alloy 18-15 at different directions:

- E_1 = 55 GPa;
- E_{21} = 45 GPa;
- E_{22} = 27 GPa.

It was assumed that E_1 and E_{21} should be equal (since both values are in the elastic region of deformation). Based on the data obtained, for all specimens $E_1 > E_{21}$, that is, after the first test cycle, the value of the elastic modulus decreases. With each subsequent cycle of "load-unloading", the restoration of the shape more and more approaches the initial value (residual deformation tends to zero, for many samples on the fifth cycle it is completely absent), that is, the material "trains". We consider that such a dislocation substructure is formed in the samples, which allows martensite crystals to be oriented in a certain way, thereby reducing the energy for their formation in subsequent cycles and the stress of activation of this process. The manifestation of plasticity at the first stages of stretching may be due to the reorientation of grains with the {112} orientation, formed during annealing of the foils as a result of recrystallization and were at the beginning of the test in an orientation unstable with respect to the acting load.

4. Conclusions

1. Based on cyclic tests of annealed foils, it was shown that all the investigated Ti-Zr-Nb-based alloys are characterized by either superelasticity or shape memory effect, i.e. able to restore their initial shape.
2. It is shown that a weak (blurred) crystallographic texture is formed in deformed samples, which becomes sharper in subsequent annealing. Moreover, in samples with superelasticity, a similar texture is formed, as well as in samples with shape memory effect.
3. It has been established that alloys with stable functional properties are alloys Ti-18Zr-15Nb, Ti-18Zr-16Nb and Ti-19Zr-15Nb (at.%). To obtain optimal properties, it is necessary to conduct annealing at a temperature of 650°C for 0.5 h.
4. It has been established that alloys with stable functional properties, i.e. with high properties of superelasticity, with a maximum fraction of elastic deformation during cycling, with minimum stresses for activating martensitic transformations, are alloys Ti-18Zr-15Nb, Ti-18Zr-16Nb and Ti-19Zr-15Nb (at.%), for which the content of zirconium ranges from 18.4 to 19.5 at.%, and niobium – from 15.2 to 16.2 at.%. To obtain optimal properties, it is necessary to carry out annealing at a temperature of 650°C for 0.5 h, because annealing at t = 900°C leads to significant grain growth and sharpening of the crystallographic texture, which leads to an increase in the anisotropy of properties and their instability.
5. The Young's modulus of all annealed samples varies from 45 to 93 GPa.

Acknowledgements
This work was supported by Competitiveness Growth Program of the Federal Autonomous Educational Institution of Higher Education National Research Nuclear University MEPhI (Moscow Engineering Physics Institute) (agreement No.02.a03.21.0005).

References

[1] Kim H Y, Miyazaki S 2016 Several issues in the development of Ti–Nb-based shape memory alloys. *Shape Memory and Superelasticity* **2** 380–90
[2] Zaripova M M, Isaenkova M G, Perlovich Yu A, Osintsev A V, Fesenko V A 2019 Influence of crystallographic texture and phase composition on the effect of superelastiñity of foils from alloys based on Ti-Nb *Chelyabinsk Physical and Mathematical Journal* **4(1)** 94-107 https://doi.org/10.24411/2500-0101-2019-14109
[3] Dubinskiy S, Prokoshkin S, Brailovski V 2011 Structure of thermo-mechanical processing of Ti-Nb-Zr(Ta) alloys and manifestation of the shape-memory effect *Physics of Metals and Metallography* 529-42
[4] Isaenkova M, Perlovich Yu, Fesenko V 2016 Modern methods of experimental construction of texture complete direct pole figures by using X-ray data *IOP Conf. Series:Materials Science and Engineering* **130** 012055 doi:10.1088/1757-899X/130/1/012055
[5] Isaenkova M, Perlovich Yu 2014 Regularities in the development of crystallographic texture and substructure heterogeneity in zirconium alloys during deformation and heat treatment. M.: NRNU MEPhI 528 p.
[6] Sutton M.A., Orteu J J, Schreier H W 2009 Image Correlation for Shape, Motion and Deformation Measurements: basic concepts, theory and applications. *Springer* 321 p.
[7] The digital image correlation system VIC-3D. Available online: https://www.correlatedsolutions.com/vic-3d/ (accessed 10.10.2020)
[8] Zhang J Y et al 2017 Microstructural evolution of a ductile metastable β titanium alloy with combined TRIP/TWIP effects *J. Alloys Compd.* **699** 775–82
[9] Brozek C et al 2016 β-titanium alloy with extra high strain-hardening rate: Design and mechanical properties *Scr. Mater.* **114** 60–4
[10] Kim K M, Kim H Y, Miyazaki S 2020 Effect of Zr Content on Phase Stability, Deformation Behavior, and Young's Modulus in Ti–Nb–Zr Alloys *Materials* **13** 476

Microstructural study of duplex stainless steel after turning using EBSD and X-ray diffraction analysis

J Capek[1], P Minarik[2], M Neslusan[3], K Trojan[1] and N Ganev[1]

[1] Faculty of Nuclear Sciences and Physical Engineering, Czech Technical University in Prague, Trojanova 13, Prague 2, 120 00, Czech Republic

[2] Faculty of Mathematics and Physics, Charles University, Ke Karlovu 5, Prague 2, 121 16, Czech Republic

[3] Faculty of Mechanical Engineering, University of Žilina, Univerzitná 1, Žilina, 010 26, Slovakia

E-mail: Jiri.Capek@fjfi.cvut.cz

Abstract. The aim of this research is a microstructural study of duplex stainless steel after turning. The electron backscatter diffraction and X-ray diffraction analyses were applied to analyse the surface and subsurface regions. The gradients of Kernel Average Misorientation as a function of flank wear were investigated. It was found that the concentration of deformation depends on the subsurface depth, individual phases, and flank wear. The similar behaviour but with a different inclination of grain size (determined by electron backscatter diffraction) and crystallite size (determined by X-ray diffraction) depending on flank wear was observed.

1. Introduction

Duplex steels are dual-phase steels contain austenitic-ferritic microstructure with a similar proportion of both phases. Due to the combination of properties of both phases and mainly two-phase microstructure, duplex steels exhibit high corrosion and wear resistance in many environments, where high-alloyed single-phase steels are usually used [1]. The mechanical properties of austenite and ferrite are generally different; therefore, the properties of duplex steel strongly depend on microstructure (e.g. grain size, texture) and others (phase content, macro- and microstresses, chemical composition, etc. [2, 3]).

Our team [4] verified that major deformation mechanisms are the same as in the single-phase steels. Nevertheless, due to inter-phase interaction, their behaviour during deformation can be different in comparison with single-phase steels [5]. Therefore, the statement that austenite and ferrite phases are generally plastic or elastic, is not generally valid.

According to [2], the strain-hardening rate of austenite is higher than for ferrite. However, it is lower in comparison with single-phase austenitic stainless steel with the same chemical composition due to the very low stacking fault energy. The explanation of this behaviour is inter-phase interaction which redistributes the plastic deformation into both phases. The strain-hardening of austenite is very high at low deformations, but from certain deformation, it increasingly concentrates within the ferrite phase, which has a larger number of active slip systems and a considerably higher stacking fault energy. In other words, the austenite phase becomes harder than ferrite phase. Wroński et al. [6] and Choi et al. [7] investigated the plastic deformation in duplex steel by electron backscatter diffraction. The samples studying after tensile deformation brought the conclusion that the Kernel Average Misorientation (geometrically necessary dislocations — their density) increases faster in the austenite phase than in the ferrite phase during deformation.

During plastic deformation, the high dislocation density is generated and form low- and high-angle boundary. According to the generally known definition, the high-angle boundaries delimit grains and low-angle boundaries so-called sub-grains (in limit crystallites). Our team [3] besides other things found that the crystallite size of the plastically deformed surface layer is nearly unaffected with flank wear. Afterwards, the gradient of crystallite size decreases with flank wear due to higher dislocation density in deeper regions. Our previous study of duplex steels, Capek et al. [8], shows the influence of crystallite size depth profiles concerning inserts rake angle. We found that the gradient of crystallite size was similar for all rake angles but, the higher crystallite size was evaluated for positive rake angles. Moreover, microhardness depth profiles were steeper for positive rake angles. All used inserts were new, i.e. sharp; thus, the influence of wearing tool should be the next step.

Therefore, this study focuses on the study of the microstructure of duplex steel after turning with defined conditions (different tool wear) using the electron backscatter diffraction and X-ray diffraction analyses. The investigations of Kernel Average Misorientation, grain and crystallite size are pointed out.

2. Material and experimental methods

Experiments were carried out on the coarse-grained duplex steel SAF 2205 (EN 1.4470) with balanced ferrite and austenite content. Chemical composition is shown in Table 1.

Table 1. Chemical composition of the duplex steel 1.4470 (wt. %) [2].

Fe	C	Mn	Mo	Cr	Ni	S	P	Si	N
bal.	0.015	1	3	22	5.5	0.012	0.017	0.5	0.16

The specimens were face dry turned. Cutting conditions were as follows: cutting speed 110 m.min^{-1}, cutting depth 1 mm, feed 0.1 mm, , tool holder *DWLNR 2525 M08 KT 80* and cutting inserts *SNMG 120408* of grade P20 with TiN coating and flank wear width (the average width of the worn area on the cutting edge) $VB = 0.05$, 0.12, 0.25, 0.4, and 0.53 mm.

Deformation induced to the surface of turned samples was investigated by electron backscatter diffraction on the CD/ND cuts[1]. The samples were analysed in *Auriga Compact SEM* equipped with *EDAX EBSD* camera. The EBSD mapping was performed near the turned surface with the scan size 200×400 µm^2 and the resolution of 0.25 µm. A 10×10 grid surrounding the pixel of interest with threshold 5° was used during each misorientation calculation to obtain Kernel Average Misorientation. Experimental data were processed using the *MATLAB*™ toolbox *MTEX* software [9].

X'Pert PRO MPD diffractometer with cobalt radiation was used to the analyses of CD/TD plane of the samples by X-ray diffraction (XRD). Crystallite size was calculated using the Scherrer formula. The irradiated area was defined by experiment geometry, effective penetration depth of the XRD radiation (approx. 5 µm) and pinhole size (4×0.25 mm^2). To analyse the gradients beneath the sample surface, layers of material were gradually removed by electro-chemical polishing using the *Struers LectroPol-5* device.

[1] CD, TD, ND denote cutting, transversal, normal direction, respectively.

3. Results and discussions

For a microstructural study of grain size, crystallite size and Kernel Average Misorientation (KAM), the X-ray diffraction (XRD) and electron backscatter diffraction (EBSD) were used.

3.1. Kernel Average Misorientation

The Kernel Average Misorientation is calculated as the average misorientation between each pixel and its 3rd nearest neighbours. The gradient of KAM was investigated from the point of view of the difference between both phases and the flank wear VB. To obtain one KAM value from each depth, the values from the 4 µm subsurface layer were averaged. The average KAM distributions of both phases in comparison with flank wear are depicted in Figures 1 and 2. Due to this local misorientation from the presence of geometrically necessary dislocations, it can be said that with higher plastic deformation (higher VB), more dislocations are created near the surface and therefore, higher KAM values are observed.

As a result of the strong plastic deformation and surface roughness, the surface regions show a higher proportion of non-indexed points, see Figure 1, nevertheless, high KAM values could be expected. The results also show that high KAM value was detected around the phase boundaries.

The KAM values in both phases in relation to the flank wear VB are depicted in Figure 3. For low plastic deformation ($VB = 0.05$ mm), the austenite is due to stacking fault energy more plastic, i.e. higher KAM is for the ferrite. However, the strain-hardening is higher in the austenite than in the ferrite at low deformations and, therefore, the KAM values are higher for austenite phase for higher VB (from approx. 0.25 mm). These results are in agreement with the authors previous researches of texture behaviour [4] and residual stresses of duplex steels [8]. In these articles as well as in the literature [6], the influence of different strain hardening was observed.

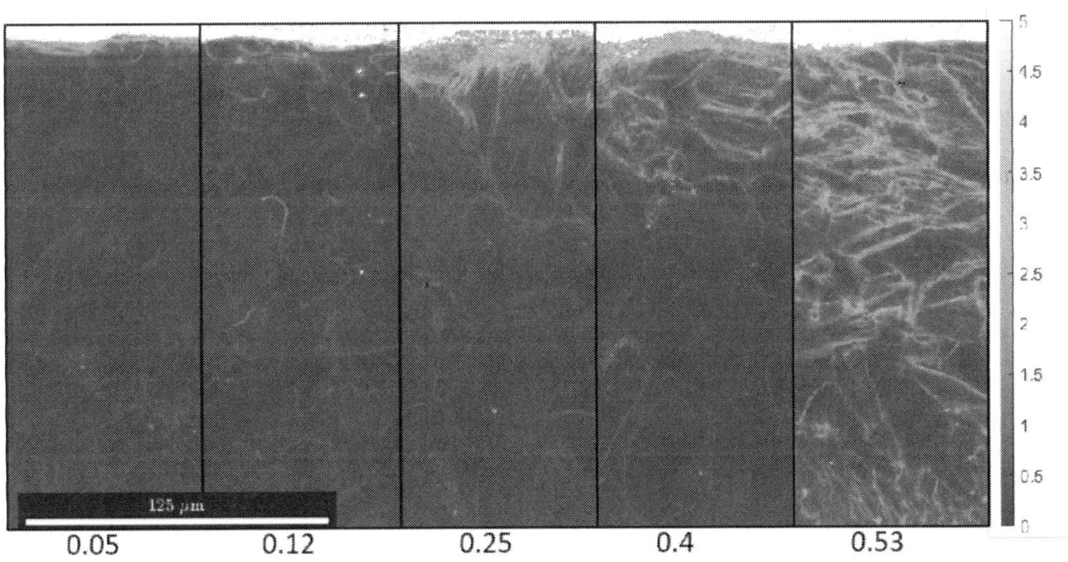

Figure 1. The sections of the KAM maps for each VB.

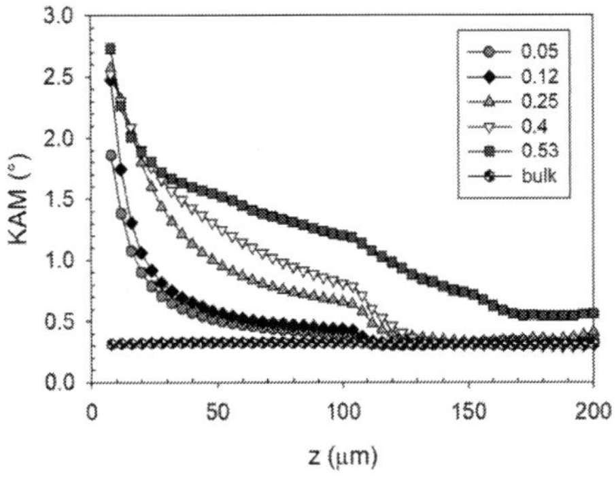

Figure 2. The gradient of the average KAM values within both phases depending on *VB*.

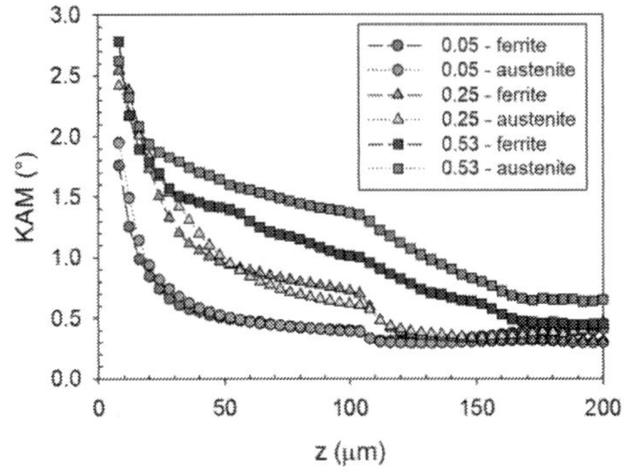

Figure 3. Comparison of the average KAM values of ferrite and austenite with respect to *VB*.

3.2. Grain size vs. crystallite size

The grain size (GS) was evaluated from EBSD data as an average of distances between high-angle boundaries (above 10°) in the CD direction[2]. Due to high data dispersion (follows from coarse-grained microstructure) and for better clarity, the GS was fitted by a sigmoid function. The average GS of bulk material is around 15 μm, see Figure 4. The crystallite size (D) was evaluated from the X-ray diffraction pattern using Rietveld refinement averaged from both phases in the CD direction. The maximum value of the D is 500 nm given by used *MStruct* program [11] and the presented error follow from *Rietveld* analysis.

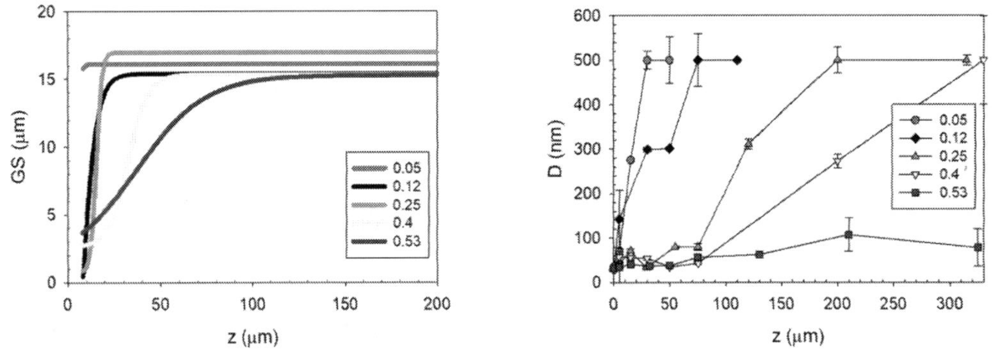

Figure 4. The gradient of grain size (left) and crystallite size (right) as a function of *VB*.

For both cases (GS and D), the samples with higher VB reach the maximum GS in the greater depth. Figures 4 depict the comparison of the gradient of GS and D depending on VB, in other words, show the difference of development of high- and low-angle boundaries with subsurface depth. Because the values of D are dependent on the rate of plastic deformation (more precisely dislocation density), D is affected by turning more than GS, see Figure 5. With higher

[2] See [10] function *grains.boundary.intersect*.

VB, this difference between *GS* and *D* is bigger. For $VB = 0.53$ mm, *D* reach the maximum even above 350 µm of subsurface depth. The explanation of this phenomenon resides in the forming of shear bands. Due to high dislocation density in these bands, much finer crystallites are generated in contrast with grains [12]. Because the low-angle boundaries define both KAM and *D*, the comparison of the KAM values with reverse *D* is comparable, see Figure 6.

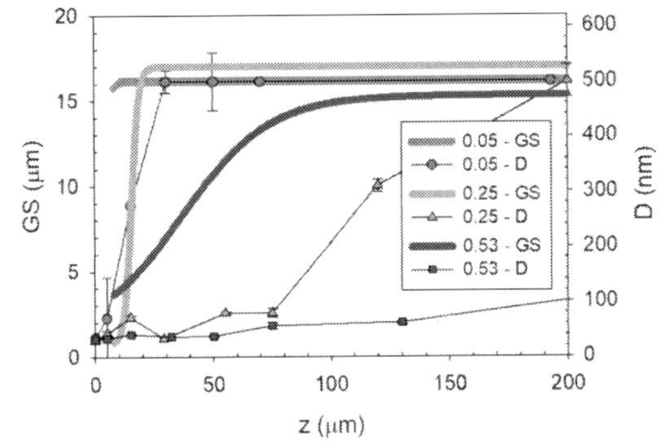

Figure 5. Comparison of the gradient of grain size (*GS*) and crystallite size (*D*) depending on *VB*.

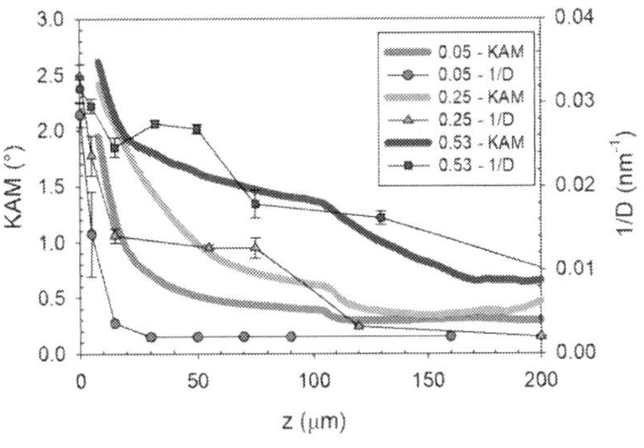

Figure 6. Comparison of the gradient of KAM and reverse crystallite size ($1/D$) with respect to *VB*.

4. Conclusions

The following results were obtained:

- The steep gradient of KAM was found with respect to flank wear. Affected subsurface depth of turned material gradually grows with higher *VB*.
- The different strain hardening rate was found for each phase.
- The steep gradients of grain and crystallite size were found.
- Flank wear influence the affected subsurface depth with higher dislocation density.
- The gradients of KAM values and reverse *D* have comparable trends.

Acknowledgments

This work was supported by the project CZ.02.1.01/0.0/0.0/16_019/0000778 "Center for advanced applied science" within the Operational Program Research, Development and Education supervised by the Ministry of Education, Youth and Sports of the Czech Republic. K.T.'s work was supported by the Grant Agency of the Czech Technical University in Prague, grant No. SGS19/190/OHK4/3T/14.

References

[1] Dakhlaoui R, Braham C and Baczmański A 2007 *Mater. Sci. Eng.: A* **444** 6–17
[2] Alvarez-Armas I 2009 *Duplex Stainless Steels* (USA: John Wiley & Sons)
[3] Neslušan M, Trojan K, Haušild P, Minárik P, Mičietová A and Čapek J 2020 *Mater. Charact.* **169** 110587
[4] Capek J, Cernik M, Ganev N, Trojan K, Nemecek J and Kolarik K 2018 *IOP Conf. Ser., Mater. Sci. Eng.* **375** 012025
[5] Ryś J, Ratuszek W and Witkowska M 2006 *Arch. Metall. Mater.* **51** 495–502
[6] Wroński S, Tarasiuk J, Bacroix B and Baczmański A 2012 *Mater. Charact.* **73** 52–60
[7] Choi J Y, Ji J H, Hwang S W and Park K T 2012 *Mater. Sci. Eng.: A* **535** 32–9
[8] Čapek J, Kolařík K, Neslušan M, Pitrmuc Z, Beránek L, Trojan K, Němeček J, Ganev N, Kyncl J and Mikeš P 2018 *Famena Trans.* **42** 1–14
[9] Bachmann F, Hielscher R and Schaeben H 2010 *Solid State Phenomen.* **60** 63–8
[10] MTEX Toolbox `https://mtex-toolbox.github.io`
[11] Matěj Z, Kužel R and Nichtová L 2010 *Powder Diffr.* **25** 125–31
[12] Iza-Menia A, Pinol-Juez A, Urcola J J and Gutiérrez I 1998 *Metall. Mater. Trans. A* **29** 2975–86

η-fiber microstructure and texture evolutions in ultra-thin silicon steel

N Zhang[1]*, L Meng[1], B Zhang[1], C X He[2], G Ma[2], Y Han[2], X Chen[2]

[1]Metallurgical Technology Institute, Central Iron & Steel Research Institute, Beijing, China; [2]State Key Laboratory of Advanced Power Transmission Technology, Global Energy Interconnection Research Institute Co., Ltd, Beijing, China.

Corresponding author's email: zhangn@126.com

Abstract. 0.08mm ultra-thin silicon steel is prepared with 0.30mm commercial grain-oriented silicon steel as raw material, and the evolutions of η-fiber microstructure and texture are investigated with emphasis. During rolling deformation, initial Goss orientation shows crystal rotation to {111}<112> orientation. With the increase of rolling reduction, the retention of Goss orientation is reduced and more observed near the sheet surface. For initial deviated Goss oriented grains, {111}<112> and η-fiber oriented areas are also observed in 0.08mm rolled sheet, while the accuracy and concentration of these two components are decreased. During annealing, η-fiber nucleation superiority in γ-fiber deformed regions is significant, and thus contributes to strong η-fiber recrystallization texture. When the rolled sheets are heated at 800℃ for 15 min, strong η-fiber recrystallization texture and uniform microstructure is beneficial for the magnetic properties of ultrathin silicon steel sheets.

1. Introduction

Ultra-thin silicon steel with the thickness lower than 0.10 mm is paid special attention for its applications in intermediate and high frequency devices [1-2]. It could be prepared by rolling and annealing grain-oriented silicon steel sheets with strong Goss ({011}<100>) texture[3-6]. The low iron losses under medium and high frequencies show the effect of ultra-low steel sheet thickness and are influenced by microstructure, and the magnetic induction could be improved by texture optimization, namely increasing the intensity of η-fiber ({0kl}<100>, <100>// rolling direction) recrystallization texture[3,7-9].

Considering the strong Goss texture and coarse microstructure of raw material, the deformation and recrystallization behaviors of Goss oriented grains greatly affect the microstructure as well as texture evolution. It is well known that Goss orientation rotate to {111}<112> orientation under rolling deformation, then Goss and other η-fiber nuclei could be observed inside shear bands in {111}<112> matrix during annealing [10-14]. Given that deformation behavior of ultra-thin silicon steel production is distinct from common polycrystals, in our earlier work, we discussed the deformed microstructure and orientation characteristics as well as recrystallization behaviors of initial Goss oriented grains in 0.075mm ultra-thin silicon steel [15].

In this study, ultra-thin silicon steel was prepared with 0.30mm commercial grain-oriented silicon steel, which is lower than that used in our earlier work. The aim is to clarify the orientation and

IOP Conf. Series: Materials Science and Engineering 1121 (2021) 012034 doi:10.1088/1757-899X/1121/1/012034

microstructure evolution by tracing the deformation process with the increasing rolling reduction, meanwhile the difference between the surface and interior of the rolled sheets was paid attention. It is worthy to note that rolling reduction is changed when the thickness of raw material is different, thus this work could expand the study of ultra-thin silicon steel production.

2. Experimental procedure

Plates of 30 mm (along transverse direction, TD) × 300 mm (along rolling direction, RD) were cut from a 0.30mm commercial grain-oriented silicon steel and were used as raw material to prepare ultra-thin silicon steel. The initial magnetic properties were shown to be B_8=1.889T and $P_{17/50}$=1.36 W/kg. B_8 means magnetic induction corresponding to 800A/m magnetic field intensity, and $P_{17/50}$ means core loss of sample per kg at maximum magnetic induction 1.7T and frequency 50Hz. After being moved coating layer, the starting material was 0.28mm thick. Cold rolling was performed by multiple passes to obtain 0.18mm, 0.1mm and 0.08mm rolled samples, corresponding to reductions of 35.7%, 64.3% and 71.4%. The 0.08mm rolled sheets were annealed at 700°C and 800°C to obtain partially and fully recrystallized microstructures, and the magnetic properties of fully recrystallized sheet were measured.

The microstructure and texture evolutions were evaluated with a Zeiss GeminiSEM500 field emission scanning electron microscope (SEM) equipped with EBSD system. The deformed samples were measured in rolling and lateral planes, and the measurements were performed in different stages of deformation. The annealed samples were measured in rolling plane. To decrease possible statistical error due to coarse initial grains in raw material, more than 5 specimens for each sample were evaluated, and representative results are shown in this paper. The tolerance angles for Goss and {021}<100> orientations are 10° to avoid overlap, and the angle for other orientations is 15°.

3. Results and discussions

The three image maps in Fig.1 represent the rolled sheets under reductions of 35.7%, 64.3% and 71.4% respectively. The crystal rotation trend from Goss to {111}<112> is clearly depicted, and the transiting orientation components between Goss and {111}<112> are displayed as black dots in the pole figures. With the increasing rolling reduction, {111}<112> oriented areas gradually occupy the majority of deformed microstructure, and the retention of Goss orientation is reduced. However, when the rolling reduction reaches 71.4%, Fig.1(c) still shows many Goss oriented areas, parts of which can be deduced to be retained from the initial Goss grain. Some Goss oriented areas are surrounded by high-angle (>15°) boundaries (black lines in orientation image maps) as small discrete regions, thus relating to high orientation gradient.

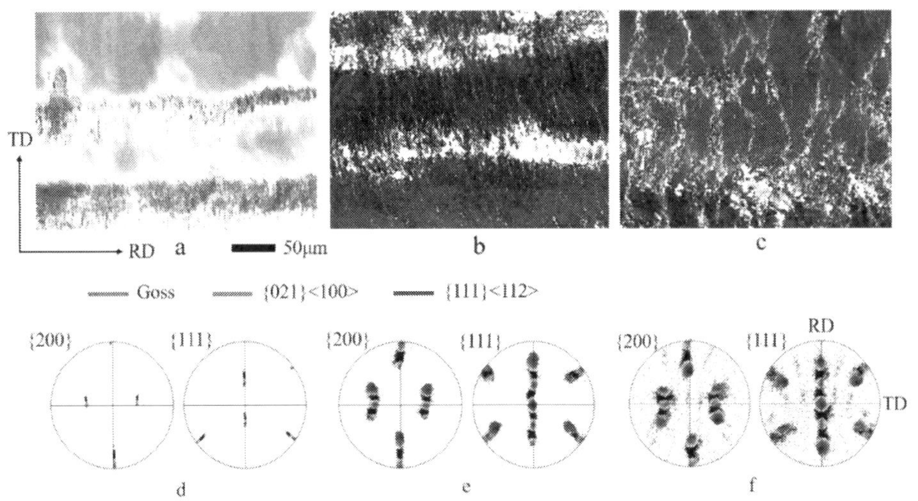

Fig.1 Deformed microstructure and texture evolution of initial Goss grains in rolling planes.
35.7% rolling reduction: a) orientation image map; d) {200} and {111} pole figures;
64.3% rolling reduction: b) orientation image map; e) {200} and {111} pole figures;
71.4% rolling reduction: c) orientation image map; f) {200} and {111} pole figures.

Fig.2 illustrates the deformation process in lateral plane, and the same gradual changes from initial Goss orientation to the end {111}<112> orientation are observed. In Fig.2(b), the retained Goss oriented areas align in specific direction, which is similar to the distribution characteristic of shear band. The slip traces in the same direction are observed in Fig.2(c), and they may be related to the activation of specific {112}<111> slip system. In Fig.2(c), it is observed that Goss and minor {021}<100> areas are mainly located near the sheet surface.

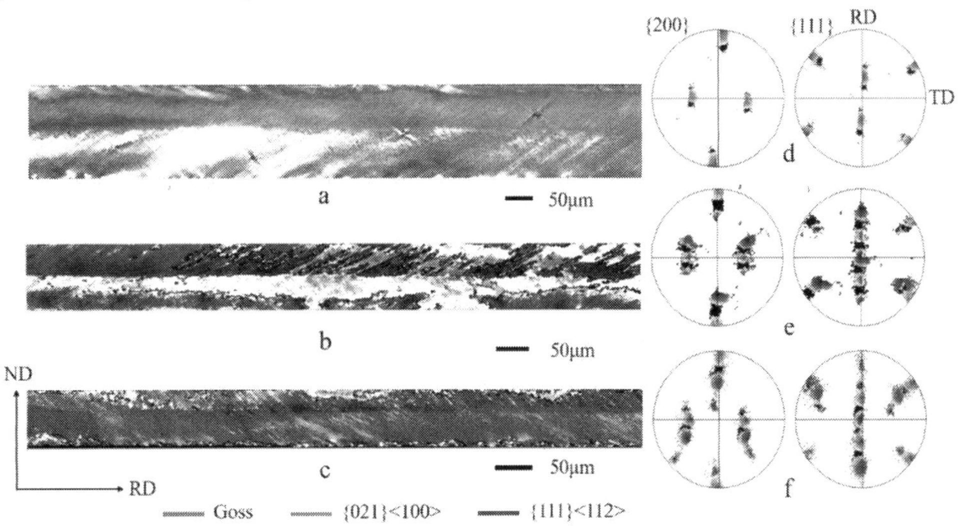

Fig.2 Deformed microstructure and texture evolution of initial Goss grains in lateral planes.
35.7% rolling reduction: a) orientation image map; d) {200} and {111} pole figures;
64.3% rolling reduction: b) orientation image map; e) {200} and {111} pole figures;
71.4% rolling reduction: c) orientation image map; f) {200} and {111} pole figures.

It is generally considered that shear bands usually occur in large γ-fiber deformed grains under the rolling reduction of 70%, and η-fiber oriented areas can be achieved inside shear bands. Shear band is not clearly identified in Fig.2(c), while its existence could not be denied for possible measurement error. However, those Goss and minor {021}<100> areas without extending trace into the interior of the rolled sheet are largely by the retention. Therefore, it can be inferred that the retention of initial Goss orientation is increased by the surface shear.

For the commercial grain-oriented silicon steel used as raw material, deviated Goss grains with the orientation deviating from exact Goss for 5°-15° degrees commonly exist. Typical deformed microstructures of this kind of deviated Goss grains are given in Fig.3. Similar orientation transition route towards {111}<112> is displayed. The majority of deformed microstructure also orients as {111}<112>, while more 'white' areas with transitional orientation are shown in Fig.3(a) and Fig.3(c). That corresponds to the lower fraction of {111}<112> deformed area and lower accuracy and concentration of {111}<112> deformation texture. Goss and {021}<100> oriented regions are observed in rolling plane. Compared with initial Goss grains in Fig.1 and Fig.2, the fraction of {021}<100> area is higher, meanwhile more η-fiber areas are located in the interior of rolled sheet. Given that no marked shear bands are observed, these η-fiber orientations are mostly linked to the orientation transition route of initial deviated Goss grain during rolling deformation. {001}<110> oriented deformation twin is depicted in Fig.2(b) in 2(d), and it is also observed in our earlier work [15].

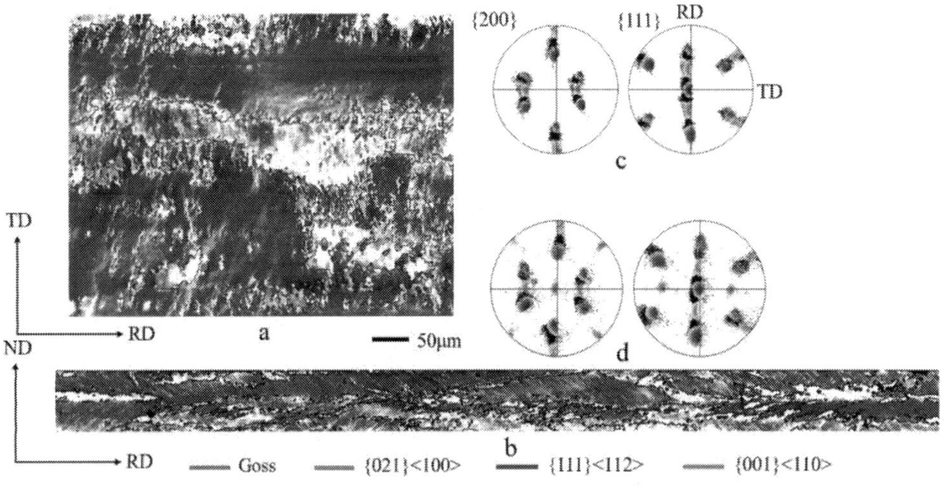

Fig.3 Deformed microstructure of initial deviated Goss grains rolled to 0.08mm.
Rolling plane: a) orientation image map; c) {200} and {111} pole figures;
Lateral plane: b) orientation image map; d) {200} and {111} pole figures.

Based on the producing method of ultra-thin silicon steel, the magnetic induction of final product is improved by strengthening η-fiber recrystallization texture. Therefore, we analyzed the fraction of η-fiber deformed areas in the regions of Fig.2(c) and Fig.3(b), and the distribution is shown in Fig.4. When Goss and deviated Goss oriented initial grains are deformed to the same strain, the area fraction of η-fiber (15° deviation permitted) region is close. However, the accuracy of η-fiber orientation is lower in the initial deviated Goss grain. Given that during annealing, nuclei originate from those pre-existed areas in deformed matrix, to choose the raw material with more exact Goss grains is more beneficial for increasing the intensity of accurate η-fiber texture.

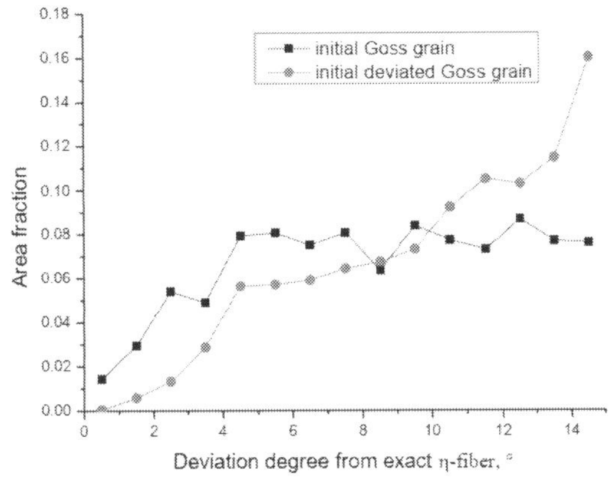

Fig.4 The distribution of η-fiber area fraction in different initial oriented grains.

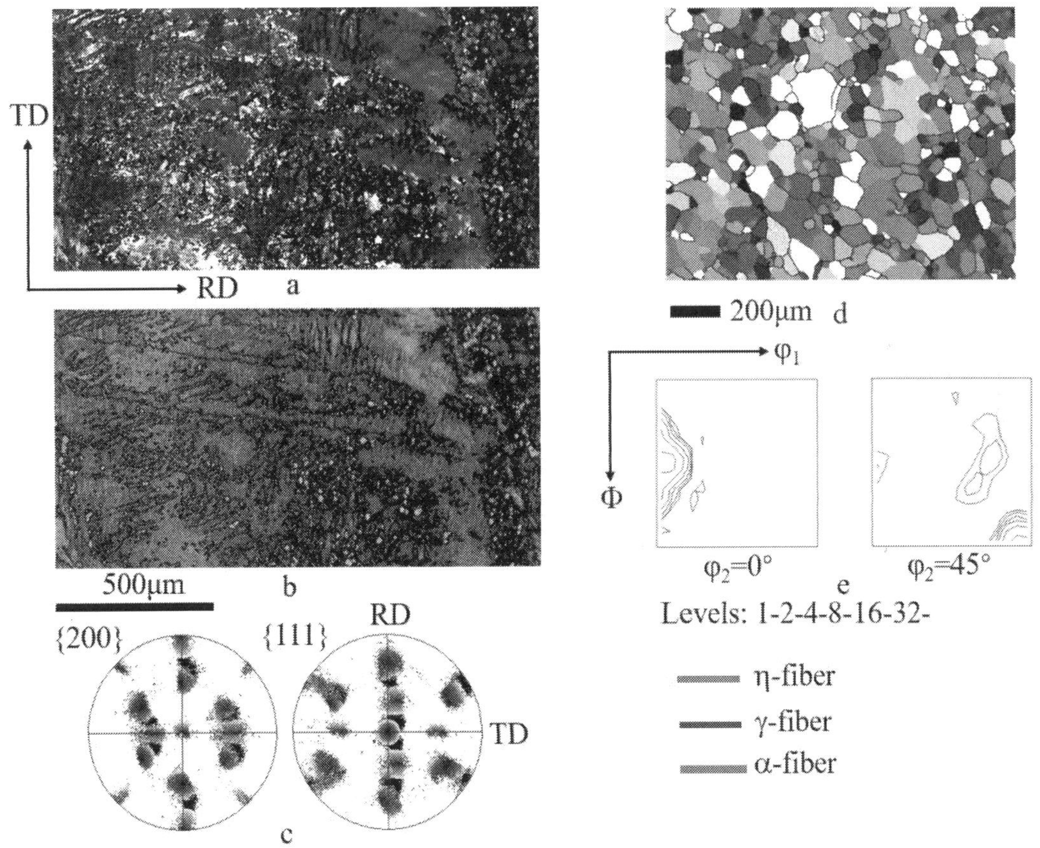

Fig.5 Recrystallized microstructures and micro-textures of 0.08mm silicon steel.
Partially recrystallized sample: a) orientation image map; b) band contrast map; c) {200} and {111} pole figures;
Fully recrystallized sample: d) orientation image map; e) ODFs at φ_2=0° and 45° sections.

After being annealed at 700°C, plenty of η-fiber nuclei in γ-fiber deformed matrix are achieved, as shown in Fig.5(a-c). New grains may be due to the retention or nucleation inside shear bands, and those locating at the boundaries in the left part of Fig.5(a-b) should be linked to the retaining of initial orientation [16]. The nucleation advantage of η-fiber grains leads to the strong η-fiber texture in fully recrystallized sample in Fig.5(d-e), which was heated at 800°C for 15min. The magnetic induction B_8 of this fully recrystallized sample is measured to be 1.802T. The microstructure is uniform, contributing to the iron loss $P_{15/400}$ of 12.6 W/kg, which is core loss of sample per kg at maximum magnetic induction 1.5T and frequency 400Hz. The average grain size is lower than 100μm, and non-η-fiber grains do not show obvious growth advantage, so the iron loss is potential to be decreased by modifying the annealing parameters.

4. Conclusions

During rolling deformation, initial Goss orientation shows crystal rotations to {111}<112> orientation. With the increasing rolling reduction, the retention of Goss orientation is reduced and more observed near the sheet surface. For initial deviated Goss oriented grains, {111}<112> and η-fiber oriented areas are also observed in 0.08mm rolled sheet, while the accuracy and concentration of these two components are decreased, and more {021}<100> oriented areas are shown in the deformed sheet. After annealing, η-fiber nucleation superiority in γ-fiber deformed regions is significant, and thus contributes to strong η-fiber texture in the fully recrystallized sheet heated at 800°C for 15min. Non-η-fiber grains do not show obvious size advantage, strong η-fiber recrystallization texture and uniform microstructure is beneficial for the magnetic properties of ultrathin silicon steel sheets.

References

[1] Lobanov M L, Redikul'Tsev A A, Risakov G M, Kagan I V and Pervushina O V 2011 *Phys. Met. Metallogr.* **111** 479-86.
[2] Moses A J 2012 *Scripta Mater.* **67** 560-65.
[3] Wang Y P, An L Z, Song H Y, Wang G D and Liu H T 2020 *J. Magn. Magn. Mater.* **499** 166290.
[4] Liang R Y, Yang P and Mao W M 2017 *J. Mater Eng.* **45** 87-96.
[5] Arai K I and Ishiyama K 1988 *J. Appl. Phys.* **64** 5352-54.
[6] Arai K I and Ishiyama K 1996 *Mater. Sci. Forum* **204-206** 133-42.
[7] Gao X H, Qi K M and Qiu C L 2006 *Mater. Sci. Eng. A* **430** 138-41.
[8] Park J T and Szpunar J A 2003 *Acta Mater.* **51** 3037-51.
[9] Daff S S F, Paolinelli S C and Cota A B 2011 *J. Magn. Magn. Mater.* **323** 3234-8.
[10] Walter J L and Hibbard W R 1958 *Trans Metall. Soc. AIME.* **212** 731-7.
[11] Dunn C G 1954 *Acta Metall.* **2** 173-83.
[12] Dorner D, Lahn L and Zaefferer S 2004 *Mater. Sci. Forum* **467-470** 129-34.
[13] Sha Y H, Sun C, Zhang F, Patel D, Chen X, Kalidindi S R and Zuo L 2014 *Acta Mater.* **76** 106-17.
[14] Liu J L, Sha Y H, Zhang F, Li J C, Yao Y C and Zuo L 2011 *Scripta Mater.* **65** 292-5.
[15] Zhang N, Meng L, Zhang B, He C X, Han Y, Yang F Y, Ma G, Chen X, Zhong S and Mao W M 2021 *J. magn. Magn. mater.* **517** 167385.
[16] Meng L, Zhang N, Zhang B, He C X, Han Y, Ma G, Chen X, Yang J X, Guo X L and Zhong S 2021 *J. magn. Magn. mater.* 10.1016/j.jmmm.2020.167590.

IOP Conf. Series: Materials Science and Engineering 1121 (2021) 012035 doi:10.1088/1757-899X/1121/1/012035

Influence of substructure inhomogeneity on the anisotropy of physical properties of textured materials

O A Krymskaya, M G Isaenkova, Y A Perlovich and V A Fesenko

National Research Nuclear University "Moscow Engineering Physics Institute", Kashirskoe shosse, 31, Moscow, 115409, Russian Federation

Corresponding authors: OAKrymskaya@mephi.ru, isamarg@mail.ru

Abstract. Calculation of the physical properties anisotropy is based on single crystal properties and information about material texture, i.e. orientation distribution function (ODF). At the same time, the grains of different orientations are known to have different substructure parameters including the lattice distortion and microstrains. Determination of these parameters is possible with the X-ray method of Generalized Pole Figures (GPF), which consists of registration of the whole X-ray reflection profile under the pole figure recording. As a result, one can obtain the FWHMs of X-ray line profiles and microstrains distributed on the stereographic projection. Despite the observable equilibrium of tensile and compressive microstrains of differently oriented grains within the studied material volume, they can affect the product properties anisotropy. In this study the calculation method for elastic properties and thermal expansion coefficients taking into account substructure inhomogeneity is offered on the basis of elastic energy minimization. Its efficiency is demonstrated for the samples of zirconium alloys.

1. Introduction

One of the main motives for crystallographic texture analysis is its effect on the anisotropy of physical and mechanical properties of materials. The anisotropy calculation of both elastic properties and linear thermal expansion coefficients (LTEC) are essentially based on models that average the single crystals properties with a weight function which is the orientation distribution function (ODF). However, a textured polycrystalline material that has undergone a certain thermo-mechanical treatment is characterized by some range of structural parameters and presence of residual elastic microstrains even in the recrystallized condition [1-3]. Therefore, in addition to the crystallites orientation, the properties are influenced by the substructural inhomogeneity of grains of different orientations.

In this paper we propose an approach for calculation of elastic moduli anisotropy as well as LTECs taking microstrains inhomogeneity into account. The algorithm was tested on a sample from a channel tube of Zr-2.5%Nb alloy, with the main α-phase having a hexagonal closed-packed (HCP) structure.

2. Principles of proposed approach

The calculation of the anisotropy of elastic properties and LTEC of textured materials is based on averaging the properties of single crystals with the ODF as a weight function ($f(g)$). Moreover, the assumption of deformations (Voight model) or stresses (Reuss model) homogeneity in a polycrystal is used for elastic moduli anisotropy estimation [4, 5]. So averaging is implemented either for components of stiffness matrix $[C_{ijkl}]$ or for compliance coefficients $[S_{ijkl}]$. However, already Hill showed that true values of the elastic coefficients are between the values determined by Voigt or Reuss.

Another so-called self-consistent approach for averaging properties developed by Lebenson and Tome [5] consists in considering individual grains as inclusions embedded in a homogeneous medium with averaged elastic properties of the entire polycrystal. In this case, it is assumed that the stresses and total strains (elastic and thermal) are constant in each grain, and the entire polycrystal experiences uniform stresses. This results in the proximity of the Hill model.

The presence of substructure inhomogeneity, i.e. microstrains, and consequently microstresses variation, results in violation of both the Voigt and Reuss models. Moreover, as noted in [4], relationship between different properties should be taken into account to prevent significant errors in such calculations. For example, LTECs define the response of the material on such an external impact as temperature, which results in the development of elastic strains, which can cause stresses between adjacent grains. However the described calculations ignore the combined effect of temperature and stresses, whereas it is necessary to additionally consider the elastic moduli when averaging the LTEC's anisotropy.

2.1. Elastic moduli anisotropy

Since a polycrystalline material is characterized by a range of elastic microstrains of differently oriented grains, it can be represented as a composite of stretched and compressed "springs", which are individual grains (figure 1). Despite the stiffness of an individual grain remains constant, due to the difference in their orientation and interaction with neighbours, the stiffness of the entire polycrystal is not equal to the mathematical averaged elastic constants. Thus, when calculating the elastic properties, it is necessary to take into account the stored elastic energy of individual grains, which is equal to [5, 6]:

$$W_c = \frac{1}{2}\{\sigma_c\}\{\varepsilon_c\} = \frac{1}{2}C_{ijkl}\varepsilon_{kl}\varepsilon_{ij}. \quad (1)$$

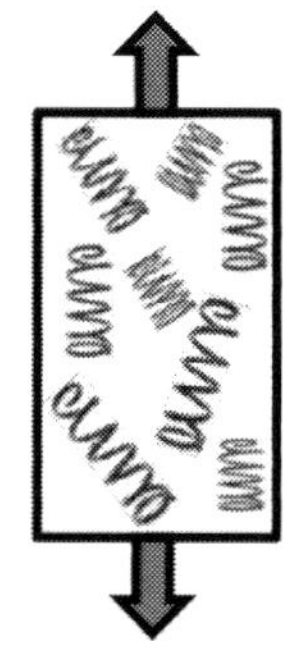

Figure 1. Model of a polycrystalline material.

Values of the crystallite's elastic microstrains (ε_c) can be obtained from the Generalized Pole Figures $\left(\frac{\Delta d}{d}\right)$ (GPF $\left(\frac{\Delta d}{d}\right)$), calculated from the Bragg's angle of the X-ray reflection profile [1-3]. Then it is possible to find the tensor of elastic stresses in the crystallite, for which the expression in matrix form is [4, 5]:

$$\{\sigma_c\} = [C_c]\{\varepsilon_c\}. \quad (2)$$

Averaging tensors of elastic strains and stresses over a polycrystalline aggregate gives [4]:

$$\{\sigma_s\} = \oint\{\sigma_c\}\cdot f(g)dg; \qquad \{\varepsilon_s\} = \oint\{\varepsilon_c\}\cdot f(g)dg. \quad (3)$$

Now the calculation of the elastic properties of a polycrystal (sample) incorporating the stored elastic energy of individual grains, due to the presence of elastic tension or compression, can be carried out on the basis of the principle of minimizing its elastic energy:

$$W_s = \frac{1}{2}\{C_s\cdot\varepsilon_s\}\cdot\varepsilon_s \rightarrow min. \quad (4)$$

This function is linear with respect to the coefficients C_s and for their estimation one can use the standard simplex minimization algorithm with constraints of $\{\sigma_s\} = [C_s]\{\varepsilon_s\}$ and the additional condition of C_s non-negativity. As textured polycrystalline materials no longer possesses the symmetry of its constituent single crystals, we suppose orthotropy of the material properties, i.e. orthorhombic sample symmetry typical for rolling products, which reduce the number of C_s coefficients to 9. Since the solution of linear programming problems is rather sensitive to the initial approximation, we used the values determined by the Hill model.

Solving linear programming problems of this type is possible by special functions which are implemented in almost any math software. We used the *DLPRS*-subroutine of *IMSL* libraries for FORTRAN.

2.2. LTECs anisotropy

The substructural inhomogeneity in textured polycrystalline materials results in the occurrence of initial tensile/compressive microstrains in grains, so during their interaction the deformation character of whole polycrystalline aggregate changes. This affects the LTECs anisotropy as well as the elastic properties.

The LTECs are related to the elastic coefficients through the Grüneisen parameters (γ) [6]. Therefore it is possible to calculate the LTECs of a polycrystal using averaging of these parameters for single crystals together with the elastic constants $[C_s]$ calculated as described above.

LTECs (α) are related to the elastic coefficients through the relations:

$$\alpha_i = \frac{c_V}{V}\sum_{j=1}^{6} C_{ij}\gamma_j, \tag{5}$$

which for the HCP single crystals with lattice parameters a and c are described by a 2nd-rank tensor of a diagonal form in the principal axes:

$$\alpha_{ij} = \begin{bmatrix} \alpha_a & 0 & 0 \\ 0 & \alpha_a & 0 \\ 0 & 0 & \alpha_c \end{bmatrix}. \tag{6}$$

At of near room temperatures, the main contribution to the LTECs value is from the crystalline lattice, so the Grüneisen parameters are also isotropic in the basal plane:

$$\begin{aligned} \gamma_1 = \gamma_2 &= \frac{dV}{\mathbf{c}_\varepsilon}[(C_{11} + C_{12})\alpha_a + C_{13}\alpha_c], \\ \gamma_3 &= \frac{dV}{\mathbf{c}_\varepsilon}[2C_{13}\alpha_a + C_{33}\alpha_c], \end{aligned} \tag{7}$$

where $\mathbf{c}_\varepsilon$ – heat capacity at constant strain; dV – single crystallite volume; α_c and α_a for Zr-alloys equal to 7.4×10^{-6} and $4.9\times10^{-6}\frac{1}{°C}$, respectively [7].

Since the calculation is carried out for normal conditions and constant temperature, the lattice volume can be considered as constant, i.e. $\oint dV \cdot dg = V$. So the components of the Grüneisen parameters tensor of a single crystal can be averaged for calculating the polycrystalline Grüneisen parameters γ_s:

$$\left[\gamma_{s_{ij}}\right] = \oint[\gamma_{ij}] \cdot f(g)dg, \tag{8}$$

and then determine the LTECs of polycrystal by formula (5) using tensor $[C_s]$, calculated earlier. The value of $\frac{c_V}{V}$ will cancel out.

3. Samples and research methods

The proposed algorithm was tested on samples from a channel pressure tube ∅113.2×103.6 mm made of the Zr-2.5% Nb alloy after 20% of cold rolling. The samples are characterized by a sharp texture with a predominant arrangement of basal normals in the tangential direction (*T*). Figure 2 shows typical pole figures (*PF*), GPFs$\left(\frac{\Delta d}{d}\right)$ and distributions of grain volume fractions (*VF*) by microstrains along various crystallographic directions.

The obtained data confirm the principal laws of substructural inhomogeneity in textured materials formulated in [1-3]: counterbalancing of elastic microstrains within individual texture maxima, which is seen in the GPF$\left(\frac{\Delta d}{d}_{0001}\right)$ for the left and right texture components. At the same time the microstrains equilibrium for prismatic directions, <11$\bar{2}$0> and <10$\bar{1}$0>, apparently associated with macroscopic stress-strain state determined by rolling, under which the sample is compressed along the normal direction (*R*) and elongated along the rolling direction (*L*). After unloading the inhomogeneity of the stress-strain state in different tube' layers results in tension along *R*. However, the balancing of microstrains along basal normals occurs at the expense of grains' interaction within texture maxima having different origins, i.e. formation due to activation of different deformation systems.

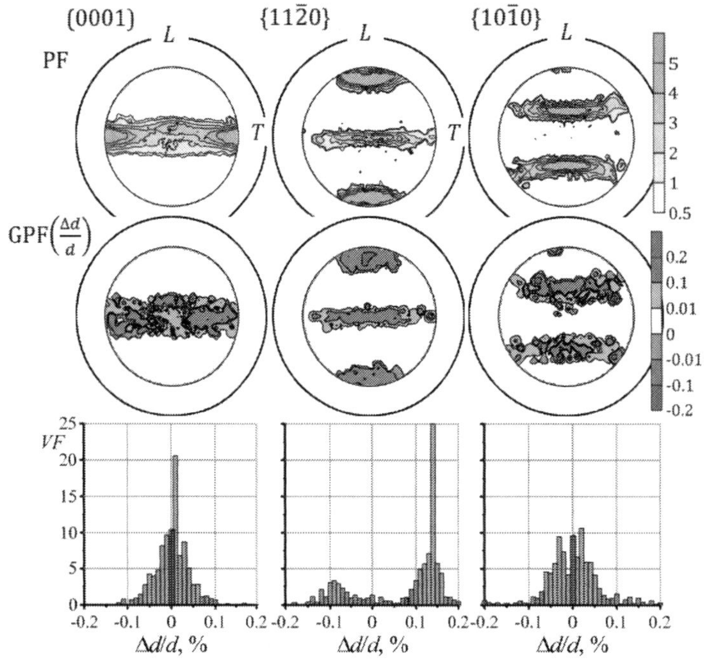

Figure 2. PFs and GPFs$\left(\frac{\Delta d}{d}\right)$ of the channel tube sample of the Zr-2.5%Nb alloy and the distributions of grain volume fractions (*VF*) by microstrains

The crystallographic directions <0001>, <11$\bar{2}$0> and <10$\bar{1}$0> represent the basis of the hexagonal lattice; therefore, the set of obtained GPFs$\left(\frac{\Delta d}{d}\right)$ can be converted into the elastic microstrain tensor of individual crystallites $\{\varepsilon_c\}$ by assigning proper Euler angles. Assuming the absence of shear components:

$$\{\varepsilon_c\} = \begin{bmatrix} \varepsilon_x & 0 & 0 \\ 0 & \varepsilon_y & 0 \\ 0 & 0 & \varepsilon_z \end{bmatrix} = \begin{bmatrix} (\Delta d/d)_{10\bar{1}0} & 0 & 0 \\ 0 & (\Delta d/d)_{11\bar{2}0} & 0 \\ 0 & 0 & (\Delta d/d)_{0001} \end{bmatrix}. \quad (9)$$

Since the construction of the full function of microstrains, similarly to an ODF, is a rather difficult task, in this work extrapolation was carried out to the unregistered regions of Euler angles using available GPFs. Thus, each set of angles (φ_1, Φ, φ_2) is associated with an ODF value and three components of the tensor $\{\varepsilon_c\}$.

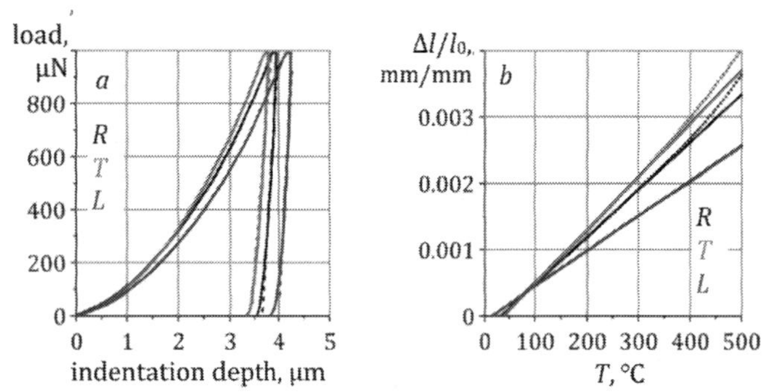

Figure 3. Typical indentation loading diagrams (*a*) and dilatometric curves (*b*) of the channel tube obtained for different sample surfaces

The elastic moduli for different sample's directions (*R*, *T*, and *L*) were measured by the instrumented indentation method with registration of loading diagrams [8-10] using indentometer DNT1/5. Ten measurements were carried out for each surface under a load of 1000 μN with a Berkovich pyramid. Examples of loading diagrams for various sample surfaces are shown in figure 3-a. Based on the obtained data the mean value and dispersion were estimated.

The statistical error of the hardness determining does not exceed 5.5%, and for elastic modulus – 7.8%. The experimental LTECs were estimated by the slope of the temperature $\Delta l/l_0$ dependences for the three directions, obtained using a NETZSCH DIL 402 dilatometer on cubic samples with dimensions of 4×4×4 mm (figure 3-b).

4. Results

Table 1 and figure 4 show the results of the measurements and calculation of the elastic modulus (E) according to both Hill's averaging and the proposed algorithm. In the calculation ODFs obtained from three perpendicular surfaces were used [11]. In addition, computational methods make it possible to determine the elastic modulus not for individual directions, but to construct its distribution over the entire stereographic projection. In this case the elastic moduli for an arbitrary direction y in orthotropic sample is determined by the compliances tensor $[S_S] = [C_S]^{-1}$:

$$\frac{1}{E_y} = y_1^4 \cdot S_{11} + y_2^4 \cdot S_{22} + y_3^4 \cdot S_{33} + 2 \cdot y_1^2 \cdot y_2^2 \cdot (S_{12} + 2S_{66}) + 2 \cdot y_1^2 \cdot y_3^2 \cdot (S_{13} + +2S_{55}) + 2 \cdot y_2^2 \cdot y_3^2 \cdot (S_{23} + 2S_{44}), \quad (10)$$

where y_1, y_2, y_3 are the direction cosines of the studied direction.

The obtained data testifies that calculation of the elastic moduli without taking into account the microstrains inhomogeneity leads to higher deviations from the values obtained by instrumental indentation, the value of anisotropy is significantly lower than the experimental one. In the case of calculations by the proposed algorithm, the anisotropy coefficient is much closer to the experimental one.

Table 1. Comparison of the elastic moduli for different directions of the chosen sample obtained by various methods.

parameter	elastic moduli						
	indentation	Hill model			proposed algorithm		
		ODF *R*	ODF *T*	ODF *L*	ODF *R*	ODF *T*	ODF *L*
E_R, GPa	101.2±6.6	97	98	98	99	105	100
E_T, GPa	113.0±7.8	102	103	103	110	115	114
E_L, GPa	93.3±5.4	98	98	98	96	97	96
$\frac{E_{max}-E_{min}}{E_{max}}$, %	17.4	4.9	4.85	4.85	12.7	15.7	15.8

Table 2 show the results of experimental and calculated LTECs of the studied sample. The obtained data again show that the calculation of the LTECs without taking into account elastic constants gives a lower anisotropy compared to the experimental value, while calculation by the proposed algorithm reveal a large value of anisotropy, which approaches to the experimental data.

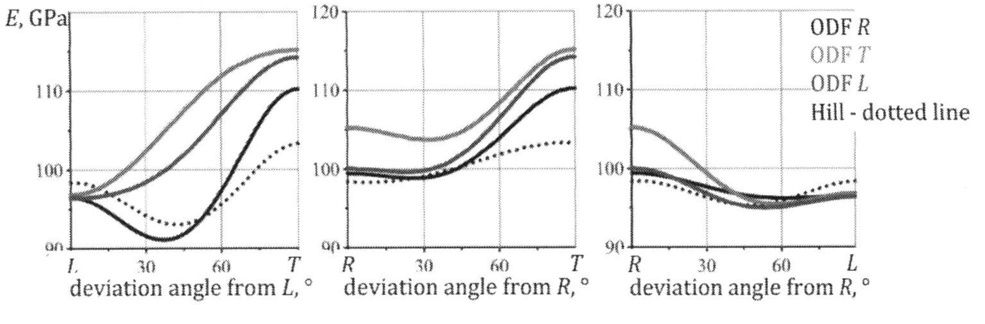

Figure 4. Dependences of elastic moduli in different sample sections.

Table 2. Comparison of LTECs for different directions of the studied sample obtained by various methods.

parameter	LTEC $\times 10^{-6}, \frac{1}{^{\circ}C}$		
	dilatometry	Bunge formulation	proposed algorithm
α_R	6.48	5.84	6.16
α_T	7.62	6.31	6.60
α_L	5.70	5.05	4.80
$\frac{\alpha_{max}-\alpha_{min}}{\alpha_{max}}$, %	25.2	19.9	27.2

5. Conclusions

This work proposes an approach for the calculation of the anisotropy of elastic moduli and LTECs with incorporation of substructural inhomogeneity expressed in the presence of tensile/compressive microstrains in grains of different orientations.

Algorithms and programs for calculating the anisotropy of elastic properties and LTECs, taking into account the substructure inhomogeneity, have been developed, the effectiveness of which is demonstrated by the example of a textured zirconium sample. The possibility of calculating the anisotropy of properties is shown in the presence of information about the texture of the material, measured from any of its surfaces, which significantly reduces the laboriousness of preparing samples for various tests. This is especially urgent for thin-walled zirconium alloy cladding tubes.

References

[1] Perlovich Y, Bunge H-J, Isaenkova M 1998 *Materials Science Forum* **273-275** 655-66
[2] Perlovich Y, Isaenkova M 2015 Recrystallization of Rolled α-Zr Single Crystals *Recrystallization in materials processing* Ed Glebovsky V. (Croatia, Rijeka: InTech) chapter 3 pp 101–124
[3] Perlovich Y, Isaenkova M, Fesenko V, Krymskaya O and Dobrokhotov P 2015 *IOP Conf. Series: Materials Science and Engineering* **82** 012075
[4] Bunge H-J, Park N-J, Klein H 1993 *Physical properties of Textured Materials* (Gottingen: Cuviller Verlag) 150 p
[5] Kocks U F, Tome C N, Wenk H R 1998 *Texture and anisotropy* (Cambridge University Press) 675 p
[6] Novikovs S 1974 *Teplovoe racshirenie tverdyh tel* (Moscow: Nauka, in Russian) 293 p
[7] Douglass D *The metallurgy of zirconium* 1971 (Vienna: International atomic energy agency) 466 p
[8] ISO 14577 2015 *Metallic materials-Instrumented indentation test for hardness and materials parameters*
[9] Isaenkova M, Perlovich Y, Krymskaya O and Zhuk D 2016 *IOP Conf. Series: Materials Science and Engineering* **130** 012053.
[10] Zhuk D, Isaenkova M, Perlovich Y and Krymskaya O 2017 *Russian Metallurgy (Metally)* **2017-5** 390-96
[11] Perlovich Y, Isaenkova M, Krymskaya O, Fesenko V and Babich Y 2016 *IOP Conf. Series: Materials Science and Engineering* **130** 012056.

Acknowledgment

The reported study was supported by the MEPhI Academic Excellence Project (agreement with the Ministry of Education and Science of the Russian Federation of August 27, 2013, project no. 02.a03.21.0005).

Dependence of Thermal Expansion of Zr-Based Products on their Crystallographic Texture

Sergey Stolbov[1, a)], Margarita Isaenkova[1, b)], Yuriy Perlovich[1], Andrey Tenishev[1], Olga Krymskaya[1], Vladimir Mikhalchik[1] and Kristina Klyukova[1]

[1]National Research Nuclear University "Moscow Engineering Physics Institute", Kashirskoe shosse, 31, Moscow, 115409, Russian Federation

Corresponding authors: a) stolbser@rambler.ru, b) isamarg@mail.ru

Abstract. The accident at Fukushima Daiichi in 2011 highlighted the increased interest in predicting the materials properties under extreme conditions. In this work, it is considered the behaviour of cubic samples cut from the wall of channel tubes made of Zr-2.5% Nb alloy during heating and cooling in the temperature range of 20-1200 °C. The anisotropy of changes in the dimensions of cubic samples in different structural states has been studied. Thermal tests were carried out in three mutually perpendicular directions: radial, tangential and axial. The structural state of tubes was estimated from the features of their crystallographic texture. The significant anisotropy of the size change is observed in the Zr-2.5%Nb alloy product with an unstable crystallographic texture of deformation due to the $\alpha\leftrightarrow\beta$-phase transformation inhomogeneity. In the case of complete recrystallization and orientation of the $<11\bar{2}0>$ axes along the tube axis, the anisotropy of the dimensions change is minimal, due to uniform nuclei formation of new phases in different orientations.

1. Introduction

The tightening of requirements for structural materials in connection with emergencies in recent years at nuclear power plants (Chernobyl, Fukushima) explains the increased interest in predicting the materials properties under extreme conditions. The need to preserve the tightness of fuel elements under operating conditions with temperature drops and to ensure the possibility of subsequent repair work brings to the fore the issues of stabilizing the dimensions of products as a result of their cyclic heating and cooling. In this regard, it is necessary to know not only the thermal coefficients of linear expansion of fuel elements to operating temperatures, but also their behavior in the event of a sharp increase in temperature in an emergency.

According to numerous studies of the kinetics of changes in the dimensions of claddings and channel tubes [1-6], the thermal expansion of tubes during their heating in the region of existence of a low-temperature hexagonal phase is determined with the distribution of basal axes. This makes it possible to observe the proportional dependence of the coefficient of linear thermal expansion (LTEC), on the integral texture f-parameters [1-6]. The reduction in size as a result of cooling the tubes fully corresponds to the LTEC for the single-phase region if there were no phase transformations in the sample during heating. If the temperature interval of heating the sample is extended to the region of existence of the β-phase, for example, up to 1200 °C, then as a result of phase transformations (PTs) the crystallographic texture changes, which also leads to changes in the LTEC [5-6]. The repetition of the heating and cooling cycles in the future does not affect the changes in the crystallographic texture and, consequently, the LTEC [6].

This paper considers the regularities of PTs $\alpha \rightarrow \beta \rightarrow \alpha$ in tubes made of Zr-2.5% Nb alloy, which are implemented during the heating-cooling cycle of thermal tests in the temperature range of 20-1200 °C. The tests were carried out in three mutually perpendicular directions for cubic samples cut from the wall of the different channel tubes. This work is devoted to the study of the influence of the crystallographic texture on the process of thermal linear expansion of samples from the Zr-2.5% Nb alloy in the different directions of the studied tubes.

2. Samples and methods

Most of the works on the study of thermal expansion have been carried out on finished products, since researchers are mainly interested in their performance properties. However, the expansion of tubes ensures their volumetric changes in such a way that changes in linear dimensions in different directions are dependent on each other. In this regard, it is necessary to prepare free samples on which it is possible to establish a real change in dimensions in three mutually perpendicular directions.

For this purpose, in this work, samples for thermal tests have been cut from thick-walled channel tubes made of Zr-2.5% Nb alloy pre-annealed in different modes. Samples of the first series were annealed at a temperature of 400 °C for 24 hours (hereinafter samples # 1), and the second series - at a temperature of 580 °C for 3 hours (samples # 2). Then samples of a cubic shape were cut from the walls of the tubes, the cutting scheme is shown in figure 1. The edges of the cubes were oriented along the main directions of the channel tube: radial *R*, tangential *T*, and axial *L*. The final dimensions of the prepared samples were approximately 4x4x4 mm.

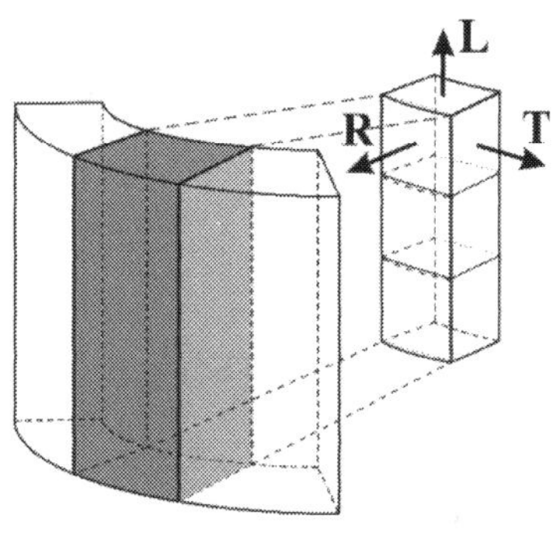

Figure 1. Scheme of cutting samples from a channel tube

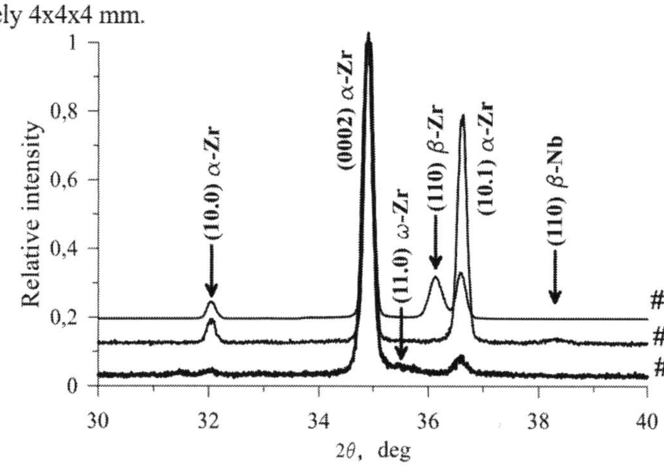

Figure 2. Diffraction patterns of the studied tubes #1 and # 2 (curves #1 and #2, correspondingly) before and after testing (curve #3)

The study of samples expansion in three mutually perpendicular directions: R, T and L, in the temperature range of 50-1200 °C was carried out on a Netzsch 402 C dilatometer in a flow of high-purity helium (99.9999%) with its additional purification by a Monotorr getter catalytic filter. An additional oxygen getter OTS manufactured by Netzsch was located next to the sample. The rate of heating and subsequent cooling of the test sample was 5°/min. The method of temperature experiments is described in detail in the works [5-6].

X-ray studies of the structure and crystallographic texture of the initial samples, as well as the samples after a heating and cooling cycle in the temperature range of 50-1200 °C, were carried out on DRON-3 and D8 Discover diffractometers using Cr Kα and Cu Kα radiation, respectively. Based on incomplete direct pole figures (DPFs) taken from three mutually perpendicular sides of a cubic sample, the complete DPFs of the sample for a plane perpendicular to the R-direction were reconstructed by the PF combination [7-8]. Based on the calculated complete DPF (0001), the integral texture parameters of

IOP Conf. Series: Materials Science and Engineering 1121 (2021) 012036 doi:10.1088/1757-899X/1121/1/012036

Kearns were estimated for three directions *R*, *T* and *L* [9]. The Kearns parameter is the sum of the effective fractions of the basal axes [0001] oriented along the chosen direction in the polycrystal material. This parameters for different directions are used to evaluate the properties of textured material with known properties for a hexagonal single crystal along the crystallographic axes *a* and *c* [9-11].

3. Experimental results and discussion

According to diffraction spectra of tubes No. 1 and No. 2 shown in figure 2, the material of the tubes differs significantly in composition. The main phase of both tubes is the α-phase, solid solution of Nb in the hcp-Zr. An additional phase in the tube # 1 was the ω-Zr phase, which is typical for these alloys with this kind of heat treatment [4]. It may also indicate a small degree of preliminary plastic deformation of the tube # 1. In the tube # 2, the β-phase with a high niobium content (90 wt.%) is turned out to be an additional phase, which proves the equilibrium of the final state of the phases in this tube, corresponding to the equilibrium phase diagram of the Zr-Nb alloys [12].

The difference in the structural state of the studied tubes is also evidenced by the DPFs (0001) and $\{11\bar{2}0\}$ shown in figure 3-a, b. Both tubes are characterized by a pronounced axial component with a predominance of different texture components. In the tube # 1, the axes $<10\bar{1}0>$ are oriented along the rolling direction. This texture component is corresponded to the rolling texture of the α-zirconium. But, in the tube # 2 the axes $<11\bar{2}0>$ are oriented along the rolling direction, confirming the occurrence of recrystallization in the tube through grain growth misoriented relative to the deformed matrix at an angle of 30°. The distributions of basal axes in the R-T-section of the DPF (0001) are also different. In tube # 1, the basal axes are predominantly oriented in the T-direction, and in the tube No. 2, the basal axes are deflected from the R-direction towards T by 30-40°.

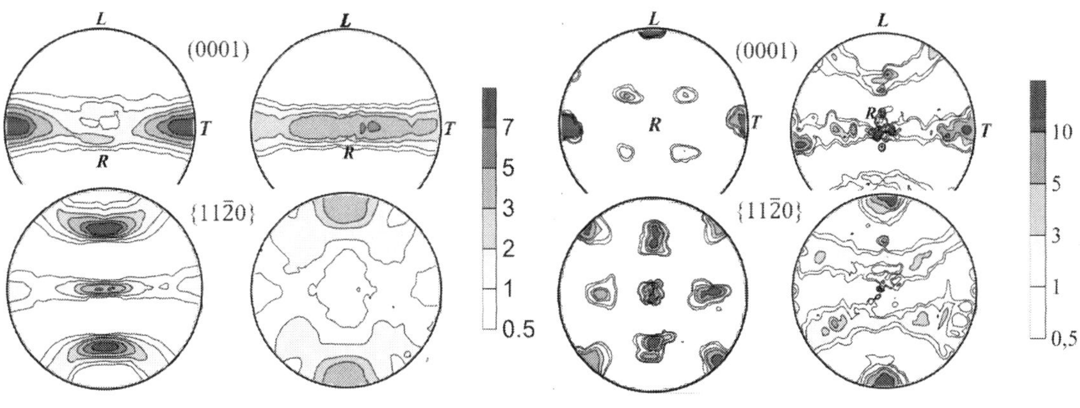

a b c d

Figure 3. Complete DPFs (0001) and $\{11\bar{2}0\}$ for the initial (a-b) and tested (c-d) samples of the tubes No. 1 (a, c) and No. 2 (b, d)

As a result of high-temperature tests of the described samples, their crystallographic texture changes in different ways. DPFs (0001) and $\{11\bar{2}0\}$ after the heating-cooling cycle in the temperature range of 20-1200 °C are shown in figure 3-c, d. The given DPFs are characterized by irregularity of the contours, which is due to the large size of β-grains formed in the high-temperature region of the state diagram, a decrease in the number of reflecting grains, and violation of measurement statistics. Nevertheless, the main regularities of the texture of PTs are obvious.

First of all, it should be noted that PTs proceed in accordance with the orientation Burgers relation, in which $\{110\}_\beta \parallel (0001)_\alpha$ and $<111>_\beta \parallel <11\bar{2}0>_\alpha$ [12]. As noted in [8, 11], the localization of PTs significantly depends on the distribution of stored energy in grains of different orientations. As a result of an inhomogeneous PTs in a sample with a less stable structural state, the α→β-PTs are localized mainly in grains, the basal axes of which are oriented in the tangential direction (figure 3-c). In this case, in a sample #2, α→β-PTs flow more uniformly in grains of different initial orientations, i.e. distribution of axes along the R-T-section of the DPF (0001) is preserved (figure 3-d) [8, 11]. The appearance of additional texture maxima on the DPF (0001) is determined by the orientation of the prismatic axes, the symmetry of the cubic lattice, and a high repeatability factor of the $\{110\}_\beta$ planes, parallel to which the unique basal planes of the α-phase are located at the inverse-PT. The theoretical arrangement of texture maxima is described in a large number of works [4, 8, 11, 13-14]. The obtained experimental results completely coincide with theoretical calculations. The reverse PT can be accompanied by the predominant growth of grains of different orientations and is determined by the level of external stresses [15]. However, in the context of this work, we will not dwell on the differences in the DPFs for the samples on which measurements were carried out in different directions. All samples cut from the same tube have the same type of final texture.

Figure 4 shows the thermal expansion curves for all studied samples, measured during heating (solid lines) and cooling (dashed lines) in the temperature range 20-1200 °C. The results of testing cubic samples in different directions *R*, *T* and *L* are shown in figure 4 by curves of different shades: black is corresponded *R*-direction, gray - *T* and finally light gray - *L*. The dimensions of the tested samples were measured before and after thermal tests. At the same time, different size changes were recorded in different directions, which are shown in Table 1.

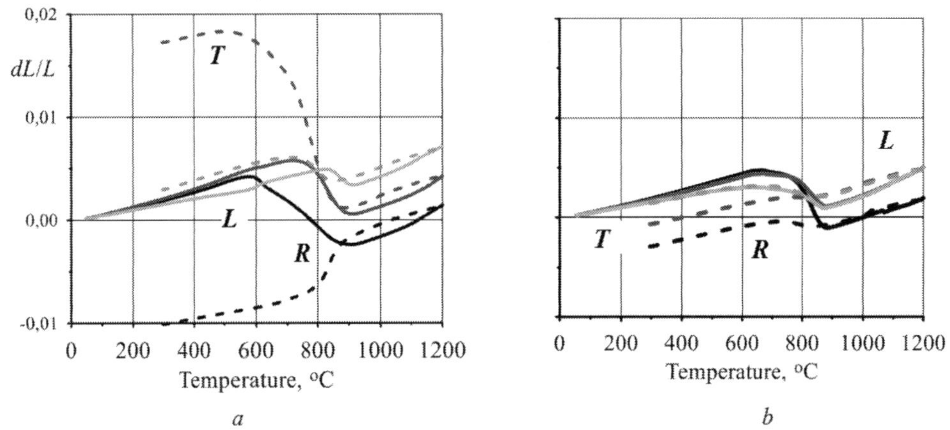

Figure 4. Curves of linear expansion and contraction in three main directions at the heating (solid lines) or cooling (dashed lines) of cubic samples of the tubes annealed at temperatures of 400 °C during 24 h (*a*) and 580 °C during 3 h (*b*)

The sizes of the tested samples of tube # 1 vary widely, from –1.3 to 2.3%, while the sizes of the samples of tube # 2 vary from – 0.3 to 0.2%. Therefore, the anisotropy of the change in the dimensions of the sample of tube # 1 is 4-5 times greater than for the tube # 2.

The final change in the size of the samples is completely determined by the processes of α→β→α–PTs in the temperature range 600-850 °C, occurring both during heating and during cooling of the samples. Let us consider the main processes that can lead to a change in the dimensions of the samples under study. First of all, heating of samples in the temperature range of existence of the α-phase is accompanied by their expansion, at which the LTEC is proportional to the integral texture parameter f for the considered direction [1-5].

When the temperature of the monotectoid transformation 610 °C reaches, the α-β transformation begins, at which the sizes of the samples begin to decrease in all directions, as shown in [1-4, 6] and can be seen in figure 4. Such a decrease is due to a reduction in the size of the unit cell of the bcc phase as compared to the hcp. Moreover, in the direction of the *c* axis, this decrease is less than along the *a* axis, as was shown in [6] (Δc = - 3.26%, Δa = - 5.5%). The sharp crystallographic texture explains the difference in size variation in the *R*- and *T*-directions. The largest decrease in size occurs in the radial direction, and the smallest decrease is experienced by the sample in the axial direction.

Table 1. Changing the size of cubic samples in different directions as a result of a cycle of thermal tests in the temperature interval 20-1200 °C

Tube number	Test direction	Resizing the sample, %			Initial state
		R	*T*	*L*	
1	*R*	-1.0	2.3	0.3	Anneal 400 °C - 3 h
	T	-0.8	2.1	0.1	
	L	-1.3	1.9	0.1	
2	*R*	-0.2	0.1	0.1	Anneal 580 °C - 5 h
	T	-0.1	-0.1	0.2	
	L	-0.3	-0.1	0.1	

Depending on the initial structural state, the onset of the PT shifts relative to the temperature corresponding to the onset of the PT in the equilibrium phase diagram. If the structure is less stable, as observed in the case of tube # 1, the PT process proceeds inhomogeneously and depends on the orientation, then the effect of size reduction in different directions will be recorded at different temperatures. It should not be forgotten that PTs occur throughout the entire volume of the material and affect changes in dimensions in all directions. But, since these changes are anisotropic, different directions are sensitive to different volumetric rearrangements. For example, in the case of tube # 2, for almost all directions, the sample dimensions change simultaneously (synchronously) (figure 4-b). For the *L*-direction of both tubes, the smallest reduction in sample size is recorded.

In the region of existence of the β-phase, the coefficient of linear expansion is the same for all directions, and within the limits of error, it can be assumed that the samples have the same dimensions at a temperature of 1200 °C.

At the stage of cooling the samples, the main changes in their dimensions are noted, which are then recorded at room temperature (Table 1). The largest increase in dimensions is observed for the *T*-direction of tube # 1, while in the *L*- and *R*-directions there is a reduction in dimensions. What processes can lead to size changing in the two-phase region of the phase diagram of Zr-Nb alloys?

With a decrease in the temperature of the single-phase Zr-2.5% Nb alloy to the two-phase region (α + β), the formed crystals of the α-phase are characterized by larger sizes in comparison with β-crystals. Since $(0001)_\alpha \parallel \{110\}_\beta$, the change in interplanar distance is $\varepsilon_c = \frac{d_{110}-d_{0001}}{d_{110}} = 1 - \frac{d_{0001}}{d_{110}} = 1 - \frac{c_\alpha}{\sqrt{2}a_\beta}$; and for directions $<11\bar{2}0>_\alpha \parallel <111>_\beta$ $\varepsilon_a = \frac{d_{111}-d_{11\bar{2}0}}{d_{111}} = 1 - \frac{d_{11\bar{2}0}}{d_{111}} = 1 - \frac{2a_\alpha}{\sqrt{3}a_\beta}$. With the substitution of specific values, it was shown [6] that an increase in the size of the cells of the hcp phase compared to the bcc phase should be observed both in the basal plane and perpendicular to it (Δc = + 1.8%, Δa = + 4.2%). The magnitude of changes in the parameters during forward and reverse phase transformations depends most of all on the concentration of niobium in the β-phase, the amount of which differs significantly and is estimated by the position of the β-phase line in the patterns (figure 2). Then all temperature dependences should increase with decreasing temperature. However, in figure 4-a, b it can be seen that along with an increase, a decrease in size is also possible (for example, for the *R*-direction). An additional process with decreasing temperature is the redistribution of niobium between phases. Moreover, in accordance with the phase diagram [12], the increase in the niobium content in the bcc phase occurs at a higher rate than niobium in the hcp phase. In this case, the parameter of the crystal structure of the bcc phase in accordance with Vegard's law decreases by an order of magnitude larger than due to the thermal decrease in the size of the β-phase in accordance with its LTEC [12].

These two described processes occur simultaneously in the material, and the diffusion process is more likely to occur at higher temperatures of the two-phase region, which can be seen from the temperature dependence of the cooling of the sample in the *R*-direction (figure 4-a). With a decrease in the temperature of the two-phase region from 860 to 610 °C, the curve of decreasing dimensions in the

R-direction changes the angle of inclination near temperatures of 780-800 °C, which indicates a change in the prevailing mechanism. For the *T*-direction, which was predominant in the original tube for the orientation of basal axes, the process of formation of the α-phase is of priority, which ensures a significant increase in dimensions in this direction with the predominant orientation of the basal axes in the *T*-direction.

Thus, it has been shown that in the presence of a sharp crystallographic texture in the product, significant anisotropy of the size change is observed. This can lead to the development of significant macro stresses in the case of heating the pipe to the two-phase region and subsequent cooling: high compressive stresses should develop in the tangential direction due to the need for the pipe to increase its dimensions in this direction, while a decrease in dimensions is observed in the radial direction.

4. Conclusions

1. It is shown that in the presence of an unstable crystallographic texture of deformation in a product made of the Zr-2.5%Nb alloy, a significant anisotropy of thermal change in product dimensions is observed as a result of the α↔β-phase transformation inhomogeneity.
2. If the material is characterized by a recrystallization texture, then the formation of nuclei of new phases occurs uniformly in different orientations, which ensures a significantly smaller change in the dimensions of the product as a whole.

5. Anknowledgment

The reported study was funded by RFBR according to the research project No. 19-32-90041 and was supported by the MEPhI Academic Excellence Project (agreement with the Ministry of Education and Science of the Russian Federation of August 27, 2013, project no. 02.a03.21.0005).

6. References

[1] Luscher W G, Geelhood K J, and Porter I E 2014 *Material property correlations: Comparisons between FRAPCON-3.4, FRAPTRAN 1.4, and MATPRO (NUREG/GR-7024, Rev.1).* Richland, WA 99352: Report of Pacific Northwest National Laboratory 153 p

[2] Bunnell L R, Bates J L, Mellinger G B 1983 *J. Nucl. Mater.* 116 No 2/3 219–232

[3] Fong R W L, Fazeli F, Smith T 2015 *35th Annual Conference of the Canadian Nuclear Society*, Canada, Curran Associates, Incorporated, p.1-12

[4] Fong R, Vogel S et al. 2012 *Metallurgical and Materials Transactions A* 43 No.3 806-821

[5] Isaenkova M G, Tenishev A V, Perlovich Yu A et al. 2020 *Fizika i khimiya obrabotki materialov (Physics and chemistry of materials treatment)* 3 p.53-65 (in Russian)

[6] Isaenkova M G, Tenishev A V, Perlovich Yu A et al. 2020 *Fizika i khimiya obrabotki materialov (Physics and chemistry of materials treatment)* 4 51-64 (in Russian)

[7] Perlovich Y, Isaenkova M, Fesenko V *2016 IOP Conf. Series: Materials Science and Engineering* 130 012055

[8] Isaenkova M G, Perlovich Yu A 2014 *Regularities of the development of crystallographic texture and substructural heterogeneity in zirconium alloys during deformation and heat treatment*. Moscow, NRNU MEPhI. 528 p (in Russian)

[9] Kearns J J 1965 *Thermal expansion and preferred orientation in Zircaloy*. Pittsburgh P.A.: Bettis Atomic Power Lab. 40 p

[10] Nye J *Physical Properties of Crystals: Their Representation by Tensors and Matrices*. 1957. 325p

[11] Kocks U F, Tome C N, Wenk H R 1998 *Texture and anisotropy* / Cambridge University Press.

[12] D.l. Douglass *The Metallurgy of Zirconium*. International atomic energy agency, Atomic Energy Review, Supplement 1971. IAEA, Vienna 350 p

[13] Perlovich Yu., Isaenkova M. 1997 *Textures and Microstructures* 30 55-70

[14] Cheadle B A, Ells C E 1966 *Electroch. Techn.* 4 (7-8) 329-336

[15] Vishnyakov Ya D, Babareko A A, Vladimirov S A et al. *The theory of texture formation in metals and alloys.* Moscow: Nauka. 344 p (in Russian)

IOP Conf. Series: Materials Science and Engineering 1121 (2021) 012037 doi:10.1088/1757-899X/1121/1/012037

Effect of post-rolling cooling on the hot-rolled microstructure and texture of a new medium-carbon steel

V Javaheri[1], S Sadeghpour[1], A Kaijalainen[1], M R Kamali[2] and J Kömi[1]

[1]Materials and Mechanical Engineering, Centre for Advanced Steel Research, University of Oulu, 90014 Oulu, Finland.
[2]Department of Mining and Metallurgical Engineering, Yazd University, Iran.

E-mail: vahid.javaheri@oulu.fi

Abstract. Thermomechanical processing consisted of hot-rolling in the austenitic region with deformation both above and below the non-recrystallization temperature. Immediately after rolling, specimens were directly quenched in water to three different temperatures of 560 °C, 420 °C and room temperature. The first two samples, which were quenched to 560° C and 420°C, immediately cooled slowly in the furnace. The microstructure of samples quenched to 560 °C mostly comprised of upper bainite whereas the samples quenched to 420 °C mainly consisted of lath-type bainite. The microstructure of sample direct-quenched to room temperature was mainly martensite. The transformation texture of all samples at the mid-thickness position showed the same general texture, consisted of mainly α and γ fibers components with high intensities close to the transformed copper {112}<110>$_\alpha$, transformed brass {111}<112>$_\alpha$ and rotated cube {001}<110>$_\alpha$ components. However, the direct-quenched sample produced slightly more intense texture compared to the bainitic samples. The local texture of samples near the rolled surface owing to sever deformation showed the shear features consisting of major components of {112}<111>$_\alpha$, {110}<112>$_\alpha$ and {110}<111>$_\alpha$.

1. Introduction

Thermomechanical controlled processing (TMCP) is a technological way to enhance the strength and toughness of steel plates at the same time by i) controlling the prior austenite structure through the rolling parameters and ii) controlling the subsequent phase transformation via control of the cooling path. Typically, TMCP of bcc steels is performed by applying a multi-stage hot deformation process, i.e. rough rolling and finish rolling stage, both above and below the non-recrystallization temperature (T_{nr}) [1,2]. Throughout the rough rolling stage, at above T_{nr}, deformation and repeated recrystallization is taken place simultaneously resulting in very fine austenite grain structure which will be elongated into narrow stretched grain structure (known as the pancake shape) after further deformation below T_{nr}. This unrecrystallized and elongated austenite grains are subsequently transformed to a desired fine microstructure which its characteristic depends on the applied cooling path. Crystallographic texture of the parent austenite develops as a result of both recrystallization and deformation without recrystallization. Moreover, owing to orientation relationships between the parent austenite and the daughter ferritic products such as bainite and martensite, the final ferritic microstructure also shows crystallographic texture [3]. Therefore, the cooling path may affect the microstructure and texture evolution during final stages of TMCP. Though that extensive research activities have so far been conducted to investigate the hot rolling process and physical metallurgy involved, especially texture development during deformation [4–6], the effect of post-rolling cooling condition is not yet fully studied and understood. Hence, the present work is intended to study the microstructural and textural changes during hot rolling and subsequent cooling of three different post-rolling cooling patterns. The cooling paths have been designed based on the studied material's time-temperature-transformation (TTT) diagram to have upper bainite, lower bainite and martensite as the final microstructures.

2. Material and experimental procedures

The material used in this work (designed by the authors) was a new medium-carbon, low alloy steel microalloyed with Nb with the following composition: **0.4 C**, **0.2 Si**, **0.25 Mn**, **0.90 Cr**, **0.50 Mo** and **0.013 Nb** (wt. %). Initially, the studied material was cast using vacuum-induction melting (VIM) furnace and then cut to the slab-shape block (51x200x75 mm). Afterward, the blocks were reheated at 1200 °C for 3 hours and then were rolled on a pilot rolling mill to a final thickness of 10 mm. As illustrated in figure 1, rolling was performed in two stages, a 4-pass rough rolling above the T_{nr} in the temperature range 1200-1100 °C with a total reduction of 48 % followed by also a 4-pass finish rolling stage below T_{nr} such that the finish rolling temperature was 800 °C, slightly above the austenite finish temperature (A_3). Immediately, the rolled strips were directly quenched in three different ways; for first two cooling cycles as highlighted in figure 1, the rolled strips were directly quenched in water to two quench-stop temperatures of 560 °C and 420 °C and then transferred to a furnace at the same temperature with related quench-stop temperature and allowed to furnace cool (approx. 0.01 °C/s) to ensure achieving upper bainite and lower bainite microstructure, respectively. For the third cycle, the rolled strip was directly water quenched to the room temperature to producing as-quenched martensite microstructure. The temperature of the material during the whole process was monitored via a thermocouple inserted in the middle of the blocks before rolling. The samples were labeled according to their expected final microstructure as Upper Bainite, Lower Bainite, and Martensite.

Regarding the microstructure and microtexture characterization, a Sigma Zeiss field emission scanning electron microscope (FESEM) equipped with electron backscatter diffraction (EBSD) was employed to examine the sub-surface and mid-thickness regions of all samples. EBSD mappings were recorded using an accelerating voltage of 15 kV, a working distance of 15 mm, a tilt angle of 70° and a step size of 0.3 μm. A detailed microstructural analysis was also performed on the EBSD image quality (IQ) data using a deconvolutional technique based on the method developed by DeArdo et al. [7].

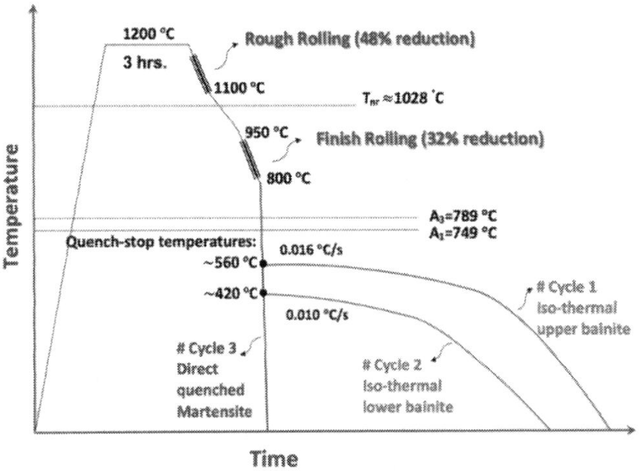

Figure 1. The schematic infograph of hot-rolling schedule along with the post-rolling cooling paths including Cycle #1, #2, and #3 intended to produce final as-rolled microstructure of upper bainite, lower bainite and martensite, respectively.

3. Results and discussion

The micrographs of the final structures in the form of EBSD image quality along with the phase fraction calculation on the basis of normalized image quality numerical analysis are presented in figure 2. In general, all three samples showed deformation of the prior austenite grains along the rolling direction resulted a very fine as-rolled microstructure. It has been earlier reported that different morphologies varying in intrinsic dislocation density and consequently give the different IQ values [8]; accordingly, different microstructural constituents were detected in each sample based on their IQ value and marked on the microstructure images given in figures 2a-c.

The normalized IQ graphs (solid black lines in figures 2d-f) exhibited three different general outlines indicating three different microstructures, upper bainite with an augmented peak around ~50-60 (figure 2d), lower bainite with an augmented peak around ~30-40 (figure 2e), and martensite with a maximum peak around ~20-25 (figure 2e). To determine the fraction of each microstructural components, the normalized IQ curve was deconvoluted into multiple normally distributed peaks. Then, each peak was attributed to a specific morphology based on the location of peak (IQ value) and the ratio of area under each peak to the area of normalized IQ was considered as fraction associated to each component. The calculated values are given in the legend boxes.

The local crystallographic characteristics of the specimen were examined using EBSD measurement. The inverse pole figure (IPF) maps of sub-surface and mid-thickness of all samples from a randomly selected rolling – normal direction (RD-ND) section are presented in figure 3. The IPF images acquired from the sub-surface exhibited a very fine final microstructure which is originated from the extremely fine prior austenite grain structure due to the heavy deformation on the surface. Although the mid-thickness samples showed a bit coarser structure compared to the surface, the microstructural components were still very fine.

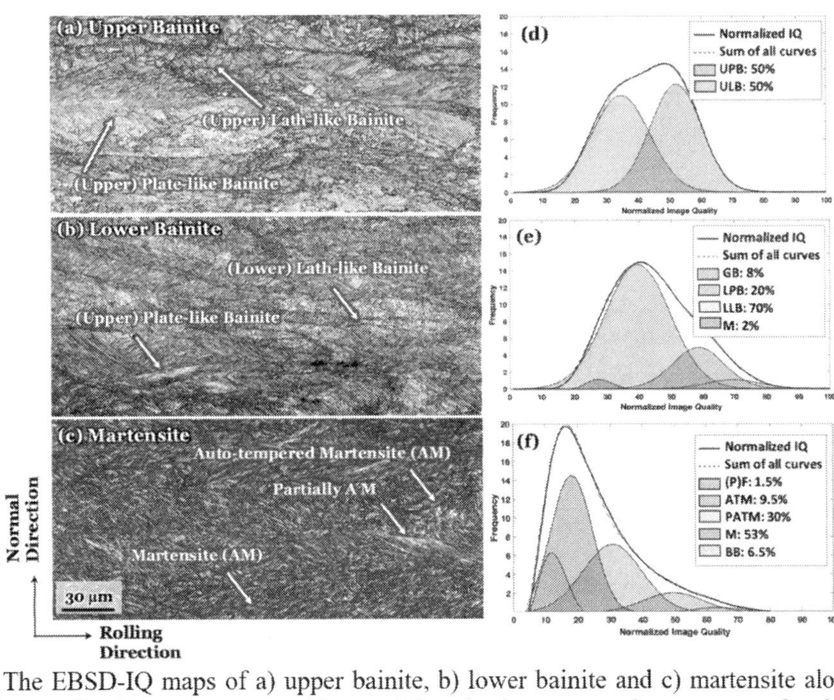

Figure 2. The EBSD-IQ maps of a) upper bainite, b) lower bainite and c) martensite along with the associated normalized IQ value curves (d, e, and f) and microstructural components fraction based on the IQ deconvolutional analysis. (UPB: (upper) plate-like bainite, ULB: (upper) lath-like bainite, GB: granular bainite, LPB: (lower) plate-like bainite, LLB: (lower) lath-like bainite, M: martensite, (P)F: (polygonal) ferrite, ATM: auto-tempered martensite, PATM: partially auto-tempered martensite, BB: block boundaries.)

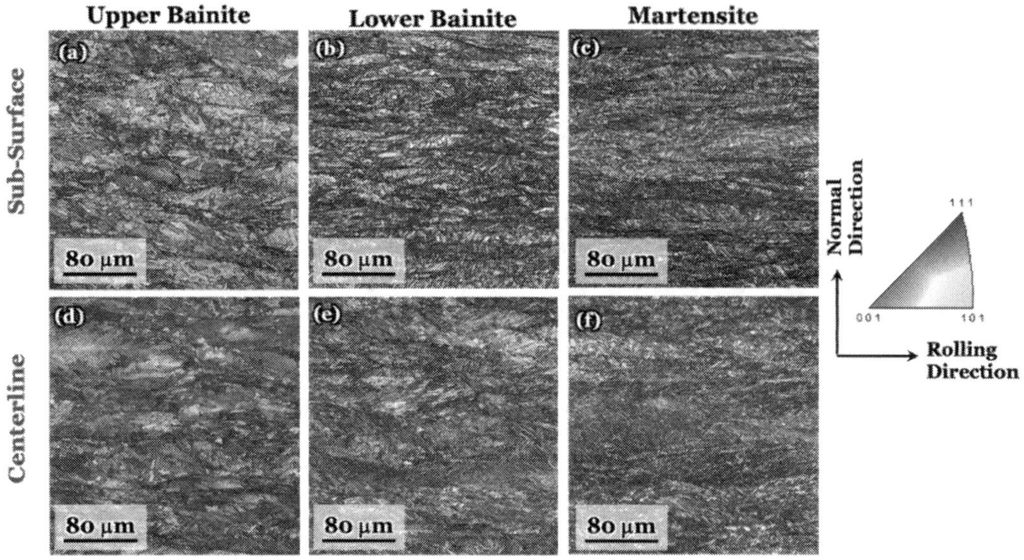

Figure 3. Invers pole figure (IPF) maps obtained from RD-ND section of both sub-surface and centreline of upper bainite (a and d), lower bainite (b and e), and martensite (c and f).

The EBSD data obtained from an area of 250×250 µm similar to figure 3 were used to construct the orientation distribution functions (ODF) in three-dimensional Euler space using OIM TSL software. ODF is a common mathematical way to describe the occurrence frequency of popular/particular crystal orientations such that, on the orientation space of the polycrystalline specimen, a volume percentage of crystals with a specific orientation is calculated for each orientation. In BCC rolled materials (like the studied steel) the major texture components and fibers can be found in the $\varphi_2 = 45°$ section of Euler space [9]. Figure 4 presents a schematic illustration of the ideal position for these fibers and components in the $\varphi_2 = 45°$ section under both shear and planar deformation. Figures 5 (a, c, and e) shows the ODF $\varphi_2 = 45°$ section for the sub-surface EBSD data. Comparing figures 4 and 5, the sharp BCC shear texture components of $\{112\}\langle111\rangle_\alpha$, $\{110\}\langle112\rangle_\alpha$ and $\{110\}\langle111\rangle_\alpha$ were observed almost in all cooling conditions. It has been reported [10,11] that since austenite is severely deformed by rolling below T_{nr} the intense shear texture components of $\{112\}\langle110\rangle_\gamma$ and $\{111\}\langle211\rangle_\gamma$ form in the austenite close to the rolled surfaces that later, during cooling, they transform to the above-mentioned BCC shear components. However, the intensity of ferritic shear components close to the rolling surface can be also because of formation of ferrite (phase) on the surface that subsequently deformed in shearing form during the rolling process.

ODF maps at $\varphi_2 = 45°$ of the centerlines are demonstrated in figures 5 (b, d, and f). As expected, the ODF sections show that the texture of the samples was the typical texture of rolled carbon steel under planar strain condition when the pancaked austenite rolling texture produces transformation BCC texture components. In the other words, the centerline texture scheme of the alloys was essentially the same for all samples comprising mainly $\langle111\rangle$//ND (γ) and $\langle110\rangle$//RD (α) fibers, i.e. the main components of $\{113\}\langle110\rangle_\alpha$, $\{111\}\langle121\rangle_\alpha$ and $\{323\}\langle131\rangle_\alpha$. However, the intensity of the martensite sample was slightly higher compared to the both bainitic conditions. The texture intensity depends on several parameters including mainly steel chemistry, amount of deformation, initial austenite structure and grain size, and cooling rate during transformation [3]. As all of the above parameters were retained the same for all the specimen except post-rolling cooling condition, it could be assumed that the slight increase in texture intensity by increasing the cooling rate, especially in the martensite sample could be owing to higher rate of cooling.

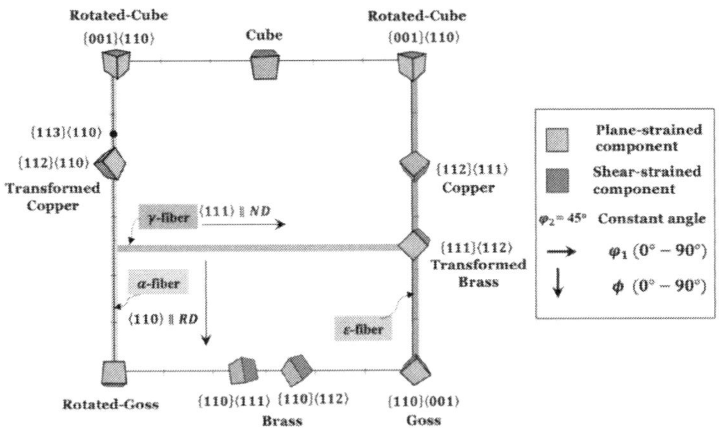

Figure 4. The schematic infograph of the position of most common bcc rolled texture components and fibers in the ODF $\varphi_2 = 45°$ section under both shear and planar strain along with the orientation of unit cell for each component.

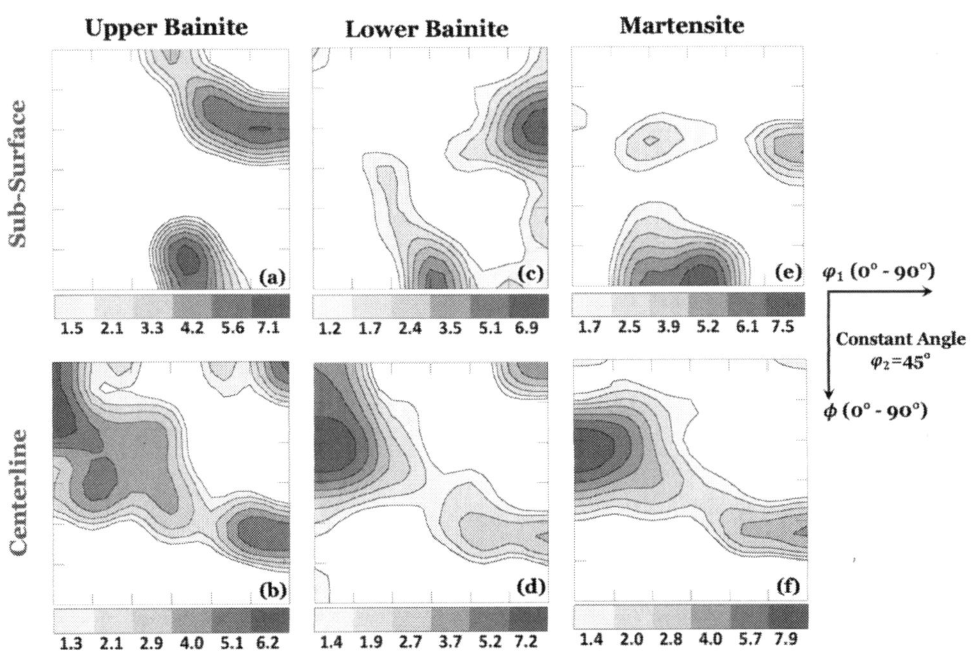

Figure 5. ODF maps at $\varphi_2 = 45°$ calculated from the EBSD data from both sub-surface and centreline of upper bainite (a and d), lower bainite (b and e), and martensite (c and f).

4. Conclusion

A novel medium-carbon low-alloy steel was subjected to a controlled rolling process in order to reduction of thickness from 50 mm to 10 mm. Directly after hot rolling, samples were quenched through three different cooling conditions. The microstructure and microtexture analysis revealed the main following results:

- According to the image quality analysis, quenching to the different quench-stop temperatures of 560 °C, 420 °C (following with subsequent furnace cooling) and room temperature resulted in different microstructure of upper bainite (50 % plate-like and 50 % lath-like), lower bainite (8 % granular, 20 % plate-like, 70 % lath-like, and 8 % martensite) and martensite (~50 % fresh martensite and (~50 % partially/fully auto-tempered martensite), respectively.

- Samples showed almost the same general crystallographic characteristics consisted the typical BCC shear features near to the rolled surface and transformation texture components (under plane strain) at the mid-thickness. However, the texture was a bit more intense in martensite sample compared to the upper and lower bainite.

Acknowledgements
The authors are grateful for financial support from Academy of Finland (#311934-Genome of Steel Project). Vahid Javaheri would also like to thank the Jenny and Antti Wihuri Foundation for awarding a personal grant.

References

[1] Eskandari M, Mohtadi-Bonab M A and Szpunar J A 2016 Evolution of the microstructure and texture of X70 pipeline steel during cold-rolling and annealing treatments *Mater. Des.* **90** 618–27
[2] Nishioka K and Ichikawa K 2012 Progress in thermomechanical control of steel plates and their commercialization *Sci. Technol. Adv. Mater.* **13** 023001
[3] Ray R K, Jonas J J, Burton-Guillen M P and Savoie J 1994 Transformation textures in steels *ISIJ Int.* **34** 972–942
[4] Storojeva L, Ponge D, Kaspar R and Raabe D 2004 Development of microstructure and texture of medium carbon steel during heavy warm deformation *Acta Mater.* **52** 2209–20
[5] Petrov R, García O L, Sánchez Mouriño N, Kestens L A I, Bae J H and Kang K B 2007 Microstructure - Texture Related Toughness Anisotropy of API-X80 Pipeline Steel Characterized by Means of 3D-EBSD Technique *Mater. Sci. Forum* **558–559** 1429–34
[6] Gazder A A, Sánchez-Araiza M, Jonas J J and Pereloma E V. 2011 Evolution of recrystallization texture in a 0.78 wt.% Cr extra-low-carbon steel after warm and cold rolling *Acta Mater.* **59** 4847–65
[7] DeArdo A J, Garcia C I, Cho K and Hua M 2010 New method of characterizing and quantifying complex microstructures in steels *Mater. Manuf. Process.* **25** 33–40
[8] Javaheri V, Pohjonen A, Asperheim J I, Ivanov D and Porter D 2019 Physically based modeling, characterization and design of an induction hardening process for a new slurry pipeline steel *Mater. Des.* **182** 108047
[9] Javaheri V, Khodaie N, Kaijalainen A and Porter D 2018 Effect of niobium and phase transformation temperature on the microstructure and texture of a novel 0.40% C thermomechanically processed steel *Mater. Charact.* **142** 295–308
[10] Kaijalainen A J, Liimatainen M, Kesti V, Heikkala J, Liimatainen T and Porter D A 2016 Influence of Composition and Hot Rolling on the Subsurface Microstructure and Bendability of Ultrahigh-Strength Strip *Metall. Mater. Trans. A Phys. Metall. Mater. Sci.* **47** 4175–88
[11] Saastamoinen A, Kaijalainen A, Porter D and Suikkanen P 2017 The effect of thermomechanical treatment and tempering on the subsurface microstructure and bendability of direct-quenched low-carbon strip steel *Mater. Charact.* **134** 172–81
[12] Hutchinson W B, Ryde L and Bate P S 2005 Transformation Textures in Steels *Mater. Sci. Forum* **495–497** 1141–50
[13] Raabe D and Lücke K 1992 Texture and microstructure of hot rolled steel *Scr. Metall. Mater.* **26** 1221–6
[14] Joo M S, Suh D W, Bae J H, Sanchez Mouriño N, Petrov R, Kestens L A I and Bhadeshia H K D H 2012 Experiments to separate the effect of texture on anisotropy of pipeline steel *Mater. Sci. Eng. A* **556** 601–6
[15] Nafisi S, Arafin M A, Collins L and Szpunar J 2012 Texture and mechanical properties of API X100 steel manufactured under various thermomechanical cycles *Mater. Sci. Eng. A* **531** 2–11

IOP Conf. Series: Materials Science and Engineering 1121 (2021) 012038 doi:10.1088/1757-899X/1121/1/012038

Texture-related biological properties of severely deformed titanium

D Wojtas[1,2,*], A Mzyk[2,3], J Kawałko[4], K Trembecka-Wójciga[2], K Wierzbanowski[1], G Imbir[2], M Marzec[4], Ł Maj[2], A Jarzębska[2], M Bieda-Niemiec[2], R Chulist[2], K Sztwiertnia[2], W Pachla[5]

[1] AGH University of Science and Technology, Faculty of Physics and Applied Computer Science, Reymonta 19, 30-059 Kraków, Poland
[2] Institute of Metallurgy and Materials Science, Polish Academy of Sciences, Reymonta 25, 30-059 Kraków, Poland
[3] Groningen University, University Medical Center Groningen, Department of Biomedical Engineering, Antonius Deusinglaan 1, 9713 AW Groningen, The Netherlands
[4] Academic Centre for Materials and Nanotechnology, Mickiewicza 30, 30-059 Kraków, Poland
[5] Institute of High Pressure Physics (Unipress), Polish Academy of Sciences, Sokołowska 29/37, 01-142 Warszawa, Poland

E-mail: wojtas@agh.edu.pl

Abstract. Pure titanium manufactured by hydrostatic extrusion has been investigated with the aim to find the clear origin of superior biological properties observed in the materials processed by various severe plastic deformation techniques. In so doing, physicochemical properties of the surface were characterised as well as protein adsorption tests and cell culture examinations were thoroughly carried out. It has been found that, irrespective of the grain size, the basal planes exposed to the surface favour protein adsorption, whereas it is prismatic planes that experience pronounced cell activity on the surface of hydrostatically extruded titanium substrates. Biological behaviour of severely deformed titanium-based materials should be attributed to crystallographic orientation of grains, chemical composition of the surface as well as the presence of surface irregularities in the form of various nano-peaks or nano-grooves, while the effect of grain size might be of less importance.

1. Introduction

Stainless steel, aluminium and titanium represent the most commonly strengthened materials by means of severe plastic deformation (SPD) techniques [1]. A remarkable increase in mechanical characteristics is accomplished while using the SPD approaches and a variety of other functional properties are also enhanced [2]. It has been well-documented that early cell response on the surface of microstructurally refined titanium is more pronounced with a comparison to its coarse-grained counterpart [3,4]. In addition, improved *in vitro* bioactivity of normally inert titanium surface, enhanced protein adsorption and substantially higher alkaline phosphatase activity have also been reported for severely deformed titanium-based materials [5]. The origin of such extraordinary behaviour remains inadequately understood, yet is typically associated with grain refinement or changes in the physicochemical properties of the surface, i.e., wettability and roughness [3–6]. Recently, the effect of a significant share of high-angle grain boundaries (HAGB) in the volume of a material as well as crystallographic orientation of grains on the biological properties of the SPD-obtained materials have also been considered [7,8].

Equal channel angular pressing (ECAP), accumulative roll-bonding (ARB) and high-pressure torsion (HPT) make up for the most frequently practiced and extensively researched SPD methods, although a great deal of novel manufacturing techniques have come to the fore over the past years [1]. Hydrostatic extrusion (HE), an unconventional SPD process, has been shown to enhance the strength of pure titanium so exceptionally that it reaches the level characteristic to that of the Ti-6Al-4V alloy [9,10]. The HE method is known to be especially advantageous in reinforcing the mechanical properties of hard-to-deform materials, such as zinc or tungsten, yet it tends to produce lengthened wires and rods, therefore its use is somehow limited [11,12]. The possible application of HE includes small-sized medical equipment, parts of advanced appliances and tools, as well as dental implants.

Within the present study, titanium fabricated by the multi-stage HE process has been analysed with respect to its biological behaviour, using cell culture studies and protein adsorption tests. The physicochemical properties of the substrates, varying significantly in the crystallographic orientation of grains, have been additionally examined so the origin of superior biological properties observed in titanium-based materials processed by SPD approaches is to get fathomed. The entire analysis is supported by a thorough characterisation of the material's microstructure.

2. Materials and experimental details

Pure titanium (grade 2) was manufactured by the HE technique realized in four consecutive steps without the interstage and stress-relief annealing, yet cooling with a stream of cold water was performed every time the material exited the die extruder. Prior to the deformation process, the billet was homogenized at 700°C for 2 hours and left air-cooled. Different cross-sections taken from a final rod were cut, then ground with a set of silicon carbide papers and electronically polished, using the A3 Struers electrolyte. Afterwards, the specimens were cleaned in isopropanol and dried. Overall, mirror-finished specimens were prepared.

2.1. Microstructure and texture

FEI Quanta 3D FEG SEM was used to execute the microstructural and textural characterisations by means of the electron backscatter diffraction (EBSD) technique. Texture of the investigated materials was additionally examined by using X-ray powder diffractometry (Bruker D8 diffractometer). Moreover, FEI TECNAI SuperTWIN G2 FEG (200 kV) combined with HAADF/ STEM/ EDAX attachments was used in order to support the analyses of the deformed microstructures conducted employing the EBSD method.

2.2. Biological properties

Adsorption of bovine fibronectin protein and bovine serum albumin was characterised by using the Qubit® Protein Assay Kit and Qubit® fluorometer, following the manufacturer's instruction. Statistical significance of the received protein concentrations was evaluated. Human umbilical vein endothelial cells (HUVECs) were studied in the cell-substrate interactions completed wholly in 72 hours. A confocal laser scanning microscope (CLSM) Exciter 5 AxioImager was implemented in order to reveal the cells' morphology and the extent of proliferation processes.

2.3. Physicochemical properties

An Innova commercial instrument, DSA 100 Krüss contact angle goniometer and a PHI VersaProbeII Scanning XPS system were utilized to carry out roughness, wettability and chemical composition measurements, respectively. The data obtained was analysed in regard to its statistical significance.

3. Results and discussion

3.1. Texture and microstructure

Generally, by undergoing plastic deformation via HE, the texture of a material is changed from the weak one to $(10\bar{1}0)$ fiber [10]. Within the present study, the grains analysed in the transverse cross-section of the final rod were oriented parallelly to the $(10\bar{1}0)$ planes, as seen in the inverse pole figure illustrated in Fig. 1a. On the other hand, the grains were distributed between (0001) (main maximum) and $(2\bar{1}\bar{1}0)$ planes, while considering the samples sliced so the longitudinal cross-section was observed (see Fig. 1e and f). Therefore, for convenience, Ti-$(10\bar{1}0)$ and Ti-(0001) designate the surfaces parallel to the transverse and longitudinal cross-sections of the investigated substrates, respectively.

The EBSD orientation map gathered from the Ti-$(10\bar{1}0)$ specimen is depicted in Fig. 1b. The microstructure consisted of wavy grains, both coarse and refined. The mean grain size was calculated to be 6.5 μm ± 5.7 μm, implying that a fraction of ultrafine-grains existed within the volume of a material. Contrarily, as seen from the EBSD orientation map collected from the Ti-(0001) sample and shown in Fig. 1f, the micro-grains were elongated in the extrusion direction, marked by a black arrow. Their mean grain size was estimated to be 12.8 μm ± 10.3 μm. A worth-mentioning discrepancy between the substrates was found in the value of high-angle grain boundaries (HAGBs) as the Ti-$(10\bar{1}0)$ demonstrated 20% higher density of HAGBs in comparison to the Ti-(0001). It indicates the Ti-$10\bar{1}0)$ surface to be more greatly enriched with structural defects.

The bright field (BF) images, seen in Fig. 1c and g, revealed that the Ti-(0001) and Ti-$(10\bar{1}0)$ were characterised by the presence of small grains, whose size lied within the sub-microcrystalline range. In addition, large grains were composed of sub-grains and exhibited high density of dislocations. The boundaries between adjacent grains were barely distinguishable, what implies a significant share of low-angle grain boundaries (LAGBs) in the material. The anisotropic microstructure of the investigated substrates is typical of most hydrostatically extruded metals. It is obvious that such property reflects on the mechanical strength of a material, what has already been proved [9,10].

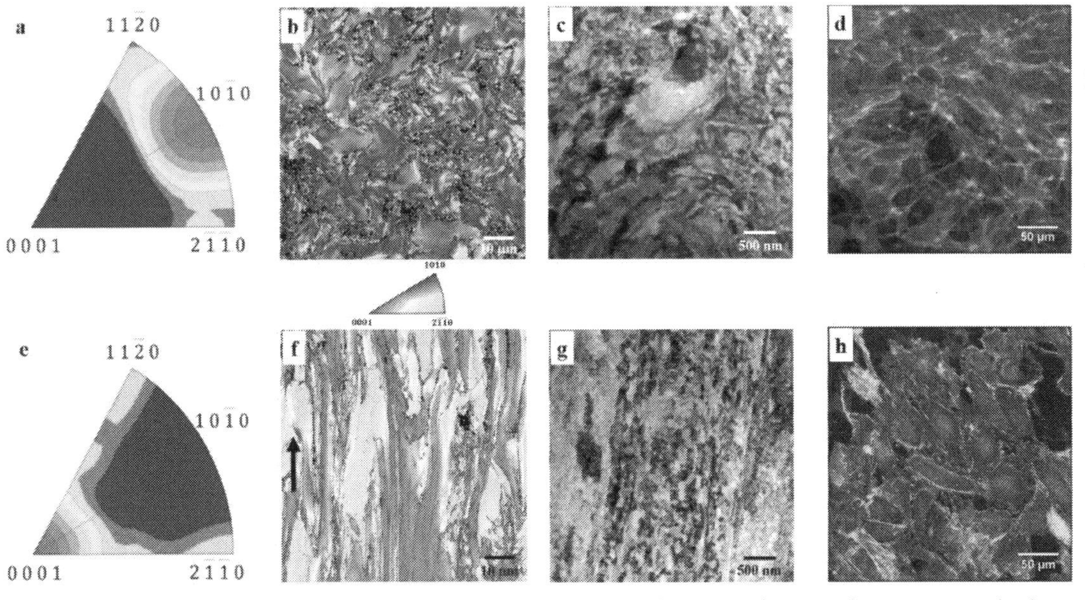

Fig. 1. (a), (b), (c) and (d) shows {001} IPF, EBSD map, TEM image and CLSM image, respectively, for the Ti-$(10\bar{1}0)$, (e), (f), (g), (h) shows {001} IPF, EBSD map, TEM image and CLSM image, respectively, for the Ti-(0001).

3.2. Biological properties

It should be expected that the Ti-($10\bar{1}0$) samples, having microstructures distinctly more refined with comparison to the Ti-(0001) ones, are those demonstrating superior biological properties. The CLSM image, taken for the Ti-($10\bar{1}0$) covered with HUVECs is displayed in Fig. 1e. The cells grew vividly on the entire surface, forming a few confluent monolayers. Both polygonal and flattened shapes of the cells may be easily viewed. The morphology of HUVECs attached to the Ti-(0001) is illustrated in Fig. 1h. Interestingly, the overwhelming majority of cells were positioned in a preferential manner and the active processes of filopodia forming could be observed. Possibly, the HUVECs were lined up with the [$10\bar{1}0$] crystallographic direction, overlapping with the extrusion direction. In addition, the elongated shape of cells differs greatly from those matured on the Ti-($10\bar{1}0$) specimens. Overall, the extent of proliferation is more noticeable for the Ti-($10\bar{1}0$) than for the Ti-(0001) substrates.

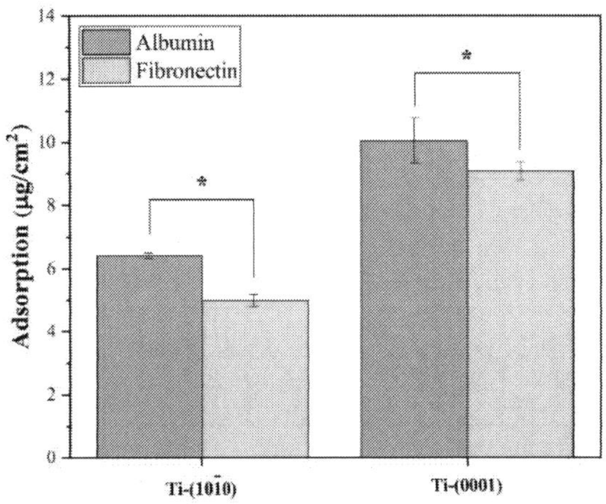

Fig. 2. Proteins adsorption on the surfaces of the investigated cross-sections. The asterisk sign stands for statistical significance between the probes ($p < 0.05$).

The adsorption of bovine fibronectin protein and bovine serum albumin on the surfaces of the analysed cross-sections is displayed in Fig. 2. Rather unexpectedly, the Ti-(0001) samples exhibited a clearly greater adsorption of both the examined proteins, although their cell-substrate response was less pronounced. The difference between the analysed probes was statistically significant ($p < 0.05$).

3.3. Physicochemical properties

Roughness and wettability data for the analysed substrates is listed in Table 1. The effect of surface properties on the biological performance of the hydrostatically extruded titanium should be fully discarded as the prepared specimens demonstrated mirror-finished surfaces of comparable nano-roughness and hydrophobicity (statistical insignificant differences, $p < 0.05$).

Table 1. Wettability and roughness of the examined cross-sections.

Cross-section	Water contact angle [°]	Roughness [nm]
Ti-($10\bar{1}0$)	76.9 ± 1.4	1.5 ± 0.4
Ti-(0001)	77.8 ± 0.7	1.8 ± 0.2

Table 2. The elements present on the characterised surfaces.

	C			O		Ca	Ti			
Energy [eV]	284.8	286.8	289.1	530.3	532.5	347.3	453.2	455.1	457.2	458.1
Groups/ Oxidation state	C-C	C-O	O=C-O	O_2^-	OH^-	Ca^{2+}	Ti(0)	Ti(II)	Ti(III)	Ti(IV)
Ti-$(10\bar{1}0)$	28.2	3.6	3.1	34.2	12.2	0.5	1.9	1.0	2.6	12.7
Ti-(0001)	36.1	4.0	3.6	27.9	13.0	1.0	0.5	0.3	1.8	11.8

A slight difference in chemical composition, shown in Table 2, could substantiate various protein adsorption among the examined cross-sections. It is also worth noticing that the thickness of the titania layer on the Ti-$(10\bar{1}0)$ surface was lower in comparison to that on the Ti-(0001) surface, although the same grinding and polishing procedures were implemented. The presence of carbon and calcium on the examined surfaces might stem from various contamination compounds, e.g., calcium carbonate or calcium oxide.

3.4. Texture-biological properties relationship

It is well-known that titanium strongly reacts with oxygen forming a thermodynamically stable, thick and well-adherent film on its surface. Thus, while investigating the biological performance of titanium and its alloys, it is the passive layer of titanium that is characterised, not the metal itself as designed biological environments are oxygen-containing [3].

In the present study, although the Ti-$(10\bar{1}0)$ substrates experienced superior grain refinement and cell proliferation than the Ti-(0001) ones, the adsorption of proteins was enhanced for the latter. Hence, it seems reasonable to state that the downscaled microstructure of titanium-based materials fabricated by the SPD techniques may not be the major factor governing their biological properties. However, its significance on cell-biomaterial interactions cannot be completely overlooked or rejected as biocompatibility of coarse-grained materials is generally unsatisfactory, therefore they cannot be readily used for medical applications.

The processes of protein adsorption, cell attachment and proliferation are dependent on the physicochemical nature of the surface [13]. Herein, the discrepancies in wettability and nanoscale roughness between the examined cross-sections were found to be negligible. Therefore, varied endothelial cell response may be attributed to the crystallographic orientation of grains as well as to diversified composition and conformation of the adsorbed proteins entangled with differences in the richness of nanostructured defects on the surface. As a matter of fact, proteins tend to conform differently if a surface of a material is covered with various structural defects, in the form of nano-grooves or nano-peaks [14]. Moreover, grain boundaries have shown to strongly influence preosteoblast cells activity on the surface of pure titanium produced by ECAP [7]. In addition, it has been demonstrated that the prismatic planes tend to be more susceptible to etching [13], thereby the surfaces of markedly greater biological activity could be produced.

On the other side, various adsorption of both the bovine fibronectin protein and bovine serum albumin on the characterised cross-sections could result from surface chemistry. It has been reported that the hydroxyl groups tend to modulate proteins to get adsorbed on the surface of a material [15]. In addition, the basal planes have shown to promote the accumulation of the OH^- moieties on the surface [8]. Within the present study, the amount of hydroxyl groups was substantially higher on the Ti-(0001) substrates and so was the protein concentration.

As shown, not only does titanium fabricated by the HE process demonstrate anisotropy of mechanical properties, but also its biological behaviour is anisotropic. To the authors' knowledge it is unclear, whether late-cell events, such as differentiation, are also affected by crystallographic orientation of grains, therefore such studies will be performed in the future.

4. Conclusions

Crystallographic orientation of grains combined with defects-enriched surface and its chemical composition has shown to strongly impact the biological behaviour of HE-manufactured pure titanium. The substrates having the prismatic planes exposed to the surface experienced superior grain refinement as well as more pronounced endothelial cells activity. Contrarily, the basal planes mediated the accumulation of hydroxyl groups on the surface of a material and favoured the adsorption of albumin and fibronectin, yet they were less refined.

References

[1] Bagherpour E, Pardis N, Reihanian M and Ebrahimi R 2019 An overview on severe plastic deformation: research status, techniques classification, microstructure evolution, and applications *Int. J. Adv. Manuf. Technol.*

[2] Valiev R Z, Estrin Y, Horita Z, Langdon T G, Zehetbauer M J and Zhu Y 2016 Producing Bulk Ultrafine-Grained Materials by Severe Plastic Deformation: Ten Years Later *Jom* **68** 1216–26

[3] Kubacka D, Yamamoto A, Wieciński P and Garbacz H 2019 Biological behavior of titanium processed by severe plastic deformation *Appl. Surf. Sci.* **472** 54–63

[4] Faghihi S, Azari F, Zhilyaev A P, Szpunar J A, Vali H and Tabrizian M 2007 Cellular and molecular interactions between MC3T3-E1 pre-osteoblasts and nanostructured titanium produced by high-pressure torsion *Biomaterials*

[5] Nie F L, Zheng Y F, Wei S C, Wang D S, Yu Z T, Salimgareeva G K, Polyakov A V. and Valiev R Z 2013 In vitro and in vivo studies on nanocrystalline Ti fabricated by equal channel angular pressing with microcrystalline CP Ti as control *J. Biomed. Mater. Res. - Part A* **101 A** 1694–707

[6] Reshadi F, Faraji G, Moghtaderi H and Faghihi S 2020 Surface and Bulk Modification of Titanium Grade 2 Substrates for Enhanced Biological Activity *Jom* **72** 721–9

[7] Lowe T C, Reiss R A, Illescas P E, Davis C F, Connick M C and Sena J A 2020 Effect of surface grain boundary density on preosteoblast proliferation on titanium *Mater. Res. Lett.*

[8] Hoseini M, Bocher P, Shahryari A, Azari F, Szpunar J A and Vali H 2014 On the importance of crystallographic texture in the biocompatibility of titanium based substrate *J. Biomed. Mater. Res. - Part A* **102** 3631–8

[9] Kawałko J, Wroński M, Bieda M, Sztwiertnia K, Wierzbanowski K, Wojtas D, Łagoda M, Ostachowski P, Pachla W and Kulczyk M 2018 Microstructure of titanium on complex deformation paths: Comparison of ECAP, KOBO and HE techniques *Mater. Charact.* **141** 19–31

[10] Wojtas D, Wierzbanowski K, Chulist R, Pachla W, Bieda-Niemiec M, Jarzębska A, Maj Ł, Kawałko J, Marciszko-Wiąckowska M, Wroński M and Sztwiertnia K 2020 Microstructure-strength relationship of ultrafine-grained titanium manufactured by unconventional severe plastic deformation process *J. Alloys Compd.* **837** 155576

[11] Jarzębska A, Bieda M, Kawałko J, Rogal, Koprowski P, Sztwiertnia K, Pachla W and Kulczyk M 2018 A new approach to plastic deformation of biodegradable zinc alloy with magnesium and its effect on microstructure and mechanical properties *Mater. Lett.* **211** 58–61

[12] Zhaohui Z and Fuchi W 2001 Research on the deformation strengthening mechanism of a tungsten heavy alloy by hydrostatic extrusion *Int. J. Refract. Met. Hard Mater.* **19** 177–82

[13] Baek S M, Shin M H, Moon J, Jung H S, Lee S A, Hwang W, Yeom J T, Hahn S K and Kim H S 2017 Superior pre-osteoblast cell response of etched ultrafine-grained titanium with a controlled crystallographic orientation *Sci. Rep.* **7** 1–10

[14] Lotz E M, Olivares-Navarrete R, Berner S, Boyan B D and Schwartz Z 2016 Osteogenic response of human MSCs and osteoblasts to hydrophilic and hydrophobic nanostructured titanium implant surfaces *J. Biomed. Mater. Res. - Part A* **104** 3137–48

[15] Thevenot P, Hu W and Tang L 2008 Surface chemistry influences implant biocompatibility. *Curr. Top. Med. Chem.*

IOP Conf. Series: Materials Science and Engineering 1121 (2021) 012039 doi:10.1088/1757-899X/1121/1/012039

Secondary Recrystallization of Grains with Cube Orientation for Pure Iron Tape

D Okai[1]*, A Yamamoto[1], T Doi[2] and H Adachi[1]

[1] 1Department of Materials and Synchrotron Radiation Engineering, Graduate School of Engineering, University of Hyogo, 2167 Shosha, Himeji 671–2280, Japan.

[2] Department of Energy Science and Technology, Graduate School of Energy Science, Kyoto University, Yoshida-honmachi, Sakyo-ku, Kyoto 606–8501, Japan.

E-mail:okai@eng.u-hyogo.ac.jp

Abstract. The formation mechanism of secondary recrystallized grains with cube orientation has been investigated for a pure iron tape prepared by a three-stage cold-rolling method. The crystal orientation before the final cold-rolling affected the appearance of secondary recrystallized grains with cube orientation. The $\{0\ \bar{1}\ 2\}\langle 1\ 0\ 0\rangle$ orientation before the final cold-rolling led to the formation of secondary recrystallized grains with cube orientation on the tape surface.

1. Introduction

Secondary recrystallization has been used for controlling the crystal orientation of silicon steel sheets. The secondary recrystallization of grains with {0 1 1}<1 0 0>, Goss orientation, is well known for silicon steel sheet with 3% silicon. The secondary recrystallized grains with Goss orientation align <1 0 0> axis of grains to parallel to the rolling direction (RD) for the silicon steel sheet, which is fabricated by rolling and annealing. Pure irons and silicon steels, which are soft magnetic materials, have anisotropy of magnetization. The <1 0 0> axis is the direction most easily magnetized as compared with the <1 1 0> and <1 1 1> axes [1]. The easily magnetization direction for the sheet with Goss orientation is one direction which is parallel to the RD on the sheet surface. On the other hand, the sheet with {0 0 1}<1 0 0>, cube orientation, has two easily magnetization directions on the sheet surface, which are parallel to the RD and the transverse direction (TD). The cube oriented silicon steel is attractive as a core material with a low iron loss in transformers. It is difficult to develop the cube orientation in silicon steel with a bcc structure. The fabrication of silicon steel sheet with cube orientation has been attempted by various methods based on rolling and annealing processes. The cube oriented silicon steel has been fabricated using a cross cold-rolling technique, which the silicon steel was rolled alternately along two perpendicular directions for the cross rolling process [2]. The cube oriented silicon steel has been prepared by the cross rolling of 3% Si steel containing AlN [3]. The 3% Si steel sheet with cube orientation has been fabricated by the manganese removal and decarburization of steel with a chemical composition of Fe-3Si-1.0Mn-0.05C [4].

From the viewpoint of manufacturing industrial products of the silicon steels with cube orientation, it is desirable to develop the cube orientation on the silicon steel sheet by the simplest method possible. It is important to clarify the mechanism of secondary recrystallization of the grains with cube orientation for metals with bcc structure. In this paper, the secondary recrystallization of grains with cube orientation has been reported for a pure iron tape prepared by a three-stage cold-rolling method. The pure iron with bcc structure was selected for investigating the essential mechanism of the secondary recrystallization in pure iron with few impurities. The initial orientation before final cold-rolling have been pointed to be important for development of secondary recrystallization of grain with cube orientation for the silicon steel [4]. The relationship between initial orientation before final cold-rolling and the secondary recrystallization of grains with cube orientation was investigated for the pure iron.

2. Experimental procedures

For the fabrication of iron tape with a cube orientation, an iron ingot was prepared by arc melting. The chemical composition of the iron metal used in this study is shown in Table 1. Rectangular rod specimen with dimensions of approximately W8× T12mm^2 was cut into from the iron ingot. For the third-stage cold-rolling process, the reduction rates in thickness were 15% for first rolling, 75% for second rolling and 92% for third rolling, which was final rolling. The annealings were performed at 1323K×10.8ks for the first intermediate-annealing, at 1473K×10.8ks for the second intermediate-annealing, and at 1163K×3.6ks for the final annealing. All of the annealings were performed in a vacuum. The thickness of tape fabricated is ca. 0.2mm. The surface of the iron tape was electropolished with a solution of perchloric acid and ethanol (= 1:9) for EBSD observation. The orientation of the iron tape was analyzed using an SEM-EBSD system (JEOL JSM-6360 equipped with a TSL MSC-2200 EBSD camera). The orientation characteristics of the iron tape were analyzed using TSL orientation imaging microscopy (OIM) analysis software (version 6.1).

Table 1. Chemical composition of pure iron used (mass%).

	C	P	S	Si	Mn	Cu	O	N	H	Fe
Pure iron	<0.0020	<0.0005	<0.0005	<0.0005	<0.0005	<0.0005	<0.0005	<0.0010	<0.0005	Bal.

3. Results

The {0 0 1} pole figure and IPF map for tape surface of the iron tape (sample-1) fabricated by the third-stage cold-rolling process are shown in Figure 1. The white and black lines in the IPF map denote low-angle grain boundaries with angles < 15°, and high-angle grain boundaries with angles ≥ 15°, respectively. The pole figure shows that the orientation of the tape surface is the cube orientation. The coarse grains with a grain size over ca. 1mm formed on the tape surface shown in Figure 1 (b). These results show that the secondary recrystallized grains with cube orientation forms on the tape surface of iron tape. The grain with cube orientation for secondary recrystallization grows in a vacuum atmosphere according to the following the growth rate (G) of grain for pure iron:

$$G = M\left(\frac{\gamma_B}{r} + \frac{2\Delta\gamma_s}{t}\right) \quad , \qquad (1)$$

where M, γ_B, r, $\Delta\gamma_s$ and t are the mobility of the grain boundary, the grain boundary energy, the average primary grain radius, the average difference in the surface energy (γ_S) between the {0 0 1} plane and the other {h k l} planes, and the tape thickness [5]. For the secondary crystallization of grains with cube orientation in a vacuum, the grains with {0 0 1} plane grow by the driving force of grain growth related to the grain boundary energy and the surface free energy of {0 0 1} plane, which is based on the $\Delta\gamma_s$ during the annealing in the vacuum atmosphere. Vacuum annealing leads to growth of grains with {0 0 1} orientation, because the surface energy of the {0 0 1} plane become low in vacuum atmosphere.

IOP Conf. Series: Materials Science and Engineering 1121 (2021) 012039 doi:10.1088/1757-899X/1121/1/012039

It has been pointed out that the cube orientation for secondary recrystallization is related to orientation of tape surface before final cold-rolling. The crystal rotation for specimen with the orientation of {0 1 2}<1 0 0> and {0 1 4}<1 0 0> by the final rolling and annealing results in the formation of cube orientation on the sheet surface for the Fe-3%Si sheets [4, 6]. The cube oriented pure iron tape was fabricated by the final rolling and annealing of the specimen with an orientation of $\{\bar{2}\ \overline{11}\ 26\}\langle 31\ \bar{8}\ 1\rangle$ shown in Figure 2. The $(\bar{2}\ \overline{11}\ 26)$ plane is a near-$(0\ \bar{1}\ 2)$ plane with a misorientation of ca. 5° from the $(0\ \bar{1}\ 2)$ plane. The crystal rotation occurred by final cold-rolling and annealing for the pure iron tape, which is the crystal rotation from $\{0\ \bar{1}\ 2\}$ <1 0 0> to {0 0 1} <1 0 0>, is similar to those for the Fe-3%Si sheets.

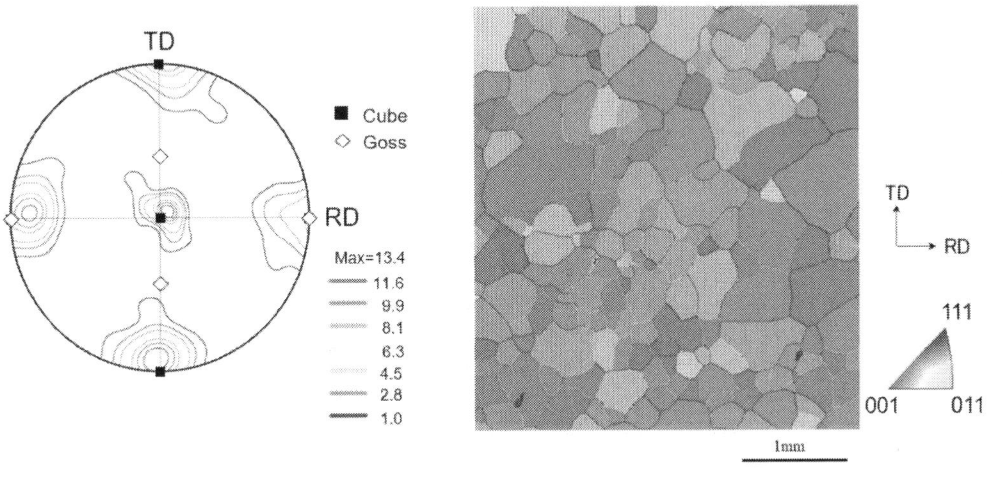

(a) (b)

Figure 1. (a) {0 0 1} pole figure and (b) IPF map for tape surface of iron tape (sample-1) fabricated by the three-stage cold-rolling method.

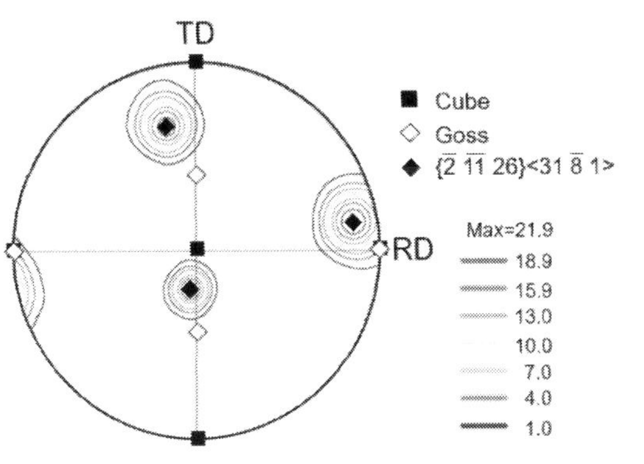

Figure 2. {0 0 1} pole figure for pure iron tape (sample-1) before final cold-rolling.

IOP Conf. Series: Materials Science and Engineering 1121 (2021) 012039 doi:10.1088/1757-899X/1121/1/012039

An iron tape (sample-2) was fabricated by the cold-rolling and annealing of the specimen with an orientation of γ-fibers shown in Figure 3, which are ND//<4 5 6> and ND//<2 1 1>. The cold-rolling with a reduction rate in thickness of 89% and annealing at 1073K×3.6ks in a vacuum were performed for the specimen. The {1 1 1} pole figure and IPF map for tape surface of the iron tape (sample-2) fabricated are shown in Figure 4. The recrystallized grains with an orientation of γ-fiber (ND//<1 1 1>) grew on the tape surface. The grains with a grain size of less than 300μm formed on the tape surface. For the specimen with the orientation of γ-fibers before the cold-rolling, the origin of grains with cube orientation for secondary recrystallization is unlikely to be formed in the rolled structure of iron tape. These results show that the crystal orientation before final cold-rolling affects the formation of secondary recrystallized grains with cube orientation. In the secondary recrystallization for pure iron, the $\{0\ \bar{1}\ 2\}$<1 0 0> orientation before cold-rolling resulted in the formation of origin of grains with cube orientation in the rolled structure of the tape. The origin of grains with cube orientation grows to secondary recrystallized grains mainly by a driving force of the surface free energy of {0 0 1} plane under the vacuum annealing.

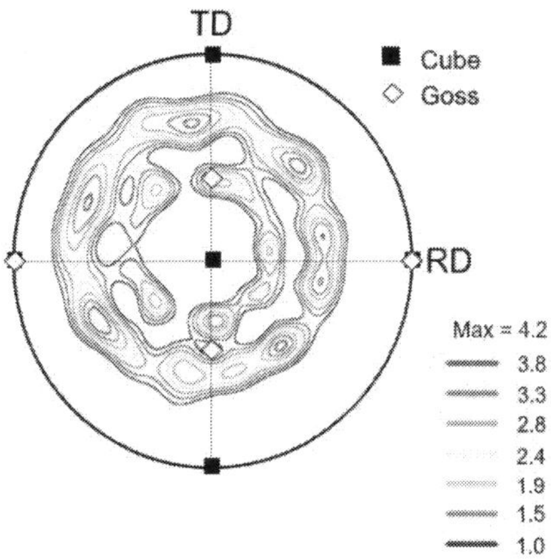

Figure 3. {0 0 1} pole figure for specimen (sample-2) of pure iron before cold-rolling.

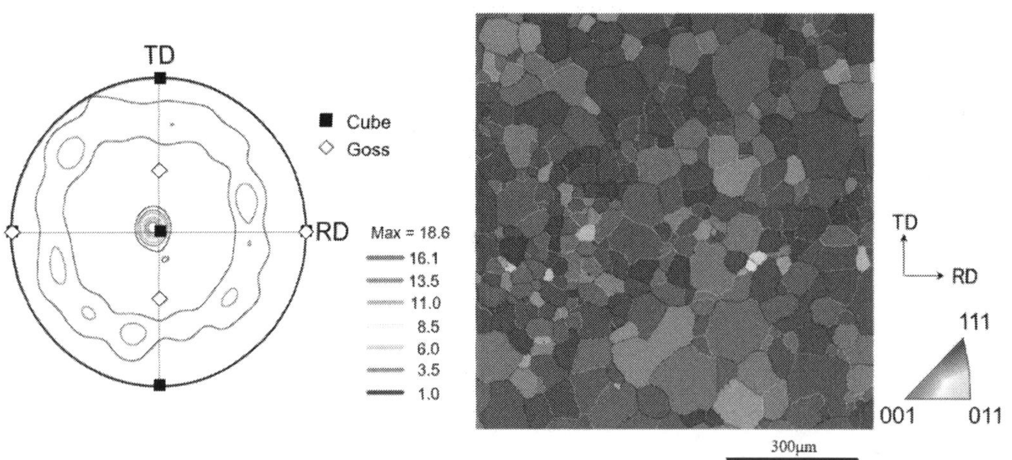

(a) (b)

Figure 4. (a) {1 1 1} pole figure and (b) IPF map for tape surface of iron tape (sample-2) fabricated by the cold-rolling and annealing of specimen with the orientation of γ-fibers of ND//<4 5 6> and ND//<2 1 1>.

4. Conclusion

The formation mechanism of secondary recrystallized grains with cube orientation was investigated for a pure iron tape prepared by the three-stage cold-rolling method. The crystal orientation before the final cold-rolling affected the appearance of secondary recrystallized grains with cube orientation. The $\{0\ \bar{1}\ 2\}\langle 1\ 0\ 0\rangle$ orientation before the final cold-rolling led to the formation of secondary recrystallized grains with cube orientation on the tape surface.

Acknowledgments

This work was supported partly by the JFE Steel 21st Century Foundation.

References

[1] Honda K and Kaya S 1926 *Sci. Rep. Tohoku Imp. Univ.* **15** 721
[2] Fiedler H C 1977 IEEE Trans. Magn. **13** 1433
[3] Sakai T *et al* 1984 Tetsu-to-Hagané **70** 2049
[4] Tomida T *et al* 2003 *Mater. Trans.* **44** 1106
[5] Foster K *et al* 1963 *Trans. Metall. AIME* **227** 185
[6] Walter J L and Hibbard W R 1958 *Trans. Metall. AIME* **212** 731

Evolution of recrystallization texture for Cu-30%Zn alloy sheets with high Young's modulus in the transverse direction

Hirofumi Inoue[1], Fumito Ituchi[2] and Tetsuo Cho[2]

[1] Department of Materials Science, Graduate School of Engineering, University Public Corporation Osaka, Osaka Prefecture University, Sakai, Japan

[2] Department of Materials Science, College of Engineering, University Public Corporation Osaka, Osaka Prefecture University, Sakai, Japan

The corresponding author's e-mail address: inoue@mtr.osakafu-u.ac.jp

Abstract. Miniaturization of electric connecters with higher stability in the coupling force is demanded as components of electric vehicles. Copper alloys are attractive materials from the perspective of electric conductivity. It is considered that Brass orientations {110}<112> has high Young's modulus along the transverse direction (TD) since the Young's moduli of copper single crystals show a maximum value at the <111> direction. The authors could successfully develop the near-Brass orientation in TD of the annealed sheets by performing additional warm rolling at a low reduction in thickness for cold rolled Cu-30% Zn alloy (brass) sheets with material cost lower than pure copper. The near-Brass recrystallization texture with a main component {110}<223> showed maximum orientation density after annealing at 723 K when warm rolling was performed at 623 K. In addition, we discussed the mechanism of the recrystallization texture evolution for Cu-30% Zn alloy sheets, which were subjected to the combined rolling consisting of cold and warm rolling using a conventional rolling mill and subsequently annealed at 723 K, in view of annealing twinning in the early stage of recrystallization.

1. Introduction

Miniaturization of electronic devices is proceeding in recent years. Materials with good properties of the strength, conductivity, bendability and stress relaxation resistance, and so on are demanded for electric connecters. Among the copper alloys for connecters, solid solution strengthening Cu-Zn alloys are low costs as raw materials and conventionally used for automobiles. Recently a Cu-Zn alloy for onboard connecters are developed and it is reported that it has good stress relaxation resistance [1]. A strong coupling force is required as copper alloys for connecters and therefore materials with high Young's moduli are promising. However it is difficult to greatly increase the Young's moduli by adding a small amount of alloy elements.

The Young's modulus of copper single crystals shows great dependence on crystallographic orientation. It is known that the maximum value is the <111> direction (205.9 GPa) about three times higher than the minimum one of <100> (66.7 GPa) [2]. The authors have recently reported that for cold rolled and asymmetrically warm rolled Cu-30%Zn alloy sheets the recrystallization texture has the {011}<322> main components close to Brass orientations {011}<211> after annealing [3]. In the

IOP Conf. Series: Materials Science and Engineering 1121 (2021) 012040 doi:10.1088/1757-899X/1121/1/012040

case of the Brass orientations, the Young's modulus in the transvers direction (TD) perpendicular to the rolling direction (RD) is a maximum, namely TD//<111>. Since in polycrystalline metals the properties are leveled by individual grains, they cannot reach those of copper single crystals. However there is a possibility that high Young's modulus in TD of Cu-30%Zn alloy sheets is obtained. It is shown in the previous study [3] that asymmetric rolling is related to the asymmetry with respect to TD in rolling texture, and that the recrystallization texture of the annealed sheets is affected by warm rolling temperature. Since the Brass orientations {011}<211> are symmetrical with respect to TD, (symmetric) warm rolling is performed instead of asymmetric warm rolling, and if the <111> direction in TD can be strongly developed for the annealed sheets, a great increase in the Young's modulus of TD is possible. In the present study, the Cu-30%Zn alloys were cold rolled, warm rolled and subsequently annealed. The Brass orientations symmetrical with respect to TD in the annealed sheets were developed by recrystallization annealing, and the influence of warm rolling temperature on the recrystallization texture and the Young's modulus was investigated. The recrystallization textures were quantitatively analyzed by orientation distribution functions (ODFs). Using data of the Young's modulus in copper single crystals, a change in the Young's modulus of the 90° direction (TD) at warm rolling temperature for annealed sheets was predicted from ODFs and compared with the experimental result. In addition, a change in recrystallization texture at 623 K warm rolling, where was the most favorable for the Young's modulus, was investigated in the early stage of recrystallization by EBSD, and then the evolution of the recrystallization texture through annealing twins has been discussed in this paper.

2. Experimental

The annealing condition we adopted the recrystallization-completed temperature and time which were measured in the micro-Vickers hardness test. Hereinafter, a cold rolled and annealed sheet, and cold and warm rolled and annealed sheets are called the CR sample, and the WR samples, respectively.

Four Pole figures of {111}, {200}, {220} and {311} are measured in the mid-thickness of the sheets at tilt angles of ϕ = 15°-90° with a step of 5° by CuKα radiation using Schultz reflection method [4], and then the ODFs were calculated by the iterative series expansion method [5]. In preparation of the specimens for pole figure measurements, they were carefully polished to the #1500 water-proof paper, not to enter the strain by mechanical grinding.

By using the resonance method at room temperature, the Young's moduli were measured specimens with a size of 50 mm in length and 8 mm in width cut out from the annealed sheets, and the in-plane anisotropy of the Young's moduli were investigated along three directions of 0° (RD), 45° and 90° (TD) to RD. In addition, the Young's moduli in 90° direction were predicted from the calculated ODFs using the Voigt and Reuss methods, and the Hill approximation which their arithmetic mean is [6,7]. The predicted results were compared with the measured values. To discuss the evolution of recrystallization texture, the annealing twins were observed by the EBSD analysis in the RD-ND section (the TD plane).

3. Results and Discussion

3.1 Texture. In the cold rolled sheet, the rolling texture showed the alloy type (α-fiber) with Brass orientations as main components. In the sheets cold rolled and warm rolled at temperatures higher than 623 K, pure-metal type (β-fiber) rolling texture was observed other than the α-fiber. This is a similar effect to cold rolled metals with a high staking fault energy (SFE). When these rolled sheets were recrystallization-annealed, in the CR sample a conventional alloy type recrystallization texture consisting mainly of the {236}<385> orientations close to {113}<121> was formed as main components (Fig. 1(a)). On the other hand, as seen in the ODFs of the WR samples (Fig. 1(b)-1(c)), the recrystallization texture consisting mainly of the (110)[2-23] (about the 8° angle difference with the Brass orientation, φ_1 = ~43°, Φ = 90°, φ_2 = 45°) close to the Brass orientation (110)[1-12] was observed with a spread around the ND//<110> axis. The orientation components of the β-fiber were observed other than this orientation were observed. This corresponds to the transition of rolling texture from the α-fiber to the β-fiber. Although a reason that the {011}<322> orientations are developed is not clear, by performing warm rolling after cold rolling, the orientations close to Brass orientations present in both the α-fiber and the β-fiber are main components of the recrystallization texture.

3.2 Young's modulus. Figure 2 shows rolling temperature dependence of the Young's modulus in annealed sheets. The Young's modulus in the 90° direction (TD) for the WR samples increased greatly. It was the highest at 623 K warm rolling and decreased as the rolling temperature was raised further. In the 0° (RD) and 45° directions, it is not so much changed from the CR sample compared to that in the 90° direction. Since this will be related to a change in recrystallization texture by warm rolling which is conducted after cold rolling. The maximum orientation density in the {011}<322> orientation (φ_1 = 40°, Φ = 45°, φ_2 = 0°) was determined. As shown in Fig. 3, there is a clear correlation between the {011}<322> orientation density and the Young's modulus in TD. It is concluded that 623 K warm rolling is the most effective in increasing the Young's modulus in TD. It is considered that the transition from alloy type (α-fiber) to pure-metal type (β-fiber) occurred since deformation by cross slips are possible on heating in the furnace during warm rolling. This corresponds to raising stacking fault energy (SFE). It is unclear whether the SFE was really raised at rolling temperatures not less than 573 K. In austenitic stainless steel sheets, it is known that the transition from alloy type to pure-metal type occurs as rolling temperature rises [8]. It is considered that a similar phenomenon occurred even in Cu-30%Zn alloy.

3.3 Prediction of the Young's modulus from ODF. Recrystallized polycrystalline metals are composed of many grains with various orientations. Since there is a possibility that texture components other than the {011}<322> orientations affect the Young's moduli, they was predicted from ODFs.

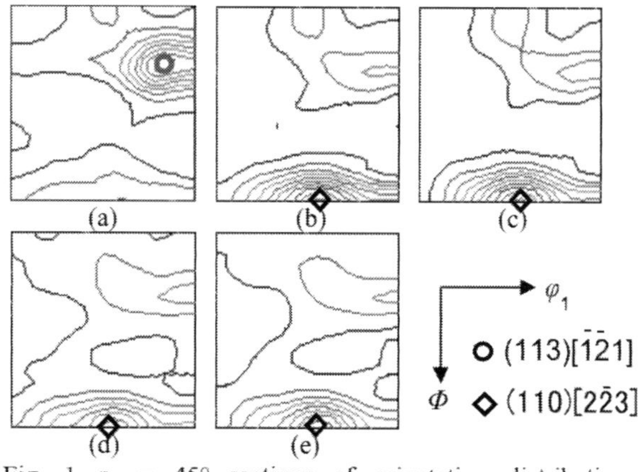

Fig. 1 φ_2 = 45° sections of orientation distribution functions for Cu-30%Zn alloy sheets, (a) cold-rolled, (b-e) cold-rolled and warm-rolled at (b) 573 K, (c) 623 K, (d) 673 K and (e) 723 K, and subsequently annealed for 1.8 ks at 723 K. Contour levels are 0.5 to 5.0 at a step of 0.5.

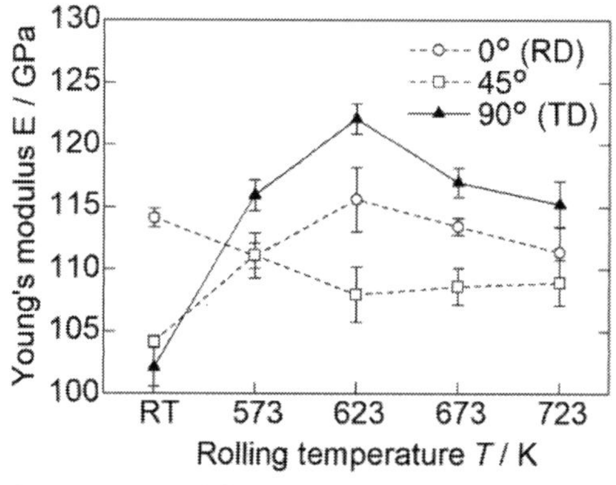

Fig. 2 Young's moduli at 0°, 45° and 90° directions for annealed Cu-30%Zn alloy sheets as a function of rolling temperature.

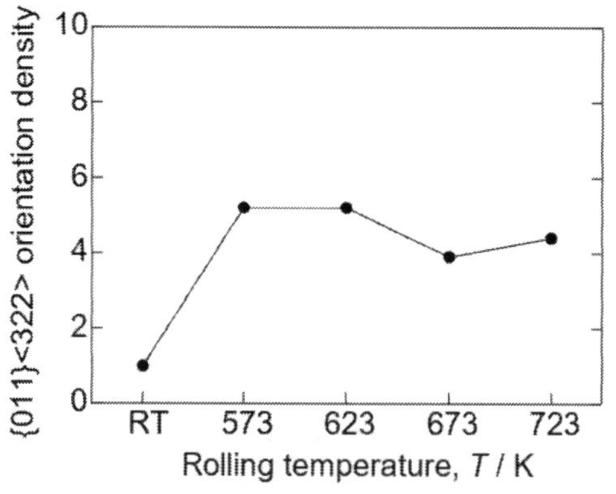

Fig. 3 Orientation density at {011}<322> orientation (φ_1 = 40°, Φ = 45°, φ_2 = 0°) for annealed Cu-30%Zn alloy sheets as a function of rolling temperature.

Figure 4 shows the calculated and measured results. The measured values are closer to the Reuss method than the Hill method. We used copper single crystals' data instead of Cu-30%Zn alloy. Since zinc (48 GPa [9]) with a lower value than copper (129.8 GPa [10]) is contained 30%, the Young's modulus prediction of Cu-Zn alloys (brass, 103 GPa [10]) with the same face-cantered cubic structure is necessary to quantitatively consider the Zn content. However, a qualitative tendency of the predicted value, on the whole, corresponds to the measured value. It is suggested that the prediction of the Young's modulus as a function of rolling temperature is possible. A large number of future problems such that the reduction of the Young's modulus at 723 K and the distribution condition of the Zn content in the thickness direction are present. Fig. 5 Rolling and recrystallization textures for cold-rolled and additionally warm-rolled Cu-30%Zn sheets and only cold-rolled ones.

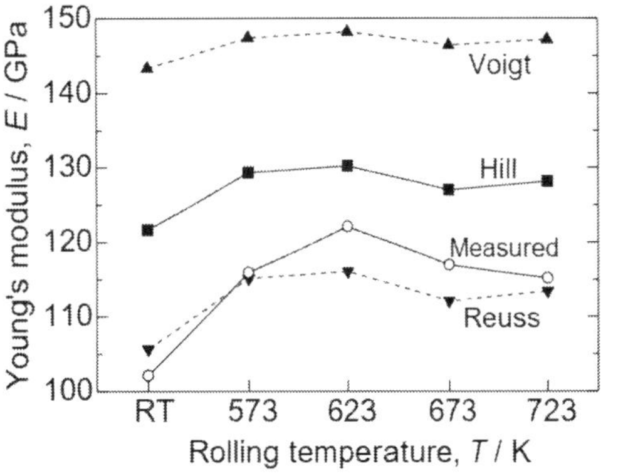

Fig. 4 Calculated and measured Young's moduli at a 90° direction for annealed Cu-30%Zn alloy sheets as a function of rolling temperature.

3.4 Effect of warm rolling on recrystallization texture. Rolling and recrystallization textures of the sample 85% cold rolled and 40% warm rolled at 623 K (the WR sample), and 91% cold rolled sample (the CR sample) are shown in Fig. 5. The rolling textures are nearly the same, but their recrystallization textures are quite different.

It is possible that the recrystallization texture is changed by adding warm rolling with a low reduction. Texture control is a very effective means to change material properties with large anisotropy in single crystals such as the Young's modulus. A reason for preferred orientations of {011}<322> close to Brass orientations as main components of the recrystallization texture is unclear at present. As this reason, since two equivalent Brass orientation variants have a twin relationship each other, it is considered that annealing twins of the Brass orientations are formed and grown when recrystallized nuclei of the Brass orientations grow to recrystallized grains. Although the rolling textures are similar to each other, this explains the different recrystallization textures well after recrystallization was completed. Adding warm rolling leads to slip deformation and recovery. Alloy type rolling texture (α-fiber) consisting mainly of the Brass orientations, which will form annealing twins in partial regions and will grow to recrystallized grains. The mechanism of the {011}<322> recrystallization texture evolution is investigated using EBSD analysis.

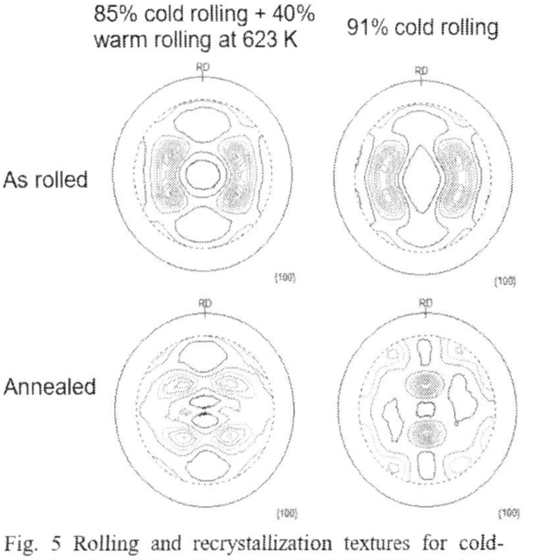

Fig. 5 Rolling and recrystallization textures for cold-rolled and additionally warm-rolled Cu-30%Zn sheets and only cold-rolled ones.

IOP Conf. Series: Materials Science and Engineering 1121 (2021) 012040 doi:10.1088/1757-899X/1121/1/012040

3.5 Discussion for the {011}<322> recrystallization texture evolution. A change in hardness with recrystallization annealing (softening curve) was measured. The results showed a large change in hardness when the samples were heated to 723 K. Therefore it is considered that softening occurs at 723 K heating. To observe a change in orientation in the early stage of recrystallization, microstructures of 723 K-12 s and 723 K-15 s annealed samples were investigated by EBSD measurements, as time condition is 0 s when samples were entered in the furnace of 723 K holding. The results were shown in Figure 6. The Brass orientations {011}<211> and the near-Brass {011}<322> orientations clearly increased with increasing annealing time. The Ishii et al. [3] mentioned that the near-Brass orientations were developed through asymmetric warm rolling after cold rolling. The effect of asymmetric rolling (additional shear deformation) contributed to only the slight asymmetry with respect to TD of pole figure. The (symmetric) warm rolling was expected to occur the transition of rolling texture, and it is considered to contribute to the evolution of the near-Brass orientations. As described in the reference [3], it is suggested that this is related to the twin relationship. An orientation change from the Brass orientations {011}<211> to the near-Brass {011}<322> orientations was observed, as shown in Figure 6. This is suggested that an orientation change which leads to grain boundaries migration in grain growth during primary recrystallization (a rotation around the <011> axis due to the twin relationship is considered.) As a result, the {011}<322> recrystallization texture with a wide spread would be formed by longer time (1.8 ks) annealing. The volume fractions of the Brass orientations and the near-Brass orientations {011}<322> obtained from EBSD analysis are shown in Figure 7. It is clear that these orientations increased with an increasing annealing time for any orientation. In other words, it is suggested that the nucleation of the Brass orientation {011}<211> and thereafter the evolution of {011}<322> orientations may be attributed to the formation of annealing twins with high order.

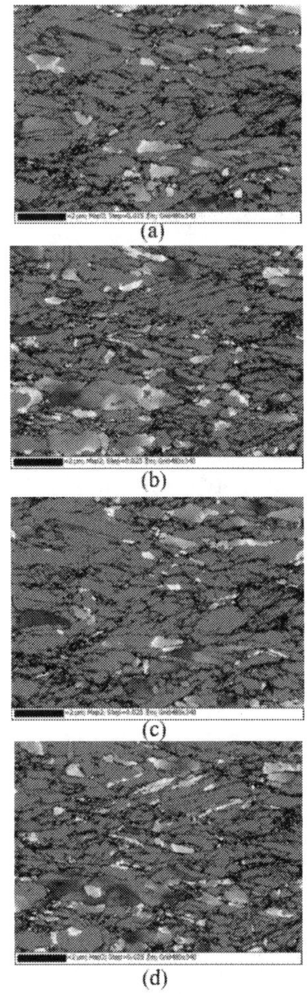

Fig. 6 Changes in grain with an increase of annealing time. (a, b) {011}<211> and (c, d) {011}<322> orientations. (a, c) a 12 s annealed sample and (b, d) a 15 s annealed one.

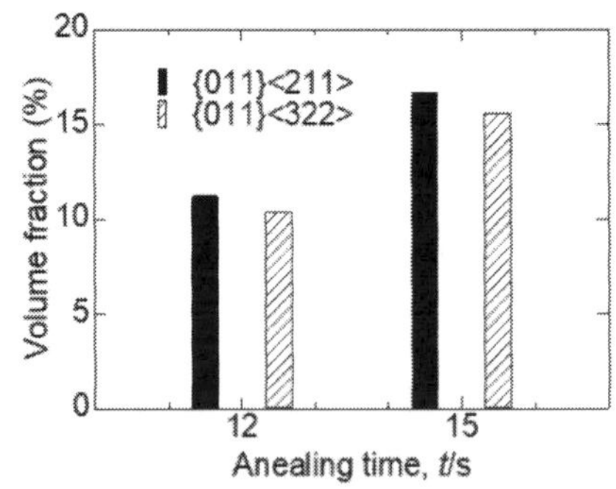

Fig. 7 Change in volume fraction of each oriented grain in the early stages of recrystallization.

4. Conclusions

Cu-30%Zn alloys were cold rolled to a high reduction in thickness and warm rolled to a low reduction. The relationship between recrystallization texture and the Young's modulus was investigated, and the mechanism of recrystallization texture evolution was discussed. The results obtained in this study are as follows:

(1) By performing warm rolling at temperatures more than 573 K for a cold rolled Cu-30%Zn alloy sheet, the recrystallization texture consisting mainly of the {011}<322> orientations was obtained for the annealed sheet.

(2) Through the evolution of the above recrystallization texture, the Young's modulus in TD was greatly increased. The WR sample warm rolled to 40% reduction at 623 K showed a relatively high Young's modulus of 122 GPa.

(3) A change in the Young's modulus with warm rolling temperature can be qualitatively predicted from the ODFs for cold rolled, warm rolled and annealed sheets.

(4) An increase in volume fraction of annealing twins in each oriented grain was observed in the early stages of recrystallization.

Acknowledgements

The authors are grateful to the Furukawa electric Co., Ltd for preparing the starting materials of Cu-30%Zn hot rolled alloy sheets with 10 mm thick. The present study was partly carried out by the 2019 grant of the Japan Copper and Brass Association. The authors express a sincere appreciation.

References

[1] Mori H., Maki K. and Yamasita D.: Materia 53 (2014), 69-71.
[2] Karashima S.: *Strenghth of Metals and Alloys*, Japan Inst. Met (1972) 6.
[3] Ishi Y. and Inoue H: Copper and copper alloys 56 (2017), 51-55.
[4] Schluz L G.: J. Appl.Phys. 20 (1949), 1030-1033.
[5] Inoue H. and Inakazu N. : J. Japan Inst. Met 58 (1994), 892-898.
[6] Bunge H. J.: *Texture Analysis in Materials Science*, Translated by Morris, Butterworths, (1982), 321-327.
[7] Inoue H. and Iwata J.: Copper and copper alloys 50 (2011), 204-209..
[8] Goodman S. R. and Hu H.: Trans. Metall. Soc. AIME 230 (1964), 1413-1419.
[9] Koide S.: *Phyics*, Syokabou (2003), 89.
[10] Takano K.: *How to Choose and Use Plastic Materials for prevent Trouble*, Kogyo Chosakai Publishing Co., Ltd. (2005), 61.

IOP Conf. Series: Materials Science and Engineering 1121 (2021) 012041 doi:10.1088/1757-899X/1121/1/012041

Stereological analysis of triple line orientations

B J Schuessler[1,2], **D P Field**[1]

[1] School of Mechanical and Materials Engineering, Washington State University, Pullman WA 99164, USA
[2] Pacific Northwest National Laboratory, 902 Battelle Boulevard, Richland WA 99354, USA

Corresponding Author: benjamin.schuessler@wsu.edu

Abstract. Determining underlying interface geometries in polycrystalline materials is a daunting task and one that is an ongoing field of materials research. This work utilizes a method of determining structural anisotropy through stereological methods. The orientations of simulated triple-lines were characterized by analysing intersections of the triple-lines on randomly orientated planar sections in a given volume. Using randomly oriented sections, the triple-line orientation distribution, $L_V(\varphi,\theta)$, can be estimated. After approximately 10-100 sections, the true triple-line orientations can be determined with reasonable accuracy. The stereological method proposed is being used to show how it may be useful to the characterization of triple junction character in a real material system. The efficacy of the method was discussed along with considerations to reducing the overall variance in the distributions as well as applying the stereological procedures to real polycrystalline triple junction networks.

1. Introduction

In materials science, the polycrystalline triple junction has often been neglected as a studied microstructural feature. Since triple junctions are inherently three-dimensional objects, studying the geometry usually results in a disregard of the spatial orientation and underlying geometries. There have been many ways of stereologically determining the spatial arrangement and orientation of lineal features [1–3] in three-dimensions by quantifying line-length per unit volume (L_V), but there has been relatively little mention of using these methods to study triple junctions in polycrystalline systems. In the 1960's Hilliard presented a stereological method for extracting the orientation of lineal features embedded in an arbitrary volume [4–6] which bares resemblance to Buffon's needle experiment [7]. Hilliard's work had stated that when randomly sectioning a given volume, the distribution of the number of intersections (N_A) of the lineal features on the oriented section can be used to estimate the total line-length per unit volume, L_V. Utilizing the relationship between the probabilities of a section intersecting a lineal feature and the orientation of the lineal feature, a distribution of line orientations, $L_V(\varphi,\theta)$, can be measured. This distribution will give some indication of the anisotropy of interfaces in a volume.

Determining the 3D structure of materials is an on-going and continuously advancing science. Being able to characterize the total area of interfaces or understand grain boundary character in polycrystalline systems is extremely useful to the design of materials [8–11]. Knowing the total length of interfaces such as fibers in composites or triple junctions in polycrystals would be of great importance to modeling and study of the structure-properties-performance of a material. It is generally understood that the orientation of triple junctions with respect to an observed free surface has an impact on properties such as recrystallization, grain growth, precipitation and various mechanical properties [12–16]. However, the actual orientation of the triple junction geometry is difficult to determine, making the study of structure-property-performance effects of triple junctions cumbersome.

While there are methods of gathering three-dimensional information of interfaces in a material, i.e. X-ray chromatography (CT), micro-CT, atomic probe tomography (APT) or high-energy diffraction microscopy (HEDM), these methods can be timely and/or costly to use and tend to be limited by small sample sizes. The use of stereology has been employed for relatively large samples and can be used readily to extract statistical and geometrical information about a given material. The grain boundary character distribution (GBCD) is widely studied in polycrystalline materials using stereological methods [10,17–20]. Since most forms of crystallographic information come in two-dimensional forms like electron backscatter diffraction (EBSD), the use of stereology to characterize interfaces become easier to manage experimentally. However, applications of stereological methods to characterization of triple junctions has been slow to develop. While some researchers have used stereological methods to study specific types of triple junctions [21], most common forms of triple junction characterization are done by observing the available information from a single two-dimensional section [8,10,16,22–24], neglecting the underlying three-dimensional information, which was acceptable for the given application. If the underlying geometrical information is desired, then additional methods that provide statistically viable datasets must be developed.

The purpose of this work is to shed light on the efficacy of determining $L_V(\varphi,\theta)$ and whether the stereological method can be applicable to material interfaces. Simulations of the method are done using multiple geometrical scenarios. The results of the stereological simulations indicate that it is possible to measure the orientation distributions of the triple junction interface, with some limitations. The type of feature geometries and the number of cuts through the volume that are needed to reliably extract the orientations of lineal features affect the efficacy of the stereological method.

2. Methods

Using a spherical reference frame, the set of coordinates (φ,θ) will represent the polar and azimuthal angles of the triple-line orientation or "line sense". The section, which is used to intersect the volume with the embedded triple junctions, will be defined by a plane with a set of spherical coordinates (ω,ψ) and a centroid P_0. The specification of $L_V(\varphi,\theta)$ according to Hilliard is

$$L_V = \int_0^{\pi}\int_0^{\pi} L_V(\phi,\theta)\sin\phi \, d\phi d\theta \quad (1)$$

It is assumed that randomly oriented sets of triple-lines have uniform density of the surface of the reference hemisphere, thus the result from Eq. 1 shows that for uniform density $L_V(\phi,\theta) = L_V/2\pi$ [5]. The full derivation of the method can be found in [5] but, for the sake of brevity, we will present only the most pertinent equation that provides the basis for the stereological procedure which was used in this analysis.

To test this hypothesis, synthetic microstructures and triple junction geometries were generated via the open-source Dream.3D microstructure analysis software [25]. Information of grain interfaces were exported and custom routines to reconstruct the triple junction networks were created in MATLAB R2019a.

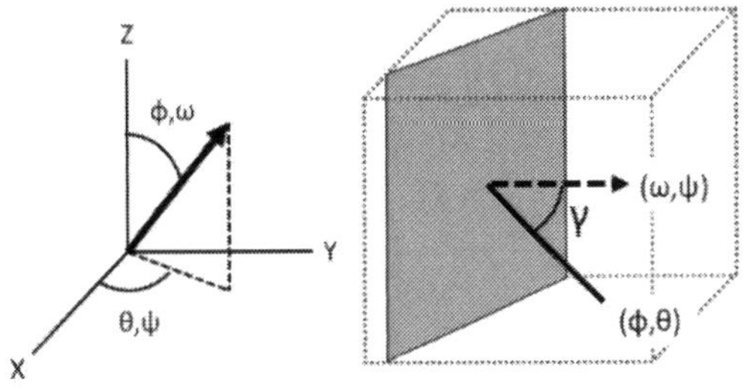

Figure 1: (Left) The reference frames for the orientation of the triple-line and the normal to the section. (Right) The interaction geometry of a planar section with a simple lineal feature. The angle between the section normal (ω,ψ) to the line sense (φ,θ) is γ. The number of intersections in this example is $N_A = 1$.

A point P_0 was defined in the bounds of the volume with randomly chosen normal angles (ω,ψ) used to define a section centered on P_0. The number of intersections the plane makes with the triple-line network were counted and subsequently divided by the area of the section. The result would be a section plane with polar angles (ω,ψ) = (φ,θ), and intensity of N_A/A, where A is the area of the section. After a user-defined number of section planes, a harmonic representation of $N_A(\omega,\psi)$, the number of sections per unit area, can be made and normalized by $1/2\pi$ to estimate line-length per unit volume $L_V(\varphi,\theta)$.

The open-source crystallographic analysis package MTEX [26] for MATLAB was used to estimate $N_A(\omega,\psi)$ and $L_V(\varphi,\theta)$ and to visualize the orientation distributions. All distributions were estimated using spherical harmonics up to order $M = 8$. All distributions are observed with respect to the Z-axis with the X-axis to the east and Y-axis to the north.

3. Results

To test the efficacy of the solution, simple geometries were first tested to see if the method was able to extract the orientation of a single triple-line. Figure 2 presents three simple geometries of triple-lines. A series of section planes were made through the volume and N_A was calculated.

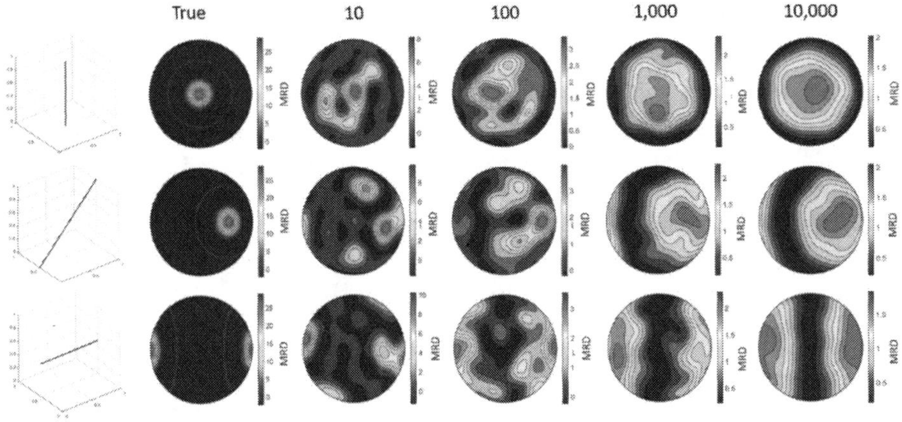

Figure 2: Line length per unit volume density distributions for a single lineal feature in differing orientations. Each column corresponds to the number of sections used in Hilliard's stereological method. Between 10-100 sections, the orientation of the lineal feature could be extracted with 1,000 sections showing a distinct peak in the distribution corresponding to the correct orientation.

For each case of line geometry, 10-100,000 sections were made. After ~10-100 sections the appearance of peaks formed in close proximity to the true line orientation. Smoothing of the orientation distribution can be seen after 1,000 sections with 100,000 sections resulting in a uniform Gaussian like distribution centered at the location of the true line orientation.

IOP Conf. Series: Materials Science and Engineering 1121 (2021) 012041 doi:10.1088/1757-899X/1121/1/012041

Studying an increasingly complex system of triple-lines, Figure 3, a grouping of straight lines were created at random locations and orientations within a unit volume. After repeating the same stereological procedure as before it appears that 100 sections through the volume was enough to extract the orientation of the random set of features. It should be noted that the resolution of the $L_V(\varphi,\theta)$ is dependent on the harmonic order used. In the MTEX analysis software, the distribution of N_A was first estimated using a harmonic approximation up to order M=8, followed by convoluting the harmonic estimation with spherical de la Valle Poussin kernel of halfwidth 10°.

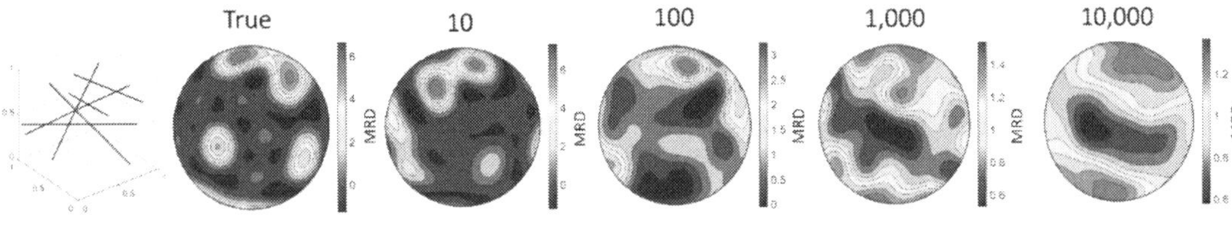

Figure 3: A selection of randomly oriented lineal features in a unit volume. L_V distributions indicate that between 100-1000 sections, the orientations of the lineal features were able to be extracted. Hilliard's stereological method appears to work for increasingly complex geometries of lineal features.

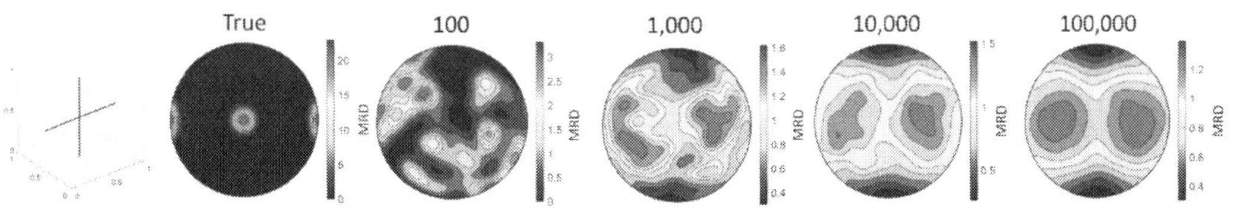

Figure 4: A geometry of lineal features that was not able to be resolved through stereological procedures. Peaks were shifted ~45° about the y-axis. The location of the peaks after 1,000 slices indicate that there are certain geometries of lineal features that may not be accessible via Hilliard's stereological procedure.

The stereological method has additional drawbacks, however. Presented in Figure 4 is a case where the geometry of the triple-lines was not able to be accurately determined. Two lines perpendicular to each other and intersecting at their midpoints produced a stereologically-derived distribution that did not accurately portray the orientation of the lines. The peaks in the resultant distribution were shifted by 45° in-plane of the triple junctions. Comparing the true distribution to the distributions after 1,000 section planes, it is apparent that the peaks show a φ=45° shift. In real material systems, triple junction geometries such as that presented in Figure 4 are not possible. These could be possible with other lineal systems of interest, however, such as fiber orientations.

4. Discussion

Line-length per unit volume is a measure of the average orientation of a lineal feature, more specifically to the current work, triple-lines. The resultant distribution $L_V(\varphi,\theta)$ is a density of these orientations having no knowledge of their true orientations *a-priori*. What $L_V(\varphi,\theta)$ does not tell the observer is the physical topology of the interfacial network. Much in the same way that a grain boundary character distribution (GBCD) tells the researcher the statistical distribution of grain boundary parameters, it does not indicate the connectivity of the grain boundary network in three dimensions. It is theoretically possible for two triple junction networks to have completely different topologies but result in the same orientation distribution, $L_V(\varphi,\theta)$. The spatial locations of triple junctions are indeterminate using this technique. It is anticipated that this method is material dependent since highly anisotropic grain shapes will affect the ability to accurately determine $L_V(\varphi,\theta)$ in real systems. For materials that exhibit grain size gradients, this method may be limited in its ability.

In [5], Hilliard points out that there are issues of which the observer must be aware when estimating $L_V(\varphi,\theta)$. First, the choice of section plane can have an impact on minimizing the standard deviation of the distribution. The section used in this work was a section plane; a more useful section would be a hemispherical surface or sphere [3]. Using a hemispherical section instead of section planes could be used in a similar manner and would result in minimizing the overall variance of $L_V(\varphi,\theta)$. It is noted that a hemispherical section is near impossible to do practically. Second, the optimum number of section planes depends on two factors; first being identifying the degree at which the triple junctions deviate from that of a random distribution. For a random distribution, a single section plane would suffice to determine $L_V(\varphi,\theta)$, but increasing anisotropy would elicit the need to have some prior knowledge of the grain morphology. The other factor is keeping a balance between the nonuniformity of the orientation distribution and spatial distribution of the section. Ideally, one would use section planes that sweep over all Cartesian and polar space as this would capture the triple junction orientations the best, but this is experimentally unreasonable. Thus, care must be taken when determining the type of sectioning done and having additional grain morphology information would help determine the spatial distributions of section planes and triple junction orientations. Real material systems are never truly random. Any deviation from "randomness" would negate the stereological assumption that the method is homogeneous. When determining $L_V(\varphi,\theta)$, the observer must understand that there are limitations since the material is more often than not inhomogeneous and may require other forms of creating an unbiased estimation of $L_V(\varphi,\theta)$.

The work presented here shows the efficacy of the stereological method of determining $L_V(\varphi,\theta)$ for triple-line orientations. While the results indicate that more than ten to one hundred randomly oriented planar sections would be needed to determine $L_V(\varphi,\theta)$, for practical purposes this is a daunting task, and likely should be substituted with a more systematic means of determining L_V.

Knowing the orientation distributions of triple junction networks would be of great benefit to interfacial science and real materials systems. Since the geometries of polycrystalline triple junctions are inherently 11-dimensional [21,27], additional geometries will need to be added to $L_V(\varphi,\theta)$. By showing that it is possible to stereologically produce the orientation distribution of triple-lines, a way of characterizing real triple junction geometries can be developed.

5. Conclusion

The efficacy of stereologically determining line-length per unit volume was studied on simplistic and simulated triple junction networks from the use of randomized section planes. The number of intersecting points on the section planes were used to construct a distribution of line-length per unit volume $L_V(\varphi,\theta)$. It was determined that for simplistic triple-line geometries, the stereological procedure was able to capture the line directions of the interface network after ~10-100 randomized section planes. By showing $L_V(\varphi,\theta)$ can be determined from isotropic-uniform-random sections in simulated triple-line system, applications towards a triple junction characterization method for real polycrystalline systems can be developed.

References

[1] Gokhale A M 1993 Utility of the horizontal slice for stereological characterization of lineal features *J. Microsc.* **170** 3–8
[2] Hanisch K-H, Klimanek P and Stoyan D 1985 Stereological analysis of dislocation arrangements in crystals from TEM images *Cryst. Res. Technol.* **20** 921–30
[3] Mouton P R, Gokhale A M, Ward N L and West M J 2002 Stereological length estimation using spherical probes *J. Microsc.* **206** 54–64
[4] Hilliard J . 1967 Determination of structural anisotropy *Stereology* 219–27
[5] Hilliard J E 1962 Specification and Measurement of Microstructural Anisotropy *Trans. Metall.*

Soc. AIME **224** 1201–11
[6] Hilliard J E 1972 Stereology : An Experimental Viewpoint *Adv. Appl. Probab.* **4** 92–111
[7] Buffon G L . 1777 *Essai d'Arithmétique Morale* vol Supplément (Imprimerie Royale, Paris)
[8] Hu C, Xia S, Li H, Liu T, Zhou B, Chen W and Wang N 2011 Improving the intergranular corrosion resistance of 304 stainless steel by grain boundary network control *Corros. Sci.* **53** 1880–6
[9] Cao W, Xia S, Bai Q, Zhang W, Zhou B, Li Z and Jiang L 2017 Effects of initial microstructure on the grain boundary network during grain boundary engineering in Hastelloy N alloy *J. Alloys Compd.* **704** 724–33
[10] Fortier P, Miller W a. A and Aust K T T 1997 Triple junction and grain boundary character distributions in metallic materials *Acta Mater.* **45** 3459–67
[11] Kobayashi S, Inomata T, Kobayashi H, Tsurekawa S and Watanabe T 2008 Effects of grain boundary- and triple junction-character on intergranular fatigue crack nucleation in polycrystalline aluminum *J. Mater. Sci.* **43** 3792–9
[12] Zhao B, Ziemons A, Shvindlerman L S and Gottstein G 2012 Surface topography and energy of grain boundary triple junctions in copper tricrystals *Acta Mater.* **60** 811–8
[13] Czubayko U, Sursaeva V G, Gottstein G and Shvindlerman L S 1998 Influence of triple junctions on grain boundary motion *Acta Mater.* **46** 5863–71
[14] Faulkner R G, Shvindlerman L S and Yin Y 2016 Heterogeneous nucleation theory revisited: Effect of triple junction line energy *Mater. Lett.* **174** 180–3
[15] Gottstein G, King A H and Shvindlerman L S 2000 Effect of triple-junction drag on grain growth *Acta Mater.* **48** 397–403
[16] Zhao B, Gottstein G and Shvindlerman L S 2011 Triple junction effects in solids *Acta Mater.* **59** 3510–8
[17] David M Saylor, El-Dasher, Adams R and David M Saylor E-D A R 2004 Measuring the Five Parameter Grain Boundary Distribution From Observations of Planar Sections *Mater. Sci.* **35** 1981–9
[18] Bagri A, Hanson J, Lind J, Kenesei P, Suter R, Gradečak S and Demkowicz M 2017 Measuring Grain Boundary Character Distributions in Ni-Base Alloy 725 Using High-Energy Diffraction Microscopy *Metall. Mater. Trans. A* **48** 354–61
[19] Saylor D M, Morawiec A and Rohrer G S 2003 The relative free energies of grain boundaries in magnesia as a function of five macroscopic parameters *Acta Mater.* **51** 3675–86
[20] Adams B L and Field D P 1992 Measurement and Representation of Grain-Boundary Texture *Metall. Trans. A* **23A** 2501–13
[21] Hardy G B and Field D P 2016 Reliability of twin-dependent triple junction distributions measured from a section plane *Acta Mater.* **103** 809–22
[22] Johnson O K and Schuh C A 2014 The triple junction hull: Tools for grain boundary network design *J. Mech. Phys. Solids* **69** 2–13
[23] Kobayashi S, Tsurekawa S and Watanabe T 2006 Structure-dependent triple junction hardening and intergranular fracture in molybdenum *Philosophical Magazine* vol 86 pp 5419–29
[24] Yi Y S and Kim J S 2004 Characterization methods of grain boundary and triple junction distributions *Scr. Mater.* **50** 855–9
[25] Groeber M A and Jackson M A 2014 DREAM.3D: A Digital Representation Environment for the Analysis of Microstructure in 3D *Integr. Mater. Manuf. Innov.* **3** 56–72
[26] Bachmann F, Hielscher R and Schaeben H 2010 Texture Analysis with MTEX - Free and Open Source Software Toolbox *Solid State Phenom.* **160** 63–8
[27] Hardy G B and Field D P 2015 The Parameters and Fundamental Zones of Twin-Dependent Triple Junction Distributions *Metall. Mater. Trans. A Phys. Metall. Mater. Sci.* **46** 2273–84

IOP Conf. Series: Materials Science and Engineering 1121 (2021) 012042 doi:10.1088/1757-899X/1121/1/012042

Depth Profile of Residual Stresses to Analyze Textures in Extruded A6XXX

Shogo Oda[1, 2], and Shun-Ichiro Tanaka[1]

[1]Tohoku University, Sendai, Japan.
[2]YKK AP Inc., Toyama, Japan.

E-mail: sh_oda@ykkap.co.jp

Abstract. The extruded profiles of A6XXX alloys have a textured surface structure, different from those having the inner cube and Goss orientations. This structure possibly contributes to the decrease in bending strength. Although the mechanism of degradation has been discussed for precipitates, it is necessary to reconsider it from the viewpoint of residual stress distribution. In this study, we first determine the optimal method to evaluate the residual stress in a textured structure. The cosα method with 3-axis oscillation successfully yielded highly precise residual stress values even in extruded aluminum alloys. Although the inner layers of A6063 and A6005C had the cube and Goss orientation, the surface layer at a depth of ~400 μm had a (112) orientation in A6063 and that at ~200 μm had a (110) orientation in A6005C. The residual stress increased further from the surface, and changes in the preferred orientation corresponded well with those of residual stress, especially in A6005C. It is suggested that the residual stress increases as the tensile strength increases.

1. Introduction

The A6XXX alloys, undergo aging and precipitation to form Mg_2Si precipitates. Because of their lower deformation resistance, the extruded profiles of A6XXX alloys have been used mainly in the field of architectural products and transportation equipment. Their mechanical properties are influenced by the recrystallized structure having a preferential orientation.

The decreased bending strength of the extruded A6XXX alloys may be due to their textured structure, which consists of both surface and inner cube and Goss orientations in the extruded direction. This is caused by the shear friction of the flowing aluminum in the die bearing area[1)]. It is important to determine the formation mechanism of the texture due to shear stress as well as understand how the profile texture is controlled by controlling the applied stress and improving the mechanical properties of the profile.

Previous studies have attempted to explain the texture formation mechanism in extruded profiles of alloys or metals from the viewpoints of precipitation density, size, and existence area in the grain boundaries or matrix[2)]. However, the extruded profile properties have not been discussed in terms of the stress field applied from the die and aluminum flow. In this study, we have conducted high-precision residual stress measurements of the aluminum extrusion profiles with preferred orientation and large crystal grains using the cosα method.

The residual stress is usually measured from the diffracted X-ray peak shift with incident angle ψ, which is well known as the $\sin^2\psi$ method. The residual stress values can be quantitatively calculated using the following equation[3)]:

$$\sigma_x = -\frac{E}{2(1+\nu)} cot\theta_0 \frac{\pi}{180} \frac{\partial 2\theta}{\partial sin^2\psi} \quad (1)$$

where, σ_x : residual stress
E : Young's modules
ν : Poisson's ratio
θ_0 : standard Bragg angle
η : complementary angle, θ
ψ : X-ray incident angle

Through the $\sin^2\psi$ method, the diffracted peak shift with ψ can be measured; however, it is difficult to apply textured material with large crystal-grain-like extruded aluminum profiles to this research because they recrystallized easily through a highly thermodynamic process. Therefore, X-ray diffraction analysis subjected to the $\sin^2\psi$ method shows a discontinuous Debye-Scherrer ring (D-S ring), preventing accurate calculation of the peak shift. We applied the cosα method constructed with 3-axis oscillation and quickly obtained a full diffraction ring.

The cosα method, first proposed by Taira and Tanaka[4)], utilizes the entire D-S ring recorded on a two-dimensional detector taken by single exposure to X-rays. Normal and shear stresses are obtained simultaneously. The residual stress values were quantitatively calculated using the following equation:

$$\sigma_x = -\frac{E}{1+\nu} \frac{1}{sin^2\eta \, sin^2\psi_0} \frac{\partial \varepsilon_{\alpha 1}}{\partial cos\alpha} \quad (2)$$

where, α : D-S ring angle
σ_x : residual stress
E : Young's modules
ν : Poisson's ratio
η : complementary angle, θ
ψ_0 : X-ray incident angle
$\varepsilon_{\alpha 1}$: strain

Although Taira's method takes a long time to detect the D-S ring using X-ray films, the use of an imaging plate detector solved this problem, making this method applicable for stress analysis. The simple optical system of the cosα method made the stress analyzer portable, smaller, lighter, and more convenient to use for on-site and field measurements. By using a new cosα-based analyzer, the time required for a single stress measurement is shortened to the order of minutes. We investigated the correlation between the residual stress distribution and cross-sectional grain orientation and explored the possibility of structural control by a stress field to improve mechanical properties.

2. Experimental

2.1. Specimen preparation

In this study, typical ISO, JIS-A6063, and A6005C alloys, whose chemical compositions are listed in Table 1, were used as the specimen. A6063 is the most commonly used alloy for extrusion, with a tensile strength of approximately 200 MPa. The tensile strength of the A6005C, which falls in the middle range of the A6XXX alloy series, is approximately 280 MPa. The A6005C has a higher content of Mg, Si, and Cu components and poorer extrudability than those of A6063. The effect of strength on the residual stress was investigated by comparing these two alloys having different tensile strengths.

IOP Conf. Series: Materials Science and Engineering 1121 (2021) 012042 doi:10.1088/1757-899X/1121/1/012042

Table 1 Chemical composition of A6063 and A6005C

Alloy	Component (mass%)						
	Mg	Si	Cu	Fe	Mn	Cr	Al
A6063	0.55	0.40	0.10	0.16	0.00	0.00	Bal.
A6005C	0.60	0.60	0.20	0.15	0.02	0.04	Bal.

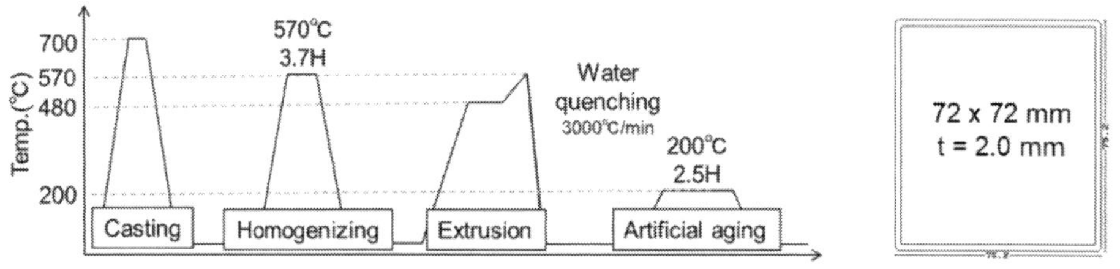

Fig. 1 Thermal cycle for extrusion and cross-section of the extruded profile.

The thermal cycle for extrusion and the cross-section of the extruded profile are shown in Fig. 1. Casted aluminum billets were homogenized at 570 °C for 3.7 h and extruded using a 2300 Metric-ton direct extrusion press machine. The extruded profiles were immediately cooled from 570 °C to room temperature by a water spray at 3000 °C/min, followed by artificial aging treatment at 200 °C for 2.5 h as T6 treatment. The cross-section of the extruded profiles had a square hollow shape.

2.2. Experimental procedure
Specimens were cut as ~ 20 × 20 mm square plates from the extruded profile. To measure the residual stress distribution in the depth direction from the surface, the specimens were electropolished 30–400 μm from the surface, which was masked on the opposite side to precisely identify the polishing amount. The electrolyte used was a solution of 6 vol% perchlorate acid ethanol at 0 °C and an applied voltage of 15 V. The polishing amount was measured by a micrometer and was approximately 50 μm after 20 min of polishing.

The X-ray measurement conditions of the $\sin^2\psi$ and cosα methods are listed in Table 2. The SmartLab system (Rigaku Corp.) was used for the X-ray $\sin^2\psi$ method. We used (422) diffraction with Cu-Kα radiation at 2θ = 137.46 deg and an oscillation angle of 5 deg in the ϕ axis; we obtained stresses using Young's modulus (E) = 69.3 GPa and Poisson's ratio (ν) = 0.35. The X-ray diffraction in the cosα method was measured using a portable μ-X360s analyzer manufactured by PULSTEC Industrial Co., Ltd. We used (311) diffraction under Cr-Kα radiation at 2θ = 138.48 deg and obtained stresses using the same E and ν values. The μ-X360s analyzer used robotic 3-axis oscillation (ψ), in-plane rotation axis (ϕ), and was perpendicular to the incident X-ray axis (ω) by 10 deg (±10 deg) for each, obtaining a continuous D-S ring in 60 s. The X-ray $\sin^2\psi$ method of the 1-axis swing achieved no accurate peak shift and an unreliable residual stress value because of the large grain size and preferred orientation of the aluminum profiles.

Table 2 Measurement conditions for extruded profiles by the X-ray $\sin^2\psi$ and cosα methods

Method	$\sin^2\psi$ iso-inclination	cosα
Apparatus	Rigaku Corp. SmartLab	Pulstec Ind. μ-X360s
X-ray type	Cu-Kα, λ = 1.54059 Å	Cr-Kα, λ = 2.28970 Å
X-ray power	45 kV, 200 mA	30 kV, 1.5 mA
Collimator size	10 mm × 1 mm	φ 1.0 mm
Diffraction	Al (422) 2θ = 137.46 deg	Al (311) 2θ = 139.32 deg
X-ray incident angle	0 ~ 40.2 deg	30 deg
Oscillation angle	φ = 5 deg	ψ, φ, ω = 10 deg (±10 deg)
Irradiation area	11.0 mm²	φ 2.0 mm

3. Results and discussion

3.1. Residual stress obtained by the two measurement methods

Figure 2 shows the Al (422) diffraction peak shift measured by the X-ray $\sin^2\psi$ method and the 2θ - $\sin^2\psi$ diagram with ϕ angle oscillation in A6063 at the surface. Irregular variation in the peak position and intensity prevented the observation of an accurate peak shift. The $\sin^2\psi$ diagram was not straight, and the calculated σ_x was 50±147 MPa, which had an unreliably high standard deviation.

Figure 3 shows a typical D-S ring obtained by the X-ray cosα method with ψ, ϕ, and ω oscillation for Al (311) of the extruded A6063 profile at the surface. Although the specimen has a large crystal grain and textured surface, a continuous ring was successfully obtained. The calculated σ_x was −27±5 MPa, which had a reliable standard deviation. Thus, residual stress distribution was measured by the cosα method hereafter.

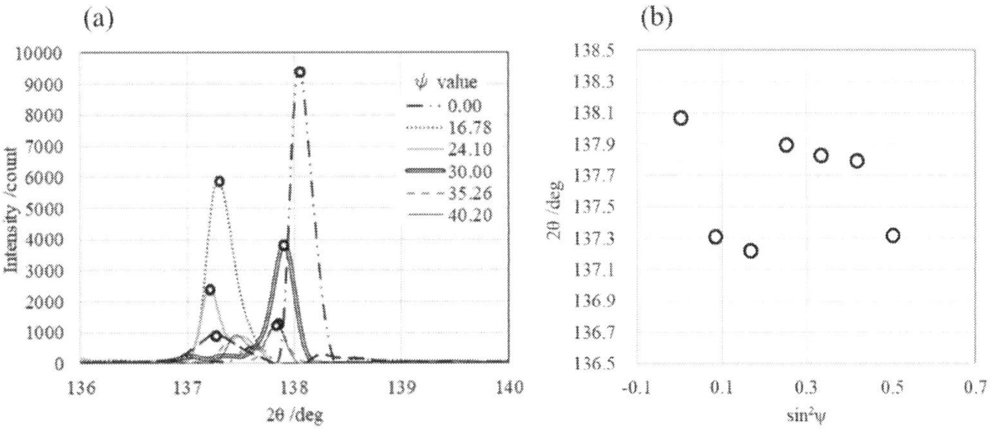

Fig. 2 (a) Al (422) diffraction peak shift measured in A6063 by the X-ray $\sin^2\psi$ method and (b) 2θ - $\sin^2\psi$ diagram with only ϕ axis oscillation. Accurate peak shift could not be identified because of irregular variation in peak position and intensity. The $\sin^2\psi$ diagram was not straight. The calculated σ_x was 50±147 MPa.

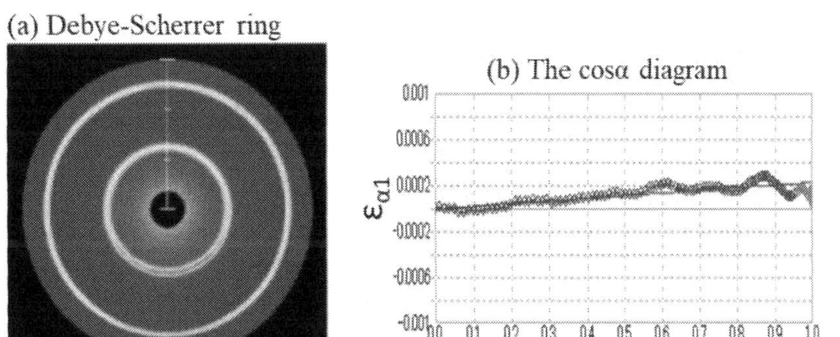

Fig. 3 (a) D-S ring obtained by the X-ray cosα method with ψ, ϕ, and ω oscillation for Al (311) of the extruded A6063 profile and (b) the cosα diagram. Although the specimen has a large crystal grain and textured surface, a continuous ring was successfully obtained. The calculated σ_x was −27±5 MPa.

3.2. Residual stress distribution of extruded A6063 profile

Figure 4 (a) shows a cross-sectional inverse pole figure (IPF) map of the A6063 profile, in which strong cube and Goss orientations of the inner layer can be seen. The surface layer at a depth of ~400 μm exhibited the (112) orientation[5, 6)]. Fig. 4 (b) shows the residual stress distribution from the surface to a depth of 150 μm.

The principal stress, σ_1, ranged from 4 to −4 MPa from the surface to 40 μm and gradually increased to 11 MPa at a depth of 150 μm. The shear stress, τ_{xy}, was −3 MPa at the surface and increased gradually to 27 MPa at a depth of 150 μm. The von Mises stress, σ_{vM}, was 10 MPa at the surface and increased to 66 MPa as the depth increased.

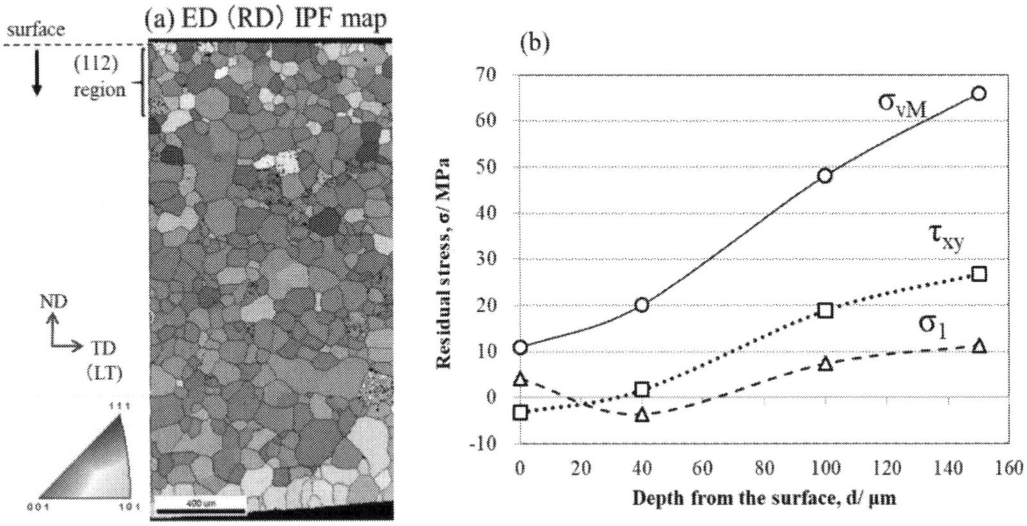

Fig. 4 (a) Cross-sectional view of IPF map (ED) of A6063 profile. (b) Depth profile of stresses: principal stress σ_1, shear stress τ_{xy}, and von Mises stress σ_{vM}.

3.3. Residual stress distribution of extruded A6005C profile

Figure 5 (a) shows the same correspondence of A6005C. The inner layer structure had cube and Goss orientations, in which (100) faced to the extrusion direction and the surface layer had the (110) orientation.

The depth profiles of the residual stresses in A6005C are shown in Fig. 5 (b). The principal stress, σ_1, was compressive from the surface to a depth of 75 μm and increased at a depth of ~105 μm, showing a maximum of 27 MPa, followed by a compressive change at a depth of 220 μm, finally increasing to 300 μm and plateauing near zero to 400 μm. The shear stress, τ_{xy}, exhibited the opposite tendency. The von Mises stress, σ_{vM}, which was the lowest at the surface, increased to 105 μm and showed a maximum of 118 MPa, similar to σ_1.

The boundary between the inner and surface layers was clear with a grain growth region just below the boundary. The first maximum value of σ_{vM} at 105 μm corresponded well to the (110) region, and the range between the first maximum at 105 μm and the second local maximum at 300 μm corresponded to the grain growth region.

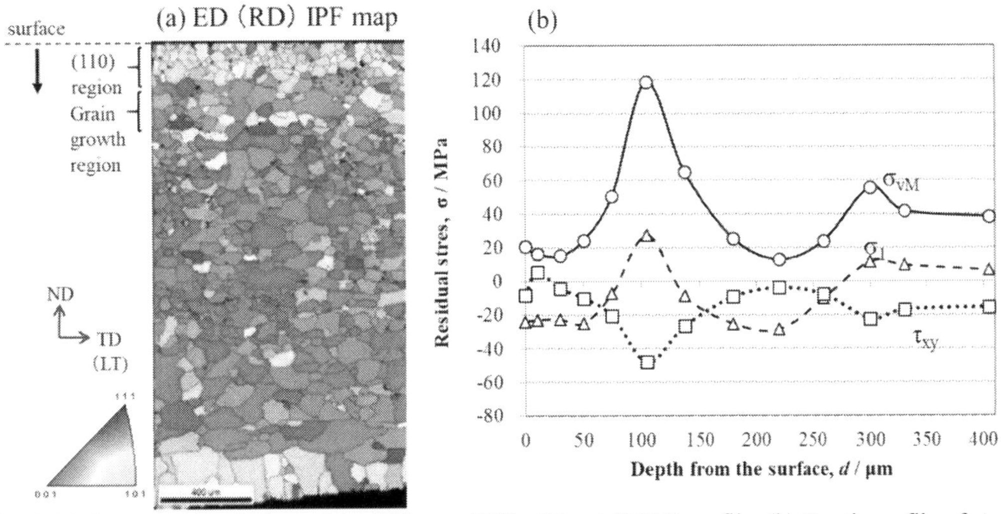

Fig. 5 (a) Cross-sectional view of the IPF map (ED) of the A6005C profile. (b) Depth profile of stresses in A6005C: principal stress σ_1, shear stress τ_{xy}, and von Mises stress σ_{vM}.

4. Conclusion

The study proposed the method to precisely measure stresses in an extruded profile of A6XXX alloy with coarse grains and preferred orientation. In addition, we clarified the relationship between the stress distribution in the cross section and the IPF map of the texture.
The results are summarized as follows:

(1) The cosα method with 3-axis oscillation allowed for the high-precision measurement of the aluminum extrusion profile with a preferred orientation and large crystal grain. The $\sin^2\psi$ method could not obtain an accurate peak shift or reliable σ_x value.

(2) The inner layer structures of A6063 and A6005C had cube and Goss orientations, with a dominant cube orientation. The surface layer at a depth of ~400 μm had a (112) orientation in A6063 and that at a depth of ~200 μm had a (110) orientation in A6005C. The residual stress increased further from the surface. However, the absolute value of σ_{vM} of A6063 was lower than that of A6005C. It is suggested that the residual stress increases as the tensile strength increases.

(3) The changes in the preferred orientation corresponded well with those of residual stress. The boundary of the surface preferred orientation (110) and inner (100) matched well with the first local maximum of σ_{vM}, whereas the grain growth area of A6005C ranged from the first to the second local maximum of σ_{vM}.

References

[1] N P Goss, 1935 *Trans. Am. Soc. Metals*, **23** 1107
[2] I Westermann, K E Snilsberg, Z Sharifi and B Holmedal, 2011 *Metallurgical and Materials Transactions A*, **42 A** 3386-3389
[3] S Tanaka and Y Takahashi, 1990 *ISIJ International*, **30** 12 1086-1091
[4] S Taira and K Tanaka, 1979 *Transactions Iron and steel Institute of Japan*, **19** 411-418
[5] H Inoue, 2002 Journal of Japan Institute of Light Metals, 52 11 524-529
[6] J. Baumgarten, W. Bunk and K. Luäcke, 1981 Zeitschrift für Metallkunde, 72 162-168

Acknowledgement:
We acknowledge Mr. T. Kurokawa, YKK Inc., for his help with stress measurement by the $\sin^2\psi$ method.

IOP Conf. Series: Materials Science and Engineering 1121 (2021) 012043 doi:10.1088/1757-899X/1121/1/012043

Using synchrotron radiation XRD technique to investigate active slip systems during tensile deformation in pure magnesium

Masahiro Hirata, Daisuke Okai, Hiroki Adachi

University of Hyogo, Himeji, Hyogo, Japan

em20j003@steng.u-hyogo.ac.jp

Abstract. Active slip systems in pure magnesium specimens with different grain sizes were investigated by the in-situ X-ray diffraction (XRD) technique during tensile testing. From the XRD measurement results, the inhomogeneous strain anisotropy formed by dislocations was obtained. Inhomogeneous strain anisotropy differs in each slip system because hexagonal close-packed metals such as magnesium have anisotropic elasticity. In this study, the dislocation amounts belonging to each active slip system were evaluated utilizing this difference. Coarse-grained specimens had isotropic inhomogeneous strain corresponding to basal slip. Fine-grained specimens showed high elongation and had anisotropic inhomogeneous strain. It is considered that the improvement in ductility occurred by non-basal slip activation near grain boundaries, which increased with grain refinement. Similarly, the ratio of non-basal slip evaluated from the crystal rotation axis increased in the fine-grained specimens.

1. Introduction

Magnesium and magnesium alloys are some of the lightest metal materials in practical use and are used in a variety of applications. However, they have low ductility caused by their low plastic deformability, which is a disadvantage in practical use. In von Mises' criterion [1], five independent slip systems are required to freely deform each grain in polycrystalline materials. Magnesium has a hexagonal close-packed (HCP) structure and basal slip system as the main slip system, which is less than the required five independent slip systems and leads to the observed low ductility. Therefore, since the activation of non-basal slip systems such as prismatic slip and pyramidal slip can increase the ductility, it is important to evaluate the non-basal slips. The critical resolved shear stress (CRSS) of the basal slip in pure magnesium single crystals at room temperature has been reported to be approximately 0.5 MPa [2]. On the other hand, the CRSS of non-basal slips is far larger than that of the basal slip, and the activation of the non-basal slips rarely occurs. However, the activation of the non-basal slips has been reported under several conditions, such as in samples with grain refinement [3, 4] and those undergoing deformation at higher temperature [5]. The identification of active slip systems has been mainly conducted by transmission electron microscopy (TEM). Although the Burgers vector can be identified relatively easily by this method, it is difficult to evaluate active slip systems from the results of many grains because the identification of the slip plane requires time and effort.

Due to its HCP structure, magnesium has different values of inhomogeneous strain anisotropy for each slip system [6]. It was speculated that qualitative evaluation of the dislocation amount belonging to each active slip system is possible by comparing the calculated and measured values of inhomogeneous strain anisotropy using these differences. Here, "inhomogeneous strain anisotropy" means a change in the size of the inhomogeneous strain field introduced by dislocations existing in the crystal depending on the crystal orientation. Therefore, in this study, we attempted to qualitatively evaluate the dislocation amount belonging to each active slip system by obtaining the inhomogeneous strain anisotropy, using the results of in-situ X-ray diffraction (XRD) measurements during tensile deformation of pure magnesium with different grain sizes and comparing the results with the calculated values.

2. Experimental procedures

Samples with a diameter of 30 mm and a thickness of 1 mm were prepared from a 99.9% pure magnesium ingot for high pressure torsion (HPT) processing [7, 8]. The rotation anvil was turned 7 times at a speed of 0.2 rpm under a compressive stress of 2 GPa. The HPTed samples were annealed at 473 K for 7.2, 18 or 36 ks in order to obtain samples with several grain sizes, and then tensile specimens having a parallel length of 10 mm, a width of 3 mm and a thickness of 0.5 mm were prepared by a wire-electrical discharge machine. The average grain sizes of the HPTed sample and annealed samples were measured by electron backscatter diffraction (EBSD) measurements at an acceleration voltage of 15 kV using an orientation imaging microscopy (OIM) system (TSL Solutions) with a scanning electron microscope (JSM-6500F, JEOL). The average grain size, d, was defined as the interval between large-angle grain boundaries of a misorientation angle >15°. In the HPTed sample, d=2.1 μm, and in the samples annealed at 473 K for 7.2, 18 or 36 ks, d=4.8, 6.4, and 8.3 μm, respectively. In this paper, these samples are called the 2.1, 4.8, 6.4, and 8.3 μm samples, respectively.

In-situ XRD measurement during tensile deformation was conducted using synchrotron radiation (SPring-8) [9]. The energy of the incident X-ray was 30 keV, and the beam size was 0.5 mm long and 0.2 mm wide. A 6-unit MYTHEN detector was positioned 22° above the transmission direction and the camera length was 730.2 mm in order to measure diffraction peaks over a large range at the same time. The tensile test was conducted with an initial strain rate of 3.3×10^{-4} s^{-1} while oscillating the tensile tester in the Z direction at a speed of 1 mm/s and a width of 2 mm, because it is necessary to increase the number of grains in the X-ray irradiation volume. The measurement was performed with a time resolution of 3 s. The diffraction peak angle and full width at half maximum were calculated from the observed diffraction peak profiles from the (100), (002), (101), (102), (110), (103), (200), (112), (201), (004), (202), (104), (203), (211), (114), (212), (105), (204), (213), and (302) diffractions.

Dragomir et al. calculated the inhomogeneous strain anisotropy introduced by the dislocations belonging to each slip system under the assumption that it is a continuous elastic body and only a basal, prismatic or pyramidal slip system exists, respectively [6, 10]. Figure 1 shows the calculated inhomogeneous strain anisotropy of the basal <a> slip: $\{0001\}\langle 2\bar{1}\bar{1}0\rangle$, the prismatic <a> slip: $\{10\bar{1}0\}\langle 2\bar{1}\bar{1}0\rangle$ and the pyramidal <c+a> slip: $\{2\bar{1}\bar{1}2\}\langle 2\bar{1}\bar{1}3\rangle$ when a density of dislocations belonging to each slip system is 10^{14} m^{-2}. This figure is represented in polar coordinates, the argument is the angle between the basal plane and the direction of inhomogeneous strain, the radius of the curve is the amount of inhomogeneous strain, the vertical axis shows the amount of inhomogeneous strain along the c-axis direction and the horizontal axis shows the amount of inhomogeneous strain along the in-plane direction of the basal plane. The dislocations belonging to different slip systems have different values of inhomogeneous strain anisotropy. For example, the dislocations of the basal <a> slip have a relatively isotropic inhomogeneous strain, the dislocations of the prismatic <a> slip have a 1.2-fold larger inhomogeneous strain anisotropy toward the in-plane direction than that of the basal <a> slip, and the dislocations of the pyramidal <c+a> slip have a 3-fold larger inhomogeneous strain anisotropy toward the c-axis direction than that of the basal <a> slip. Qualitative evaluation of the dislocation amount belonging to the active slip systems was performed by comparing the inhomogeneous strain anisotropy with the measured values with Figure 1.

The crystallite size and inhomogeneous strain are the two main sources contributing to XRD peak broadening. For HCP metals with elastic anisotropy, separation by the Williamson-Hall method [11], which is valid for the analysis of isotropic materials, is not appropriate. Therefore, the modified

Williamson-Hall method [12] was used to separate the two effects [13-15]. The modified Williamson-Hall equation is the following,

$$\Delta K_{hkl} = \frac{0.9}{D} + \left(\frac{\pi M^2 b^2}{2}\right)^{\frac{1}{2}} \rho^{\frac{1}{2}} \overline{C_{hkl}}^{\frac{1}{2}} K_{hkl} + O(K_{hkl}^2 \overline{C_{hkl}}) \quad (1)$$

where K_{hkl}=2sinθ/ λ, ΔK_{hkl}=$\Delta 2\theta$cosθ/ λ, the subscript *hkl* indicates data for the diffraction peak obtained from the *hkl* diffraction, θ is Bragg diffraction angle, $\Delta 2\theta$ is full width at half maximum (FWHM), λ is the wavelength of incident X-rays, D is the crystallite size, b is the size of the Burgers vector, ρ is the dislocation density, M is a constant representing the degree of dislocation arrangement and $\overline{C_{hkl}}$ is the average dislocation contrast factor for the *hkl* diffraction. $O(K_{hkl}^2 \overline{C_{hkl}})$ represents higher-order terms in *KC*, which usually are small compared to the first two terms. The coefficient part of K_{hkl} is the part corresponding to the inhomogeneous strain (ε_{hkl}) of the conventional Williamson-Hall equation, and can be expressed as the following equation from (1),

$$\varepsilon_{hkl} = \sqrt{\left(\frac{\Delta K_{hkl} - \alpha}{K_{hkl}}\right)^2} \quad (2)$$

where $\alpha = 0.9/D$. By calculating the amount of inhomogeneous strain in the *hkl* diffraction plane normal direction from *hkl* diffraction peak, the inhomogeneous strain anisotropy was obtained.

EBSD measurement has been used as a method for evaluating active slip systems [16, 17]. Kashihara et al. [16]. evaluated an active slip system by determining the axis of crystal rotation in deformation along the [100] axis of an aluminum bicrystal by EBSD measurement and comparing it with the calculated rotation axis. In this study, EBSD measurement was performed at the same field of view for the 2.1 and 6.4 μm samples before and after tensile deformation, and the crystal rotation axes of 20 crystal grains were determined. The angle formed by the measured crystal rotation axis and the crystal rotation axis of the basal slip was investigated, and the ratio of the basal slip and non-basal slip was qualitatively evaluated. The results were compared with the qualitative evaluation results of the active slip systems obtained from the inhomogeneous strain anisotropy.

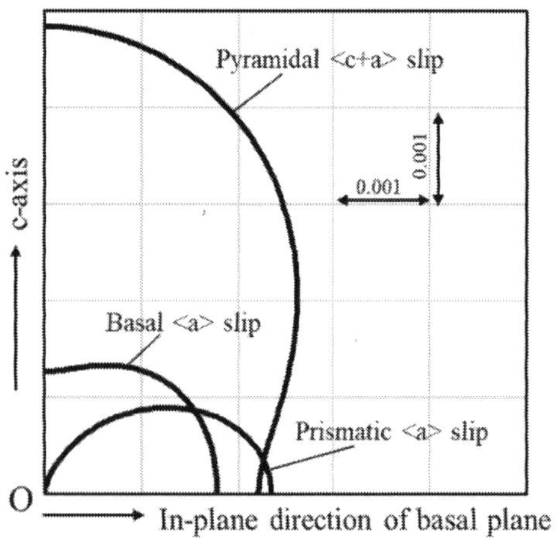

Figure 1 The inhomogeneous strain anisotropy of each slip system created from calculated values. This figure is expressed in polar coordinates in arbitrary units (a.u.); the argument is the angle between the basal plane and the direction of inhomogeneous strain, the radius of the curve is the amount of inhomogeneous strain, the vertical axis shows the amount of inhomogeneous strain in the c-axis direction and the horizontal axis shows the amount of inhomogeneous strain in the in-plane direction.

3. Results & Discussion

3.1. In-situ XRD measurement

The nominal stress – nominal strain curves of each sample are shown in Figure 2. The total elongation of the 2.1, 4.8, 6.4 and 8.3 μm samples was 34.5, 10.6, 5.1 and 2.9%, respectively, and the uniform elongation values were 10.1, 9.7, 4.1 and 2.4%, respectively. Similar to previous reports on magnesium alloys, the ductility increased for samples with fine crystal grains [3, 4, 18, 19].

Figure 3(a) shows typical in-situ XRD profiles for the 2.1 μm sample before tensile deformation, during elastic deformation and during plastic deformation, with nominal strain of 0, 0.18 and 2.0%, respectively. In order to clearly observe the change in the shape of the diffraction peak, enlarged views of the (110) diffraction peaks are shown in Figure 3(b). Compared with the diffraction peak before the tensile deformation, the diffraction peaks during the deformation were shifted to the low angle side because the interplanar spacing increased. In addition, the FWHM increased during plastic deformation due to the introduction of inhomogeneous strain.

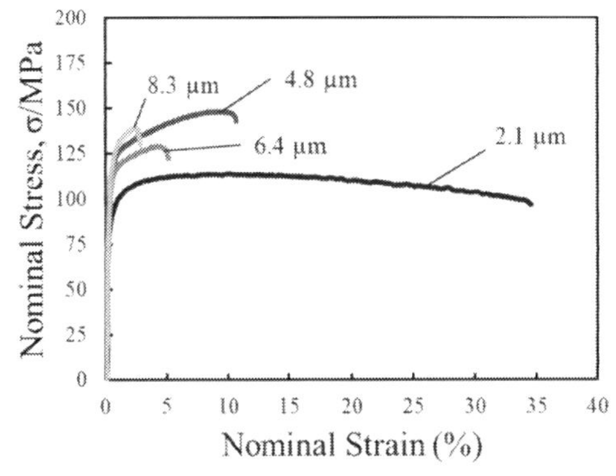

Figure 2 Nominal stress – Nominal strain curves of each sample.

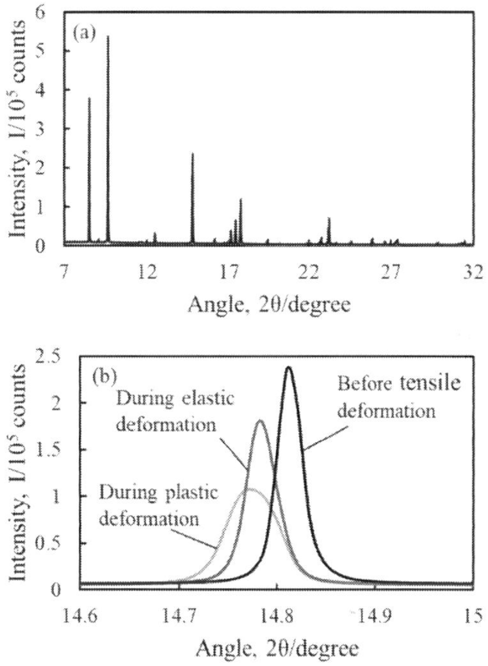

Figure 3 (a) The typical In-situ XRD profiles in 2.1μm sample in the nominal strain of 0, 0.18 and 2.0 %. (b) is an enlarged view of the (110) diffraction peaks.

3.2. Qualitative evaluation of the dislocation amount belonging to each active slip system

Figure 4 shows the changes in the inhomogeneous strain anisotropy in the 2.1 (a), 4.8 (b), 6.4 (c) and 8.3 μm (d) samples during tensile deformation. In each sample, the amount of inhomogeneous strain increased with the progress of tensile deformation. This is due to the increase in the dislocation density. The samples showing high ductility with small grain size and uniform elongation of about 10% (Figure 4(a, b)) and the samples with a lower ductility (Figure 4(c, d)) had different shapes for the inhomogeneous strain anisotropy. At 10.1% in Figure 4 (a) and 9.7% in (b), the amount of inhomogeneous strain in the c-axis direction and the in-plane direction of basal plane was 1.5 and 1.7 times larger than the amount of inhomogeneous strain in the 45° direction, respectively. The anisotropy of the inhomogeneous strain was large. On the other hand, at 4.1% in Figure 4 (c) and 2.4% in (d), the difference in the amount of inhomogeneous strain depending on the direction was 1.1 and 1.2 times, respectively, and the inhomogeneous strain was almost isotropic.

The dislocation amount belonging to each active slip system was qualitatively evaluated by comparison with Figure 1. In (a) and (b) of Figure 4, the 2.1 and 4.8 μm samples have a large amount of inhomogeneous strain along the c-axis and in-plane direction of the basal plane. Therefore, it is considered that the prismatic <a> slip and pyramidal <c+a> slip, which cause large inhomogeneous strain along the c-axis and in-plane direction of basal plane, respectively, were activated. Panels (c)

IOP Conf. Series: Materials Science and Engineering 1121 (2021) 012043 doi:10.1088/1757-899X/1121/1/012043

and (d) of Figure 4 show the isotropic inhomogeneous strain of the 6.4 and 8.3 μm samples; this suggests that there is a lot of activity in the basal <a> slip.

Focusing on the change in inhomogeneous strain anisotropy during tensile deformation, the difference in the direction-dependent amount of inhomogeneous strain at nominal strain of 0.25% in Figure 4(a, b) is 1.3 times at the maximum, which is smaller than the value at nominal strain of 10.1% in (a) and 9.7% in (b). This suggests that the basal <a> slip is active in the early stage of plastic deformation, and the ratios of active prismatic <a> slip and pyramidal <c+a> slip increase as the deformation progresses. On the other hand, in Figure 4(c, d), the difference in the amount of direction-dependent inhomogeneous strain was about 1.1 to 1.2 times. Compared with Figure 4(a, b), there was no significant change in the shapes of the inhomogeneous strain anisotropy curves, and it is considered that a lot of basal slip was activated during tensile deformation.

The non-basal slips are considered to be activated by the additional stress generated by their compatibility in the region near the grain boundary, and fine grains occupy a larger proportion of the region near the grain boundary than coarse grains [4, 20]. Therefore, it is considered that the non-basal slips were more active in samples with fine grains. The reason why high ductility was exhibited in the 2.1 and 4.8 μm samples was that the plastic deformability of magnesium was improved by the activation of the non-basal slips.

3.3. Evaluation by crystal rotation

Figure 5 shows the angles formed by the crystal rotation axis obtained by EBSD measurement and the crystal rotation axis of the basal slip in the 2.1 and 6.4 μm samples. The "0.5%" and "1.0%" in Figure 5 are the angles formed by the crystal rotation axis between the condition before tensile deformation and at nominal strains of 0.5% and 1.0%, respectively, and the rotation axis of the basal slip. When the angle is close to 0°, this indicates that the measured rotation axis is close to the rotation axis of the basal slip, which means that the crystal rotation is caused only by the basal slip. The average angle was 52.5° and 55.4° for the 2.1 μm sample and 20.4° and 21.2° for the 6.4 μm sample, respectively, at nominal strains of 0.5% and 1.0%, respectively. Compared with the 6.4 μm sample, the crystal

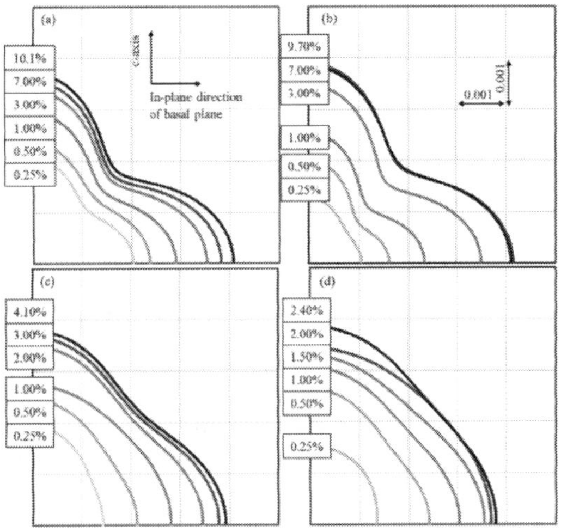

Figure 4 The change of inhomogeneous strain anisotropy during tensile deformation in (a) 2.1, (b) 4.8, (c) 6.4, and (d) 8.3 μm samples, shown as % nominal strain.

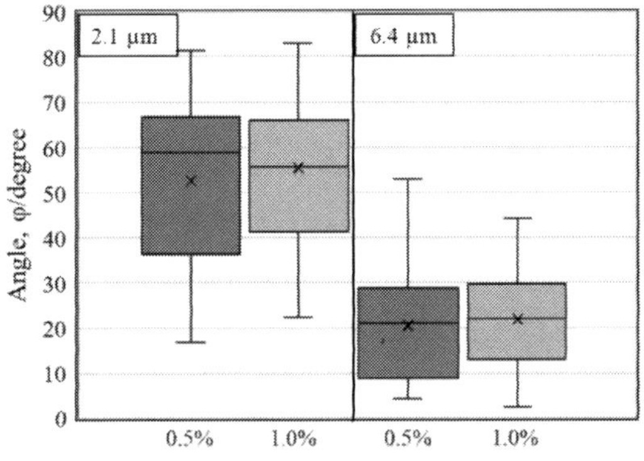

Figure 5 The angles formed by the crystal rotation axis obtained by EBSD measurement and the crystal rotation axis of the basal slip in the 2.1 and 6.4 μm samples. The dark gray shows the results of the rotation axis between the condition before tensile deformation and at nominal strain of 0.5%. The light gray shows the corresponding rotation axis at nominal strain of 1.0%.

rotation axis in the 2.1 μm sample had a large deviation from the rotation axis of the basal slip, suggesting that the activation ratio of non-basal slips was high. Since these results are in agreement with the results obtained by in-situ XRD measurement, it is considered that the evaluation of active slip systems using inhomogeneous strain anisotropy in this study is valid.

4. Conclusions

Active slip systems were qualitatively evaluated from the inhomogeneous strain anisotropy derived from the results of in-situ XRD measurements during tensile deformation of pure magnesium samples with different grain sizes.

(1) Different shapes of inhomogeneous strain anisotropy plots were obtained from samples with different grain sizes.
(2) The anisotropy of the inhomogeneous strain was large in the 2.1 and 4.8 μm samples, suggesting that the prismatic <a> slip and the pyramidal <c+a> slip were active.
(3) The anisotropy of the inhomogeneous strain was small in the 6.4 and 8.3 μm samples, suggesting that the basal <a> slip was active.
(4) As a result of evaluation of the active slip systems based on the crystal rotation, the activation ratio of non-basal slips was higher in the 2.1 μm sample than in the 6.4 μm sample, showing the same tendency as the result obtained from measurements of inhomogeneous strain anisotropy.

Acknowledgement

The synchrotron radiation experiments were performed at the BL19B2 and BL46XU beamlines of SPring-8 with the approval of the Japan Synchrotron Radiation Research Institute (JASRI) (Proposal No. 2018A1029 and 2017A1006).

References

[1] Von Mises R and Agnew Z 1928 *Math. Mech.* **8** 161
[2] Numakura H 1998 *Materia Jpn.* **37** 117-124
[3] Kobayashi T, Koike J, Yoshida Y, Kamada S, Suzuki M, Maruyama K and Kojima Y 2003 *J. Jpn. Inst. Met.* **4** 149-152
[4] Zheng R, Bhattacharjee T, Gao S, Gong W, Shibata A, Sassaki T, Hono K and Tsuji N 2019 *Sci. Rep.* **9** 11702
[5] Wu G, Nodooshan H R J, Zeng X, Liu W, Li D and Ding W 2018 *metals* **8** 980
[6] Dragomir I C and Ungár T 2002 *J. Appl. Cryst.* **35** 556-565
[7] Bridgman P W, 1935, *Phys. Rev.* **48** 825
[8] Zhilyaev A P, Langdon T G, 2008 *Prog. Mater. Sci.***53** 893-979
[9] Adachi H, Mizowaki H, Hirata M, Okai D and Nakanishi H 2020 *J. Jpn. Inst. Light Met.* **70** 274-280
[10] Borbély A, Dragomir J C, Ribárik G and Ungár T 2003 *J.Appl. Cryst.* **36** 160-162
[11] Williamson G K and Hall W H 1953 *Acta Metall* **1** 22-31
[12] Ungár T and Borbély A 1996 *Appl. Phys. Lett.* **69** 3173
[13] Ungár T, Révész Á and Borbély A. 1998 *J. Appl. Cryst.* **31** 554-558
[14] Ungár T, Dragomir I C, Révész Á and Borbély A 1999 *J. Appl. Cryst.* **32** 992-1002
[15] Ungár T, Gubicza J, Ribárik G and Borbély A 2001 *J. Appl. Cryst.* **34** 298-310
[16] Kashihara K and Wert J A, 2006 *Mater. Trans.* **47** 233-238
[17] Kashihara K, 2008 *Mater. Trans.* **46** 419-423
[18] Sakaoka Y, Kuramoto S, Kawabata H and Kurumada A 2019 *J. Jpn. Inst. Light Met.* **69** 332-338
[19] Miura H, Yang X and Sakai T 2008 *Mater. Trans.* 49 1015-1020
[20] Miyanno H, Takemoto K, Tsushida M, Kitahara H and Ando S 2020 *J. Jpn. Inst. Light Met.* **70** 117-121

Evaluation of active slip systems during deformation by In-situ XRD in precipitation hardening Mg Alloys

Tomoki Yoshikawa [1], Masahiro Hirata[1], Daisuke Okai[1] and Hiroki Adachi[1]
[1] Graduate School of Engineering, University of Hyogo, Himeji, Japan

y.tomoki10@gmail.com

Abstract. The effect of precipitates on active slip systems was evaluated in precipitation-hardening Mg Alloys. In a Mg-5% Y-4% Nd (WE54) alloy, the radius and thickness of disc-shaped β″ precipitates were measured by small angle X-ray scattering measurements. The active slip system was then measured during tensile deformation by in situ X-ray diffraction measurements. The average radius and thickness of the precipitates increased with aging time, and approached 19.4 and 3.85 nm, respectively, at a peak aging time of 2160 ks. The uniform elongations of the as-quenched, 1.08 ks aged and 360 ks aged alloys were determined to be approximately 9.7, 5.5 and 2.3%, respectively. Various slip systems were active in the as-quenched alloy. On the other hand, in the alloy aged for 360 ks, non-basal <a> slip was found to be dominant.

1. Introduction

Lightweight, high-specific-strength magnesium has gained attention for use in the transport industry. However, magnesium shows low ductility at room temperature due to the anisotropy of plastic deformation because of its crystal structure. There are multiple deformation mechanisms involving dislocation slip in the hexagonal close packed (HCP) structure of magnesium, such as basal <a> slip, prism <a> slip and pyramidal <c+a> slip. At room temperature, the critical resolved shear stress (CRSS) for basal <a> slip in pure magnesium is reported to be about 0.5 MPa [1]. On the other hand, the CRSS for prism <a> slip and pyramidal <c+a> slip is reported to be more than 10 times higher than that for basal <a> slip [2]. Therefore, basal <a> slip occurs preferentially in magnesium, and the number of independent slip systems is small, so that the von-Mises criterion cannot be satisfied [3]. For this reason, non-basal slip mechanisms such as prism <a> slip and pyramidal <c+a> slip are necessary to improve the ductility of magnesium.

It has been reported that the addition of yttrium enhances non-basal slip [4,5]. Mg-Y alloys are well-known precipitation hardened alloys; therefore, it is important to investigate the effect of the precipitates on the active slip systems in order to control the mechanical properties. Transmission electron microscopy (TEM) observations of dislocations are generally used to identify active slip systems in HCP metals. However, in TEM observations, although the Burgers vectors of dislocations can be identified easily, much effort is required to identify the slip planes, and it is difficult to obtain statistical data from many grains. On the other hand, methods such as X-ray diffraction (XRD) can obtain statistical information from many grains during tensile deformation using synchrotron radiation [6,7]. The purpose of this study is to evaluate the effect of the precipitate size on active slip systems during tensile deformation by in situ XRD measurements of Mg-Y-Nd alloys.

2. Experimental Procedures

Mg-5 wt% Y-4 wt% Nd (WE54) extruded alloys were solution treated at 823 K for 9 ks, subsequently quenched in water, and aged at 473 K to cause precipitation of the β″ phase. Samples with different precipitate sizes were prepared by varying the aging time between 1.08 and 2160 ks. For the samples for the tensile tests, in order to refine the crystal grains, high-pressure torsion (HPT) was performed after a 9 ks solution treatment at 823 K and water quenching. The samples were disks with a thickness of 0.9 mm and produced at a pressure of 2 GPa, and 7 rotations were performed at a rotation speed of 0.2 rpm. The tensile-test specimens had a length of 10 mm, a width of 3 mm, and a thickness of 0.6 mm. For comparison, pure Mg was prepared. The specimens were subjected to electron beam backscatter diffraction (EBSD) measurements at an acceleration voltage of 15 kV, in an oriented imaging microscopy (OIM) system provided by TSL, and equipped on a JSM-6500F scanning electron microscope provided by JEOL Ltd.

To measure the change in the precipitate size with aging time, small angle X-ray scattering (SAXS) measurements were performed at the BL19B2 beamline of the SPring-8 synchrotron radiation facility. The X-ray energy was 25 keV, the exposure time was 60 s, the camera length was 3046 mm, and the scattering intensity for each sample was measured using a two-dimensional pixel detector (PILATUS-2M, DECTRIS). The scattering profile of the as-quenched (A.Q.) alloy was subtracted so that only the scattering profile of the precipitate was obtained. The precipitates in the Mg-Y-Nd alloys were disk-shaped and lay on $(1\bar{1}00)$ prism plane in the matrix, as determined by TEM observations [8]. The data are presented as scattering intensity $I(k)$ vs. scattering vector k ($=4\pi\sin\theta/\lambda$). The Guinier approximation was used to measure the precipitate size [9]. In the low-k region of the scattering curve, the relationship between $I(k)$ and k is expressed as $lnI(k)\propto k^2$, and its slope is $-(1/3)Rg^2$ using the Guinier radius, Rg. Therefore, Rg was calculated by finding the slope of the $lnI(k)$ vs. k^2 plot (Guinier plot). Rg is a size parameter that is not dependent on the shape of the precipitates. Assuming that the actual radius and the thickness of the cross section of the disk-shaped precipitate are r [nm] and t [nm], respectively, the relationship between Rg, r, and t is expressed as $Rg^2 = r^2/2 + t^2/12$. In addition, in the medium-k region where k is approximately $1/Rg$ or more, the relationship between $I(k)$ and k is expressed as $ln(I(k)k^2)\propto k^2$, and its slope is $-(1/12)t^2$ [10]. In the same way as when the Guinier radius was calculated, the thickness of the cross section of the disk-shaped precipitates was calculated by finding the slope of the $ln(I(k)k^2)$ *vs.* k^2 plot (thickness plot). By substituting the obtained t and Rg values into the relational expression of Rg, t, and r, the radius r of the disk-shaped precipitates was obtained.

To evaluate active slip systems during tensile deformation, in situ XRD measurements were performed at the BL46XU beam line of SPring-8 using the measurement system shown schematically in Fig. 1. The X-ray energy was 30 keV, and the incident beam was 0.5 and 0.2 mm in the horizontal and vertical directions. The detector system was an array of six MYTHEN detectors (DECTRIS) and was positioned about 22° from the transmission direction with a 721.24 mm distance between the specimen and the MYTHEN detectors. The tensile test was performed with an initial strain rate of 1.6×10^{-4} s^{-1}, while oscillating the tensile tester at a rate of 1 mm/s and a width of 3mm. Oscillation was performed to increase the number of grains in the irradiated volume and to obtain XRD peaks of sufficient intensity [11]. The time resolution in this experiment was 4 s. Profile fitting of the obtained diffraction peaks was performed using the Voigt function, and the diffraction angle and full width at half maximum (FWHM) were obtained. The Williamson-Hall equation [12] is often used to separate the FWHM into the effect of crystallite size and the effect of nonuniform strain introduced by dislocations. However, this equation does not consider elastic anisotropy and is not appropriate for application to HCP metals with large elastic anisotropy. Therefore, a modified Williamson-Hall equation that takes elastic anisotropy into account was used in this study [13]:

$$\Delta K_{hk.l} = \frac{0.9}{D} + \left(\frac{\pi M^2 b^2}{2}\right)^{\frac{1}{2}} \rho^{\frac{1}{2}} \overline{C_{hk.l}}^{\frac{1}{2}} K_{hk.l} + O(K^2 \overline{C_{hk.l}}), \quad (1)$$

where K is the diffraction vector ($=(2\sin\theta)/\lambda$), $\Delta K=(\Delta 2\theta\cos\theta)/\lambda$, θ is the diffraction angle, $\Delta 2\theta$ is the FWHM, λ is the wavelength of the incident X-rays, and D is the crystallite size. b is the magnitude of the Burgers vector, ρ is the dislocation density, M is a constant that depends on the effective outer cut-off radius of dislocations, and $\overline{C_{hk.l}}$ is the average dislocation contrast factor that depends on the diffraction plane. $O(K^2\overline{C_{hk.l}})$ is a higher-order term and is typically ignored. The first-order coefficient of K represents the nonuniform strain $\varepsilon_{hk.l}$. The transformation of Eq. (1) is as follows:

$$\varepsilon_{hk.l} = \sqrt{\left(\frac{\Delta K_{hk.l}-\alpha}{K_{hk.l}}\right)^2}. \quad (2)$$

The subscript $hk.l$ in Eq. (2) corresponds to the XRD peak data obtained from the diffraction plane ($hk.l$), i.e., $\varepsilon_{hk.l}$ represents the nonuniform strain in the direction normal to ($hk.l$) planes. The nonuniform strain in the direction normal to each set of diffraction planes was obtained using Eq. (2). To express the anisotropy of the nonuniform strain, polar coordinates were created with the nonuniform strain for each set of diffraction planes as the radial diameter and the angle between the direction normal to each set of diffraction planes and the basal planes as the declination. An approximate curve was then created in the polar coordinates, and this is referred to as the nonuniform strain distribution in this study.

For comparison with the experimental values, Fig. 2 shows the nonuniform strain distribution reported by Dragomir and Ungár that was calculated assuming that only one type of slip system is active and dislocation densities for each slip system is 10^{14} m^{-2} [14]. From Fig. 2, when basal <a> slip is active, the nonuniform strain distribution becomes relatively isotropic. When prism <a> slip is active, nonuniform strain is generated in the in-plane direction of basal plane, and when pyramidal <c+a> slip is active, the nonuniform strain is approximately twice as large in the c-axis direction as in the in-plane direction of basal plane. The active slip systems were evaluated by comparing the nonuniform strain distributions shown in Fig. 2 with those obtained experimentally.

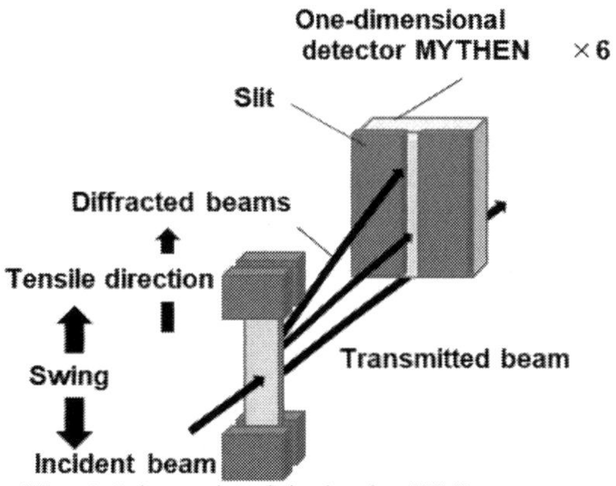

Fig. 1 Schematic of the in-situ XRD measurement with tensile test.

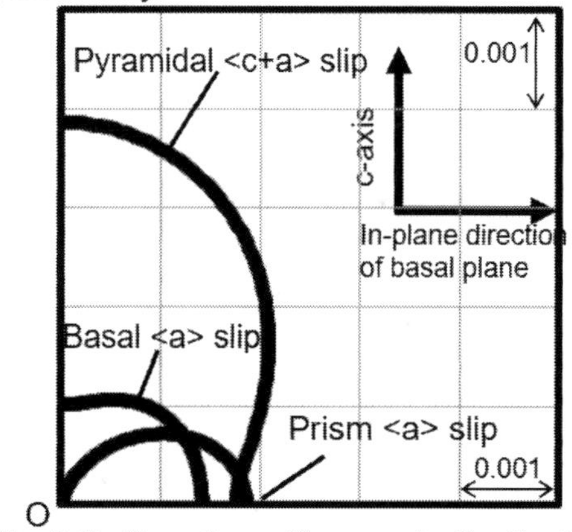

Fig. 2 Outline of ununiform strain distribution of each slip system created using calculated values.

3. Results

Fig. 3 shows the radius and thickness of the disk-shaped precipitates as a function of the aging time. When the aging time was 1.08 ks, the radius and thickness were 0.98 and 0.61 nm, respectively, and after increasing gradually up to 36 ks, they increased rapidly up to 180 ks. The radius then continued to

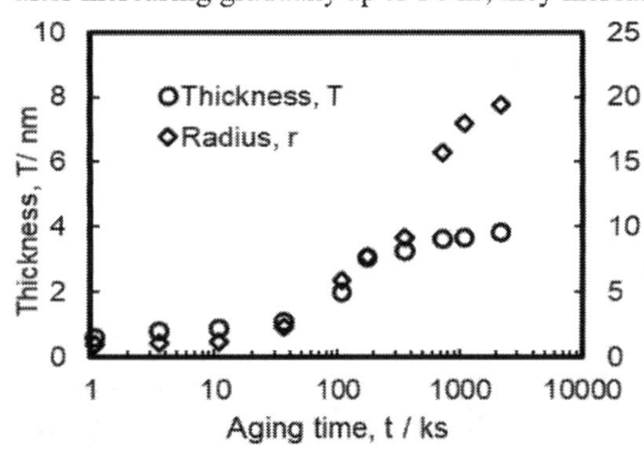

Fig. 3 Average precipitates radius and thickness change with aging time.

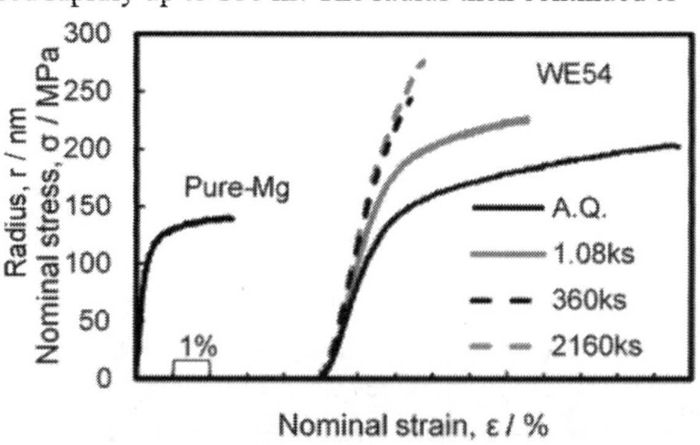

Fig. 4 Nominal stress – nominal strain curves of WE54 alloys.

increase rapidly, while the increase in thickness slowed down. Finally, the radius and thickness at an aging time of 2160 ks were 19.4 and 3.85 nm, respectively. The EBSD measurements results for the A.Q. WE54 alloy and pure Mg, indicated that the grains in both alloys were both coarse with a size of about 10 μm. The change in grain size with aging time was not so large. Fig. 4 shows tensile test results for WE54 at each aging time and those for pure Mg. The uniform elongation for pure Mg was about 2.6%, while that for the A.Q. WE54 alloy indicated a high ductility of about 9.7%. In addition, as the aging time increased, the strength tended to increase while the ductility decreased. The tensile strength and uniform elongation of the alloy aged for 2160 ks were 280 MPa and 2.9%, respectively. In addition, EBSD measurements of the gauge section after fracture of pure Mg and the WE54 alloy indicated no twinning in any of the samples, and the main cause of deformation was dislocation slip.

Fig. 5 shows XRD results for the A.Q. WE54 alloy before tensile testing, during elastic deformation, and during plastic deformation. Compared to that before tensile deformation, the peak angle during elastic deformation shifted downward. This represents an increase in the diffraction plane spacing in the tensile direction as a result of elastic deformation. The increase in peak width during plastic deformation is due to an increase in the dislocation density and the amount of nonuniform strain. Nineteen peaks from the low angle side were used for the analysis.

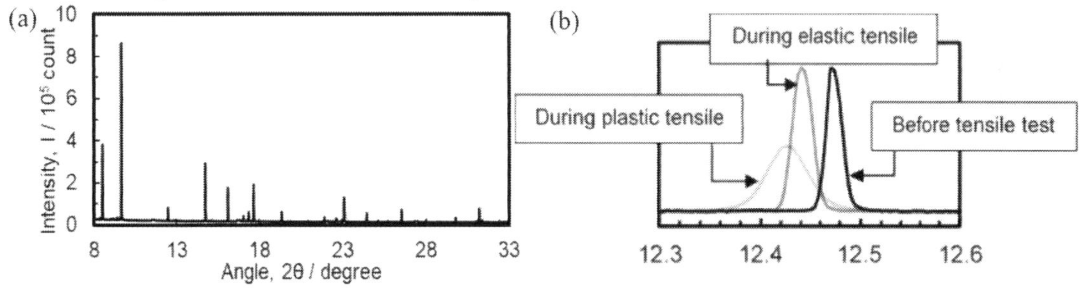

Fig. 5 (a) XRD plofile of WE54 A.Q. before tensile (b)Change in peak position and shape.

Fig. 6 shows the nonuniform strain distribution for each nominal strain of the A.Q. alloy and each aging time of the WE54 alloys. As shown in Figs. 6(a) and 6(b), the nonuniform strain at a nominal strain of 1%, which is the elastic deformation region, was small in the sample where aging was not so advanced. On the other hand, as shown in Figs. 6(c) and 6(d), nonuniform strain was present in the elastic deformation region in the sample with advanced aging. For all samples, the graph expanded due to the increase in nonuniform strain as the deformation progressed. In the A.Q. alloy, the nonuniform strain in the c-axis direction and the in-plane direction of basal plane was about 1.2 times larger than that in the 45° direction, as shown in Fig. 6(a). Compared to Fig. 2, not only basal <a> slip where the nonuniform strain is relatively isotropic, but also prism <a> slip where a large strain is generated in the in-plane direction of basal plane and pyramidal <c+a> slip, where a large strain is generated in the c-axis direction, were active. Therefore, the high ductility of the A.Q. WE54 alloy is due to activation of non-basal slip. Figure 6(b) shows that in the alloy aged for 1.08 ks, the nonuniform strain distribution changed at the deformation stage. Up to a nominal strain of 4%, the nonuniform strain in the c-axis direction was about 1.5 times larger than that in the in-plane direction of basal plane, compared to Fig. 2, which suggests that pyramidal <c+a> slip was active. When the nominal strain was 5.5%, both the nonuniform strain in the c-axis direction and that in the in-plane direction of the basal plane were about 0.0033. Therefore, it is inferred that prism <a> slip is active in the latter stage of plastic deformation. As shown in Fig. 6(c), the nonuniform strain in the in-plane direction of basal plane in the alloy aged for 360 ks was approximately twice as large as that in the c-axis direction at any stage during plastic deformation. Compared to Fig. 2, it can be seen that prism <a> slip was active. Figure 6(d) shows that the amount of nonuniform strain in the alloy aged for 2160 ks increased again in the c-axis direction and in the in-plane direction of basal plane. Compared to Fig. 2, not only basal <a> slip, but also prism <a> slip and pyramidal <c+a> slip were active. In addition, the nonuniform strain in the 45° direction was smaller than that for the A.Q. WE54 alloy shown in Fig. 6(a). Therefore, the alloy aged for 2160 ks had less activity for basal <a> slip than the A.Q. alloy.

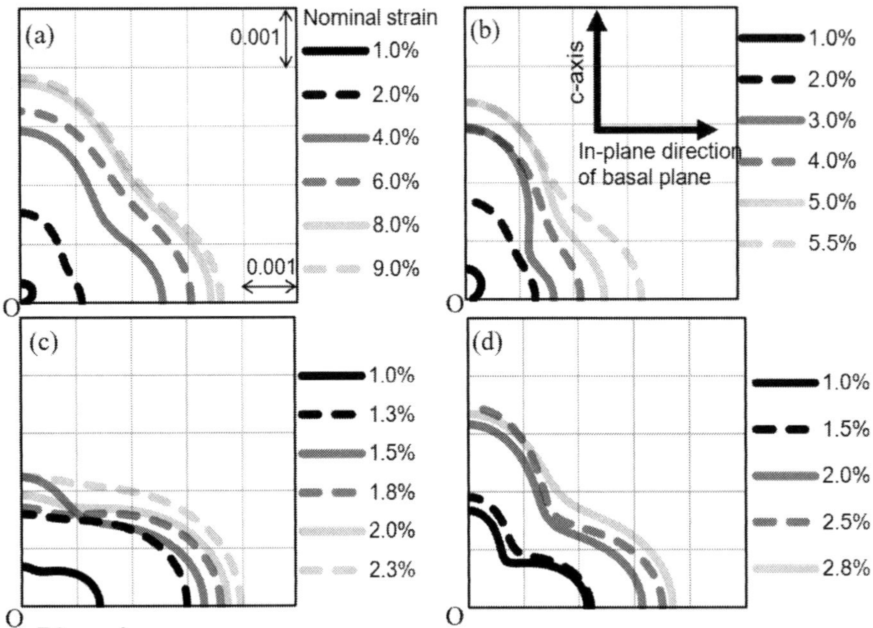

Fig. 6 Nonuniform strain distribution at each stage of deformation for (a) A.Q., (b) 1.08 ks aged, (c) 360 ks aged, and (d) 2160 ks aged WE54.

4. Discussions

To investigate the effect of the precipitates generated by aging on each slip system, the increase in CRSS for each slip system was calculated. The Orowan mechanism and shearing mechanism are well-known precipitation hardening mechanisms [15]. In the Orowan mechanism, dislocations move around the precipitates and leave an Orowan loop, where the amount of strengthening is given by [16]:

$$\Delta\tau_{Orowan} = \frac{Gb}{2\pi\lambda\sqrt{1-\nu}} \ln\frac{d_p}{r_0}, \tag{3}$$

where d_p is the mean planar diameter of the point obstacles, r_0 is the core radius of dislocations, λ is the effective planar interparticle spacing on the slip plane, G and ν are the shear modulus and Poisson's ratio of the matrix phase (17.3 GPa and 0.291 for Mg). In the shearing mechanism, dislocations move while shearing precipitates, and the amount of strengthening is given by [8]:

$$\Delta\tau_{Shear} = \frac{\gamma_{APB}}{2b}\left(\frac{d_p}{\lambda} - \frac{d_p}{L_p}\right), \tag{4}$$

where L_p is the mean planar center-to-center interparticle spacing on the slip plane, and γ_{APB} is the anti-phase boundary (APB) energy for basal <a> dislocation shearing of the precipitates (210 mJ m^{-2} [8]). In past reports, TEM observations of Mg-4 wt% Y-3 wt% Nd (WE43) alloys confirmed that basal <a> slip occurs via the shearing mechanism, and non-basal slip occurs via the Orowan mechanism with respect to the precipitates [8]. Therefore, the increase in the CRSS for each slip system was calculated geometrically using Eq. (4) for basal <a> slip and Eq. (3) for non-basal slip, based on the SAXS results assuming that the precipitates are rationally oriented. The calculation results are shown in Fig. 7. The increase in the CRSS of the prism <a> slip shown in Fig. 7 is large, and that of basal <a> slip is small during the initial stage of aging. The increase in CRSS for prism <a> slip decreases significantly with aging time, and becomes smaller than that for pyramidal <c+a> slip and basal <a> slip after aging for 108 ks. In addition, the increase in CRSS for basal <a> slip increases monotonically with aging time. The calculation results in Fig. 7 were used to consider the results for the nonuniform strain distribution shown in Figs. 6(b)-(d). As shown in Fig. 6(b), for the alloy aged for 1.08 ks, the increase in CRSS for prism <a> slip is large; therefore, the amount of prism <a> slip is small during the initial stage of deformation. Prism <a> slip was active in the alloy aged for 360 ks, as shown in Fig. 6(c). This is because the increase in CRSS for prism <a> slip is smaller than that for the other slip systems, so that it is more easily activated. In the alloy aged for 2160 ks, the activity of basal <a>

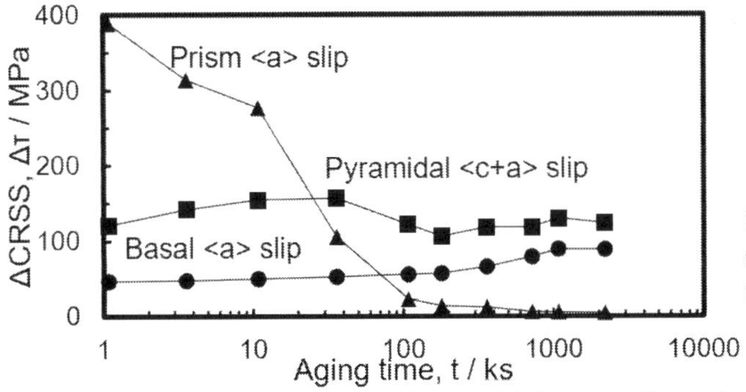

Fig. 7 Increase in ΔCRSS for basal slip, prism slip and pyramidal slip as function of aging time.

slip is small, while the activities of pyramidal <c+a> slip and prism <a> slip are large, as shown in Fig. 6(d). This is because the increase in CRSS for basal <a> slip became large and the difference from the CRSS for pyramidal <c+a> slip narrowed; therefore, the activity of pyramidal <c+a> slip became relatively large.

5. Conclusions

SAXS and in situ XRD measurements were performed on WE54 alloys to evaluate the precipitate size and the active slip system for different aging times.

1. In the A.Q. alloy, the nonuniform strain distribution indicated that not only basal <a> slip, which is the main slip system, but also non-basal slip, were active.
2. In the 360 ks aged alloy, pyramidal <c+a> slip activity decreased and prism <a> slip activity increased, which is in agreement with the calculated results that indicated that the amount of precipitation hardening due to prism <a> slip decreases as aging progresses.
3. Pyramidal <c+a> slip was also active in the alloy aged for 2160 ks because the difference in CRSS between basal <a> slip and pyramidal <c+a> slip narrowed.

Acknowledgments

The synchrotron radiation experiments were performed at the BL19B2 and BL46XU of SPring-8 with the approval of the Japan Synchrotron Radiation Research Institute (JASRI) (Proposal No. 2018A1029 and 2017A1006).

Reference

[1] Sandlobes S, Zaefferer S, Schestakow I, Yi S and Gonzalez R 2011 *Acta Mater.* **59** 429
[2] Yoshinaga H and Horiuchi R 1963 *Trans. JIM* **41** 1
[3] Von Mises R 1928 *Z. Agnew. Math. Mech.* **8** 161
[4] Tsuru T, Udagawa Y, Yamaguchi M, Itakura M, Kaburaki H and Kaji Y 2013 *J. Phys. Condens. Matter.* **25** 02202
[5] Miura S, Imagawa S, Toyoda T, Ohkubo K and Mohri T 2008 *Mater. Trans.* **49** 952
[6] Adachi H, Miyajima Y, Sato M and Tsuji N 2015 *Mater. Trans.* **56** 671
[7] Adachi H, Karamatsu Y, Nakayama S, Miyazawa T, Sato M and Yamasaki T 2016 *Mater. Trans.* **57** 1447
[8] Bhattacharyya J J, Wang F, Stanford N and Agnew S R 2018 *Acta Mater.* **146** 55
[9] Guinier A and Fournet G 1955 Small-angle Scattering of X-rays
[10] Kratly O and Glatter O 1982 Small-angle X-ray Scattering
[11] Adachi H, Mizowaki H, Hirata M, Okai D and Nakanishi H 2020 *J. Jpn. Inst. Light Met.* **70** 274
[12] Williamson G K and Hall W H 1953 *Acta Metall.* **1** 22
[13] Ungár T and Borbély A 1996 *Appl. Phys. Lett.* **69** 3173
[14] Dragomir I C and Ungár T 2002 *J. Appl. Cryst.* **35** 556
[15] Gerold V and Haberkorn H 1966 *Phys. Stat. Sol.* **16** 675
[16] Nie J F 2003 *Scr. Mater.* **48** 1009

IOP Conf. Series: Materials Science and Engineering 1121 (2021) 012045 doi:10.1088/1757-899X/1121/1/012045

3D simulation of texture evolution induced grain coarsening in FCC polycrystals during severe plastic deformation

Chi Zhang[1,2*] and Laszlo S Toth[2,3]

[1]School of Materials Science and Engineering, Dalian University of Technology, Dalian, China

[2]Laboratoire d'Etude des Microstructures et de Mécanique des Matériaux (LEM3), Université de Lorraine, CNRS, Arts et Métiers ParisTech, F-57045 Metz, France

[3]Laboratory of Excellence on Design of Alloy Metals for Low-mAss Structures (DAMAS), Université de Lorraine, F-57045 Metz, France

* E-mail: zhangchi@dlut.edu.cn

Abstract. In the present work, results obtained in 3D polycrystal simulations are reported on the coalescence effect of neighbouring grains due to texture evolution. A 3D cellular automaton model was developed for this purpose, which permits to take into account the effect of topology on coalescence. The grains constituting the polycrystal were divided into voxels to have realistic representations of grain shapes. The Taylor polycrystal plasticity approach was applied to calculate the orientation change for each voxel. When the disorientation angle between neighbour voxels belonging to different grains was less than 5°, the voxel volume was reallocated to the neighbouring grain. For a random initial texture, after a shear strain of 6, the relative volume that was re-assigned between neighbours was 29.7%, which is not negligible. The effect of initial texture and topology was also investigated. The 3D morphologies of some typical coarsening grains were monitored to illustrate the simulation results.

1. Introduction

The grain refining effect during severe plastic deformation processes (SPD) is well known, and one of the major reasons why SPD is a very effective way for obtaining ultra-fine grained or even nano-structured materials [1]. However, at extreme large strains a steady state develops in the microstructure and the average grain size remains constant [2-4]. Therefore, the grain fragmentation process is balanced by a coarsening effect. It is proposed that coarsening is due to continuous dynamic recrystallization in this stage by grain boundary migration [5]. Nevertheless, a displacement of a grain boundary can be also produced as an effect of reducing the orientation difference between the two sides of the boundary. Such an effect can be produced by an evolution of the grain orientations on the two sides. If the orientations are approaching each other, the disorientation is diminishing. So by setting a minimum angle (usually 5°), if it is falling below this critical value, the grain boundary can be detected at a shifted position within the grains. Progressively, this effect is increasing the volume of one grain while reducing the neighbor's one, so the grain size changes. Indeed, during texture evolution, grain orientations are approaching ideal positions in Euler space, and if they are neighbor grains, coalescence into one grain can take place. Such an effect has been reported in sheet-ECAP deformation of a low carbon steel in reference [6] and was also modelled successfully in a 2D simulation. The purpose of the present study is to explore the magnitude of the coalescence effect due to texture evolution in a 3D modeling approach. The simulation work shows that the effect is not negligible; up to 30% of the sample volume can be affected by the coalescence process at sufficiently large strains.

2. Simulation procedure

2.1. Generation of a 3D polycrystal structure by cellular automaton (CA)

A 3D CA algorithm was developed to generate a 3D polycrystal aggregate. A cubic space was divided into voxels and a certain number of grain-sites were generated randomly in this space. Then the nuclei were let grow until occupying the whole space using a probability switching rule. During the growth procedure the Moore neighborhood approach was used, that considers the nearest 6 voxels and the second-nearest 12 voxels in the state switching rule. Grain IDs were assigned to each grain in order to track the grains; the voxels belonging to one grain had the same grain ID. Finally, crystallographic orientations were assigned to the grains. Periodic boundary conditions were applied to the cube for simulating an infinite system.

In this work, the polycrystal model was constructed to compose 150×150×150 voxels in the x, y, z axis directions containing 10000 grains in total. So, in average, 150×150×150 / 10000 = 338 voxels composed a grain. The voxel size was set as 1 μm ×1 μm ×1 μm. It should be noted that all grain size statistics data in the following are based on this voxel size, however, the fraction and frequency data are irrelevant to the voxel size. Figure 1(a) shows the established polycrystal geometry with a random texture generated using the ATEX software [7]. The grain size was calculated here as the diameter of a sphere having the same volume as an irregular shaped grain. The initial grain size distribution is shown in figure 1(b) in number fractions. It infers that a homogeneous equiaxed grain structure with Gaussian distribution in grain size was obtained using the developed CA model.

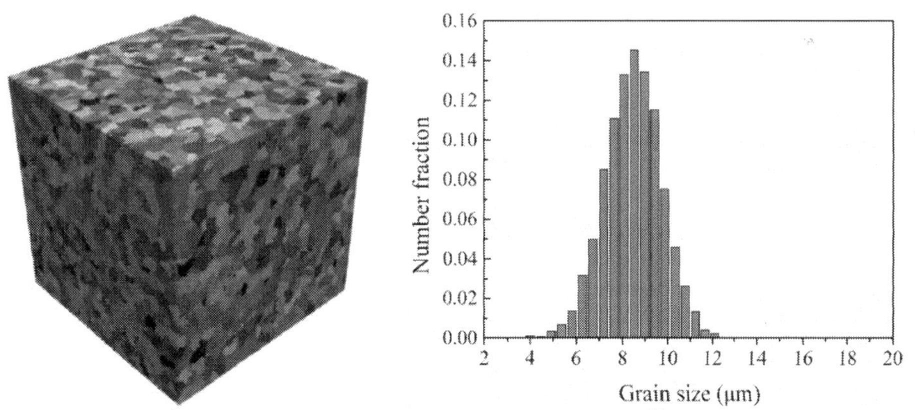

(a) (b)

Figure 1. (a) 3D model polycrystal and (b) its grain size distribution generated by CA.

2.2. Taylor polycrystal plasticity analysis

Generally, the crystallographic texture evolution of a polycrystal during deformation needs to consider not only the orientation evolution of single grains but also the interaction between neighbor grains. Also, the grain shape would change with the progress of plastic deformation. Even for one specific grain, both the deformation and orientation evolutions are inhomogeneous within the grain, depending on its initial orientation, on the loading conditions, and also on the disorientation with its neighbors. Besides, grain fragmentation usually occurs during deformation process, resulting in a very fine microstructure after large plastic strain.

This work focuses on the texture induced grain coarsening effects during large plastic strain. Because of the good ability and efficiency for predicting orientation evolution in FCC and BCC metal polycrystals at high strain conditions [8], the full constraints Taylor model was employed in this work to simulate the orientation evolution during deformation. In this model, the interaction between neighbor grains is not considered and the voxels belonging to one grain were estimated to undergo the same changes. Nevertheless, using this approach, the effects of texture induced coarsening can be captured and the tendencies can be examined.

In the full constraints Taylor model all grains undergo the same shape change as the whole polycrystal. This means that the local velocity gradient ($l_{ij}^{(g)}$) is equal to the macroscopic one (L_{ij}):

$$l_{ij}^{(g)} = L_{ij} \quad . \tag{1}$$

The imposed deformation of a grain is obtained as the sum of independent shears in the slip systems:

$$l_{ij}^{(g)} = \sum_{s=1}^{N} m_{ij}^{s} \cdot \dot{\gamma}^{s} \quad , \tag{2}$$

where m_{ij}^{s} is the Schmid orientation matrix of slip system indexed by s, and $\dot{\gamma}^{s}$ is the shear strain rate. The local stress-strain relation is modelled by the usual constitutive viscoplastic power law relationship between the shear rate ($\dot{\gamma}^{s}$) and the resolved shear stress (τ^{s}):

$$\tau^{s} = \tau_{0}\,\mathrm{sgn}(\dot{\gamma}^{s})\left|\frac{\dot{\gamma}^{s}}{\dot{\gamma}_{0}}\right|^{m} = \tau_{0}\frac{\dot{\gamma}^{s}}{\dot{\gamma}_{0}}\left|\frac{\dot{\gamma}^{s}}{\dot{\gamma}_{0}}\right|^{m-1} \quad . \tag{3}$$

Here m is the strain rate sensitivity index, τ_0 and $\dot{\gamma}_0$ are the reference shear stress and reference shear rate, respectively. The resolved shear stress is related to the macroscopic stress tensor ($\boldsymbol{\sigma}$) by the relation:

$$\tau^{s} = \sigma_{ij} \cdot m_{ij}^{s} \quad . \tag{4}$$

Eqs. (1-4) are the basic equations of the Taylor model with strain rate sensitivity slip to obtain the stress state of a given crystal [9]. The stress tensor provides the slip distribution, from which the orientation change of the grain can be calculated. The 12 {111}<110> slip systems were considered for dislocation slip. Hardening was not taken into account in the simulation. It can be justified by several arguments: i. during large strains the hardening saturates, ii. as the objective is to obtain orientation evolution, isotropic hardening would not influence it. Thus, the results obtained are valid for isotropic hardening, without actually explicitly introducing it into the simulation.

The simple shear deformation was selected for studying the grain coalescence process, by applying a macroscopic velocity gradient with the only non-zero component $L_{12} = \dot{\gamma}$, corresponding to shear on plane 2 in direction 1.

2.3. *Grain coalescence detection and visualization*

The 3D topology of the polycrystal and its orientation evolution during deformation were tracked during the simulation. A grain coalescence detection procedure was developed to count the volumes that were reallocated between neighbor grains. This was done when the disorientation angle between two voxels belonging to neighbor grains was less than 5°. After the coalescence detection process, the grain size distributions were calculated in both number-weighted and volume-weighted versions, as well as the average grain size.

For visualization of the 3D orientation data, the initial and deformed orientations of the polycrystal were output to a set of section data with positions and corresponding Euler angles. The 3D data were then analyzed by the DREAM.3D software [10]. After that, the Paraview software was used to display the generated microstructure [11]. The initial and the deformation induced textures of the polycrystal were calculated and plotted in pole figures using the ATEX software.

3. Results and discussion

Figure 2 plots the (111) pole figures (PFs) of the texture evolution during shear deformation of the polycrystal with random initial texture. The PFs present typical shear texture of FCC polycrystals, corresponding to the Taylor model used in this work. It infers that the orientations rotate near to preferred orientations very fast at the beginning of shear deformation. By increasing the shear strain, the texture becomes sharper and its maximum density increases.

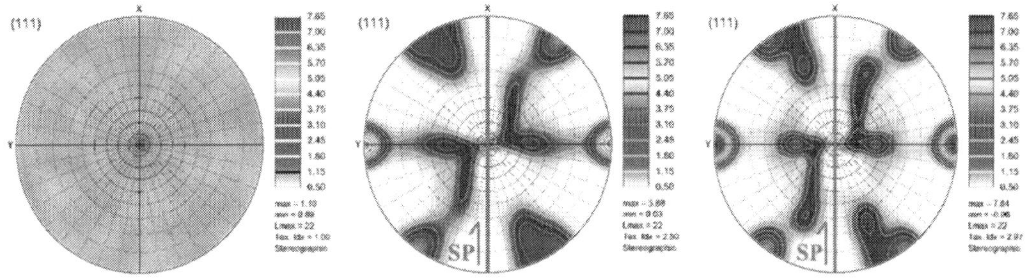

(a) (b) (c)

Figure 2. Texture evolution at different shear strains of the 3D polycrystal with random initial texture. (a) initial texture, (b) texture at shear strain of 2 (c) and at shear strain of 6. (SP indicates the shear plane and the arrow is oriented in the shear direction.)

Typical morphologies of some selected grains with their orientation evolution were tracked, as shown in figure 3. The colors of the grains indicate the crystallographic orientations according to the color code. It clearly shows that with the shear strain increasing to 6, some orientations rotated to similar orientations which have similar colors. Their misorientation angles became below 5°, so they were combined to form a larger grain. Figure 3(a) and (b) shows the evolution of two initial neighbor grains while the example in figure 3(c) and (d) show that five initial neighbor grains coalesced together. The frequency of the number of coalescing grains was analyzed. It indicated that two-grain events accounted for about 60% of the coalesced volume at a shear strain of 6. With the number of coalescing grains increasing, this frequency decreased rapidly, meaning that the coalescence frequency of more than two grains into one was increasing.

The grain coalescence detection procedure was utilized to track the grain coarsening tendency during the shear deformation. The obtained results are listed in Table 1. Note that during the random initial texture assigning procedure, the misorientation angles between some neighbor voxels with different grain IDs happened to be less than 5°. This resulted in the grain number of the initial polycrystal to be 9934 instead of 10000. By increasing the shear strain, the grains rotated near to preferred orientations, forming the texture as shown in figure 2. Meanwhile, the misorientation angles between some adjacent grains decreased below 5°. Therefore, the grain number of the polycrystal decreased with increasing shear strain as listed in Table 1. The accumulated coalescing volume fraction was also calculated. It increased dramatically at the beginning and then reached a saturation state from about 4-8 shear strain. The coarsening volume fraction reached 29.7%. (A value of 17% was reported by Gu et al. in their 2D simulation for low carbon steel [6].) This means that as much as about 30% volume fraction of the polycrystal was participating in the grain coarsening effect induced by the texture evolution. Obviously, this high volume fraction cannot be ignored during large strains. The changes in average grain sizes, however, are relatively smaller, see Table 1. In number fraction, the initial average grain size of 8.48 μm increased up to 8.82 μm, while in volume fraction, from 9.00 μm to 10.38 μm.

Table 1. Grain coalescence analysis for random initial texture

Shear strain	0	1	2	4	6	8
Grain number	9934	9250	8763	8238	8095	8201
Average grain size (number-weighted) (μm)	8.48	8.62	8.72	8.81	8.84	8.82
Average grain size (volume-weighted) (μm)	9.00	9.38	9.76	10.27	10.45	10.38
Coalescing volume fraction (%)	1.4	13.6	20.9	27.8	29.7	28.4

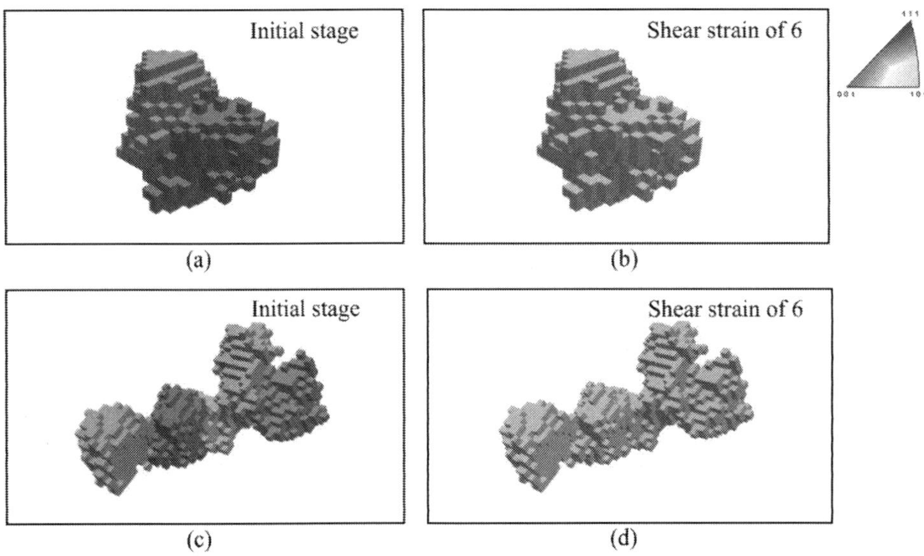

Figure 3. Typical morphologies for orientation evolution induced grain coarsening events. (Note that the deformation induced grain shape change is not shown; the deformed state is shown in the initial geometry.)

The effects of the initial texture and the topology on the texture induced grain coarsening were also investigated, as shown in figure 4. A cube-type initial texture was also considered. The change in topology was simulated by changing the number of voxels. The results show that the 3D topology had relatively small influence on the grain coarsening compared to the effect of the initial texture. As can be seen in figure 4, significantly smaller volume was concerned by grain coarsening in the case of the cube initial texture. It is also apparent from figure 4 that after the coalesced volume reached a maximum, there was a decrease in the volume. This means that grain splitting could also take place, an effect which concerned grains that were initially individual, then coalesced, and finally split in orientation. See also Table 1, which shows an increase in the grain number between shears of 6 and 8. This is also an effect of texture evolution; its origin has to be looked for in the convergent/divergent nature of the rotation field in Euler space. Namely, it has been shown in Ref. [9] that in simple shear, grain orientations can cross from the convergent side of the rotation field into the divergent one. Therefore, first orientations approach each other, then, by passing the line between the convergent/divergent regions, they deviate more and more.

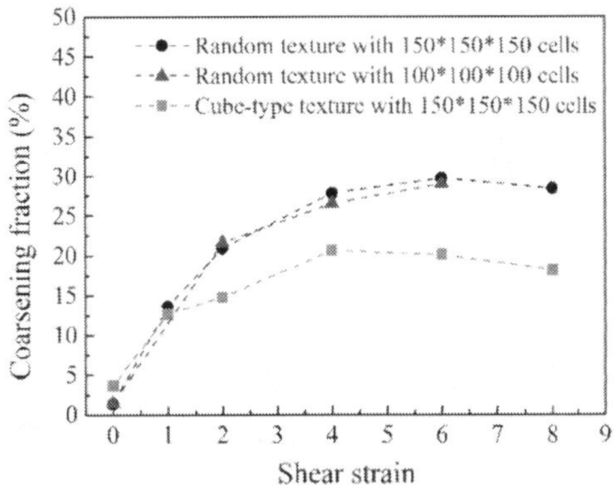

Figure 4. The volume fraction affected by coalescence of grains as a function of the applied shear. The effects of the initial texture and 3D topology are also shown.

4. Conclusion

The texture induced grain coarsening was analyzed at large strains in this work. For this purpose, 3D topological polycrystals were generated using a 3D cellular automaton model. The texture evolution of the polycrystal during shear deformation was calculated using the Taylor polycrystal viscoplastic approach. A grain detection analysis, based on disorientation between neighbor voxels, was employed for computing the texture induced grain coarsening effect. The observed accumulated coalescing volume fraction reached 29.7% at a shear strain of 6 for a random initial texture, together with variations in grain size. It was found that the initial texture had significant influence on the texture induced grain coarsening; the cube texture showed smaller coalescing tendency as compared to the random texture. It is concluded that the texture induced coarsening effect in SPD cannot be ignored and should be taken into account in grain refinement analyses. Therefore, the effect of texture evolution produced grain coarsening should be investigated further for different initial textures.

References

[1] Toth L S and Gu C 2014 Ultrafine-grain metals by severe plastic deformation *Mater. Charact.* **92** 1-14
[2] Belyakov A, Sakai T, Miura H and Tsuzaki K 2001 Grain refinement in copper under large strain deformation *Philos. Mag. A* **81** 2629-43
[3] Estrin Y and Vinogradov A 2013 Extreme grain refinement by severe plastic deformation: A wealth of challenging science *Acta Mater.* **61** 782-817
[4] Langdon T G 2013 Twenty-five years of ultrafine-grained materials: Achieving exceptional properties through grain refinement *Acta Mater.* **61** 7035-59
[5] Sakai T, Belyakov A, Kaibyshev R, Miura H and Jonas J J 2014 Dynamic and post-dynamic recrystallization under hot, cold and severe plastic deformation conditions *Prog. Mater. Sci.* **60** 130-207
[6] Gu C F, Toth L S, Rusz S and Bova M 2014 Texture induced grain coarsening in severe plastic deformed low carbon steel *Scripta Mater.* **86** 36-9
[7] Beausir B and Fundenberger J-J 2017 Analysis Tools for Electron and X-ray diffraction, ATEX-software. Université de Lorraine - Metz
[8] Suwas S and Ray R K 2014 *Crystallographic texture of materials* (UK: Springer)
[9] Toth L S, Gilormini P and Jonas J J 1988 Effect of rate sensitivity on the stability of torsion textures *Acta Metall.* **36** 3077-91
[10] Groeber M A and Jackson M A 2014 DREAM.3D: A Digital Representation Environment for the Analysis of Microstructure in 3D *Integrating Mater. Manuf. Innovation* **3** 56-72
[11] Ayachit and Utkarsh 2015 *The paraview guide: a parallel visualization application* (Kitware: ISBN 978-1930934306)

IOP Conf. Series: Materials Science and Engineering 1121 (2021) 012046 doi:10.1088/1757-899X/1121/1/012046

Process parameter influence on deformation and recrystallization textures in Al alloys

Jurij J Sidor[1], Qingge Xie[2], Purnima Chakravarty[1], Gyula Pal[1]

[1]Savaria Institute of Technology, Faculty of Informatics, Eötvös Loránd University (ELTE), Szombathely, Hungary
[2]Collaborative Innovation Center of Steel Technology, University of Science and Technology Beijing, Beijing 100083, China
Corresponding author's e-mail: js@inf.elte.hu

Abstract. Mesoscopic changes take place during the entire thermomechanical processing (TMP) of polycrystalline metallic materials. Controlling the TMP parameters is of key importance since both microstructure and texture evolution of a particular technological step severely influence the final properties of a given product. This study is focusing on the crystallographic aspect of microstructural formation in Al alloys. The effect of straining level on the crystallographic texture evolution and texture-dependent properties is discussed. This contribution clearly demonstrates that the plastic stain ratio can be modified via TMP route. Implementation of relatively small deformation could account for improvement of anisotropy of plastic yielding, necessary for advanced deep drawing qualities.

1. Introduction

Production of polycrystalline Al alloys involves continuous change on microstructural level and these mesoscopic changes strongly influence the mechanical properties of materials. In case of sheet metal products, the thermomechanical processing (TMP) involves direct chill casting, homogenization, hot and cold rolling (intermediate annealing, if necessary) and final recrystallization annealing. Although it seems that each stage of TMP chain is an independent event, the results of numerous investigations [1, 2] clearly indicate that there is a "genetic" connection between the individual processing steps. Furthermore, each TMP step affects the behavior of a consequent one as well as the final properties of a material.

Microstructure of polycrystalline aggregate, exposed to a sequence of deformation and annealing processes, is subjected to morphological changes, which depend on the straining level, strain rate, and annealing history. When it comes to crystallographic aspect of mesoscopic changes, the evolution becomes less apparent, compared to morphological one, since one type of texture tends to replace the preceding one and the connection between the two counterparts is not always obvious. A typical example is the evolution of recrystallization texture during discontinuous annealing in face centered cubic (FCC) metals. Particularly, the α and β fibers, which typically evolve during rolling, tend to transform to a qualitatively new one, characterized by the strongly evolved θ-fiber components mixed with the weakly developed α and γ orientations (see Tab. 1).

Both experimental evidence and implementation of numerical approaches are necessary in order to reveal the process parameters influence on the evolution of deformation and recrystallization textures. The present study aims to clarify the correlation among the TMP parameters, crystallographic texture and related properties. The major goal of this contribution is to show how the deformation affects the recrystallization texture and the plastic strain ratio.

Table 1. Main orientations and fibers, observed in materials with FCC crystal structure [1, 3].

Fiber	Common axis of orientations
α	$\langle 011\rangle$ ‖ Normal Direction
β	$\{h,\ 1,\ h+1\}\left\langle \frac{h(h+1)}{3/4-h},\ \frac{2h(h+1)}{1/2-h},\ \frac{h^2}{h-3/4}+\frac{2h}{h-1/2}\right\rangle$
γ	$\langle 111\rangle$ ‖ Normal Direction
θ	$\langle 001\rangle$ ‖ Normal Direction
η	$\langle 001\rangle$ ‖ Rolling Direction

2. Materials, experimental and computational procedure

The evolution of crystallographic texture was studied in Al-Mg-Si alloy (AA6016 series) in the present investigation. Two investigated materials (A and B) featured different pre-rolling textures and were subjected to diverse straining levels. Material A was cold rolled with 86% thickness reduction, whereas material B was subjected to 30% (material B1) and 47% (material B2) reductions. Finally, the deformed sheets were annealed at 550°C with the aim to ensure a fully recrystallized state.

The initial, rolled and annealed samples were exposed to textures measurements across the thickness by means of electron backscattering diffraction (EBSD) technique. The orientation data, obtained from the plane perpendicular to the sample transverse direction (TD-plane), were collected and post-processed by the commercial OIM-TSL-8® software. The texture data were measured by the Hikari-type EBSD detector, which was attached to the scanning electron microscope (SEM) FEI®. In case of annealed samples, the orientation imaging microscopy (OIM) data were collected at the acceleration voltage of 20 kV. In the deformed materials, the acquisition was performed at lower acceleration voltages, to avoid overlapping of acquired pattern with ones originating from the deeper layers. Application of 12-16 kV guaranteed appropriate OIM data quality. During OIM measurements, the investigated sheets were 70° tilted with respect to the EBSD detector and the mapping was performed on hexagonal scan grids. The textures were displayed in the φ_2=45°, φ_2=65° and φ_2=90° sections respectively, which show majority of components evolving during TMP.

Sample preparation for OIM was performed according to the standard procedure, which comprises mechanical grinding and polishing as well as electrolytic polishing. The mechanical polishing procedure was finished with the DiaDuo-2 Struers®-type 1 μm diamond paste. The electrolytic polishing, as a final step of sample preparation for EBSD, was conducted for ~1 min. at voltages ranging from 18 to 30 V with A2 Struers® electrolyte, cooled to temperatures ranging between -5 and 0°C.

The plastic strain ratio (q-value) was simulated by a well-established Taylor-type homogenization approach Alamel [4]. The plastic strain ratio (q-value) is defined as a fraction of width to elongation in tension. The average q-value, measured at different angles with respect to RD, describes the normal anisotropy whereas the planar anisotropy Δq is defined as a difference between the maximum and minimum q-values. The calculation of q-value profiles was performed by crystal plasticity model by taking into account the {111}<110> octahedral slip systems, which typically operate during deformation at room temperatures in materials with FCC crystal structure.

3. Results and Discussions

3.1. Pre-rolling textures

The pre-rolling textures of materials A and B are shown in Fig. 1. The bunch of orientations, mainly distributed along the α, β, θ and η fibers, has evolved in the investigated materials. The textures presented in Fig. 1 a and b reveal significant qualitative and quantitative diversities. Material A is characterized by the mixture of cube ({001}⟨100⟩) and β-fiber orientations. In contrast, material B shows strongly developed cube component, {113}⟨121⟩ orientation, a weak Goss texture ({011}⟨100⟩) and traces of β-fiber orientations.

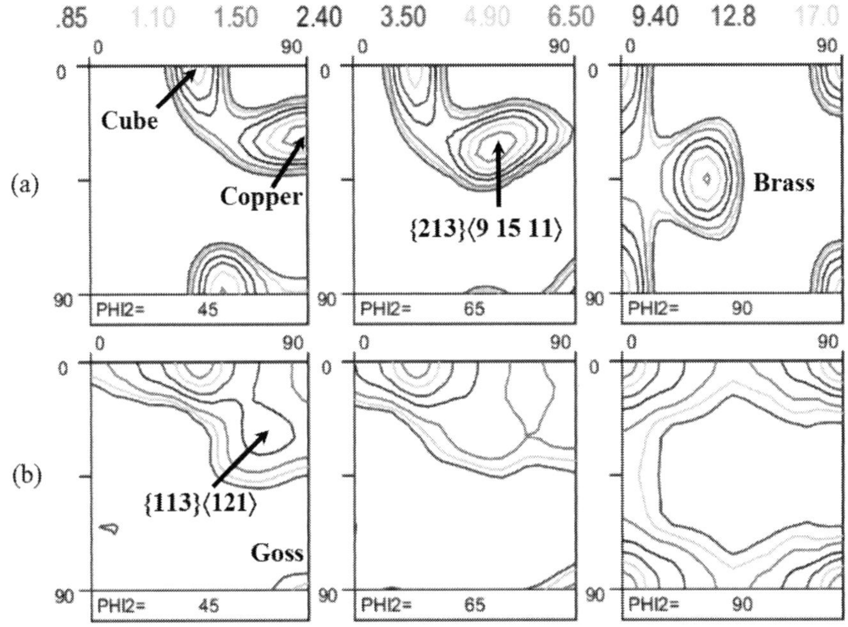

Fig.1. Pre-rolling texture of investigated materials: a) material A; b) material B.

3.2. Deformation textures

The development of texture during cold rolling, shown in Fig. 2, is characterized by the α and β fibers. In case of severe straining level (material A, 86%), the rolling components are aligned along the β-fiber. The reference orientations of the β-fiber can be computed by means of equation presented in Table 1, according to which the position of each β-fiber component is a function of a single miller index *h*. The deformation texture orientations in material A (Fig. 2a) show somewhat unequal distribution along the β-fiber ($6.5<f(g)<11$) with a maximum at ~{213}⟨9 15 11⟩. As it is shown in Fig. 2a, the severe reduction of 86% is not capable of complete reorientation of cube component towards the deformation fiber texture. Compared to material A, material B, with strongly developed cube component, was subjected to less intense straining. The intensities of components along the skeleton line in samples B1 and B2, connecting the copper and brass in Euler space, tend to decline with an increase of *h*, i.e., orientation intensity *f(g)* follows slight downward trend while moving from the {112}⟨111⟩ (h=1) via {213}⟨9 15 11⟩ (h=2) to {011}⟨112⟩ ($h\to\infty$). The cube component in samples B1 and B2 revealed fairly high stability against reorientation, as it was also observed in the material A. The major qualitative difference between the texture evolutionary patterns in materials A and B is related to the appearance of α-fiber in samples B1 and B2, which was not present in material A (see Fig. 2 a-c).

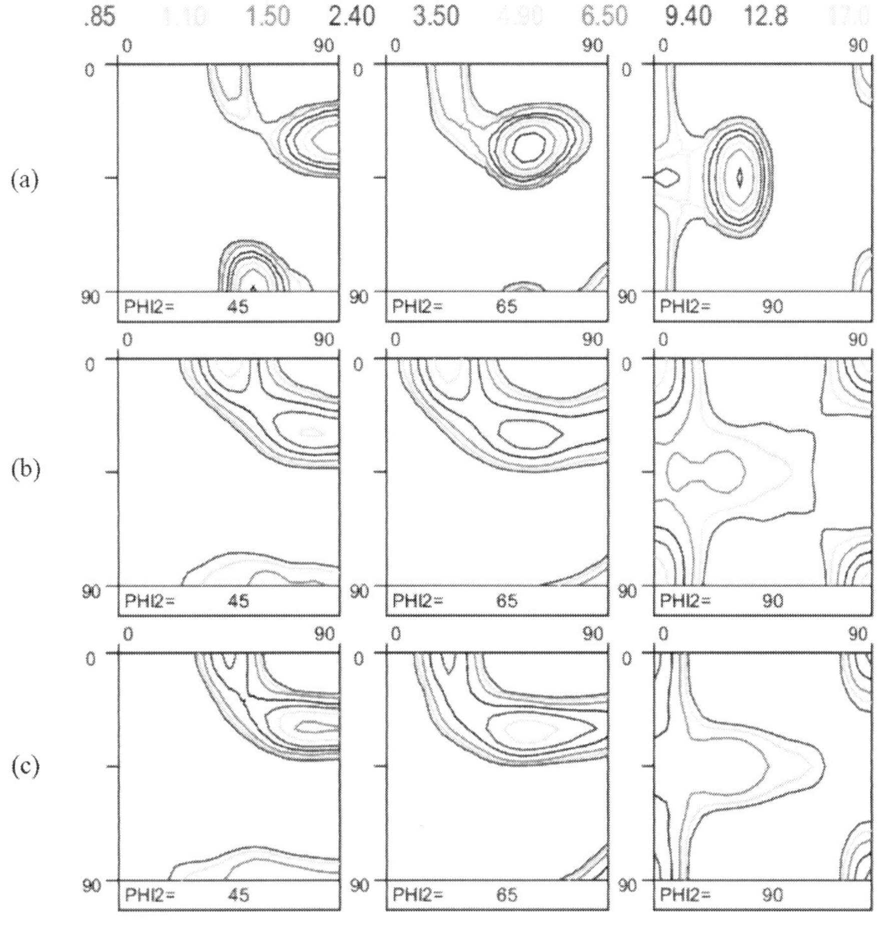

Fig.2. Deformation textures of investigated materials: a) material A, subjected to 86% reduction; b) material B, subjected to 30% reduction (B1); c) material B, subjected to 47% reduction (B2).

3.3. Recrystallization texture

By comparison of Figs. 2 and 3, it becomes evident that the evolution of deformation texture has a great impact on the crystallographic aspect of microstructure development during recrystallization. The combined cube-β-fiber type deformation texture (Fig. 2a) has ensured a well evolved θ-fiber, Goss, P ({011}⟨233⟩) texture mixed with a week γ-fiber orientations (Fig. 3a) during recrystallization. In case of less intense deformation (30% and 47%), the cube-α-β-fiber type rolling textures (Fig. 2 b and c) tended to transform to a cube dominating annealing texture (Fig. 3b and c). Both qualitative and quantitative differences in texture change might be explained by the varieties in the pre-rolling and deformation textures as well as diversities in the degree of reduction. Although both the initial and deformation textures of materials B1 and B2 showed strong cube components, the recrystallization ODFs of these samples exhibited weaker θ-fiber components as compared to material A. Analysis of texture evolution presented in Figs. 2 and 3 suggests that a broad spectrum of orientations in the deformed state, obtained after relatively small straining levels, is capable of ensuring a qualitative diversity in the recrystallized matrix.

IOP Conf. Series: Materials Science and Engineering 1121 (2021) 012046 doi:10.1088/1757-899X/1121/1/012046

The evolution of recrystallization textures shown in Fig. 3 can be explained by employing modeling approaches [2, 5, 6], where the nucleation spectrum is determined by orientation selection, which is based on the diversity of stored energy in differently oriented crystals. Apart from the cube component, which typically appears in metals with FCC crystal structure, weak γ-fiber orientations, P, Goss, Q ({013}⟨231⟩), or a ~22° rotated cube (CH) texture components tend to evolve in the recrystallized matrix of the investigated materials (Figs. 3 a-c). These orientations originate from diverse annealing phenomena and accounting for stain mode heterogeneities in the vicinity of non-deformable particles [2, 7] or texture evolution in the shear-bands [8], the recrystallization models are capable of explaining the evolution of mentioned orientations. The modelling issues, are out of the scope of this paper, but it should be underlined that the local events such as nucleation in the shear bands or particle stimulated nucleation [2], which takes place within a particle deformation affected zone, have a great impact on both qualitative and quantitative characteristics of texture evolved during final annealing.

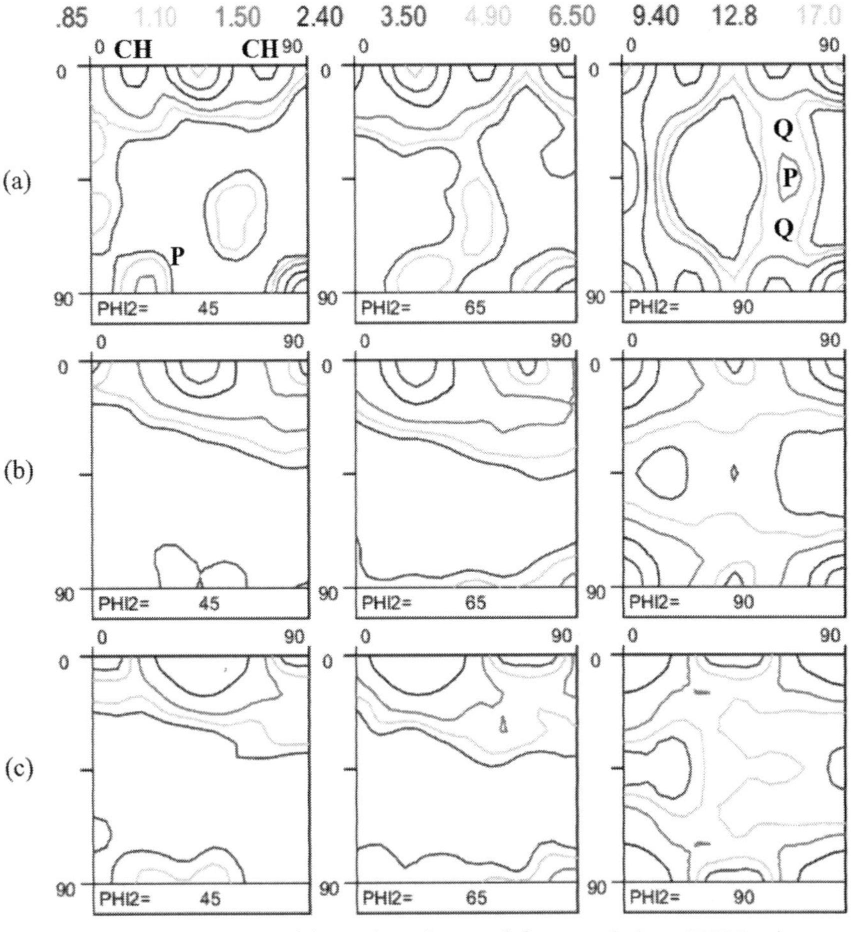

Fig.3. Recrystallization textures of investigated materials annealed at 550°C: a) material A; b) material B1; c) material B2.

3.4. Plastic strain ratio

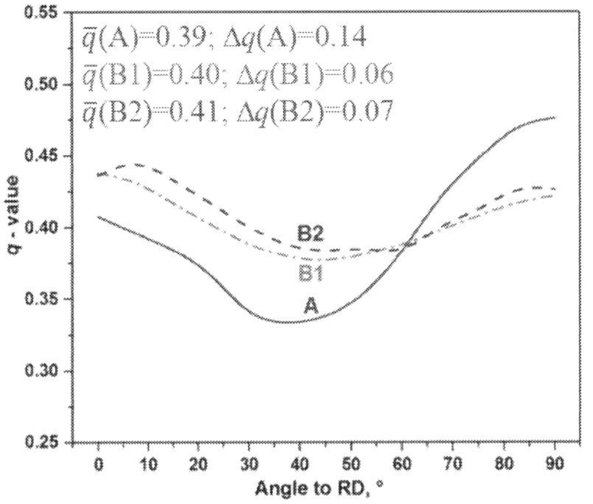

Fig.4. Calculated q-value profiles for investigated materials A, B1 and B2 with the Alamel model.

As it was already claimed in the previous studies [1, 9], the crystallographic texture strongly influences the anisotropy of plastic yielding, and therefore, texture control during TMP is of key importance. Both normal ($\bar{q}$) and planar (Δq) anisotropy appear to show evidence whether a given material has appropriate deep drawing quality (ideally, $\bar{q}$ should be above 0.5 and Δq=0). The assessment of plastic strain ratio (see Fig. 4) in the recrystallized materials A, B1 and B2 (shown in Fig. 3), is performed by employing a crystal plasticity model Alamel. This type of Taylor-type homogenization approach is capable of simulating the plastic anisotropy with a high accuracy [10] for a vast variety of textures. The investigated recrystallization textures (Fig. 3) reveal noticeable quantitative varieties. Since the ODFs of materials B1 and B2 are weaker in terms of texture intensity, the corresponding q-value profiles reveal less anisotropy, compared to material A, which shows a pronounced V-shaped profile. Although the $\bar{q}$ and Δq values are far from ideal, the current study clearly shows that the proper choice of TMP parameters is capable of changing the behavior of a material during deep drawing operations.

4. Conclusions

Examination of texture evolution during deformation and recrystallization suggests that a broad spectrum of orientations aligned along the α and β fibers in the deformed state, obtained after relatively small straining levels (30-47%), is capable of ensuring qualitative diversity in the recrystallized matrix. By way of contrast, relatively large quantity of cube component embedded in the deformation matrix, characterized solely by the β fiber orientations account for stronger recrystallization texture.

The emerged weak textures are of particular interest due to enhanced formability characteristics while the strongly textured materials ensure strong planar anisotropy which is detrimental for deep drawing.

Acknowledgement

This research was funded by the EFOP-3.6.1-16-2016-00018 project: "improving the role of research + development + innovation in higher education through institutional developments assisting intelligent specialization in Sopron and Szombathely".

References

[1] Humphreys J Rohrer G S and Rollett A 2017 *Recrystallization and Related Annealing Phenomena* (Amsterdam: Elsevier)
[2] Sidor J J Decroos K Petrov R H and Kestens LAI 2015 *Int. J. Plast.* **66** 119
[3] Sidor J J and Kestens LAI 2013 *Scripta Mat.* **68** 273
[4] Van Houtte P Kanjarla A K Van Bael A Seefeldt and M Delannay L 2006 *Eur. J. Mech. A* **25** 634
[5] Kestens L and Jonas JJ 1996 *Metal. Mater. Trans.* A **27** 155
[6] Engler O 1997 *Textures and Microstr.* **28** 197
[7] Engler O Yang P Kong XW 1996 *Acta Mater.* **44** 3349
[8] Engler O 2001 *Scripta Mater.* **44** 229.
[9] Hutchinson B 2015 *Mater. Sci. Technol.* **31** 1393
[10] Sidor J J Petrov R H Xie Q Van Houtte P and Kestens LAI 2017 *Mater. Sc. Tech.* **33** 667

IOP Conf. Series: Materials Science and Engineering 1121 (2021) 012047 doi:10.1088/1757-899X/1121/1/012047

Influence of laser beam scanning strategy in the selective laser melting of 316L steel powder on macrostress

MG Isaenkova[1,a)], **A V Yudin**[1,2], **A E Rubanov**[1,b)], **A V Osintsev**[1] and **L A Degadnikova**[1]

[1]*National Research Nuclear University MEPhI, Moscow, Russia*

[2]*JSC "CNIITMASH", Moscow, Russia*

E-mail: : [a)]*isamarg@mail.ru*; [б)]*toly.rubanov@yandex.ru*

Abstract. The use of selective laser melting (SLM) leads to the formation of a complex material structure with high residual elastic stresses. The work investigates the distribution of macrostresses in SLM samples using five different scanning strategies. The stresses were measured by X-ray method and by recording the change in the shape of the specimens as a result of their separation from the platform using digital correlation image method. The combined use of the two methods provides more reliable results for SLM samples. It is shown that depending on the scanning strategy, the nature and magnitude of macrostresses change which are distributed more isotropically and have a smaller value when using scanning strategies with different directions of the laser beam movement.

1. Introduction

The selective laser melting method (SLM) is an additive manufacturing method in which the metallic part is formed layer-by-layer from metal powder. The advantage of this method is that it is possible to produce parts with complex shapes, with inner cavities [1]. The powder is melted by laser radiation and a melt pool is formed in which the material re-solidified again after shifting the laser beam to another area. This determines the formation conditions of the material - crystallization at a temperature gradient, the sequence of heating and cooling of the material. These, in turn, lead to the formation of high thermal stresses [2] and anisotropy of mechanical properties due to the complex structure of the material [3]. SLM samples contain overlapping areas of individual tracks [4] from successive laser passes filled with column grains with close crystallographic orientations [5, 6].

The high level of residual macro stresses is a negative feature of the SLM method, as it can cause the part to warp after separation from the construction platform due to stress relaxation. Optimization of the laser beam scanning strategy, scanning speed and laser power [7, 8], as well as heat treatment for stress relief before separation of parts from the construction platform can be considered to reduce this phenomenon. But, all these methods require monitoring the level of macrostress in a sample to determine their effectiveness.

Various calculation and experimental methods are used to estimate the value of macrostress in samples manufactured by additive manufacturing methods. For example, stress fields near the melting pool when applying a separate track can be calculated analytically [9] and measured in-situ using

IOP Conf. Series: Materials Science and Engineering 1121 (2021) 012047 doi:10.1088/1757-899X/1121/1/012047

synchrotron radiation [10]. The distribution of residual macrostresses in a sample can be measured experimentally using the X-ray method [11] and neutron diffraction [12], or calculated by numerical simulation as a superposition of stresses from multiple tracks [7, 8].

All these methods of determining macrostress have their advantages and disadvantages, and therefore it seems reasonable to use a combination of different methods. Therefore, the purpose of this work is to reveal the influence of the scanning strategy on the residual macrostress by combining two methods of determining the macrostress - X-ray and by changing the shape of the sample at stress relaxation. Specimen shape change was determined by digital image correlation method [13].

2. Smples and research methods

amples of 316L steel produced by SLM on MeltMaster3D-550 with ytterbium fiber laser of maximum power of 1 KW and working area of 550×450×450 mm, layer thickness of 20-250 microns were studied in this work. To print samples, the following SLM-process parameters were used: laser power 320 W, scanning speed 850 mm/s, scanning step 80 μm, layer thickness 50 μm. For each of the five manufactured samples, different scanning strategies were used, as shown in Figure 1. The sample size is 10×10×50mm. For the simplicity of further presentation, let's introduce a coordinate system: the Z-axis is selected along the direction of sample growth, the Y-axis along the long side of the sample, and the X-axis along the short side of the sample.

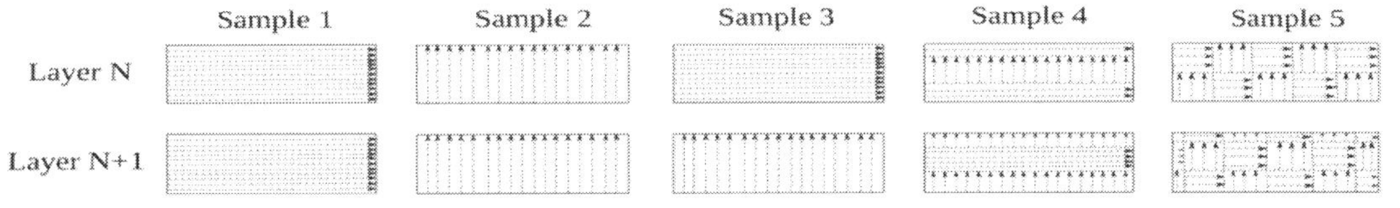

Figure 1. Laser beam scanning strategies

The samples were printed on a 22 mm thick construction platform. For easier separation of the sample from the platform, a supporting structure in the form of a grid of mutually perpendicular edges 0.3 mm thick and 1 mm step was printed below them. At the first step, the specimens were examined directly on the construction platform in the state after printing (fugure 2-a). In the second step, the supporting structure was cut off, except for a small section of one rib in the center of the sample, which allowed for stress relaxation by changing the shape of the sample (fugure 2-b). The keeping of a small segment of the supporting structure was due to the comfort of measurements. At each of these steps, the macrostresses in the sample were measured by X-ray method and the surface profile was recorded by digital images correlation.

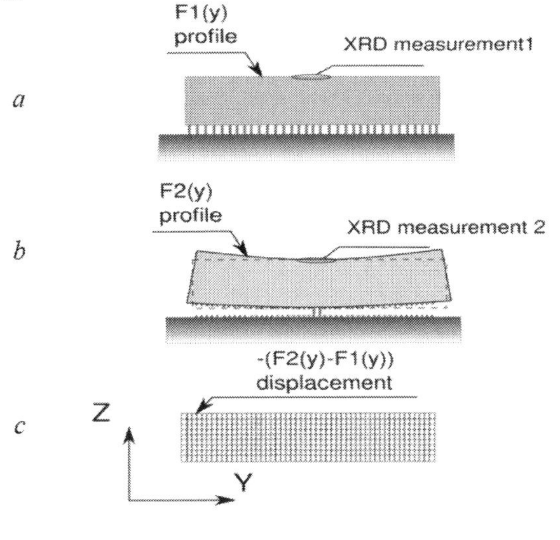

Figure 2. Scheme of the experiment:
a - measurements in the initial state;
b - measurements after removal of the supporting structure;
c - finite element model for calculation of stresses by changing the surface profile;

The measurement of residual elastic macrostresses was performed by $\sin^2\psi$ method on Bruker D8 Discover X-ray diffractometer using filtered Cu radiation. For this purpose, a line (400) in the range of angles 2Θ 115-122.5° and angles ψ=0, 10, 20, 30, 40, 50° was recorded. To exclude the influence of the sample surface roughness (measurements were made without additional surface preparation after printing), the geometry with parallel beam (i.e. Goebel mirror) was used. When measuring, the sample was set so that the beam would get into its central part. The macrostresses were determined in the X and Y directions.

Detection of the sample surface profile was carried out by the method of digital images correlation. Measurements were carried out on the upper surface of the sample, on which chaotically distributed marks-stains (speckle structure) were applied. Then, the spatial location of the applied marks was identified by optical system to determine the surface profile of the sample. Additional markings were made on the specimen surface in advance to align the coordinates of the surface points before and after removing the supports. Polynomial approximations of the upper surface profile along the midline in the initial state ($F_1(y)$) and after removal of supports ($F_2(y)$) were used for quantitative description of the sample shape change. Stresses from the specimen shape change were calculated using the finite element method (FEM). The two-dimensional beam bending problem (representing the investigated sample) was solved, where the upper surface movement was set by function $-(F_2(y) - F_1(y))$, as shown in Figure 2c.

3. Results and discussion

3.1. Experimental results

fugure 3 shows graphs of X-ray measured macrostresses in investigated samples in initial state (fugure 3-a) and after removal of supporting structure (fugure 3-b) in two directions. Macrostresses in the initial state are mainly tensile, significant compressive stresses were found only in sample 3 in the direction Y. In samples 1 and 2, the stresses along X and Y directions respectively (directions perpendicular to the scanning direction) are close to zero. After removing the Y-axis supports, the sign changes to the opposite, and for the X-axis stresses only the value changes.

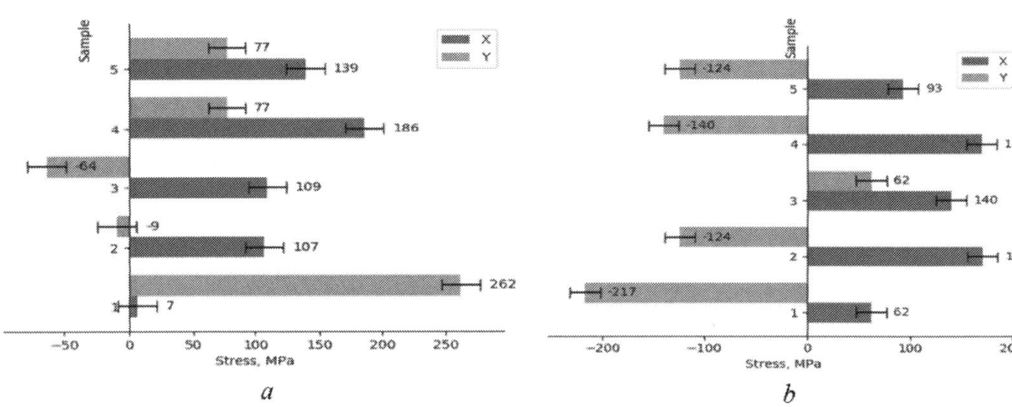

Figure 3. Results of macrostress measurement by X-ray method
a - in the initial state; b - after removing the supports;

fugure 4 shows the results of measuring the shape change of the sample as a result of removing the supporting structure: the surface height maps in the initial state (fugure 4-a) and after removing the supports (fugure 4-b), obtained by the digital images correlation. We can see that there is some bending of the sample in the initial state - the edges are located above the central part. After removing the supports, the bend along the long side of the sample (Y-axis) becomes stronger, and along the short side, the shape changes less.

Figure 4-c shows an example of the stress distribution calculated with the help of FEM on the data on changing the shape of the sample. It should be noted that the obtained character of stress changes by height of the sample well corresponds to that obtained in [11] - compressive stresses are observed in the lower part of the sample and tensile stresses in the upper part. We will compare the results of stress calculations for different samples by the value of stresses in the center of the upper surface - in the area of X-ray stress measurement. Figure 4-g shows a graph of the calculated stresses along the Y-axis in the central part of the upper surface of the samples. All stresses have the tensile nature.

3.2. Comparison of X-ray macrostress with shape change data

Comparing change of measured value of residual elastic stresses at removal of supporting structure (fugure 3) with change of sample shape (fugure 4-a, b), it can be noted that significant change of X-ray macrostresses and sample shape occurs only along Y direction. It follows that both methods register the same nature of stress relaxation and there is a good quality coincidence of results.

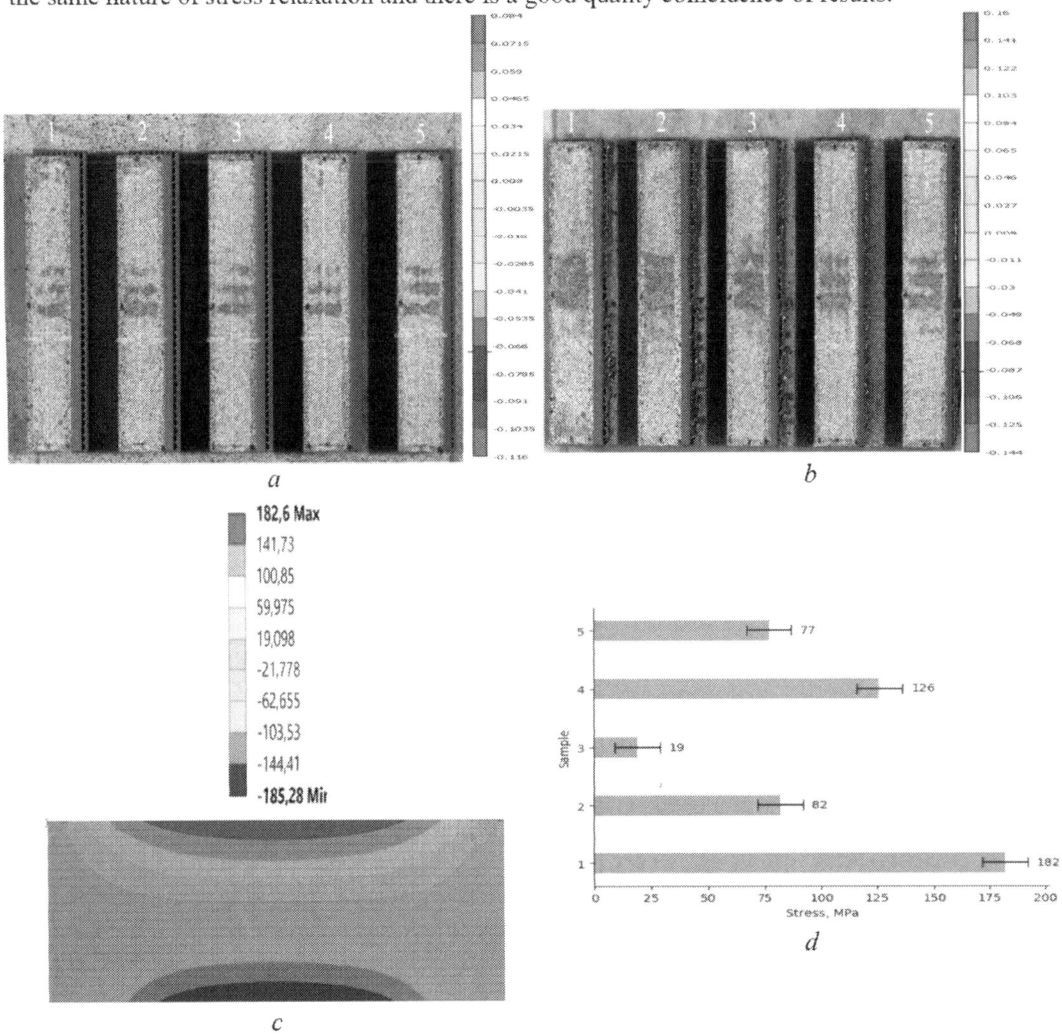

Figure 4. Evaluation results of the sample shape change: a - surface profile shape in initial state; b - surface profile shape after removal of supports; c - stress distribution calculated by FEM; c - calculated values of stresses along the Y axis in the central part of the upper surface of the sample.

On the graph shown in the fugure 5, a quantitative comparison of the results of macrostress determination by the methods used was made. The graph shows that the best match of results is observed for samples 4 and 5 - with the scanning strategies in the form of strips with change of direction and chess. The worst match was found for samples 2 and 3, with a single-pass scan strategy

IOP Conf. Series: Materials Science and Engineering 1121 (2021) 012047 doi:10.1088/1757-899X/1121/1/012047

along X and with a change of direction. Sample 1 occupies an intermediate position for matching the results.

It should be noted that in X-ray measurements, information about the state of the material is obtained only from the uppermost layer applied in the printing process, which is caused by the small depth of penetration of X-rays (~10-20 microns) relative to the track depth (~100 microns) [4]. This will explain the differences in quality of the results obtained for different printing modes. Thus, in samples 4 and 5 all used laser beam directions are presented in one layer, therefore the value of stresses in the layer is closest to the value of stresses in the sample as a whole. In sample 3, on the contrary, the scanning direction in the layers is alternating and the situation is opposite to that observed in samples 4 and 5.

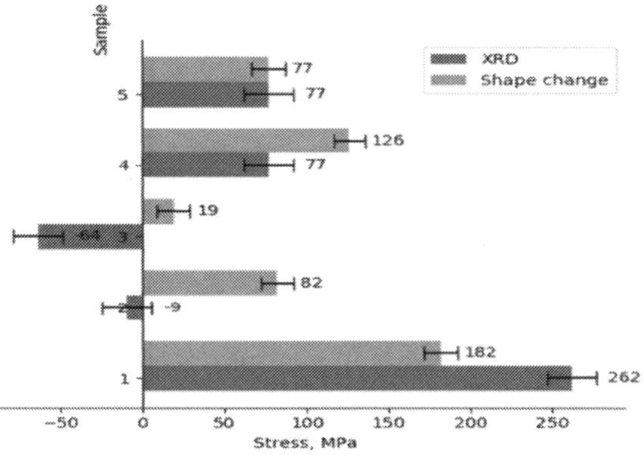

Figure 5. Comparison of results of determination of macrostresses by X-ray method and by change of sample shape

To explain the differences in the results in sample 2, where scanning was performed in the X direction in all layers, it should be taken into account that according to the results [9], when applying a single track , tensile stresses of greater magnitude are formed along the scanning direction. Thus, in sample 2, local stresses along the Y-axis in a small area under the X-ray beam are small, but due to the elongated shape of the sample along the Y-axis, they were sufficient to bend the sample.

3.3. Effect of scanning strategy on residual stresses.

We will analyze the impact of the scanning strategy on the value of macrostress in samples with different scanning strategies based on the data of both used methods. As we have shown in 3.2, although these methods may produce inaccurate results in some cases, the combination of these methods allows us to overcome this problem.

In samples 1 and 2, which were printed with laser beam scanning in one direction in all layers, a high level of macrostress along the scanning direction and a lower level perpendicular to it are detected (fugure 3-a, fugure 4-g). The reason for this is elongation of the melt bath at track application along the laser beam direction. Consequently, due to the longer length of the heated section, compression of the material during cooling leads to higher tensile stresses along the track. This is confirmed by the higher stress value in sample 1 relative to sample 2 (and the highest among all samples) - here the scanning was carried out along the long side of the sample and the tracks are longer.

In samples 4 and 5, in which at printing of each layer a part of the area of horizontal section of the sample was scanned by a laser beam along X axis, and the other along Y axis, a close level of macrostresses in these directions is observed (fugure 3-a). There is no reason to suppose that in this case the character of stresses arising at application of a separate track changes. Then we can conclude that due to the mutual influence of regions with different scanning directions, the leveling of macrostress levels along different directions occurs. Here, there is a difference in the distribution of macrostresses in layers with different scanning directions, as evidenced by the differences in the results of the X-ray method and measurements of changes in the shape of the sample. However, the alignment of the overall macrostress level in the sample is achieved by interaction of neighboring layers with each other rather than different parts of the same layer.

Thus, a more uniform distribution of stresses and a decrease in their overall level is observed when using scanning strategies that combine different scanning directions in one layer or in different layers. This is consistent with the results of macrostress simulation [7], where the minimum value and most uniform distribution of macrostresses is obtained for a strategy with frequent changes in the scanning direction.

4. Conclusions

The distribution of macrostresses formed in the samples manufactured by the method of selective laser melting (SLM) with the use of different laser beam scanning strategies, by X-ray method of measuring macrostresses and by changing the shape of the sample after separation from the construction platform is studied. It is shown that due to the specific features of SLM samples - the possibility of stress gradients formation between different layers, stress anisotropy - to obtain reliable results it is necessary to compare data of different stress measurement methods. Through the joint analysis of X-ray data and changes in the shape of the samples, it has been established that the scanning strategy has a strong influence on the distribution of macrostresses: when scanning in one direction, the distribution of stresses is anisotropic, while when combining different directions of scanning in successive neighboring layers or in one layer, the anisotropy and the stress value decreases. The results are in good agreement with the literature on experimental, analytical and numerical determination of macrostresses.

Acknowledgement

The work was carried out under Governmental Support of Competitive Growth Program of NRNU MEPhI (agreement No.02.a03.21.0005).

References

[1] Isaenkova M G, Yudin A V, Rubanov A E, Osintsev A V and Degadnikova L A 2020 *J. Mater. Res. Technol.* **9** Issue 6 15177-15184
[2] Li C, Liu X X, Fang X Y and Guo Y B 2018 *Procedia CIRP* **71** 348-353.
[3] Isaenkova M G, Perlovich Yu A, Rubanov AE and Yudin AV 2019 *CIS Iron and Steel Review* **18** 64-68
[4] Yadroitsev I, Gusarov A, Yadroitsava I and Smurov I 2010 *J. Mater. Process. Technol.* **210** Issue 12 1624-1631
[5] Yachao Wang and Jing Shi 2020 *Mater. Charact* **165** 110372
[6] Isaenkova M G, Perlovich Y A, Yudin A V and Rubanov A E 2018 *Tsvetnye Metally* **16** 69–74
[7] Sun L, Ren X, He J and Zhang Z 2021 *J. Mater. Sci. Technol.* **67** 11-22
[8] Bian P, Shi J, Liu Y and Xie Y 2020 *Optics & Laser Technology* **132** 106477
[9] Mirkoohi E, Dobbs J R and Liang S Y 2020 *J. Manuf. Process* **58** 41-54
[10] Schmeiser F, Krohmer E, Schell N, Uhlmann E and Reimers W 2020 *Addit. Manuf.* **32** 101028
[11] Liu Y, Yang Y, Wang D 2016 *Int. J. Adv. Manuf. Tech.* **87** 647–656
[12] Ghasri-Khouzani M, Peng H, Rogge R, Attardo R, Ostiguy P, Neidig J, Billo R, Hoelzle D and Shankar M R 2017 *Mater. Sci. Eng. A* **707** 689-700
[13] Osintsev AV and Ochkov K Yu 2016 *Scientific Visualization* **8**(2) 15-23

IOP Conf. Series: Materials Science and Engineering 1121 (2021) 012048 doi:10.1088/1757-899X/1121/1/012048

Regularities of Crystallographic Texture Formation in Products Obtained by Selective Laser Powder Melting

Margarita Isaenkova[1, a)], Yuriy Perlovich[†], Anatoliy Rubanov [1, b)], Vladimir Fesenko[1], Artyom Yudin[2]

[1]National Research Nuclear University "Moscow Engineering Physics Institute", Kashirskoe shosse, 31, Moscow, 115409, Russian Federation
[2]JSC "RPA "CNIITMASH", Moscow, Russian Federation

a) Corresponding author: isamarg@mail.ru
b) toly.rubanov@yandex.ru

Abstract. As examples of austenitic steel 316L, nickel alloy (Inconel 625) and titanium alloy VT1-0, the regularities of the development of crystallographic texture in monolithic samples and lattice structures obtained by selective laser melting (SLM) of powder are considered. Crystallization of all of these alloys is carried out by the formation of crystals with a cubic structure {100} <001> (bcc or fcc). Upon subsequent cooling, the titanium samples additionally undergo a $\beta \rightarrow \alpha$ phase transformation while maintaining the Burgers orientation relation. A sharp cubic texture {100}<001> is formed in the middle-height layers of a monolithic product, which determines the anisotropy of the properties of SLM samples. The layer-by-layer change in the crystallographic texture is associated with the growth of columnar crystals of the cubic phase, which are formed due to the thermal effect of the molten region on the underlying layers, which determine the orientation of the crystal during its crystallization. This texture is typical for both the fcc-phase of steel and the bcc-titanium phase. In the case of the formation of lattice structures, columnar crystals with a preferred orientation of <001> along the growth direction are formed in the central part of the ribs and nodes along the diameter of the structural elements. On the basis of the crystallographic texture of the steel lattice structures and the mechanical properties of the monolithic specimens, the strain curves of the lattices under their compression were calculated.

1. Introduction

The development of additive technologies presupposes a comprehensive analysis of the physical processes of crystallization that occur in the zone of material formation. At present, a large number of scientific studies are carried out on the construction of models for the development of the structure of products obtained by the method of selective laser powder melting (SLM) [1, 2]. A huge number of experimental results have been obtained on the study of the structure and properties of SLM samples from powders of different alloys: steel [3, 4], titanium [5, 6] and nickel [3, 7]. These questions are of great practical importance, since the listed materials are used for the manufacture of critical structural parts in various fields of science and technology. These are rocketry and the aviation industry, the nuclear industry and medicine [8]. As a rule, such parts have a complex shape (for example, blades of a gas turbine engine [9] or a hip joint [10]), and the technological process of their manufacture is a laborious task.

The method of SLM of powders is a very promising technology for producing objects of complex shape [11, 12]. Interest in additive technologies, i.e. to the "direct growing" of metal products, arose, first of all, in the aviation industry, space industry, power engineering, medicine and a number of other industries that require the manufacture of parts of complex geometry [13]. It is there that this technology is most relevant and is already widely used as an alternative to traditional technological methods for the production of not only prototypes, but quite marketable products. Moreover, the motivation here is not the ability to create something unique, with unusual properties, but economic feasibility. In the course of selective synthesis, rapid crystallization of the material occurs, which is accompanied by a high cooling rate, as a result of which a specific structure is formed in the material, which has a nonequilibrium nature. The structural-phase state of such a material can be controlled by various technological factors. One of the most effective levers of influence on the structure of the material is the energy parameters of the laser.

In the manufacture of products by the SLM method, the features of the location of the part in the working area of the 3D printer and its geometric shape determine the mode of forming the part, and, therefore, can lead to different properties of the resulting products. As was shown in the work [14] about the regularities of the structure formation in a steel product during SLM, the crystallographic texture is a source of information about the features of the crystallization process, which is influenced by the parameters of the technological process (radiation power, scanning speed, track width, etc.)). The structure formed as a result of crystallization determines the properties of the manufactured product.

In the manufacture of products by the SLM powder method, the part is formed from successively applied layers of powder under the action of laser radiation (LR) when the laser beam is scanned over the surface of the part being manufactured in accordance with a predetermined trajectory. According to the results of work [15], the processes occurring in the material after powder melting and crystallization can be divided into two stages. At the first stage, the material is in the zone of local melting by LR near the surface and is subject to rapid heating to temperatures close to the melting temperature, followed by rapid cooling, as a result of which a nonequilibrium structure is formed. At the second stage, as new layers are formed, the material is in the heat-affected zone, away from the area of direct exposure to LR, resulting in a decrease of temperature, heating and cooling rates, which contributes to stabilization (annealing of the material) and the formation of a more equilibrium structure. The crystallographic texture, the predominant orientation of the crystallographic axes of grains relative to the outer directions, is a sensitive indicator of the physical processes of grain growth in the manufacture of products by the SLM method.

Thus, the objectives of the work are to establish the regularities of the formation of the structure and texture of the different materials (steel, titanium and nickel alloy of the Inconel type), the mechanical properties of monolithic and lattice products obtained by SLM of powders:, as well as to predict their mechanical properties based on the results of structural and texture analysis and available properties for massive SLM materials.

2. Samples and research methods

The paper presents the results of layer-by-layer changes in the crystallographic texture along the product construction direction. The formation of a crystallographic texture in 316L austenitic steel, Inconel nickel alloy, and VT1-0 titanium is considered. The listed alloys have different crystal structures under normal conditions: fcc and hcp, however, the formation of the material structure is set by their high-temperature modifications, which are formed in the melt zone. The most common high-temperature modification is cubic structures. For the indicated alloys, such structures are fcc and bcc subsection.

The regularities of the formation of a crystallographic texture in cubic samples obtained by selective laser alloying of powders of different alloys were studied on monolithic cubic samples 6x6x6 mm or 10x10x10 mm in size and lattice structures of two types – 8x8x8 mm and 12x12x12 mm. The samples were printed using the following mode [6]: a laser power is equal 220-357 W, a scanning speed – 700-850 mm/s, a scanning step – 60-80 μm and a powder layer thickness – 50 μm. A powder with a spherical shape of particles and an average size of 40-50 microns was used. Namely such mode allows to obtain solid, low-porous samples [16]. At the same time, for different types of products, the optimal modes were selected, which made it possible to obtain monolithic samples with maximum density or lattice structures with cells of the correct shape.

Various scanning strategies were used in the manufacture of samples: 1) single-pass scheme; 2) cross, with a change in the scanning direction in the next layer by 60 or 90°; 3) checkerboard scanning scheme (figure 1). The Z direction (figure 2) is the product construction direction, the X direction is the main scanning direction of the laser beam and Y is the secondary scanning direction. In the case of using the scanning strategy 2 and 3, the Y and X directions are equal (equivalent).

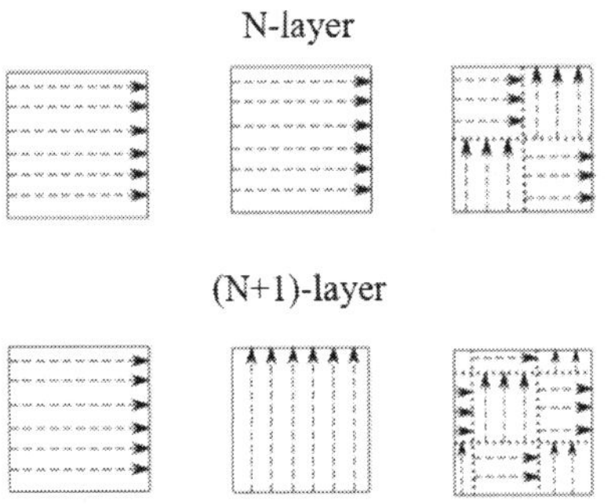

Figure 1. Alternating layers with different directions of the laser beam scanning.

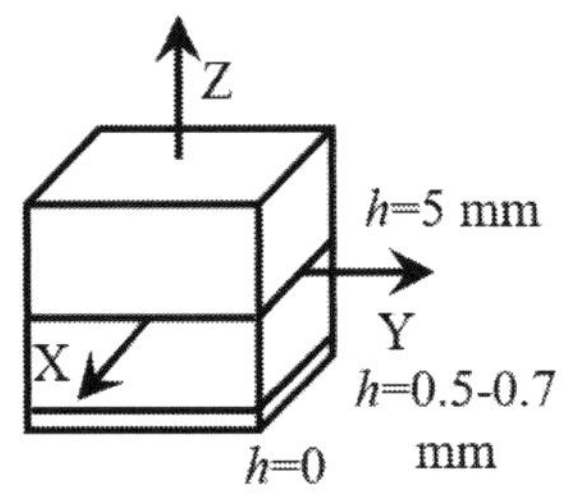

Figure 2. Layers of the studied samples. Z – the product construction direction; X – direction of the laser beam scanning.

Texture analysis was carried out by X-ray methods by constructing direct pole figures (DPFs) for a surface perpendicular to the Z-direction [17, 18]. The measurements were carried out on a D8 DISCOVER X-ray diffractometer using different radiation. For each layer of the material, 4 incomplete DPFs were measured, on the basis of which the grain orientation distribution function (ODF) and full DPFs were reconstructed in accordance with the MTEX software [19].

3. Experimental Results

Figure 3 shows changing the complete DPFs {110} or (0001) in height of the investigated steel, nickel and titanium products obtained according to the cross strategy. Since titanium has a hexagonal lattice at room temperature, the distribution of basal axes was constructed for such a crystal lattice, which are parallel to the <110> axes for the high-temperature modification of the bcc. Since the formation of the crystallization texture is initiated in the high-temperature phase, the distribution of basal axes characterizes the orientation of the bcc lattice. Figure 4 shows the graphs of changes in the pole density of the texture components <110> and <100> along the direction of the specimen growth. For hcp Ti-metal the distribution of basal normal corresponds cubic symmetry due to Burgers orientation relation between hcp and bcc-phases: (0001)||{110} and $<11\bar{2}0>||<111>$. This allows to calculate from DPF (0001) fractions of different texture components <100> and <110> for high temperature bcc-phase in which hcp metal initially crystalized at the molten metal cooling.

According to the results presented, the middle layers of all specimens are characterized by a sharp crystallographic texture {001}<100>. However, in the lower layers or at the beginning of the specimen formation from a powder, an axial texture with a predominance of the <111> component along the Z direction is observed on the supporting structure. At a distance of 0.5 mm, a change in the main texture component to <110> is observed, which becomes limited and then is replaced by a stable one <100> for the rest of the specimen. Only in the uppermost layer this specimen is violated due to the stoppage of the building process. This sequence of the crystallographic texture development can be traced for all samples, regardless of the Bravais lattice type at crystallization temperature: fcc or bcc.

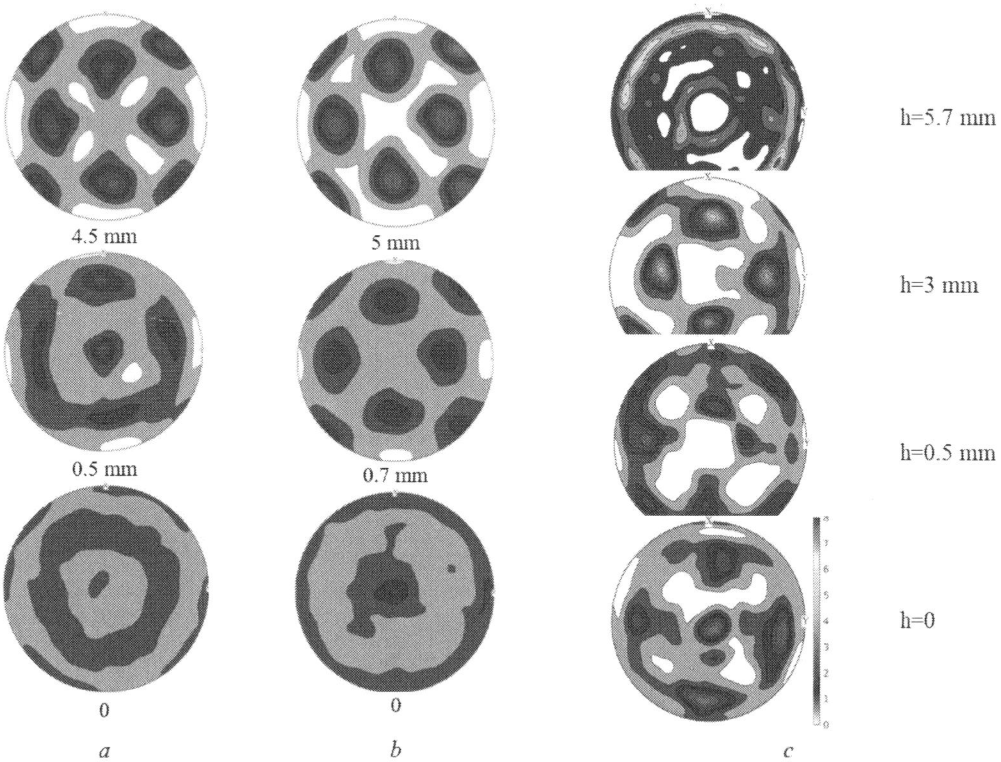

Figure 3. Changing of complete DPFs {110} (*a*, *b*) for steel (*a*) and Inconel (*b*) or (0001) for Ti (*c*) of studied samples along the growth direction Z. Height h is shown near the corresponding DPFs. Z-direction is located in the center of DPFs.

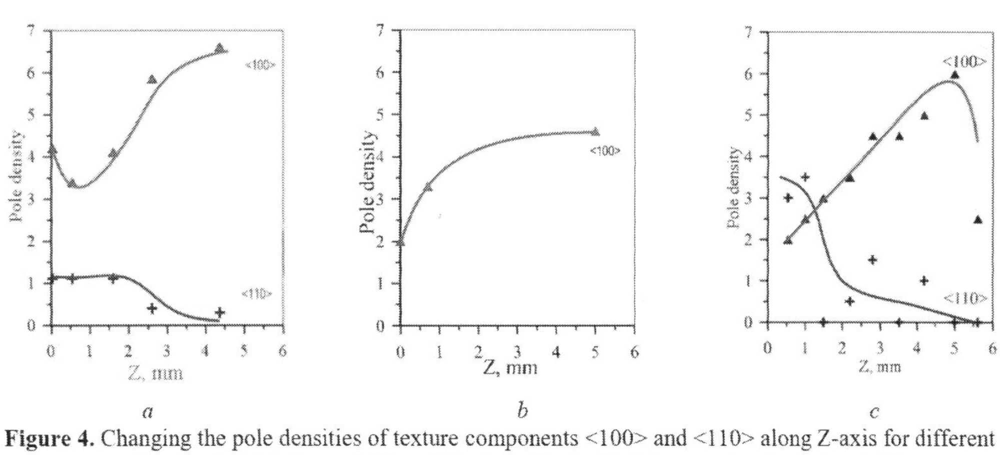

Figure 4. Changing the pole densities of texture components <100> and <110> along Z-axis for different specimens: steel (*a*), Inconel (*b*) and titanium (for the high temperature bcc-phase) (c).

4 Discussion

When the scanning strategy is changed to a single-pass one, an axial texture component appears on the DPF, which causes blurring around the X direction, the scanning direction of the laser beam. Figures 5-*a*, *b* show typical {100} DPFs for a plane perpendicular to the Z direction in the case of a cross-beam scanning strategy (*a*) and a single-pass scanning scheme (*b*). It should be noted that the scanning direction of the laser beam X for both scanning patterns is horizontal. Figure 5-*c* shows the track orientation diagram, the direction of heat removal and the main crystallographic directions in growing grains in the case of using a cross-scan strategy. For a single track, it was shown in numerous works [20, 21] that columnar crystals are oriented with the <100> axis along the direction of heat removal. Then the DPF {100} should look as shown in figure 5-*b*. The sharp crystallographic texture can be explained only if the lateral parts of the track are melted during the formation of the overlying layer. A constant shift with respect to the underlying layer or cross direction of the beam movement allows for the predominant growth of crystals of a single orientation. That is, when, in the process of forming the next layer, the lower part of the track of the previous layer acts as a seed for the molten material, and its side parts causing the scattering of the <100> orientation are melted and oriented in accordance with the existing columnar crystals. This process also explains the continuous improvement of the crystallographic texture with increasing a height along the product print direction and the texture scattering if the building process is stopped, i.e. in specimen surface layers (figures 3-c and 4-c).

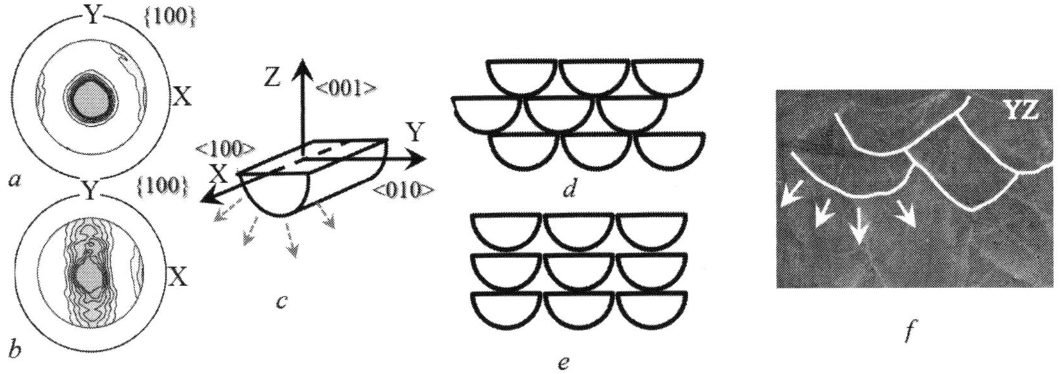

Figure 5. DPF {100} for Z-section of SLM-samples made by a cross (*a*) and single pass (*b*) scan strategies. Figure *c* shows the layout of the track relative to the external axes of the product with a single-pass scanning scheme; dashed arrows indicate the direction of heat removal during the crystallization of molten metal. Possible arrangements of successive layers of the product with a one-pass scanning strategy (*d*, *e*). Microstructure of SLM samples in the YZ section perpendicular to the scanning direction of the laser beam (*f*).

The considered mechanism of the formation of the crystallographic texture explains the appearance of significant anisotropy of properties in such specimens, as shown in [22, 23]. When printing lattice structures in the nodes and in the middle part of the ribs, the growth of columnar crystals oriented in the direction of growth of the lattice structure is also observed. The severity of the axial crystallographic texture <100>||Z in a lattice structure [24] depends on the power of the laser radiation used to print it. In the samples obtained using the minimum radiation powers, scattering of the axial texture is observed, which is caused by an increase in the number of chaotically oriented grains with a simultaneous decrease in the volume of columnar, strictly oriented crystals located mainly near the axis of the ribs of the lattice structure. The sharpness of the texture in lattice samples with a small void size is higher than in samples with a large void size. Based on the results of measuring the mechanical properties of bulk products, crystallographic texture and type of lattice structures, their deformation behavior under compression was predicted [12].

5 Conclusions

1. It was found that as the product is formed along the Z axis, the crystallographic texture of successive layers changes. For all studied materials (austenitic steel, nickel alloy and titanium) it was observed the common regularities of texture formation. Crystallites of the lower layers are characterized by an axial texture with the preferred orientation of the <111> axis along the Z direction and; at a distance of 0.5 mm, a change in the main texture component to <110> is observed, which becomes limited and then is replaced by the component <100>, which is stable for the rest of the

product. Only in the uppermost layer this pattern is violated due to the stoppage of the building process.

2. It was found that the formation of texture in the middle layers of the product is due to the growth of columnar crystals of the cubic phase with the orientation {100}<001>. In this case, the upper layers inherit the texture of the lower layers. The texture of the supporting structure does not affect the texture of the part itself, which begins to form at a distance of 0.5 mm.

3. A model of the formation of columnar crystals of a certain orientation in products produced by selective laser melting and the possibility of changing it by varying the beam scanning strategy is proposed.

4. A model has been developed for describing the deformation behavior of bulk and lattice specimens based on the results of the analysis of their crystallographic texture and properties of bulk materials.

Acknowledgment
The work was carried out within under Governmental Support of Competitive Growth Program of NRNU MEPhI (agreement No.02.a03.21.0005).

References
[1] Zinovieva O, Zinoviev A, Romanova V and Balokhonov R 2020 *Additive Manufacturing* **36** 101521
[2] Zakirov A, Belousov S, Bogdanova M et al. 2020 *Additive Manufacturing* **35** 101236
[3] Yakout M, Elbestawi M A and Veldhuis S C 2019 *J. Mater. Process. Technol.* **266** 397-420
[4] Khodabakhshi F, Farshidianfar M H and Gerlich A P 2020 *Additive Manufacturing* **31** 100915
[5] Li X P, Van Humbeeck J and Kruth J P 2017 *Materials & Design* **116** 352-8
[6] Isaenkova M G, Perlovich Y A, Yudin A V and Rubanov A E 2018 *Tsvetnye Metally* **16** 69–74
[7] Delcuse L, Bahi S, Gunputh U, et al. 2020 *Additive Manufacturing* **36,** 101339
[8] Mengke Wang, Yuwei Wu, Songhe Lu et al. 2016 *Prog. Nat. Sci.* **26**(6) 671-7
[9] Attard B, Cruchley S, Beetz Ch, et al. 2020 *Additive Manufacturing* **36** 101432
[10] Bergmann C, Lindner M, Zhang W, et al. 2010 *J Eur Ceram Soc.* **30**(12) 2563-7
[11] Isaenkova M G, Perlovich Y A, Yudin A V et al. 2020 *Inorg. Mater. Appl. Res.* **11**(3), 692-8
[12] Isaenkova M G, Yudin A V, Rubanov A E et al 2020 *J. Mater. Res. Technol.* **9**(6) 15177-84
[13] Ngo T D, Kashani A, Imbalzano G, Nguyen K T Q et al. 2018 *Compos. B. Eng.* **143** 172-96
[14] Perlovich Yu A, Isaenkova M G, Dobrokhotov P L et al. 2019 *Russian Metallurgy (Metally)* **2019** (1) 42–7
[15] Heeling T, Cloots M, Wegener K 2017 *Additive Manufacturing* **14** 116-25
[16] Yudin A V, Beregovsky V V, Tret'yakov E V, et al. 2017 *IOP Conf. Series: Materials Science and Engineering* **218** 012022
[17] Perlovich Yu, Isaenkova M and Fesenko V 2016 *IOP Conf. Series: Materials Science and Engineering* **130** 012057.
[18] Perlovich Yu, Isaenkova M and Goltzev V 1996 *J. de Physique IV Colloque C6, suppl. J. de Physique III* **6** 335-42
[19] Hielscher R and Schaeben H 2008 *J Appl Crystallogr* **41** 1024-37
[20] Zhou X, Li K, Zhang D, Liu X, Ma J, Liu W et al. 2015 *J Alloys Compd* **631** 153-64
[21] Yadroitsev I, Gusarov A, Yadroitsava I and Smurov I 2010 *J. Mater. Process. Technol.* **210**(12) 1624-31
[22] Isaenkova M G, Perlovich Yu A, Rubanov A E and Yudin A V 2019 *CIS Iron and Steel Review* **18** 64-8
[23] Kunze K, Etter T, Grässlin J and Shklover V 2014 *Materials Science & Engineering A* **620** 213–22

Microstructural anisotropy in Electron Beam Melted 316L stainless steels

Deepak Kumar[1*], Gyan Shankar[1], Satyam Suwas[1]

[1] Department of Materials Engineering, Indian Institute of Science, Bangalore, India

*Email: deepakk@iisc.ac.in

Abstract. In recent years electron beam melting has been explored to establish its suitability for product manufacturing as this additive manufacturing route offers advantages which are not achieved in other similar processes. This paper focusses on the prime issues associated with 316L manufactured using electron beam melting. Location dependent microstructure and strain accumulation is found to be completely different at central and peripheral regions in a particular layer. Coarser grains as well as lesser amount of strain value is observed at central region when compared to periphery. Crystallographic texture at centre is seen as intensified <100> parallel to build direction whereas it is weak and relatively scattered (<100> and <110> both) for periphery. BD parallel plane gives a glimpse of available energy as well as repeated thermal cycling as long elongated grains were observed and lowest strained region, depicting the high anisotropic structure altogether.

1. Introduction

Austenitic stainless steel 316L has been extensively explored to establish its manufacturing following the route of selective laser melting (SLM), an important method in additive manufacturing [1-3]. Primary reasons for adopting this non-conventional approach comes because of 316L application areas that demands intricate design, near net shape products, low buy-to-fly proportion, etc. Although SLM possesses many non-traditional behaviours in 316L such as Mo- and Si- segregated dislocation cells, crystallographic texture as <100> or <110> normal to substrate, increase of both strength and ductility altogether [5], this manufacturing route exhibits some key challenges which hinders its widespread acceptance. Inherent defects common to SLM such as lack of fusion, unmelted powders, debonding of layers, trapped gases as well as anisotropic microstructure in 316L shows a large fluctuation in mechanical properties and sometimes lead to inferior products than conventional counterparts [1].

Electron beam melting (EBM), a very similar route as SLM melts metallic powder of a single layer selectively using electron beam at comparatively high power (~1 kW) and the chamber environment is kept in vacuum [2]. Salient advantages offered for EBM manufacturing which are not observed for SLM as (a) high densification level because of comparatively higher energy density when compared to SLM, (b) minimised defects like gas traps, de-bonded layers etc. (c) reduced thermally generated residual stress as substrate temperature is kept higher (nearly 800°C) (d) comparatively more homogenised and relieved microstructure as lower cooling rate (~ 10^3 Ks^{-1}) provides more available time for diffusion [3]. Very few reports have been done for the case of EBM processed 316L that primarily gives attention to process-induced defects observation and inherent non-equilibrium microstructure [3,7]. A detailed investigation is needed that should answer questions related to phases, microstructure and its response combined with repeated heating and cooling of higher heated substrate on crystallographic texture.

This paper aims at establishing the response of location dependent microstructure on crystallographic texture for EBM manufactured 316L. Microstructure of various length scales as well as its location specific distribution and the key reasons contributing towards this observation has been discussed in detail. Additionally, factors that leads to differences in strain-gradient at these locations has been highlighted and discussed.

2. Experimental details

Manufacturing of 316L sample was done using electron beam where preheated and pre-alloyed 316L powder was taken as the starting material. Sample was built in the form of cylinder having the dimension as 13 mm height and 8 mm diameter and it is built vertical to the substrate. An interlayer hatch rotation of 90° was given and individual layers were rastered bidirectionally. After melting a particular layer of thickness 70 μm, it is lowered and powder was spread using racking mechanism for repetition of melting sequence. Substrate was maintained in a temperature range of 820 – 850°C to minimise the thermal gradient. Densification level for this particular sample was found as 99.4% calculated using Archimedes' principle.

A detailed microscopic characterisation was carried using Electron back scattered diffraction (EBSD) the help of FE-SEM attached with EBSD detector on both planes, parallel and normal to the build direction. Sample was scanned at two discrete locations as centre and periphery in BD normal plane to gain a clear understanding. Sample preparation was done using conventional polishing steps followed by electropolishing at 29V in electrolyte designated as A2. EBSD was done with a step size of 2 μm and nearly equivalent area was scanned for BD normal plane so that a clear comparison can be made. A commercially available software TSL 8.0 was used for data processing.

3. Results and discussion

3.1. Microstructure

Figure 1 (a-c) represents map of optical image micrograph (OIM), grain boundary character distribution (GBCD), and kernel average misorientation (KAM), respectively for the region of central portion in BD normal plane. Figure 1(d-f) represents the above-mentioned maps for peripheral portion of BD normal plane. As shown in figure 1 (a and d) morphology of grains is irregular in almost both locations. However, coarseness of grains seems higher at central portion (grain size ~140 μm) when compared to peripheral (grain size ~60 μm). Additionally, distribution of grain follows a wider range for periphery. The prime reason for this observation lies in location dependent cooling rate which happens to be more at periphery than central because heat can escape from more directions at periphery (towards sides of built sample and substrate) whereas it can escape only through substrate at central region. Moreover, figure 1 (b and e) highlights comparatively lower presence of low angle grain boundaries (demarcated as red, misorientation of 2 - 5°) in case of central region than periphery. Distribution of medium angle boundaries (demarcated as green, misorientation of 5 - 15°) seems identical in both cases whereas negligible number of twins (demarcated as blue, boundary of misorientation 60 ± 5°) are observed at all locations.

A very similar trend is observed for KAM distribution that is mostly used to find the strain distribution as shown in figure 1(c and f). Central region highlights comparatively more strain-free regions as this area shows a uniform colour corresponding to minimum strain at all locations as compared to periphery that has non-uniform and higher strained regions.

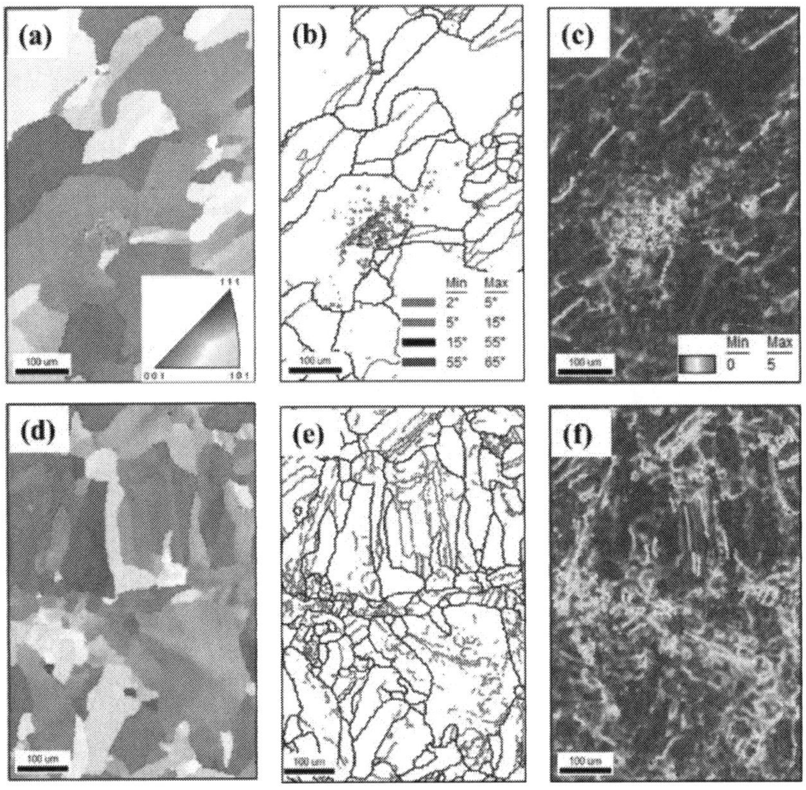

Figure 1. EBSD generated microstructures for BD normal plane where (a) Orientation image micrographs, (b) Grain boundary character distribution (GBCD) map, (c) Kernel average misorientation (KAM) map represents central region and (d) OIM, (e) GBCD map, (f) KAM map represents peripheral region

Figure 2 (a-c) represents the OIM, GBCD map, and KAM map, respectively for BD parallel plane. A wide range of colour variants in OIM clearly demonstrate the fact that direction of maximum thermal gradient is not constant thereby, this clearly will affect crystallographic texture. As shown in figure 2(b) grains possess elongated shape having longer side along build direction where length/width ratio is nearly 8 (width ~90 μm and length ~700 μm). Additionally, some grains length along build direction are nearly 2.6 mm in length. These findings clearly depict the fact that higher amount of available energy during melting as well as cyclic heating/cooling cycle in sample promotes extensive growth of grains along build direction as reported by Korner et al. [2]. Moreover, this retained heat in previously solidified layers anneal out the structure as also reported previously. This finding is supported by KAM distribution for the same area as shown in figure 2(c). This KAM distribution is lower than value seen for a particular layer both at centre and periphery.

IOP Conf. Series: Materials Science and Engineering 1121 (2021) 012049 doi:10.1088/1757-899X/1121/1/012049

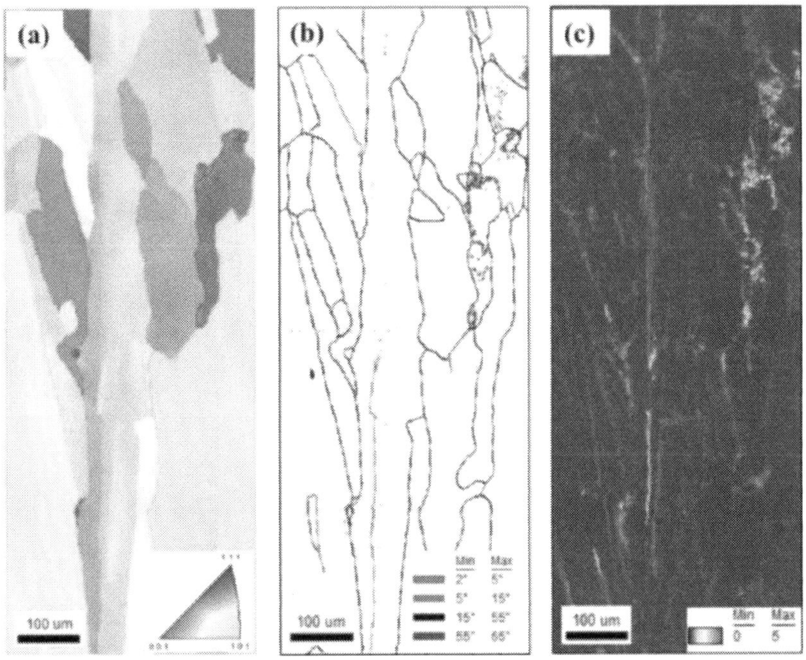

Figure 2. EBSD generated microstructures for BD parallel plane representing (a) Orientation image micrographs, (b) Grain boundary character distribution (GBCD) map, (c) Kernel average misorientation (KAM) map

Figure 3 compares the KAM plot of BD normal plane (centre and periphery region) and BD parallel plane. Central and peripheral region of BD normal plane exhibits average KAM value as 0.58 and 0.80, respectively. However, BD parallel plane exhibits a value of 0.37, the lowest KAM value out of all these locations.

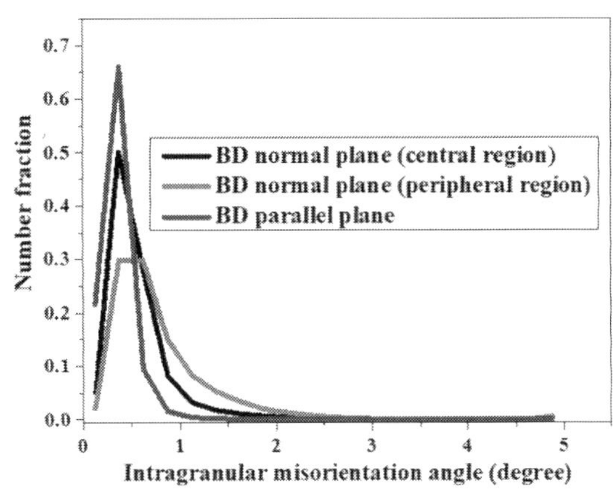

Figure 3. Kernel average misorientation (KAM) distribution plot of BD normal representing the central and peripheral regions as well as BD parallel plane

3.2. Crystallographic texture

Figure 4 (a and b) shows the crystallographic texture using inverse pole figure along the build direction for central region and peripheral region of BD normal plane. The reason for adopting inverse pole figure and reference as build direction is because of two reasons: (a) texture in most AM processed alloy is observed as <100> or <110> or a combination of both and (b) build direction is the only fixed direction as other manufacturing parameters vary from case to case hence, changes considered reference direction [1]. As observed in Fig. 4(a), central region shows texture as <100> along build direction whereas texture shown in Fig. 4(b) for peripheral region represents a combination of <100> and <110> which appears to be consistent with previous reports of AM processed 316L [6]. Moreover, intensity level in peripheral region also observed to be low than central region. The key reason for these differences in texture observation is because of thermal gradient as a result of retained heat at a particular location. Peripheral region solidifies earlier than centre because of accelerated cooling thereby, chance of randomised nucleation at these locations gets high. This condition is very similar to amount of energy available to manufacture the product using AM [6]. This led to a decreased intensity of <100> and <110> planes at periphery.

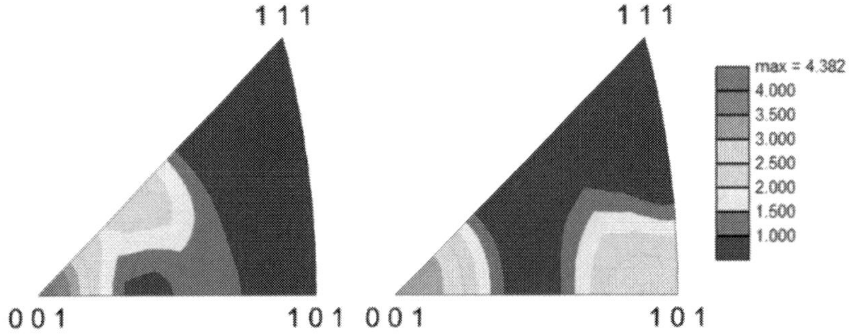

Figure 4. Inverse pole figure parallel showing texture parallel to build direction representing the region (a) centre and (b) periphery

4. Conclusions

This investigation emphasises key consideration that need to be addressed for EBM manufactured 316L. Location dependent complex thermal gradient as a result of layer-by-layer manufacturing affects morphology of grains, strain distribution as well as crystallographic texture altogether. In an individual layer, regions near to periphery shows finer grains, strained structure as well as relatively weak texture when compared to regions near to centre. The key reason for this lies in increased cooling rate of peripheral regions than centre. Additionally, texture is seen as a combination of <100> and <110> parallel to build direction in peripheral regions when compared to central region.

BD parallel plane shows a representation of highly anisotropic process as length/width ration of grains is near to 8. This anisotropy comes as a result of repeated thermal cycling of layers as well as higher amount of retained heat in EBM process than similar processes.

References

[1] DebRoy T, Wei HL, Zuback JS, Mukherjee T, Elmer JW, Milewski JO, Beese AM, Wilson-Heid A, De A and Zhang W 2018 *Progress in Materials Science* **92** 112–224
[2] Körner C 2016 *International Materials Reviews* **61** 361–77
[3] Rännar L-E, Koptyug A, Olsén J, Saeidi K and Shen Z 2017 *Additive Manufacturing* **17** 106–12

[4] Shamsujjoha Md, Agnew SR, Fitz-Gerald JM, Moore WR and Newman TA 2018 *Metall and Mat Trans A* **49** 3011–27
[5] Sun Z, Tan X, Tor SB and Chua CK 2018 *NPG Asia Materials* **10** 127–36
[6] Suwas S and Kumar D 2020 *Trans Indian Natl Acad Eng* **5** 1–10
[7] Zhong Y, Rännar L-E, Wikman S, Koptyug A, Liu L, Cui D and Shen Z 2017 *Fusion Engineering and Design* **116** 24–33

Acknowledgement

Authors are thankful to Advanced Facility for Microscopy and Microanalysis (AFMM), Indian Institute of Science for successfully conducting the microscopy.

AUTHOR INDEX

Adachi, H 239, 262, 268
Bar, H. N 173
Baudin, T 191
Bhattacharya, Basudev 155
Bieda-Niemiec, M 233
Biswas, Somjeet 155, 161, 173
Brisset, F 191
Capek, J 203
Chakravarty, Purnima 280
Chen, X 209
Cho, Tetsuo 244
Chouhan, Devesh K 161
Chulist, R 46, 233
Ciucani, U M 111, 149
Degadnikova, L A 286
Doi, T 239
Ebata, T 125
Edrisy, A 93
Fesenko, V 197, 215, 292
Field, D P 250
Fukutomi, Tatsuya 185
Ganev, N 203
Gervasyeva, I V 167
Gietl, H 149
Gottstein, Günter 1
Guo, C F 21
Han, K 76
Han, Y 209
Haus, L 149
He, C X 209
He, Youliang 93
Helbert, A-L 191
Hilinski, E J 93
Hirata, Masahiro 262, 268
Hoffmann, A 111
Hoshino, Takumi 179
Huang, Q L 21
Ichie, T 52
Imbir, G 233
Inoue, Hirofumi 244
Inoue, T 137
Isaenkova, M 197, 215, 221, 286, 292
Ito, Kunio 87
Ituchi, Fumito 244
Jarzębska, A 233
Javaheri, V 34, 227
Jensen, D Juul 81
Kaijalainen, A 34, 227
Kainuma, R 76
Kamali, M R 227
Kaneko, S 28
Kawalko, J 233
Kestens, L A I 11, 93, 143
Kimura, Y 137
Klyukova, Kristina 221
Koga, N 40
Komei, Narumi 185
Koshi, S 63
Krymskaya, O 215, 221
Kumar, Deepak 69, 298
Kurosaka, R 52
Kömi, J 34, 227
Lebel, S 191
Lee, S 28, 57
Li, R 81
Lopez, Jesus G 11
Ma, G 209
Madsen, D T 111
Maj, L 233
Mania, I 46
Marzec, M 233
Matsumoto, R 57, 63
Mehdi, M 93
Meng, L 209
Mikhalchik, Vladimir 221
Milyutin, V A 167
Minarik, P 203
Miura, Kouki 179
Moelans, N 81
Morikawa, T 52
Muchime, R 57
Murakami, K 52
Mzyk, A 233
Naruse, T 125
Natori, K 63
Neslusan, M 203
Nguyen-Minh, Tuan 11
Nousiainen, O 34
Ochi, N 63
Oda, Shogo 256
Ohmura, T 137
Okai, D 239, 262, 268
Okuda, K 76
Onuki, Y 105, 125
Osintsev, A V 197, 286
Pachla, W 233

Pal, Gyula 280
Pantleon, W 111, 149
Paul, H 46
Perlovich, Y 215, 221, 292
Petrov, Roumen H. 11
Petrzak, P 46
Pirgazi, Hadi 11
Prakash, Gautam C 173
Riesch, J 149
Rollett, Anthony D. 1
Rubanov, A 286, 292
Sadeghpour, S 227
Sato, S. 105, 125, 131
Sato, T. 125
Schuessler, B J 250
Shankar, Gyan 69, 298
Shibata, A 137
Sidor, Jurij J 280
Singh, Alok K 155
Sivaprasad, S. 173
Solas, D 191
Steen, P 34
Stolbov, Sergey 221
Suwas, Satyam 69, 298
Suzuki, S. 125
Sztwiertnia, K 233
Takayama, Yoshimasa 105, 179, 185
Takenouchi, S 28
Tanaka, Hiroki 105
Tanaka, M 52
Tanaka, Shun-Ichiro 256
Tarafder, S. 173
Tenishev, Andrey 221
Tomida, T 131
Tomono, S. 40
Toth, Laszlo S 274
Trembecka-Wójciga, K 233
Trojan, K 203
Tulonen, J 34
Uchida, M. 125
Ueji, R 137
Umezawa, O. 40
Ushigami, Y 117
Ushioda, K 137
Utsunomiya, H 28, 57, 63
Van Paepegem, W. 143
Watanabe, Hideo 179, 185
Watanabe, M. 125
Widomski, C 191
Wierzbanowski, K 233
Wojtas, D 233
Xiang, H. 143
Xie, Qingge 280
Xin, R L 21
Xu, Yihe 105
Yadav, V 81
Yamamoto, A 239
Yamanoi, T 99
Yoshida, Tsuyoshi 105
Yoshikawa, Tomoki 268
Yudin, A 286, 292
Zaripova, M M 197
Zhang, B 209
Zhang, Chi 274
Zhang, N 209
Zhang, Y 81

Institute of Physics
Dirac House, Temple Back
Bristol BS1 6BE UK

ISSN: 1757-8981
ISBN 978-1-7138-4606-2

CURRAN ASSOCIATES INC.
proceedings.com